McGRAW-HILL SERIES IN GEOGRAPHY

V. C. FINCH, *Consulting Editor*

ELEMENTS OF ·GEOGRAPHY
Physical and Cultural

ELEMENTS
OF GEOGRAPHY
Physical and Cultural

By
VERNOR C. FINCH
Professor of Geography, University of Wisconsin

and

GLENN T. TREWARTHA
Professor of Geography, University of Wisconsin

SECOND  EDITION

SIXTH IMPRESSION

McGRAW-HILL BOOK COMPANY, Inc.
NEW YORK AND LONDON
1942

ELEMENTS OF GEOGRAPHY
PHYSICAL AND CULTURAL

COPYRIGHT, 1936, 1942, BY
VERNOR C. FINCH AND GLENN T. TREWARTHA

PRINTED IN THE UNITED STATES OF AMERICA

THE MAPLE PRESS COMPANY, YORK, PA.

PREFACE

The second edition of this book, like the first, is designed to supply textual material covering the elements of geography in a form particularly suited to classroom discussion in beginning courses in college geography. The special merit of the treatment of the subject employed in this text is believed to lie in the choice of the material that has been included in it, in the structure of its organization, and in the manner of its presentation.

The selection of material for inclusion has been made with a single objective: to describe and depict the major elements of geography and to enable the student to acquire a background for interpreting the significance of their areal association. The material included is confined to the development of what may be considered a check list of the elements of natural earth and the elements of material culture. In this an attempt has been made to lay a solid foundation for studies in cultural geography by description and analysis of the habitat potentialities of the natural features of the earth and its conspicuous forms of human culture. The material is presented in a manner that the authors believe furnishes a basis not only for understanding on the part of the student but also for a full and rich classroom discussion of the subjects included.

The structure of the book's organization is considered by the authors an essential part of the presentation. It includes (a) two opening chapters which provide a degree of orientation in the field of geography, together with certain basic facts and geographical tools, and (b) two principal parts. The latter treat, respectively, of (i) the elements of natural earth and (ii) the elements of material culture.

Part I of the book receives the most extended treatment, and it has been divided into five sections of several chapters each. This organization has the merit of enabling the student to distinguish clearly between the *elements* of weather and climate and the *types* of climate into which they are combined, and of distinguishing earth *processes* from the classes of earth *features* produced by them. The emphasis has been placed deliberately upon the nature or form of the elements of geography and upon their world distribution rather than upon the processes of their origin. Not that the rational interpretation of features through the manner of their origin is neglected. It is employed constantly, but in part the discussion of process is segregated, and always it is made secondary in importance to the essential physical characteristics of the features produced. In this respect the treatment of landforms, for example, is to be distinguished sharply from that which is customary in physiography or physical geology.

Part II of the book alone deals with the features of material culture essential to geography. Omitting that part, the book functions as a basic text for a course in natural science. Just as Part I is an analytical treatment of natural features, so Part II is a similar, but briefer, analysis of the *types of features* resulting from human beings occupying regions. This manner of treatment of the subject of material culture is new to American textbooks of geography. Part III of the earlier edition, which concerned the associations of physical features characteristic of each of the great geographical realms of the earth, has been omitted as such, but certain of its features have been incorporated with Parts I and II.

The revision of the Elements of Geography from its original form has been suggested from three directions; the rapid advancement of knowledge in some of the fields upon which it touches, the practical test of five years of classroom use, and the kindly criticism of professional colleagues. Section *A* of Part I, which treats of the elements of weather and climate, has required the most thorough revision. This has been made necessary by recent and extensive changes in physical climatology, particularly in those aspects of the subject dealing with the nature and behavior of air masses, the types and significance of storms, etc. In the revision of both Sections *A* and *B*, the latter dealing with climatic types and their distribution, every effort has been made to abbreviate and simplify the numerous details in order that the essentials shall be emphasized and that the whole presentation may more readily be grasped by the beginning student.

Sections *C* and *D* of Part I, which deal, respectively, with the origin of landforms and with the characteristics and classification of landforms themselves, have seemed to require less revision. The changes that were made have, it is believed, resulted in the clarification of obscure points, the avoidance of some controversial matters, and the omission of certain details on which there is recognized difference of scientific opinion beyond the concern of an introductory course. Similar changes have been made in Section E, which deals with earth resources, particularly in the chapters which are concerned with the nature and classification of soils and the distribution of the principal soil groups of the world.

Those who are familiar with the structure of the earlier edition of the book will find the most extensive changes of all in Part II, which surveys the cultural elements of geography. As before, this discussion is concerned with the nature and classification of the significant elements of human culture manifest in the geographical scene. However, the treatment of them has been much expanded, their inherent qualities are analyzed, the bases of their classification are indicated, and the significant features of their world patterns are introduced. Many details of cultural form and feature have been added. The purpose of these, however, is not to present a brief human geography of the world but to give added significance to the bases of classification upon which the facts of world geography may be brought into rational order in other courses which may follow this introduction to the field. The present discussion is an attempt at a scheme of analysis and classification of cultural elements comparable with and parallel to that applied to the physical elements in Part I of the book. Admittedly, the development of theory and the body of knowledge adaptable to this procedure are less complete than for the physical elements, which are the special fields of several branches of science. It is not remarkable therefore that Part II of the book is not equal in extent with Part I.

It may be asked why the authors have so restricted their discussion of the cultural elements of geography and why they have not dealt at some length with the social implications of the various elements of physical earth. In some geography books the description of each of the physical features is followed by a summary of the human activities supposedly related to that feature. For example, the study of the physical characteristics of mountains will be supplemented by a description of the activities "dependent on or centered about" mountains. Such a treatment bespeaks a belief that geographical science is primarily concerned with showing how and to what degree physical earth influences human affairs. To such a philosophy of their subject the present authors cannot subscribe.

It may be asked also why the authors have not enlarged upon numerous themes suggested by the discussions of the cultural elements. Why, for example, have they not considered the world patterns of wheat production or forest exploitation or of any other of the many topics which are a part of the body of systematic economic geography? It may only be stated that this was not their objective. Neither was it their purpose to explore the complex of areal associations that comprise the field of regional study in its full geographical sense. Rather, their purpose has been, as was noted above, to show that *the elements of geography, physical and cultural, are capable of analysis and classification* and to show something of the pattern of distribution of each of these elements over the surface of the earth. Only after these functions have been performed does the student begin to distinguish the elements as such and to appreciate the significance of their areal associations. The details of these complex associations, whether treated from the systematic or the regional viewpoint, are, however, left to other authors and other courses of study.

Several grades of distinction in type have been employed in the part, section, chapter, and center headings of the book for the purpose of keeping before the student the nature of the structural outline within which he works. Also, the component *articles* of the chapters have been numbered serially through the book. It is believed that this feature will be of use in encouraging forward and backward reference by the student and in making easy the definition of class assignments by the instructor. It will be noted also that many of the numbered articles are further distinguished by being printed in slightly smaller type and shorter lines. Those articles are selected as having a secondary or elaborative place in the discussion, and they are, by their type and length of line, indicated for omission by students in briefer courses where there is not time to consider all the topics presented in the book.

The authors have striven for readability as well as explicitness in the style of the text. They have undertaken also, sometimes at the expense of brevity, to place special emphasis upon certain phases of the discussion. The interrelated nature of the subjects treated and the structure of the presentation both facilitate emphasis. The same association of facts may be, and often is, approached from two or more directions in as many different connections. This has made emphasis possible by a judicious use of repetition or by restatement to suit the new occasion.

The style of presentation seeks to avoid being merely a compendium of facts. The elements of geography are ordered, and the student is led to distinguish, by comparison and contrast, similar but not identical elements. Since this text attempts to lay a good foundation for the understanding of the geographical forms, patterns, and associations of world regions, many statements of fact and association concerning the features of specific world regions or localities have been included. To study these statements most effectively the student should make frequent reference to an atlas. Instructors are urged to see to it that students have facilities for that kind of study.

The text illustrations have been drawn or selected with the special purpose of centering attention upon significant features under discussion and of making possible a reduction in the amount of descriptive text. To that end they are placed in as close proximity to the related text as possible, although, in order to save space, some illustrations are made to serve in more than one connection. The plates that accompany the book have been prepared in blank. They are intended for student drawing and coloring as a manual aid to the appreciation of significant facts and associations in the distributions of geographical phenomena. Duplicate sets of these plates may be obtained from the publisher. Relatively few rainfall and temperature data have been presented in graphic form in the text, since it is believed that the student profits much more by the construction of these graphs for himself. A plate containing a number of coordinate paper blocks provides facilities for doing this. In addition to the classified climatic data provided for the several types of climate within the text proper, data for other stations are available in Appendix A.

Through teaching experience it has been found that in most introductory courses there is scant time for the development of the subject matter relating to forms of map projection, however much the instructor would like to present it. That has therefore been omitted from the body of the text and transferred to Appendix B, where it still is available for reference or for those teachers having time or inclination to use it. The balance of the former Chapter III, dealing with the general features of maps, has been incorporated with Chapter II. Appendix D has been added to deal with the American systems of land survey.

Reference lists are appended to those chapters, sections, or parts of the book that treat of distinct fields without conspicuous overlap in source material. These have been revised to include significant publications of recent date. The lists are not intended to be merely the references consulted by the authors, although many of those are included, and their aid is acknowledged with gratitude. The purpose of these lists is to suggest some of the more recent and authoritative general works in each field. In these the instructor or the gifted student may find supplementary reading with which to broaden his understanding of the subjects considered.

The indebtedness of the authors for valuable suggestions, illustrations, and other kinds of aid extends in many directions and to numerous individuals. This cordial cooperation is much appreciated.

VERNOR C. FINCH,
GLENN T. TREWARTHA.

UNIVERSITY OF WISCONSIN,
May, 1942.

CONTENTS

PART I

THE PHYSICAL ELEMENTS OF GEOGRAPHY

SECTION A

THE ELEMENTS OF WEATHER AND CLIMATE

SECTION B

CLIMATIC TYPES AND THEIR DISTRIBUTION

SECTION C

PROCESSES CONCERNED WITH THE ORIGIN OF LANDFORMS

SECTION D

LANDFORMS

SECTION E

EARTH RESOURCES

PART II

THE CULTURAL ELEMENTS OF GEOGRAPHY:

FEATURES RESULTING FROM MAN'S USE OF THE LAND

APPENDIX

ELEMENTS OF GEOGRAPHY
Physical and Cultural

Chapter I. The Field of Geography: Its Content, Method, and Point of View

Definition of Geography

1. Geography is the science of the earth's surface. It consists of a systematic description and interpretation of the distribution of things on the face of the earth. (As the geographer conceives of the surface of the earth, it is in the nature of a thin shell that extends slightly above and below the surface proper.) It is in this thin zone of contact between the atmosphere above and the solid and liquid sphere below that life in its various forms exists. Here organic and inorganic forms are closely intermingled and intimately interrelated, and from their combined patterns of distribution there emerges an earth's surface of variegated form and color.

The Geographic Features of the Earth's Surface

2. PHYSICAL AND CULTURAL FEATURES. It may be asked, "Specifically what is it about the earth's surface that the geographer studies?" Essentially it is the two classes of interrelated features noted in the preceding paragraph: (*a*) those which are provided by nature (among them, climate, surface configuration, soils, economic minerals, surface and underground water, and native plant and animal life) and (*b*) those which man has added through living on the earth and using its resources (population, houses, settlements, communications, farms, factories, mines, etc. These two groups are designated as the *physical* or *natural* features and the *cultural* features. The latter are composed chiefly of the *material observable features* resulting from man's productive activities in earning his livelihood, and from his creation of shelter buildings and means of communication. These are the cultural features of primary importance. Some would add to these, other less tangible aspects of human development, cultural and political, which are closely associated with the material features.

In addition to the distinctly man-made, or cultural, features, there are others of natural origin which have been modified by human beings. Cultivated soils, for instance, are not exclusively either natural or cultural, and the same is true of much of the earth's vegetation cover. *These material features, of both natural and human origin, are the elements of geography,* and it is with them that the present volume is concerned.

It is not, to be sure, in the numerous *individual* features of the earth or its regions that the geographer is primarily interested. Simply a catalogue of individual plants is not botany, nor is the listing of things to be seen within any portion of the earth's surface geography. Scientific study requires grouping and classifying and the tracing of origins and connections. When it is noted, for instance, in a study of the geography of an area, that there are *repeating patterns* of population distribution, drainage lines, fields, or any of the other very numerous features, and when these repetitions are discovered to have definite causal relation to other features (past or present) with which they are areally associated, there is then the beginning of scientific geography. The classifying of the regional features according to origin, function, or some other basis into groups and the revealing of the bonds of connection between them are the geographer's task. Characteristic and repeated *patterns* and *associations* of features, then, rather than individual features are most useful in understanding the geography of the earth's surface.

The following diagrammatic outline may help to clarify the preceding analysis:

GEOGRAPHY

The Science of the Earth's Surface

The distinctive geographic character of any portion of the earth's surface is determined by the combined patterns of the areally associated natural and cultural features.

I. *Physical or Natural Features*
  1. Climate
    a. Temperature
      (1) Of the warmest and coldest months
      (2) Length of the frost-free season

II. *Cultural (Man-made) Features*
  1. Population
    a. Density
    b. Distribution patterns
  2. Houses and settlements
    a. House types
    b. Settlements
      (1) Dispersed

b. Precipitation
  (1) Total annual amount
  (2) Distribution throughout the year
  (3) Reliability
c. Type of climate
2. Surface configuration and drainage
  a. Earth materials—nature of underlying rock
  b. Principal landform groups—relief and slope characteristics
    (1) Plains
    (2) Plateaus
    (3) Hill country
    (4) Mountains
  c. Surface features of a smaller size
  d. Drainage
3. Earth resources
  a. Water ·resources of the land
  b. Native vegetation and animal life
    (1) Forest
    (2) Grass
    (3) Shrub
  c. Soils
    (1) Physical and chemical properties
    (2) Character of profile
    (3) Soil type
  d. Economic minerals

  (2) Agglomerated
3. Features associated with production
  a. Agriculture
    (1) Size and layout of farm and fields
    (2) Crop or animal specialization
    (3) Distribution pattern of agricultural land
    (4) Types of agriculture and their world distribution
  b. Manufacturing
    (1) The industrial plant
    (2) Raw materials, power resources, and finished products
    (3) Manufactural regions of the world
  c. Extractive industries
    (1) Logging
    (2) Fishing
    (3) Hunting and trapping
    (4) Mining
4. Features associated with transportation
  a. Routes of travel—density and patterns
  b. The carriers
  c. The things transported—foreign and domestic trade

3. *Description and Explanation.* As in many other sciences, so in geography, careful, systematic, direct observation and description are preliminary to and necessary for any classification and explanation that may follow. The geographer, in his study of any region of the earth or of any single geographic element, first of all systematically observes and then records, usually on a map, the results of his obser-

vations. Unlike most scientists, a geographer needs to describe and understand things that are much larger than his range of vision. The microscope is of little or no use to a geographer. His problem is to bring the patterns of widespread and far-flung features, distributed over countries, continents, or even the world, within his range of study. He must see them in their relations to each other, and to do this he is obliged to reduce them to observable size on maps. Maps, then, with their great variety of symbols, become the technical language of geographers. No other science, social or natural, makes use of them to anything like the same degree.

The second step, following observation and description, is the search for explanations as to why the patterns· of distribution are as they ’are. No limit is placed upon *kind* of explanation. The physical earth, or natural environment, is only one of a great variety of things affecting man's use of a region, and it holds no preferred position among the several influences. There is, to be sure, no attempt to minimize the importance of the natural equipment of a region in its effects upon land use. But historical antecedents, customs and habits, laws, tariffs, and multitudes of other social forces likewise influence the character of land use, and they are as “geographic,” as far as explanation of the cultural scene is concerned, as is a coal field, a mountain barrier, a soil type, or any other feature of the natural earth. In other words, the things studied are restricted but not the type of explanation.

4. GEOGRAPHY NOT EXCLUSIVELY EITHER A NATURAL OR A SOCIAL SCIENCE. Since the earth's surface, which is the focus of a geographer's study, is composed of natural as well as of cultural features, it is obvious that geography cannot be exclusively either a natural or a social science, but belongs to both. It is inherently dual in character. If one studies a region in its totality, he is compelled to deal with both (*a*) its natural equipment and (*b*) the human imprint upon it, and such is the nature of most regional studies.

Physical Geography. It is entirely feasible, however, for one to study the patterns and associations of the natural features while ignoring the cultural, and there is a group of geographers that chooses to cultivate this more restricted physical aspect of regions. But many times physical geography has a humanized perspective, for it is often an analysis of the whole natural equipment of a region, or some element of it, in terms of its resource potentialities for human use. Such a study provides a solid foundation not only for cultural, or human, geography but for all the other social sciences as well. The associated original natural features of a region, unmodified by human beings, are designated as the *fundament.*

Cultural, or Human, Geography. On the other hand, one may, if he chooses, focus his principal attention upon the man-made features of a region, while minimizing, although certainly not ignoring, the physical aspects. The thing to be understood is still the earth's surface, but it is the surface as modified by the human beings living in and using the region. Human geography thus becomes a study of the "culture surface" and as such is a social science, claiming a place along with history, economics, anthropology, and others in an investigation of the human record. However, geography is concerned not primarily with human relationships, but rather with the features that man has inscribed upon the earth's surface, including population. The data of cultural geography are chiefly forms of land utilization. These features of human origin within regions rest upon, and grow out of, the earth's physical surface. But in no sense is the physical surface to be thought of as the sole cause of the character and distribution of material culture. It is the human group, with its particular heritage of racial endowments, customs, habits, and training, that creates the features of land utilization, and it is the human element also that largely determines their character and distribution. Physical conditions set up only certain very flexible limits to land use.

5. *Regional and Systematic Geography.* The features that exist together on the earth's surface may be studied in a number of ways. Probably the most logical way to study them is in their natural groupings, *i.e.*, by *regions*. The face of the earth may be thought of as composed of a mosaic of regions differing from one another in their natural and man-made (cultural) features. In other words, each region has individuality or distinctiveness by reason of the kinds and arrangements of the features that occupy its surface. To delimit these regions, to describe and explain their distinctive characteristics, and to understand the bonds of connection between them—this, according to many geographers, is the core of their science.

It is possible, however, to study geographic features in their *systematic* rather than their regional groupings. By this method landforms, climates, human settlements, manufacturing types, crops, and the like may be made the subject of observation, description, classification, and explanation. In the evolution of geographic science many of the systematic groupings which it formerly included and cultivated have been partly or even largely taken over by more recently developed sciences. Thus to the mother science geography was born a group of offspring—geology, botany, zoology, meteorology, climatology—and each attained independence by taking over a part of the parental estate and successfully cultivating it. Nevertheless many qualified geographers still work successfully in the several branches of systematic geography and their bordering sciences.

6. THE PRESENT BOOK; TITLE, CONTENT, AND ORGANIZATION. If the position is taken that geography is primarily concerned with a study of the earth's surface, it remains to be pointed out what particular contribution to that study this book is intended to make. It is in the nature of an introduction to geography through a systematic study of the individual elements or features that together comprise the face of the earth. The title of the book suggests this content. In no sense is it intended to be a general summary of geographic knowledge. On the contrary, the purpose is to acquaint the beginning student with the fundamentals of geography and to offer suggestions as to how they may be used in the understanding of the earth's surface. It is more in the nature of an outline of geography, the content of which provides organization and factual material on the physical and cultural earth.

Various methods have been employed by different authors in making this introductory approach to geography. One very common way has been through the channel of formal physiography, in which emphasis usually is placed upon a study of such physical *processes* and *agents* as rivers, glaciers, weathering, diastrophism, and storms. Less attention is given to physical *features*, their regional associations, potentialities for human use, and their world distribution. Some other books minimize the treatment of physical processes and emphasize instead the characteristic human developments within the several great physical realms of the world. Still others are condensed compendiums of information summarizing the whole field of geographic knowledge. As stated in the preceding paragraph, this book makes the approach to the study of earth regions through a treatment of their observable material features, these being the principal elements of geography.

REFERENCES FOR CHAPTER I

Barrows, Harlan H. Geography as Human Ecology. *Ann. Assoc. Amer. Geographers*, Vol. 13, pp. 1–14, 1923.

Bowman, Isaiah. "Geography in Relation to the Social Sciences." Charles Scribner's Sons, New York, 1934.

Brunhes, Jean. "Human Geography." Chap. I, Rand McNally & Company, Chicago, 1920.

Dickinson, R. E., and Howarth, O. J. R. "The Making of Geography." Oxford University Press, New York, 1933.

Fenneman, Nevin M. The Circumference of Geography. *Ann. Assoc. Amer. Geographers*, Vol. 9, pp. 3–11, 1919.

Finch, V. C. Geographical Science and Social Philosophy. *Ann. Assoc. Amer. Geographers*, Vol. 29, pp. 1–28, 1939.

Hartshorne, Richard. The Nature of Geography. *Ann. Assoc. Amer. Geographers*, Vol. 29, pp. 171–658, 1939.

Sauer, Carl O. Cultural Geography. "Encyclopaedia of the Social Sciences," Vol. 6, pp. 621–624.

———. Recent Developments in Cultural Geography. Chap. IV in "Recent Developments in the Social Sciences." J. B. Lippincott Company, Philadelphia, 1927.

Chapter II. The Earth: Its Shape, Planetary Relations, and Representation on Maps

7. Many familiar conditions, both in the realm of nature and in everyday life, have their origins in the shape and size of the earth and its relation to other heavenly bodies, especially the sun. Common ideas of distance, area, direction, time, and weight depend upon these conditions of earth size and planetary relation. Such phenomena as day and night, the seasons, the tides of the ocean, and indeed the very existence of the oceans and the atmosphere depend upon them also. The external relations of the earth require study, therefore, because of their fundamental importance to an understanding of the nature of earth environment and of the many complex ways in which natural features are associated with those that have been created by man.

8. THE SHAPE OF THE EARTH. So slight are the earth's departures from true sphericity that the greatest of them amounts to less than one-third of 1 per cent of its 4,000-mile radius. A slight flattening at each earth pole causes the radius from the earth center to the pole to be about 13.5 miles shorter than the distance from the center to any point on the equator. That is the earth's greatest departure from true sphericity. Great ocean deeps (6 miles or more below sea level) and high mountain peaks (5.5 miles above sea level) exist, but the height of the highest mountain above the lowest point on the ocean floor is not more than the amount of the polar flattening. If the 25,000-mile circumference of the earth be represented by a true chalk circle, the largest that can be drawn on an ordinary blackboard, the chalk line will have more than enough thickness to include all the earth's departures from true sphericity, if they could be represented properly at that scale.

9. EARTH FEATURES AND THE EARTH INTERIOR. The nature and relative smallness of the departures of the earth's surface from truly spherical form have a meaning of wider interest than their mere size. It seems surprising that some of the great mountains of the earth are not higher and

8

that the great ocean depths are not deeper than they are. Forces of crustal distortion are at work now, and have worked since the origin of the earth, at bending, breaking, and heaving the crust by unbelievably slow motion which appears capable of producing irregularities much greater than those which exist. That they are not greater seems due to a natural limit upon the size to which they may grow, a limit set by the plasticity of the earth and the inability of the interior to support the weight of huge projections upon its exterior. The earth ball appears perfectly rigid, and probably it has in fact about the rigidity of steel. Yet even this great strength seems incapable of supporting features of a greater order of height than that of the existing continental masses. If the earth be thought of as composed of a mosaic of segments or blocks, it is obvious that those which include the continents are slightly taller, measured from the center of the earth, than are those which include the ocean basins. It is believed that the higher segments are composed of rocks sufficiently lighter than the average so that they are nearly in balance with the lower but heavier segments. This state of balance is constantly disturbed by various of the earth processes, such as the removal of earth from the continents by streams and its deposition in the oceans, and is constantly regained by the slow movement of plastic material beneath the earth's crust. The polar flattening of the earth also suggests a plastic earth interior, since that form of distortion of shape would be produced in a plastic sphere by the centrifugal force caused by slow rotation. The idea that the earth is plastic will be useful later in connection with studies of the molding of the surface forms of the land.

10. LAND, WATER, AND AIR. The home of man is upon the 197 million square miles of the exterior of the earth, but the major parts of which it is composed are very unlike in their degrees of human utility. The solid mass of the earth (the lithosphere) is covered in part by water (the hydrosphere), and both are surrounded by a gaseous envelope (the atmosphere). Each of these spheres touches upon the life of man in many ways, and their many different features or phases combine and recombine in hundreds of ways to make the sets of natural features that characterize different regions of the world. Some of the combinations form regions that are eminently suited to the habitation of man and to intensive use by modern human society; others form regions that are very unsuited. In the latter group are the depressed segments of the earth crust which are filled by the oceans and the great seas. These together occupy about 71 per cent of the surface of the sphere, leaving the smaller part, about 29 per cent, as the exposed continental surfaces. Only the latter are in any degree suited to permanent human abode.

The total area of the land surface of the earth is, therefore, only about 51 million square miles, equal to about seventeen times the area of the United States. Upon this rather restricted surface the entire human population of the earth resides and endeavors to secure a living. However, there are large parts of the land which, for one reason or another, are ill suited to intensive human occupation or use. The primary purpose of this book is to direct attention to the many different phases of the major elements, land, water, and air, which are combined in the natural equipment of areas; to emphasize those features and conditions which are inherent in the earth but which go together in so

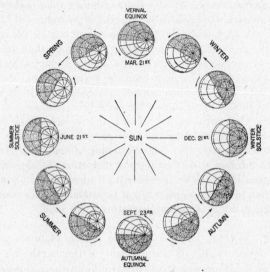

Fig. 1.—A diagram to illustrate the relation of the inclination of the earth's axis and its parallelism to the change of the seasons in the Northern Hemisphere.

many different ways and give to various regions of the earth differences of physical appearance and of human utility.

Earth Motions

11. EARTH ROTATION AND ITS CONSEQUENCES. The earth is held in space by the combined gravitational attraction of other heavenly bodies and has motions that are controlled by them. The two principal earth motions are *rotation* and *revolution*. The earth rotates upon an imaginary axis which, owing to the polar flattening, is its shortest diameter. The ends of the axis of rotation are at the earth poles. The time required for the earth to rotate once upon its axis is 24 hr. During that time each place on the sphere is turned alternately toward and away from the sun, has experienced a period of light and a period of darkness, and has been swept over twice by the circle of illumina-

tion, once at dawn and again at twilight. The direction of earth rotation is toward the east. This fact has broad significance. Not only does it determine the direction in which the sun, moon, and stars appear to rise and set, but it is related to other earth phenomena of far-reaching consequence, such as the prevailing directions of winds and ocean currents, which will be studied later.

12. EARTH REVOLUTION. The rotating earth revolves in a slightly elliptical orbit about the sun, from which it keeps an average distance of about 93 million miles. The time required for the earth to pass once completely around its orbit fixes the length of the year. During the time of one revolution the turning earth rotates on its axis approximately $365\frac{1}{4}$ times, thus determining the number of days in the year.

An imaginary plane passed through the sun and extended outward through all points in the earth's orbit is called the plane of the ecliptic. The axis of the earth's rotation has a position that is neither parallel with nor vertical to that plane. It has instead a fixed inclination of about $66\frac{1}{2}°$ from the plane of the ecliptic (or $23\frac{1}{2}°$ from vertical to it). This position is constant, and therefore the axis at any time during the yearly revolution is parallel to the position that it occupied at any previous time (Fig. 1). This is called the parallelism of the axis.

The degree of *inclination* of the earth's axis and its *parallelism*, together with the earth's shape, its *rotation* on its axis, and its *revolution* about the sun, combine to produce several earth phenomena which are of vital importance among the conditions that surround earth inhabitants. Some of these are (a) the primary distribution of solar energy over the earth, (b) the changing of the seasons, and (c) the changing lengths of day and night. These matters, and others related to them, will be discussed more fully in their connection with climate.

LOCATION ON THE EARTH

13. THE EARTH GRID. The conditions described above also are matters of great importance in another way. They furnish a convenient means of determining and describing exactly the position or relative location of any place on the earth's surface. On a true sphere that is not in motion there is neither beginning nor ending, no natural point or line of reference from which to begin to measure the relative positions of other points. If it were not for its motions and other planetary relations, the earth also would have no natural point or line from which to measure direction. Since the fact of rotation establishes the geographic poles of the earth, these serve as initial points in a scheme of imaginary lines, called the earth grid, by means of which directions and relative locations are easily indicated. Midway between the poles

an imaginary circle may be drawn upon the surface. It is a "great circle," called the *equator*. Other circles may be drawn at any desired distances from the poles. They will be smaller than the equator but parallel with it. They are called *parallels*. Upon the equator and the parallels, distance may be measured east or west of a given point. The north-south members of the earth grid, or system of coordinates, are called *meridians*. They are produced by drawing any number of circles which intersect at both poles. They are all great circles, and each of them bisects the equator and every parallel. By means of all these circles, the parallels and meridians, is developed the system of lines made familiar through the grid of a geographical globe.

14. LATITUDE. In the measurement of the earth it is customary to divide into quadrants the circle formed by each pair of meridians, the points of division being the poles and the two intersections with the equator. Each quadrant is divided into 90 parts, called degrees (°) of latitude, the sum of the number of degrees in the four parts being the 360 degrees of the meridian circle. The numbering of the degrees proceeds from the equator to either pole, and positions on the meridian

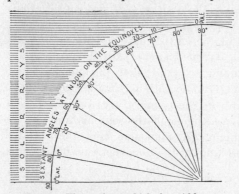

are marked by the east-west cross lines of the parallels. By means of the parallels, latitude is reckoned from the equator (0°Lat.) northward to the North Pole (90°N.Lat.) on any meridian and, in the same way, from the equator to the South Pole (90°S.Lat.). Owing to the size of the earth, the average length of a degree of latitude is about 69 miles.

FIG. 2.—The angle at which the midday rays of the sun strike any place on the earth at the time of the equinox is the complement of the latitude of the place.

15. THE LENGTH OF DEGREES OF LATITUDE. On a true sphere each degree of circumference, measured in any direction, has the same length, but this is not quite true on the earth. Because of the earth's polar flattening, degrees of latitude near the poles are slightly longer than those near the equator. The first degree of latitude from the equator has a length of 68.69 miles, while the first degree from the pole is 69.39 miles long. Each degree of latitude is divided into 60 minutes ('), and each minute into 60 seconds ("). One minute of latitude has an average length of about 1.15 miles, and one second of latitude is about 101 ft. The length of the meter, standard of measurement in the metric system is, in theory,

exactly one ten-millionth of the meridian distance from the equator to the pole.

The latitude of any place is determined by instrumental observation. It is necessary only, by means of the sextant, to measure the angle between the horizon and the zenithal position of the sun at noon. At the time of the equinoxes (about Mar. 21 and Sept. 22) the sun's rays at noon fall vertically on the equator, and the latitude of any place may be computed by subtracting from 90° the angle read on the sextant (Fig. 2). For times other than the equinoxes the results obtained by the above method must be revised by the use of tables that show the different latitudes at which the rays of the sun fall vertically for each day in the year. Latitudes may be obtained also by instrumental observation upon the North Star (Polaris).

16. PARALLELS OF LATITUDE, drawn through points equally distant from the equator on all meridians, may be constructed for any degree, minute, or second of latitude. On an ordinary globe grid, at small scale, only a few of the many possible parallels are shown—usually those of the multiples of 5 or 10°. Almost always, however, four fractional parallels are shown in addition to the others, because they have special significance. These are the parallels of approximately $23\frac{1}{2}$°N. and S. and of $66\frac{1}{2}$°N. and S. respectively. Their importance is derived from their relation to the inclination of the earth's axis to the plane of the ecliptic. The parallels of $23\frac{1}{2}$°N. and S. are called the Tropics of Cancer and Capricorn, respectively. They mark the limits of that portion of the earth where the solar rays ever fall vertically (Fig. 1). The parallels of $66\frac{1}{2}$°N. and S. are called respectively the Arctic and Antarctic Circles. They are the lines at which the midday rays of the sun are tangent to the earth's surface at the time of the shortest day of the year and at which the midnight rays are tangent at the time of the longest day (Fig. 15).

17. LONGITUDE is reckoned east or west along the parallels of latitude. Just as distances on a horizontal chalk line are measured by the vertical lines on a rule, so positions on the east-west parallels of latitude are marked by the intersections of the north-south meridians of longitude. Among the meridians there is no particular one marked by nature (as is the equator for counting latitude) from which numbering may begin. All are exactly alike, and it is possible to begin to count from any one of them as 0°Long. This was in fact done for several centuries, each important country beginning with a meridian drawn through a spot within its own borders. So much confusion resulted that, in the year 1884, the meridian passing through the Royal Astronomical Observatory at Greenwich, near London, was chosen by international agreement as the zero meridian. It is called the *prime*

meridian. It intersects the equator in the Gulf of Guinea at a point which has the distinction of having 0°00′00″Long. and 0°00′00″Lat. The 360° of longitude in the equator and each parallel are numbered 180°E. and 180°W. of the prime meridian to the opposite side of the earth.

18. DEGREES OF LONGITUDE VARY IN LENGTH. All the parallels of latitude, except the equator, are less than great circles, the diameters of those near the poles being much less than that of the equator or of the other parallels near to it (Fig. 3). Since each parallel, regardless of its circum-

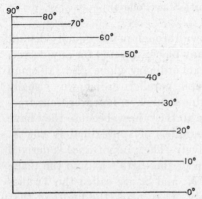

FIG. 3.—The comparative lengths of the radii of the parallels.

ference, is divided into 360°, it follows that the length of 1° of longitude, in miles, must decrease toward the poles. One degree on the equator, a great circle, has about the same length as an average degree of latitude (69.15 miles). At latitude 30°N. or S. the length of a degree of longitude is 59.94 miles; at 60° it is 34.60 miles; at 80° it is 12.05 miles; and at the poles it is, of course, zero.

The longitude of an unmapped place east or west of the prime meridian, or of a ship at sea, can be determined only by finding the difference in time between that place and the prime meridian. This was first accomplished by means of accurate timepieces (chronometers) carried on shipboard and set at Greenwich, or prime-meridian, time. Observation of the sun at the instant when it reached the highest point (zenith) in its daily course across the sky gave local noontime, which could then be compared directly with the chronometer, and the difference in time translated into degrees and minutes of longitude. Now, instantaneous communication by telegraph and radio makes accurate time comparison possible almost everywhere and, therefore, makes possible greatly improved determinations of longitude. This is of particular aid in geographical exploration.

19. ACCURATE LOCATION. The intersection of any two lines is a point; consequently, any point on the earth's surface may be located by determining that it lies at the intersection of a certain meridian with a certain parallel. Therefore, by exact determination of its latitude and longitude the location of any place may be expressed briefly and with great accuracy. Thus if one were to say that the dome of the National Capitol at Washington was located at 38°53′23″N.Lat. and

77°00′33″Long. west of Greenwich, he would state its exact position on the earth to within 10 paces.

20. LONGITUDE AND TIME. The earth rotates eastward through its entire circumference of 360° of longitude in 24 hr.; therefore through 15° in 1 hr. When noon (the zenith position of the sun) arrives at any meridian it is already 1 hr. later (1:00 P.M.) on the meridian 15° east of that one, and it lacks 1 hr. of noon (11:00 A.M.) on the meridian 15° to the west of it. For the instant, it is noon on the one meridian only, but it is noon on that meridian from north pole to south pole. Four minutes later it is noon on the meridian 1° farther west. In a generation past, each town kept the time of its own meridian, which was called apparent solar time or, in common American parlance, "sun time."

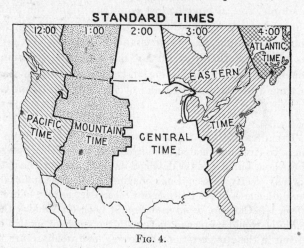

STANDARD TIMES

FIG. 4.

When rail transportation permitted rapid travel it became awkward or impossible to change one's time a few minutes with every village passed. To avoid this necessity each railroad adopted an arbitrary time scheme which differed from that of most of the places that it passed through but was the same for considerable distances on the rail line. Unfortunately, several railroads in a region often adopted different times for their own use. Consequently, it sometimes happened that a town reached by different railroads found itself required to use, or distinguish between, several different kinds of time: its own solar time and one for each of its railways. The awkwardness and confusion of this situation led to the adoption by American railways, in 1883, of a system of *standard time*. This system, in theory, supposes that all parts of a north-south zone 15° of longitude in width adopt the solar time of the central meridian of that zone. Places within the zone that are east or west of the central meridian, instead of differing in time by a few minutes from it and from each other, all have the same time. Changes of time are then necessary only in crossing the boundary of the zone, and each change is exactly 1 hr. The timepiece is set forward (*i.e.*, later, as from 12:00 to 1:00) in traveling east and back (*i.e.*, earlier, as from 12:00 to 11:00) in traveling west. In practice, these zones are not bounded by meridians but by irregular lines the location of which is dictated by railway convenience and political consideration. Figure 4 shows the present standard-time zones of the United States.

On the whole earth there should be 24 standard time zones, each extending from pole to pole, and each differing from Greenwich time by an integral number of hours. In practice the arrangement is not quite so simple, for, although most countries follow the plan, certain isolated ones have not yet adopted standard time at all, and a few small countries employ as their standard meridians that are not multiples of 15 and therefore do not differ from Greenwich time by exact hours. For example, Netherlands time is 19 min. faster, and Bolivian time 4 hr. 33 min. (instead of 5 hr.) slower, than Greenwich time.

21. THE INTERNATIONAL DATE LINE. The quickness with which the earth may be circumnavigated has introduced a problem of correction not only of the hour but also of the date and day of the week. The nature of this problem may clearly be seen if one imagines an airplane sufficiently fast to fly around the earth in the latitude of Chicago, let us say, in exactly 24 hr. If the flyer left Chicago, *going westward*, at noon on Monday the tenth of the month, he would keep exact pace with the apparent motion of the sun, would see it in the same position all the way, and would return to Chicago the same (to him) noon. To persons in Chicago a night would have intervened, and it would be noon of Tuesday the eleventh. The flyer would have *lost* a day. If he had flown *eastward*, he would have encountered midnight over Spain, noon of another day over Central Asia, a second night over the Pacific Ocean, and would have returned to Chicago at noon of the second day, though he had been gone only 24 hr. To him it would be noon of Wednesday the twelfth, while to those who remained it is, as before, Tuesday the eleventh. The flyer has *gained* a day. The fact that one who travels slowly by train and boat loses or gains this time by 24 time corrections of 1 hr. each does not alter the case in the least. Unless he sets his calendar ahead one day when traveling around the earth westward and sets it back when traveling eastward, it will be out of adjustment on his return. To avoid the confusion that would result from individual choice as to place of change, an *international date line* has been established at the 180th meridian. There, correction may be made uniformly, and no correction of date is necessary unless that line is crossed. Certain deviations of the date line

from the 180th meridian are agreed upon to prevent confusion of day and date in certain island groups or land areas that are divided by the meridian.

22. DIRECTION. The location of places with respect to each other may be expressed in terms of direction and distance as well as by relative location in latitude and longitude. Direction usually is stated in terms that signify an angular relation (azimuth) to the meridian, or geographical north. Although, in recent years, the gyroscopic compass and other devices have made it possible to maintain direction by immediate reference to true north, yet much direction finding, especially in land surveys, still is accomplished by means of the magnetic compass. The needle of this instrument aligns itself with the lines of magnetic force emanating from that great magnet the

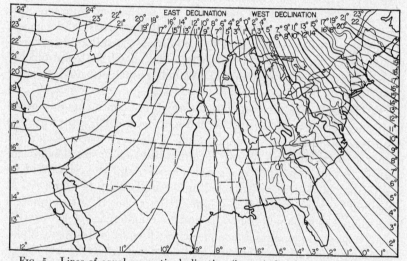

FIG. 5.—Lines of equal magnetic declination (isogonic lines) in the United States. Only at points on the agonic line (0° declination) does the magnetic compass point true north. (*Generalized from a map by U. S. Coast and Geodetic Survey.*)

earth. However, the magnetic north and south poles are not opposite one another and even are subject to slight changes of position. In consequence, there are few places on the earth where the magnetic needle points true geographical north. At all other places the compass reads at an angle with true north. These angles vary considerably in size from place to place, and their amount is called the compass declination. Figure 5 shows the lines of equal compass declination in the United States. East of the line of zero declination the compass needle has a west declination, and west of the line it has east declination. In parts of the frequented oceans the compass declination is as much as 30 to 40° from true north. It is obvious that true direction cannot be found by the magnetic compass and that true maps cannot be made without a knowledge of the degree and direction of compass declination. This may be obtained by an observation on Polaris.

The Nature and Uses of Maps

23. MAPS ARE ESSENTIAL TOOLS. Maps are graphic representations of the surface of the earth. They are used in many fields of learning but especially in earth sciences. For the student of geography *the map is an essential tool, a means of recording facts, and also a manner of expression.* Maps are almost infinite in number, size, form, and meaning, and they constitute almost a language in themselves. For their ready interpretation it is necessary that their important types and qualities be understood. To that end it is desirable that the student shall have a quick appreciation of at least three fundamental matters concerning all maps. These are (a) the size of the map representation compared with that part of the earth which it represents; (b) the nature of the plan, scheme, or "projection" employed in making the representation; and (c) the types of things represented on the map and the meanings of the various kinds of symbols or devices used to show them.

24. THE MAP SCALE. A *globe* on which the continents and ocean basins are shown in modeled relief is the form of earth representation requiring the least interpretation. Such a globe, however accurately it may show the figure of the earth, cannot be like it in size. The dimensions of the globe may be measured however, and the relation of its size to that of the earth, indicated in like units, may be expressed as a ratio. That ratio is called the *scale* of the globe. If, for example, a large globe has a diameter of 50 in. and a circumference of 157 in. (the diameter and the circumference of the earth being respectively about 500 million and 1,577 million inches), the ratio of the distance between any two places on the globe, measured in inches, to that between the same two places on the earth, measured also in inches, will be as 50 is to 500,000,000 or as 157 is to 1,577,000,000. That ratio is as 1 is to 10,000,000, and it is often written as a fraction, thus: $\frac{1}{10,000,000}$ or 1:10,000,000, and is called a fractional scale.

Maps, like globes, bear proportional relations to the parts of the earth that they represent. A statement of the proportion is printed on most maps in the form of a ratio or a fraction. It is called the *map scale*. Frequently the scale is expressed verbally also, or by means of a measured line. Maps may have large scales or small. A ratio of 1:10,000,000, indicates a small scale because one unit of map distance represents 10,000,000, units of earth distance, and the map is, by comparison, extremely small. A ratio of 1:100,000 indicates a map of much larger scale, and a ratio of 1:1 would indicate a map as large as the area mapped. Reference to a student's atlas will serve to illustrate the range of map scales ordinarily employed in such publications.

Between the application of scales to globes and to maps there is one essential difference. The scale of a globe, no matter how small, may truly be applied to it in any part and in any direction. On small-scale maps of large areas, especially of the entire earth, the indicated scale seldom is equally applicable to all the lines of the map, sometimes only to one of them. A reason for this will appear below.

25. THE NATURE OF A MAP. A map differs from a globe in that it is a representation of some part or all of the earth's curved surface on a *plane*. A map may be made on a flat sheet of paper which will show a farm or the area of a village without distortion of shape or of relative area, because the part of the earth's spheroidal surface included in either of them is so small as to be itself practically flat. To make a map of the entire earth, a hemisphere, a continent, a state, or even a county without some degree of distortion is no more possible than it would be possible to press flat all or part of a slit tennis ball without stretching or tearing the rubber. *The only true representation of the whole earth is a globe.* The greater convenience of maps as compared with globes has led, however, to the invention of many systems of arrangement of the meridians and parallels of the earth grid in ways designed to control the unavoidable distortion as to its kind, degree, or place on the map. Such a systematic arrangement of lines is called a *map projection*.

26. MAP PROJECTIONS. The distortion of the earth's surface inherent in map projections is controlled by the mathematical arrangement of the lines of the grid in such ways that either one of two objectives is attained. The map may (a) represent the *shapes* of limited areas correctly as compared with their shapes on a globe, or (b) it may represent *areas* so truly that all parts of the map are in proper areal relation to the globe. *It is impossible for any map that shows a considerable part of the earth's surface to accomplish both these objectives at the same time,* and some accomplish neither. For a more extended discussion of the nature of map projections and the appearance and properties of a few of their many forms the student is referred to Appendix B.

Representations on Maps

27. CLASSES OF MAP DEVICES. Maps are employed to show the areal distribution of many kinds of things. The devices used on the map to show distribution also are many. However, in a general way, they may be arranged in four groups which probably are not all-inclusive

or even quite mutually exclusive. The groups are (*a*) devices employed to show areal extent, shape, or outline; (*b*) devices for showing patterns of arrangement; (*c*) devices intended to convey an impression of relative land elevation or surface relief; and (*d*) devices employed to show the areal distribution of statistical values of actual or relative quantity.

In the first group may be included all those familiar devices of line and color that characterize the many kinds of regional maps which show the extent of the boundaries of areas classified upon the basis of some kind of unity. These may be countries or other political divisions, areas of unity in geological formation, climatic type, landscape com-

Fig. 6.—The wall map of Switzerland by Kümmerly and Frey, of which the above is a photographic reproduction, is printed in subdued colors and is an example of the best in maps that simulate modeled relief.

position, or of any other nature. In the second group may be found maps of drainage patterns, city-street and road patterns, the patterns of other means of transportation and communication, and patterns of the distribution of towns and cities with respect to each other. In the third group are devices such as shadings and hachures (Fig. 273) arranged to produce the effect of light and shadow, simulating modeled relief on the earth. Some of these are of great intricacy and beauty and are the supreme examples of the map maker's skill (Fig. 6). In this group also is that useful device, the contour line, which is discussed more fully below. The fourth group includes many devices, prominent among them being such things as dots or squares, denoting area; or representations of cubes or spheres, indicating volume. Each of these is intended to convey the idea of the existence of a unit of

number or value in a specific locality on the earth's surface. Maps having devices of this class are called *cartograms*. Their effectiveness

as geographic tools is generally in inverse proportion to the size of the areal units for which the values are shown. Thus a few dots or squares, each representing a large unit of value and covering a large area, show generalities. Many of them, each representing a small unit of value and distributed properly within small units of area, show valuable details of distribution. They may be used to show in an effective way the areal arrangement of many

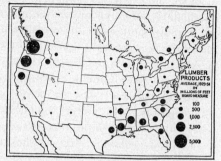

Fig. 7.—A cartogram that shows the distribution of a manufacturing industry by dots of graduated sizes. The radii of these dots are to each other as are the square roots of the numbers they represent.

kinds of things, especially such as have large space requirement but do not occupy the entire area. Such are agricultural crops, the distri-

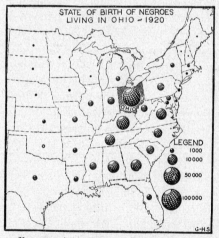

Fig. 8.—A cartogram that shows population data by means of dots that suggest volume rather than area. The radii of these dots are to each other as are the cube roots of the numbers they represent. (*Courtesy of Guy-Harold Smith and the Geographic Society of Philadelphia.*)

bution of livestock, or the distribution of rural population (Figs. 357, 358). For such uses the dot map is unexcelled because, when the pattern of distribution, and not the quantity distributed, is the thing desired to be shown, a proper arrangement of the dots most nearly reproduces the actual distribution of the thing represented. The dot map is properly effective only when shown on an equal-area projection, where the relative area of dots and space remain constant over the entire map. The dot map is not suited to the effective representation of the distribution of things that have no definite relation between area and quantity, such as urban population, volume of manufactures, or value of mineral output. For such uses other devices are indicated, particularly such as show concentration within a local area rather than general distribution. Graduated circles, spherical representations, or drawings of block piles, whose component blocks may actually be counted, are particularly effective in cartograms of that type (Figs. 7, 8).

Among the devices intended to show actual or relative quantity in map form is a generally useful one which may be called the isarithm.[1] It is a line drawn on a map through all points that have the same numerical value of amount or measure.

28. ISARITHMIC MAPS are of many kinds and commonly are used by geographers to picture elements of geography. The lines may represent either absolute or relative amounts. They may be made to show either economic data or the numerical values of natural phenomena. Examples of isarithmic maps are to be seen in several of the figures of this volume (Figs. 24, 29, 68, Plate II). Isotherms, isobars, and isohyets are isarithms of absolute value used in studies of the atmosphere. In contrast, a chart showing the distribution of relative humidity employs isarithms showing percentage, or relative rather than absolute values. In the field of economic data the isarithm may be used to indicate, for example, the number of persons per square mile of area and thereby to picture the comparative density of population in terms of actual number. Such a map may not show pattern of distribution so well as the dot map can, but it does express the distribution of people over area in exact terms. A map of the kind indicated above would show the areal distribution of actual eonomic values, but others may be made to show the distribution of relative values, such as the percentage of departures from the normal rainfall, or rainfall variability, in the different parts of the world (Fig. 79).

29. THE CONTOUR MAP is an isarithmic map the purpose of which is to show the surface irregularities of the land. So useful is that kind of map that it is more widely employed than any other for the purpose of depicting the comparative elevations of the land-surface features above sea level, *i.e.*, land-relief representation. This particular isarithm is called a *contour line*. It is drawn on the map so that it passes only through those points that, on the surface of the earth, have the same elevation above sea level. The idea of contour lines, their spacing, and their irregularities may be made clear by a simple illustration.

In an open tank one may mold an oval mound of wax $6\frac{1}{2}$ in. high, steeply sloping at one end and gently sloping at the other. If 6 in. of

---

[1] Isarithm is derived from the Greek *isos* equal + *arithmos* number. The word has been spelled isorithm also, but isarithm is believed to indicate its meaning more truly. The word *isopleth* also is much used by American geographers to indicate a line of equal number or value on a map, but its specific meaning is slightly different.

water is permitted to flow into the tank, only ½ in. of the mound will protrude. With a sharp point the position of the edge of the water upon the wax may be marked, and then the water level may be lowered by 1-in. stages, and the position of each stage marked on the surface of the wax. The marks made will now appear as contour lines on the wax mound, the lowest being everywhere 1 in. above the bottom of the tank, the next 2 in., and so on to the sixth, as in Fig. 9A. If the mound is viewed from directly above, the arrangement of the lines will be that of Fig. 9B. From this pattern of arrangement certain things may be learned which will help in the general interpretation of contour maps. Most important of these is the fact that where the slope of the mound is steep the contour lines are close together and that they are more widely spaced as the slope becomes more gentle.

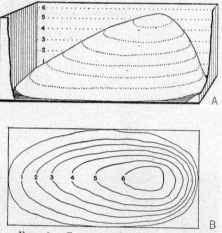

On this little model the water levels, and therefore the contour lines, have a vertical separation of 1 in. This may be called the *contour interval*. If the pattern of the

FIG. 9.—Compare this diagram with a photograph of one of the United States topographic maps shown in Fig. 187.

lines, as seen from above, is reproduced upon a sheet of paper, the result may be called a contour map, which, in this case, has a contour interval of 1 in. The lines may be numbered accordingly.

Few hills in nature are so smooth as this mound, and the example may be made more real by introducing a pair of gullies in its side (Fig. 10A). If the submergence is repeated, and the lines redrawn in the wax, it will be seen that in each gully the lines now follow along the gully side, cross its bottom, and return down its other side. If, now, the pattern of the lines, as viewed from above, are transferred to a map, it will look like Fig. 10B. From the arrangement of these lines further general facts may be learned. One is that when a contour line must cross a valley it does so by a bend such that the closed end of its loop points in the upslope direction. Conversely, contour lines bent so that their closed ends point in the upslope direction indicate gullies or valleys. Between the two gullies is a ridge. In the contour map of this hill the contour lines that emerge from the gullies and pass over the ridge appear to loop so that their bends point in the downslope direction. Thus, contour lines bent sharply toward the downslope

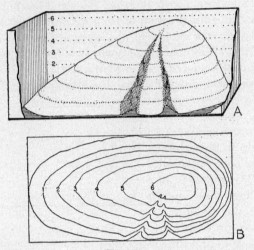

FIG. 10.

FIG. 11.—Nature's contours on an emerging shore. Wave-cut lines on a hilly slope, resulting from the intermittent withdrawal of water from an irrigation reservoir. (*Courtesy of Taylor-Rochester.*)

direction always indicate ridges. An illustration of this principle is seen in Fig. 11, where natural contour lines are marked on a hill slope as a result of wave work performed in a reservoir at different stages in the lowering of the water level. On a map that represents the irregular surface of a region these same principles may be applied.

30. INTERPRETATION OF UNITED STATES TOPOGRAPHIC MAPS. Although some countries use shaded representations of surface configuration on their official maps, the topographic maps of the United States Geological Survey depend wholly upon contour lines to produce the effect of surface relief. These maps are now available for about half the area of the country, and their use provides so much of both pleasure and profit that every educated person should be able to interpret them.

The maps are printed in either three or four colors, each having a restricted meaning. In *black* are shown those features in the surveyed area that may be classed as culture, *i.e.*, have human origin. In this color are roads, houses, towns, place names, boundary lines, and parallels and meridians. In *blue* are printed all water features, both natural and man-made, such as canals, streams, marshes, millponds, lakes, or seas. The various classes of such features are distinguished by appropriate symbols in blue. In *green*, if that color is shown, are areas covered by timber or woodland. This feature is shown on a small number of the published maps only. The contour lines and other symbols relating to the relative elevation of the land surface are shown in *brown*.

Each map is provided with a place title and with parallels and meridians that indicate its exact location and extent. Each is provided also with a scale and with a statement of the contour interval used on that map. The contour lines express the elevation of the land, in feet, above a datum plane which is mean sea level. To facilitate the reading of these brown contour lines, which often are very closely spaced, it is customary to make every fifth line heavy and to open it at intervals for the insertion of its numerical value. The intervening four lines are drawn lightly and are not numbered. Their values may be obtained by using the contour interval as a unit and counting from the nearest numbered line. If it is desired to know the height of any feature, such as that of a hill above its adjacent valley, it may be approximated by multiplying the number of contour intervals between the two points by the value of the contour interval. An error of nearly twice the contour interval is possible in this instance because of uncertainty as to just how far below the lowest contour line the valley bottom lies and how far above the highest line the hilltop extends. In each surveyed area a few carefully measured points are given permanent markers in the form of numbered metal posts called *bench marks*. The location of each of these is shown on the map of the area by the letters B.M. and figures showing its exact elevation, printed in black.

The standard United States topographic sheet includes a quadrangle of 0°15′ of latitude and 0°15′ of longitude. It is printed at a scale of 1/62,500, or approximately 1 in. to 1 mile. Some maps are printed at about twice that scale: 1/31,680 (2 in. = 1 mile), and show only one-fourth as much area. Still others are printed at one-half the standard scale: 1/125,000 (1 in. = 2 miles), and show four times as much area as the standard maps (about sixteen times as much as those at 1/31,680). A few maps are printed at still other scales. The contour intervals employed usually are 10, 20, 50, or 100 ft. On maps of extremely flat land, intervals as small as 5 ft., or even 1 ft., are used; but on maps of rugged mountains, intervals are sometimes as much as 250 ft. Both the map scale and the contour interval of *each map* must be read and considered before its true meaning can be interpreted.

If the above principles are used, it is not difficult to read the essential relief features of the ordinary topographic map. Facility in their interpretation, however, comes only with experience. In chapters to follow, the nature and arrangement of many of the landforms to be described can be made much more clear and real if the text is supplemented by selected maps from the United States topographic atlas. Although the nature of this book does not permit the inclusion of representative maps illustrating the various features discussed, specific topographic quadrangles which do illustrate them are indicated in Appendix D. It is hoped that some of these at least may be made available and that the student will acquire sufficient ability to read them so that they may make their full contribution to his understanding of the element of landforms in the natural environment.

REFERENCES FOR CHAPTER II

Adams, Mary. "A Little Book on Map Projections." George Phillip & Son, London, 1914. Simple and clearly stated.

Dake, C. L., and Brown, J. S. "Interpretation of Topographic and Geologic Maps." McGraw-Hill Book Company, Inc., New York, 1925.

Deets, C. H., and Adams, O. S. "Elements of Map Projection." Government Printing Office, Washington, D.C., 1921. General descriptions supplemented with mathematical discussions.

Finch, J. K. "Topographic Maps and Sketch Mapping." John Wiley & Sons, Inc., New York, 1920.

Johnson, Willis E. "Mathematical Geography." American Book Company, New York, 1907. An elementary treatment of the planetary relations of the earth.

Raisz, Erwin. "General Cartography." McGraw-Hill Book Company, Inc., New York, 1938.

Reeves, E. A. "Maps and Map-making.'" Royal Geographical Society, London, 1910.

Steers, J. A. "Introduction to the Study of Map Projections." University of London Press, London, 1929.

THE PHYSICAL
ELEMENTS OF GEOGRAPHY

Section A. The Elements of Weather and Climate

31. GENERAL CONSIDERATIONS. Surrounding the earth, and yet an integral part of the planet, is a gaseous envelope called the atmosphere, which extends to a height of several hundred miles. It is at the plane of contact between the atmosphere, on the one hand, and the solid and liquid earth, on the other, that life in its various forms exists. To be sure, man lives *on* the solid portion of the earth's surface but *in*, and *at the bottom of*, this sea of air. He is, as a consequence, much affected by changes that take place in the gaseous medium that surrounds him. In fact, among the several elements that comprise the natural equipment of a region (climate, native vegetation, landforms, minerals, soils, etc.) for human occupance and use, climate is the single most important one causing variations in the productive potentialities between the earth's regional subdivisions of the first order of magnitude. This results from the fact that not only is climate in and by itself a major element of a region's natural equipment, but also it directly affects vegetation, soil, and drainage characteristics and, to a degree, the nature of the landforms as well. Thus large areas with similar climates also are likely to have strong resemblances in vegetation and soil.

32. COMPOSITION OF THE ATMOSPHERE. Pure, *dry* air near sea level is largely composed of nitrogen (78 per cent) and oxygen (nearly 21 per cent).[1] There are smaller amounts of argon, ozone, carbon dioxide, hydrogen, and a number of other gases. In addition to those gases named, ordinary surface air also contains variable amounts of water vapor (up to nearly 5 per cent on

[1] The permanent gases of the atmosphere probably exist in nearly these same proportions at all heights up to the upper part of the stratosphere. Water vapor and dust are concentrated in the lower atmosphere.

hot, humid days) and numerous organic and inorganic particles that are classed as dust.

Of slight significance to the various weather and climatic phenomena are nitrogen and oxygen, even though they comprise so much of the surface air by volume. Certain of the minor gases are much more important. Thus water vapor is the source of all forms of condensation and precipitation (clouds, dew, white frost, sleet, hail, rain, and snow), and it is the principal absorber of solar energy and of radiated earth energy as well. Since water vapor is much more transparent to the sun's rays than to the energy radiated from the earth's surface, it acts as a blanket to keep the earth relatively warm. Some of the microscopic dust particles which have hygroscopic, or water-absorbing, properties provide the nuclei around which atmospheric condensation takes place. Over large cities smoke and dust act as an effective screen against incoming sunlight. As an example, the university weather station at Chicago, Ill., receives during the three winter months (December through February) only 55 per cent of the solar energy recorded by the weather station located on the university campus at Madison, Wis., a smaller and less industrial city.

33. THE ELEMENTS OF WEATHER AND CLIMATE. The condition of the atmosphere at any time or place, i.e., the weather, is expressed by a combination of several elements, primarily (a) *temperature* and (b) *precipitation* and *humidity* but to a lesser degree by (c) *winds* and (d) *air pressure* as well. These four are called the *elements of weather and climate* because they are the ingredients out of which various weather and climatic types are compounded. The *weather* of any place is the sum total of its atmospheric conditions (temperature, pressure, winds, moisture, and precipitation) for a *short* period of time. It is the momentary state of the atmosphere. Thus we speak of the weather, not the climate, for today or of last week. *Climate*, on the other hand, is a composite or generalization of the variety of day-to-day weather conditions. It is not just "average weather," for the variations from the mean, or average, are as important as the mean itself. "Certainly no picture of climate is at all true unless it is painted in all the colors of the constant variation of weather and the changes of season which are the really prominent features." (Kendrew.)

34. THE CONTROLS OF WEATHER AND CLIMATE. Weather varies from day to day, and climate differs from place to place, because of variations in the amount, intensity, and areal distribution of these several weather and climatic elements, more particularly temperature and precipitation. One may naturally inquire what it is that causes these several climatic elements to vary from place to place and season to season on the earth, resulting in some places' and some seasons' being hot and others cold, some wet and others dry. The answer is to

be found in the *climatic controls*. These are (*a*) latitude or sun, (*b*) distribution of land and water, (*c*) winds and air masses, (*d*) altitude, (*e*) mountain barriers, (*f*) the great semipermanent high- and low-pressure centers, (*g*) ocean currents, (*h*) storms of various kinds, and a number of other minor ones. It is these controls, acting with various intensities and in different combinations, that produce the changes in temperature and precipitation, which in turn give rise to varieties of weather and climate. The following diagram may help to clarify the relationship among (*a*) *elements*, (*b*) *controls*, and (*c*) the resulting weather and climate.

Climatic Controls		*Climatic Elements*		
1. Sun or latitude				
2. Land and water				Types
3. Winds and air masses		1. Temperature		and
4. Altitude	Acting	2. Precipitation		varieties
5. Mountain barriers	upon→	and humidity	Produce→	of
6. Semipermanent low- and		3. Winds and		weather
high-pressure centers		air pressure		and
7. Ocean currents				climate
8. Storms				

Although it is the composite of atmospheric conditions, called climates, and their world distribution, that is of principal interest to geographers, a description of climatic types will be more intelligible if preceded by an analysis of the characteristics, origins, and distributions of the individual elements which comprise the climatic complex. The next few chapters, dealing with air temperature, pressure and winds, moisture and precipitation, and storms, provide this background, which is desirable for understanding the origin of various types of climate and their distribution over the earth.

REFERENCES FOR SECTION A

Blair, Thomas A. "Weather Elements." Prentice-Hall, Inc., New York, 1937. A good up-to-date, nontechnical meteorology.

Brooks, Charles Franklin. "Why the Weather?" Harcourt, Brace and Company, New York, 1935. A popularly written but scientific analysis of weather.

Brunt, Davis. "Physical and Dynamical Meteorology." 2d ed., University Press, Cambridge, England, 1939. An advanced text of high quality.

Byers, Horace Robert. "Synoptic and Aeronautical Meteorology." McGraw-Hill Book Company, Inc., New York, 1937. Excellent text on air-mass analysis for relatively mature students.

"Climate and Man." Yearbook of Agriculture, 1941. United States Department of Agriculture, Washington, D.C. See especially Part 4, The Scientific Approach to Weather and Climate, pp. 579–661.

Davis, W. M. "Elementary Meteorology." Ginn and Company, Boston, 1895. Clearly and forcefully written but far out of date on numerous topics.

Gregg, Willis Ray. "Aeronautical Meteorology." 2d ed., The Ronald Press Company, New York, 1930.

Haynes, B. C. Meteorology for Pilots. *Civil Aeronautics Bull.* 25, Washington, D. C., September, 1940. Nontechnical, very concise and up to date.

Kendrew, W. G. "Climate." 2d ed., University Press, Oxford, 1930. One of the best treatments of the weather and climatic elements and their distribution.

Landsberg, Helmut. "Physical Climatology." State College, Pennsylvania, 1941.

Milham, W. I. "Meteorology." The Macmillan Company, New York, 1912. Well organized, but out of date.

Namias, Jerome, *et al.* "An Introduction to the Study of Air Mass Analysis." 5th ed., Milton, Mass., 1940. A good summary in English of air-mass methods of weather analysis.

Petterssen, Sverre. "Weather Analysis and Forecasting." McGraw-Hill Book Company, Inc., New York, 1940. A very comprehensive treatment of modern methods of analyzing and forecasting weather.

———. "Introduction to Meteorology." McGraw-Hill Book Company, Inc., New York, 1941. An abbreviation and simplification of the author's "Weather Analysis and Forecasting."

Physics of the Earth. III, "Meteorology." National Research Council, *Bull.* 79, Washington, D. C., 1931. An excellent advanced treatment of the subject.

———. V. "Oceanography." National Research Council, *Bull.* 85, Washington, D. C., 1932.

Ridgely, Douglas C., and Koeppe, Clarence. "A College Workbook in Weather and Climate." McKnight and McKnight, Bloomington, Ill., 1930.

Sutcliffe, R. C. "Meteorology for Aviators." Chemical Publishing Company of New York, Inc., New York, 1940.

Taylor, George F. "Aeronautical Meteorology." Pitman Publishing Corporation, New York, 1938. Excellent nonmathematical treatment.

Weightman, Richard Hanson. Forecasting from Synoptic Weather Charts. *Miscellaneous Publication* 236, Washington, D. C., April, 1936.

Willett, H. C. "American Air Mass Properties." Massachusetts Institute of Technology and Woods Hole Oceanographic Inst., Papers in Physical Oceanography and Meteorology, Vol. 2, No. 2, June, 1933.

Chapter III. Air Temperature
(including insolation)

Sun Energy or Insolation

35. SOURCE OF ATMOSPHERIC HEAT. The sun is the single note-worthy source of heat for the earth's atmosphere. Out into space from this gigantic body, whose diameter is more than one hundred times the earth's and whose surface is estimated to have a temperature of more than 10,000°F., streams a tremendous mass of energy. The earth, nearly 93,000,000 miles distant, intercepts less than 1/2,000,000,000 part of the solar output. Yet to this small percentage of the sun's total energy many of the physical, and all of the biotic, phenomena of the earth owe their existence. The radiant energy received from the sun, transmitted in the form of short waves (1/10,000 to 1/100,000 in. in length) and traveling at the rate of 186,000 miles a second, is called *solar radiation*, or *insolation*. A considerable part of the solar-radiation spectrum can be perceived as light. But there are other waves, some shorter (ultraviolet), and others longer (infrared), which cannot be seen. Since sun radiation is the single important source of atmospheric heat, its distribution over the earth is of outstanding significance in understanding weather and climatic phenomena and more especially those associated with temperature. Certainly the sun, or insolation, is the single greatest control of climate.

36. MAJOR FACTORS DETERMINING THE AMOUNT OF SOLAR RADIA-TION RECEIVED AT ANY PORTION OF THE EARTH'S SURFACE. In order to simplify the problem of insolation distribution, imagine for the moment that the absorbing and reflecting effects of the earth's atmospheric layers do not exist. Under that condition the amount of solar energy that any portion of the earth's surface receives will depend primarily upon two factors; (*a*) *the angle at which the rays of sunlight reach the earth* and (*b*) *the duration of solar radiation, or length of day.* Because an oblique solar ray is spread out over a larger surface than a vertical one it delivers less energy per unit area (Fig. 12). Moreover,

33

although for the moment the effects of an atmosphere are being omitted, it may be added that an oblique ray also passes through a considerably thicker layer of scattering, absorbing, and reflecting air. Winter sunlight, therefore, is much weaker than that of summer, since in late December the noon sun at Madison, Wis., located at 43°N., is only 23½° above the horizon, whereas in late June it has an elevation of 70½°. As regards the second item, it would seem to require no further explanation of the fact that the longer the sun shines (length of day) the greater the amount of solar energy received, all other conditions being equal. Thus the longest summer days (15+ hr.) in the latitude of southern Wisconsin, which have 6+ hr. more of daylight than the shortest winter days (9— hr.), allow for much greater receipts of solar energy (Figs. 13, 14). It is quite understandable, then, why in these latitudes summer temperatures are so much higher than winter temperatures, since (a) sun's rays are less oblique, and (b) days are much longer in summer.

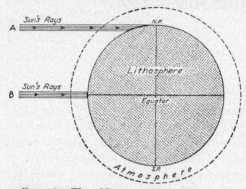

FIG. 12.—The oblique ray (A) delivers less energy at the earth's surface than the vertical ray (B) because it passes through a thicker layer of absorbing and reflecting atmosphere and likewise because its energy is spread over a greater area.

LENGTH OF THE LONGEST DAY (HENCE ALSO OF THE LONGEST NIGHT) AT CERTAIN LATITUDES

Latitude	0°	17°	41°	49°	63°	66½°	67°21′	69°51′	78°11′	90°
Duration	12 hr.	13 hr.	15 hr.	16 hr.	20 hr.	24 hr.	1 mo.	2 mo.	4 mo.	6 mo.

Since length of day and angle of the sun's rays are equal on all parts of the same parallel, it follows that all places on a parallel (save for differences in the transparency of the atmosphere) receive the same amount of solar energy. By the same reasoning, different parallels or latitudes receive varying amounts of insolation, there being a decrease from equator to poles for the year as a whole. If insolation were the only control of atmospheric phenomena, then all places in the same latitude should have identical climates. Although certainly not identical throughout, the strong climatic resemblances within latitude belts testify to the dominant, although not exclusive, rank of sun control.

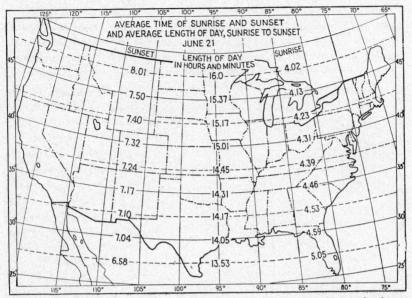

FIG. 13.—At the time of the summer solstice, days are more than 2 hr. longer in northernmost United States than they are in the extreme south. Length of day increases with latitude until north of the Arctic Circle the sun on June 21 does not set and the day is 24 hr. long. (*After Kincer.*)

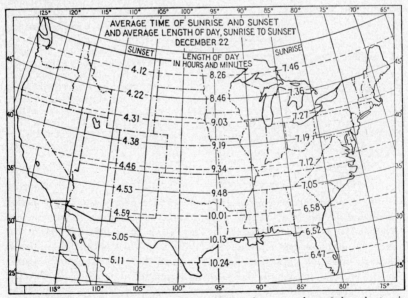

FIG. 14.—At the time of the winter solstice, days are about 2 hr. shorter in northernmost United States than they are in the extreme south. Length of day decreases with latitude until north of the Arctic Circle the sun on Dec. 22 does not rise above the horizon. (*After Kincer.*)

37. EARTH AND SUN RELATIONS. The rotation and revolution of the earth and the inclination and parallelism of its axis have been discussed in an earlier chapter (II). It remains to be analyzed, then, how these earth motions and positions act to produce the changing lengths of day and varying angles of the sun's rays, which in turn are the causes of the seasons.

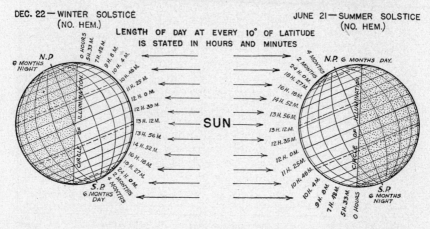

DEC. 22 — WINTER SOLSTICE (NO. HEM.)

JUNE 21 — SUMMER SOLSTICE (NO. HEM.)

LENGTH OF DAY AT EVERY 10° OF LATITUDE IS STATED IN HOURS AND MINUTES

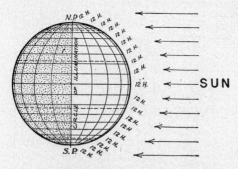

SEPT. 22 — AUTUMN EQUINOX
MARCH 21 — SPRING EQUINOX

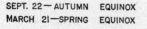

FIG. 15.—On the equinoxes, when the sun's vertical rays are at the equator, the circle of illumination cuts all the parallels in half, and days and nights are equal in length over the entire earth. At this time insolation decreases regularly from equator to poles. At the times of the solstices the sun's vertical rays have reached their greatest poleward migration. The circle of illumination cuts all the parallels (except the equator) unequally so that days and nights are unequal in length except at latitude 0°.

38. *The Equinoxes; Spring and Fall.* Twice during the yearly period of revolution, on Mar. 21 and Sept. 22, the sun's noon rays are directly overhead or vertical at the equator (Fig. 15). At these times, therefore, the circle of illumination, marking the position of the tangent rays, passes through both poles and consequently cuts all the earth's parallels exactly in half. One half of each parallel (180°) consequently is in light, and the other half in darkness. For this reason, since the path described by any point on the earth's surface during the period of rotation is coincident with its parallel of latitude, days and nights are equal (12 hr. each) over the entire earth. From this fact the two dates Mar. 21 and Sept. 22 get their names, the *equinoxes* (spring equinox Mar. 21, autumn equinox Sept. 22—Northern Hemisphere). At these seasons the maximum solar energy is being received at the equator, a latitude from which it diminishes regularly toward either pole, where it becomes zero

39. *The Solstices; Summer and Winter.* On June 21 the earth is approximately midway in its orbit between the equinoctial positions, and the North Pole is inclined $23\frac{1}{2}°$ *toward* the sun (Fig. 15). As a result of the axial inclination, the sun's rays are shifted northward by that same amount ($23\frac{1}{2}°$), so that the noon rays are vertical at the Tropic of Cancer ($23\frac{1}{2}°$N.), and the tangent rays in the Northern Hemisphere pass over the pole and reach the Arctic Circle ($66\frac{1}{2}°$N.), $23\frac{1}{2}°$ on the opposite side of it. In the Southern Hemisphere the tangent rays do not reach the pole but terminate at the Antarctic Circle, $23\frac{1}{2}°$ short of it. Thus while all parts of the earth north of the Arctic Circle are experiencing constant daylight, similar latitudes in the Southern Hemisphere (poleward from the Antarctic Circle) are entirely without sunlight. At this time, June 21, or the *summer solstice*, all parallels, except the equator, are cut unequally by the circle of illumination, those in the Northern Hemisphere having the larger parts of their circumferences toward the sun so that days are longer than nights. Longer days, plus a greater angle of the sun's rays, result in a maximum receipt of solar energy in the Northern Hemisphere at this time. Summer, with its associated high temperatures, is the result, and north of the equator June 21 is known as the summer solstice. In the Southern Hemisphere at this same time, all these conditions are reversed, nights being longer than days and the sun's rays relatively oblique, so that solar radiation is at a minimum and winter conditions prevail.

On Dec. 21, when the earth is in the opposite position in its orbit from what it was on June 21, it is the South Pole that is inclined $23\frac{1}{2}°$ *toward* the sun (Fig. 15). The latter's noon rays are then vertical over the Tropic of Capricorn ($23\frac{1}{2}°$S.), and the tangent rays pass $23\frac{1}{2}°$ over the South Pole to the Antarctic Circle ($66\frac{1}{2}°$S.). Consequently south of $66\frac{1}{2}°$S. there is constant light, while north of $66\frac{1}{2}°$N. there is a continuous absence of sunlight. All parallels of the earth, except the equator, are cut unequally by the circle of illumination, with days longer and sun's rays more nearly vertical in the Southern Hemisphere. This, therefore, is summer south of the equator but winter in the Northern Hemisphere (winter solstice), where opposite conditions prevail.

40. DISTRIBUTION OF SOLAR RADIATION AT THE EARTH'S SURFACE. *Effects of an Atmosphere Omitted.* It is clear from the previous discussion that the belt of maximum insolation swings back and forth across the equator during the course of a year, following the shifting rays of the sun, with the two variables, (*a*) angle of sun's rays and (*b*) length of day, largely determining the amount of solar energy received at any time or place.

41. *Distribution from Pole to Pole along a Meridian.* For the *year as a whole* as well as on two specific dates, the *spring* and *autumnal equinoxes*,

insolation is highest at the equator and diminishes with regularity toward the poles (table below).

TOTAL ANNUAL INSOLATION FOR VARIOUS LATITUDES EXPRESSED IN THERMAL
DAYS (Effects of an atmosphere omitted)
(The Unit, or Thermal Day, Is the Average Total Daily Insolation at the
Equator)

Latitude	Thermal Days
0°	365.2
10°	360.2
20°	345.2
30°	321.0
40°	288.5
50°	249.7
60°	207.8
70°	173.0
80°	156.6
90°	151.6

At the time of the *summer solstice*, June 21, although the noon rays of the sun are vertical only $23\frac{1}{2}°$ north of the equator, the increasing length of day in the higher latitudes tends to offset the declining angle of the sun's rays poleward from the Tropic of Cancer, so that, if the effects of an atmosphere are omitted, insolation will reach a maximum at the North Pole. Even with the absorptive effects of an atmosphere taken into consideration, the latitude receiving the maximum insolation is still well poleward of the tropic, although not at the pole, while latitude 60° receives more than does the equator. These facts of insolation distribution help to explain the warm summers of parts of the middle latitudes. It is clear also that during the course of a year there is a marked latitudinal migration of the belt of strong insolation.

42. *Annual Distribution for Various Latitudes.* The yearly insolation curves for the several latitudes can be arranged in three general groups (Fig. 16): (a) The equatorial type, which prevails between about latitudes 20°N. and 20°S., has two maxima and two minima and *at no time reaches zero.* (b) The middle-latitude type has one maximum and one minimum and likewise *does not reach zero at any time.* (c) The polar type, *i.e.*, poleward from the Arctic and Antarctic Circles, has one maximum and one minimum *but does reach zero,* for during a portion of the year there is a total absence of direct sunlight.

43. *Effects of an Atmosphere upon Insolation.* Thus far the whole problem of insolation distribution has been greatly simplified by assuming that solar radiation is received at the earth's surface without passing through an atmosphere. When that gaseous envelope is added, numerous modifications and complications result. Chief among these is a weakening of insolation at the earth's surface due to (a) *selective scattering,* chiefly of the

short wave lengths of blue light by very small obscuring particles (molecules of air, fine dust); (*b*) *diffuse reflection* of all wave lengths by larger particles (dust, cloud droplets); and (*c*) *absorption* of selected wave lengths, chiefly the longer ones, by water vapor and in a very minor degree by oxygen and ozone (see solid lines in Fig. 16). A part of that energy which is scattered and reflected is sent back into space and is lost to the earth. Some of it, however, reaches the earth's surface in the form of diffuse blue light of the sky, called diffuse daylight, and is transformed into heat and other forms of energy. It is this diffuse daylight which prevents absolute darkness on cloudy days, indoors, or in the shade where direct sunlight is absent. The energy transmitted to the earth in this form probably amounts to one-quarter of the energy of direct sunlight.

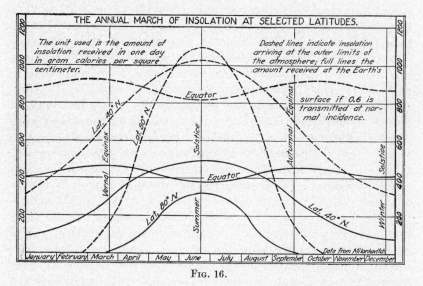

FIG. 16.

The amount of depletion of insolation by reflection and absorption in passing through the atmosphere depends upon (*a*) the length of the passage, or, in other words, the angle of the sun's rays; and (*b*) the transparency of the atmosphere. The former factor can be arrived at mathematically, but the second is variable according to time and place. It is estimated that 42 per cent of the total insolation reaching the outer limits of the air layer is lost by *scattering and reflection* from clouds, small dust particles, molecules of air, and the earth's surface and so has no part in heating either the earth or its atmosphere. Fifteen per cent is *absorbed* directly by the atmosphere, most of it by water vapor. The remaining 43 per cent reaches the earth's surface either as direct sunlight or as diffuse daylight, is absorbed by it, heats it, and eventually heats the atmosphere as well. From the preceding analysis it is obvious that only some 58 per cent of the solar radiation (15 per cent absorbed by the atmosphere directly and

43 per cent absorbed by the earth's surface) is available for heating the atmosphere.

Absorption of Insolation at the Earth's Surface; Processes Associated with the Heating and Cooling of the Earth's Surface and Atmosphere

HEATING AND COOLING OF LAND AND WATER SURFACES

44. LAND AND WATER CONTRASTS. Thus far the discussion has been concerned largely with distribution of solar energy, the single important source of atmospheric heat. But sun energy is of such short wave lengths that only relatively small amounts (15 per cent) of it can be absorbed directly by the earth's atmosphere. All bodies whatever their temperature give off radiation. The hotter the body the more intense the radiation and the shorter the wave lengths. Low-temperature long-wave radiation like that of the earth is invisible, whereas much of the sun's high-temperature short-wave radiation is visible. In order to be readily absorbed by the air sun energy first must be converted into terrestrial energy, which is composed of longer wave lengths. (Ratio of wave lengths of solar and terrestrial energy is roughly 1:25.) This conversion from short-wave solar to long-wave terrestrial energy takes place principally at the earth's surface, by which insolation is much more readily absorbed than it is by the relatively transparent atmosphere. Absorbed at the earth's surface, the solar energy is there converted into heat, after which the earth itself becomes a radiating body. Thus the atmosphere receives most of its heat only *indirectly* from the sun but *directly* from the earth's surface, which in turn had previously absorbed and consequently been warmed by solar energy. It is obvious, therefore, that preliminary to a discussion of heating and cooling the atmosphere, it is necessary to understand the comparative reactions to solar energy (in terms of reflection,[1] absorption, transmission) of the various kinds of terrestrial surfaces. Here the greatest contrasts are between land and water

---

[1] It is a common misconception that water is a much better reflector of insolation than are land surfaces. Recent investigations seem to indicate that instead of being a better reflector, water actually may be less efficient than land. Unfortunately the published data by different investigators of the problem are not entirely in agreement so that simple and direct comparisons are made more difficult. A fair estimate for the average amount of insolation reflected by the great variety of land surfaces is 10 to 15 per cent. For a water surface the estimates vary between 8 and 20 per cent. Based exclusively upon the comparative amounts of insolation lost by reflection, therefore, it appears that there is no great difference in the heating and cooling of land and water surfaces.

surfaces, although, to be sure, there are no fixed values for all land areas, because of such variables as snow cover, soil color, vegetation cover, and others.

The most striking contrasts between land and water areas, relative to their reactions to isolation, may be summarized as follows:

45. *Movement and Mixing.* Since water is a fluid, its movements in the form of waves, drifts, currents, and tides tend to distribute the absorbed solar energy throughout the whole mass. Moreover, when a water surface begins to cool, convectional currents are set up, the cooler, heavier surface layers sinking and being replaced by warmer water from underneath. Consequently the whole mass of water must be cooled before the surface layers can be brought to a low temperature. As a result, a larger mass of water (as compared with land) imparts its heat to the surrounding air, and the supply of heat is maintained for a longer period of time. It is largely because the upper layers of the ocean are always in a state of violent stirring, with the heat gains and losses at the surface thereby being distributed throughout large volumes of water, that the surface temperatures of water bodies change relatively little between day and night or between winter and summer. Over lands, on the other hand, where there can be no turbulence or mixing, diurnal and seasonal surface-temperature fluctuations are much more striking.

46. *Transmission.* Since water is relatively transparent to insolation, the sun's rays penetrate to considerable depths so that their energy is distributed throughout a larger mass. On the other hand, the relatively opaque land concentrates the solar energy close to the surface, which results in more rapid and intense heating. This same concentration of energy close to the surface likewise permits the land area to cool more rapidly than is true of the more deeply warmed water body.

47. *Specific Heat.* For a given volume of dry ground and water, approximately five times as much energy is required to raise the temperature of the water, say, 1° as to raise the temperature of the dry ground by the same amount. This relationship is expressed by saying that the *specific heat* of water is higher than that of land, which causes the water to heat (and cool) more slowly.

48. *Summary of Land and Water Contrasts.* From the above comparisons of land and water as regards their reactions to insolation, it becomes evident that, with the same amount of solar energy falling upon each, a land surface will reach a higher temperature, and reach it more quickly, than a water surface. Conversely, a land surface also cools more rapidly. Land-controlled, or continental, climates, therefore, should be characterized by large daily and seasonal extremes of temperature, whereas ocean-controlled, or marine, climates should be more moderate. The ocean surface probably changes temperatures not more than 1° between day and night, and seasonal changes also are very small. The relatively slower heating and cooling of water bodies quite naturally lead to a lag in the seasonal temperatures of marine climates.

HEATING AND COOLING THE ATMOSPHERE

49. Being acquainted now, as a result of the previous discussion, with (a) the distribution of solar energy over the earth and (b) the contrasting reactions of land and water surfaces to this solar energy, and (c) being aware that the air receives most of its energy directly from the surface upon which it rests and only indirectly from the sun, the background is sufficient to proceed with an analysis of the processes involved in heating and cooling the atmosphere.

50. HEATING PROCESSES. *Absorption of Direct and Reflected Insolation.* The earth's atmosphere is relatively transparent to direct and reflected solar radiation, which is short-wave energy, only about 15 per cent being absorbed, and that chiefly by small amounts of water vapor. About one-half of this absorption takes place in the lower two kilometers of air, but this is a large mass of air through which to spread $7\frac{1}{2}$ per cent of the solar radiation. The process is not very effective therefore in producing the normal daytime rise in temperature close to the earth's surface. Evidence of this is suggested by the fact that often on a clear winter day, when the land surface is blanketed by a reflecting snow cover, air temperatures may remain extremely low in spite of a bright sun. At the same time, on the south side of an absorbing brick wall or building, where short-wave sun energy is being converted into long-wave terrestrial energy, it may be comfortably warm. Dust, an impurity in the air, readily absorbs insolation, each particle thereby becoming a tiny focus for radiated terrestrial energy.

51. *Conduction.* When two bodies of unequal temperature are in *contact* with one another, energy in the form of heat passes from the warmer to the colder object until they both attain the same temperature. Thus, during the daylight hours, the solid earth (without a snow cover), being a much better absorber of insolation than air, attains a higher temperature. By conduction, therefore, the layer of air resting upon the warmer earth becomes heated. But air is a poor conductor, so that heat from the warmed lower layer is transferred very slowly to those above. Unless there is, through movement, a constant replacement of the warmed layer in contact with the earth, only the lower few feet will be heated by this process during the course of a day. Through air currents and winds, however, large masses of air are brought into contact with the heated earth's surface and consequently

are warmed. Heating by conduction is primarily a daytime and a summer process.

Just as a warm earth on a summer day heats the air layer next to it by conduction, so a cold earth, chilled by terrestrial radiation on a winter night, has exactly the opposite effect. It not infrequently happens that, during clear, calm, winter nights, as a result of radiation and conduction, the atmospheric strata adjacent to the earth become colder than those at some distance above its surface (59).

52. *Radiation.*   Short-wave solar energy, absorbed at the earth's surface, is there transformed into heat. Through this absorption and conversion of insolation, the heated earth becomes a radiating body. But although the atmosphere is capable of absorbing only relatively small amounts (15 per cent) of short-wave incoming solar energy, it is, on the other hand, able to retain $75\pm$ per cent of the outgoing long-wave earth radiation. As stated before, water vapor is the principal absorbing gas. This absorptive effect of water vapor upon outgoing earth radiation is illustrated by the rapid night cooling in deserts, the dry air and clear sky permitting a more rapid escape of energy. Obviously the effect of the atmosphere is analogous to that of a pane of glass, which lets through most of the incoming short-wave solar energy but greatly retards the outgoing long-wave earth radiation, thus maintaining surface temperatures considerably higher than they otherwise would be. This is the so-called *greenhouse effect* of the earth's atmosphere.

Radiation of terrestrial energy from the earth's surface upward toward space is a continuous process. During the daylight hours up to about midafternoon, however, receipts of energy from the sun are in excess of the amount radiated from the earth, with the result that surface-air temperatures usually continue to rise until two to four o'clock in the afternoon. But during the night, when receipts of solar energy cease, a continued loss of energy through earth radiation results in a cooling of the earth's surface and a consequent drop in air temperature. Being a better radiator than air, the ground during the night becomes cooler than the air above it. When this condition prevails, the lower layers of atmosphere lose heat by radiation to the colder ground as well as upward toward space. This process is particularly effective during the long nights of winter when, if the skies are clear and the air is dry and calm, excessively rapid and long-continued radiation takes place. If a snow cover mantles the ground, cooling is even more pronounced, for not only is most of the incoming solar radiation during the short day reflected, but at night, the snow, which is a very poor conductor of heat, allows little to come up from the ground below to replenish that lost by radiation. As a result, the snow surface becomes excessively cold, and then in turn the air layer resting upon it.

Water, like land, is a good radiator, but the cooled surface waters keep constantly sinking to be replaced by warmer currents from below. Extremely low temperatures over water bodies are impossible, therefore, until they are frozen over, after which they act like a snow-covered land surface. Humid air or a cloudy sky tends to prevent rapid earth radiation so that air temperatures remain higher, and frosts are less likely on humid nights and especially when a cloud cover prevails. There are authentic cases, in the dry air and under the cloudless skies of Sahara, of day temperatures of 90° followed by night temperatures slightly below freezing. When clouds cover the sky all the earth radiation is completely absorbed at the base of the cloud sheet, which in turn reradiates a part of it back to the earth so that cooling of the earth is retarded. Under a sky with low clouds the net loss of heat from the ground is only about one-seventh the loss with clear skies. Water vapor likewise absorbs and reradiates outgoing terrestrial energy but not so effectively as cloud particles.

Through the first three heating processes described above (50, 51, 52) there is actually an *addition* of energy to the atmosphere. Through the three processes the description of which follows (53, 54, 55) there is no addition of energy but only a *transfer* from one place to another, or from one air mass to another, of that which already has been acquired.

53. *Convectional Currents.* The surface air, after being heated by conduction and radiation, expands in volume and consequently

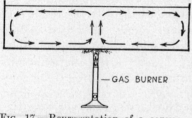

— GAS BURNER

Fig. 17.—Representation of a convectional circulation.

decreases in density. Because of expansion, a portion of the warmer, lighter column of air overflows aloft, thereby decreasing its own pressure at the surface and at the same time increasing that of the adjacent cooler air. This causes a lifting of the warmer, lighter air column by the heavier, cooler, settling air that flows in at the surface to displace it. Such a circulation, as described above and illustrated in Fig. 17, is called a *convectional system.* Warm surface air, expanded, and therefore less dense, is like a cork that is held under water; *i.e.*, it is unstable and inclined to rise. This convectional principle (which applies to liquids and gases only) is employed in the ordinary hot-air and hot-water heating systems. The rising masses of warmed air on a hot summer day make air transport relatively bumpy, since the plane alternately crosses rising and sinking air masses. While heating processes 2 (conduction) and 3 (radiation) are especially effective in heating the lower layers of atmosphere, convection, on the other hand, is capable of carrying terrestrial heat to the upper air strata as well. It, too, is primarily a daytime and a summer process.

54. *Importation by Air Masses and Winds.* Even the layman has come to recognize that in Northern Hemisphere middle latitudes a south wind is usually associated with unseasonably high temperatures. In such a case the wind acts simply as the conveyor or importer of heat from lower latitudes where higher temperatures are normal. Such an importation of southerly warmth in winter results in mild weather, with melting snow and sloppy streets. In summer, several days of south wind may result in a "hot wave" with maximum temperatures of over 90°.

If tropical air masses with associated south winds from regions that are usually warmer (Northern Hemisphere) import higher temperatures to the regions toward which they blow, then polar air masses with associated north winds from colder, higher latitudes, or from the cold interiors of continents, should in turn bring lower temperatures. These importations are particularly effective where there are no mountain barriers to block the wind movement. In eastern North America where lowlands prevail, great masses of cold polar air periodically pour down over the Mississippi Valley, occasionally carrying severe frosts even to the Gulf States.

55. *Heating by Compression and Cooling by Expansion.* When a mass of air descends from higher to lower altitudes, as, for instance, when it moves down a mountain slope, it is being transferred from regions of lower atmospheric pressure to those where it is higher. Because there is an increasingly thicker layer of air pressing down upon it as lower altitudes are attained, the descending mass of air gradually is being compressed in volume. Work is being done upon it, and as a result of compression its temperature is increased.

Just as descending air heats as a result of compression, so rising air cools as a result of expansion. In the latter case the upward current is traveling from a lower altitude where atmospheric pressure is greater to a higher altitude where pressure is less. As a consequence, the rising air continues to expand as the weight of atmosphere upon it becomes less. Work is done in pushing aside other air in order to make room for itself. This work done by the rising and expanding air consumes energy, which is subtracted from the ascending currents in the form of heat, resulting in a lowering of their temperature.

56. *Heat Balance in the Atmosphere.* Since the mean temperature of the earth remains about the same, getting neither colder nor warmer, it follows that the heat lost by the earth through radiation to space is identical with the amount of energy received from the sun. But although this balance is true for the earth as a whole, it is not true for individual latitudes. In the low latitudes, equatorward from about 37°, the incoming solar energy exceeds the outgoing earth energy,

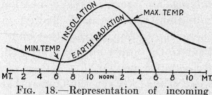

Fig. 18.—Representation of incoming solar radiation and outgoing earth radiation for a period of 24 hr. at about the time of an equinox.

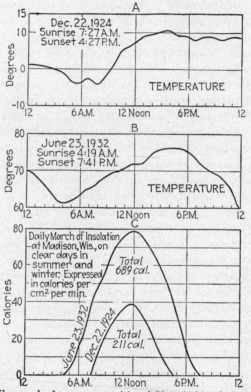

Fig. 19.—Daily march of temperature (*A* and *B*) and of insolation (*C*) on *clear days* in winter and summer at Madison, Wis. The total solar energy received was 3¼ times as great on June 23 as on Dec. 22. Note that temperature lags behind insolation. South winds prevented normal night cooling on Dec. 22.

whereas poleward from latitude 37° exactly the reverse is true. Unless there is to be a constant increase in the temperatures of low latitudes and a constant decrease in the temperatures of the middle and higher latitudes, this situation requires a continuous transfer of energy from low to high latitudes of the earth. This transfer is accomplished by the winds of the earth. *In fact, in this unequal latitudinal distribution of solar and terrestrial radiation is to be found the ultimate cause for the earth's atmospheric circulation and for much of its weather.*

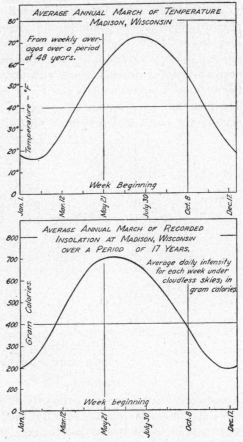

DAILY AND SEASONAL MARCH OF TEMPERATURE

57. All average temperatures for a month, season, year, or even a long period of years are built upon the *mean daily temperature* as the basic unit. The daily mean is the average of the highest and the lowest temperatures recorded during the 24-hr. period.

The mean daily march of temperature chiefly reflects the balance between incoming solar radiation and outgoing earth radiation (Fig. 18). From about sunrise until 2:00 to 4:00 P.M., when energy is being supplied by incoming solar radiation faster than it is being lost by earth radiation, the temperature curve usually con-

FIG. 20.—Note that temperature lags behind insolation. Insolation curve has been smoothed slightly.

tinues to rise (Figs. 18, 19). Conversely, from about 3:00 ± P.M. to sunrise, when loss by terrestrial radiation exceeds receipts of solar energy, the daily temperature curve usually falls.

The annual march, or cycle, of temperature reflects the daily increase in insolation (hence heat accumulated in the air and ground) from midwinter to midsummer and the decrease in the same from midsummer to midwinter (Fig. 20). Usually there is a temperature lag of 30 to 40 days after the periods of maximum or minimum insolation. This reflects the balance between incoming and outgoing energy.

Distribution of Temperature: Vertical and Horizontal

VERTICAL DISTRIBUTION OF TEMPERATURE

58. TEMPERATURE DECREASES WITH ALTITUDE. Numerous temperature observations made during mountain, balloon, airplane, and kite ascents show that under normal conditions there is a general *decrease* in temperature with *increasing* elevation. Although the rate of decrease is not uniform, varying with time of day, season, and location, the average is approximately 3.3°F. for each 1,000-ft. rise (Fig. 21*B*). The fact that air temperature is normally highest at low elevations next to the earth and decreases with altitude clearly indicates that

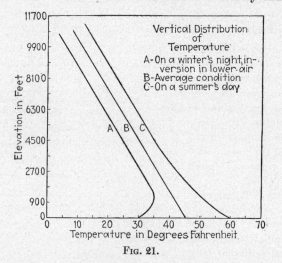

FIG. 21.

atmospheric heat is received primarily directly from the earth's surface and only indirectly from the sun. But the lower air is warmer, not only because it is closest to the direct source of heat, but also because it is denser and contains more water vapor and dust, which cause it to be a more efficient absorber of terrestrial radiation than is the thinner, drier, cleaner air aloft. Two exceptions to this general rule of decreasing temperature with increasing altitude are (*a*) the stratosphere and (*b*) conditions of temperature inversion.

Above an elevation of approximately 10 miles at the equator, 6 miles in latitudes 45 to 50°, and 4 miles at the poles, the normal decrease in temperature halts abruptly and thermal conditions remain relatively constant for another 12 miles or more. It is possible, then, to think of the earth's atmosphere as composed of two shells, or layers. The higher, or outer, shell, in which temperature remains much the same throughout, is known as the *stratosphere*. In it temperatures are very low, clouds are absent, dust and water vapor are at a minimum, convectional currents are lacking, and all air movement is horizontal. Below the stratosphere is the turbulent, dusty layer known as the *troposphere*, which contains much water vapor and also clouds and in which temperature decreases with increasing altitude.

59. INVERSIONS OF TEMPERATURE. Although the *normal* vertical temperature gradient (lapse rate) shows a decrease in temperature with altitude up to the bottom of the stratosphere, it frequently happens on clear, calm, nights, especially in the cooler seasons, and when the ground is snow covered, that the air close to the earth becomes colder than that at higher altitudes. Under this arrangement, with the coldest air next to the earth, the normal situation is reversed, and a *temperature inversion* is said to exist (Fig. 21*A*). This condition is dependent upon a cold land surface which is chilled as a result of rapid nocturnal cooling by radiation. Ideal conditions for temperature inversion are (*a*) long nights, as in winter, so that there will be a relatively long period when outgoing earth radiation exceeds incoming solar radiation; (*b*) a clear sky so that loss of heat by terrestrial radiation is rapid and unretarded; (*c*) cold dry air that absorbs little earth radiation; (*d*) calm air so that little mixing shall take place, and the surface stratum will, as a consequence, have time, by conduction and radiation, to become excessively cold; and (*e*) a snow-covered surface, which, owing to reflection of solar energy, heats little by day and, being a poor conductor, retards the upward flow of heat from the ground below. At the Eiffel Tower in Paris there is, throughout the year, an increase in temperature upward from the base to top between midnight and 4:00 A.M. Strong surface inversions make the landing of an airplane difficult, for the added lift exerted by the dense cold air near the ground may make it difficult for the pilot to penetrate the inversion. A very close relationship exists between temperature inversions and frost phenomena, since conditions favorable for the one are also ideal for the other. Although temperature inversions are common on flattish land surfaces, they are, nevertheless, more perfectly developed in depressions.

60. *Air Drainage.* In regions of uneven surface configuration, the cold stratum of air next to the earth's surface, because of its greater density, slips off the uplands and flows down to surrounding lowlands (Fig. 22). This phenomenon of the cold air, drained from the adjacent slopes, collecting in valleys and lowlands is designated as *air drainage*. It is a well-known fact that the first frosts of autumn and the last in spring occur in bottomlands, while the lowest minima on calm,

clear, winter nights are found in similar locations. On one occasion, during a cold spell, a temperature of −8.9° was registered on top of Mount Washington, N. H., while records of −23 to −31° were recorded in the surrounding lowlands. Citrus orchards in California, which are quite intolerant of frost, are located on the upper slopes of alluvial fans where air drainage causes a slipping off of the frosty air, while the colder lower slopes and bottoms are given over to hardier deciduous

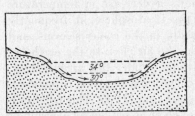

FIG. 22.—Cold air, because it is denser, tends to settle into the valley bottoms. For this reason frost is more prevalent in low places than it is on adjacent slopes.

fruits and nuts or to field crops. Coffee in Brazil is prevailingly planted on the rolling uplands, while the frosty valleys are avoided. Resort hotels in the Swiss Alps shun the cold, foggy valleys and choose instead sites on the brighter and warmer slopes. So definite and sharp is the autumn frost line along certain of the valley slopes in the Blue Ridge Mountains that one can trace it by means of the color line between the darkened, frozen vegetation below and the brighter, living green of that above. At times the lower part of a bush may be frozen while the top is untouched.

On clear, cold nights when air drainage and temperature inversions are prevalent the atmosphere is very stable. The heaviest air is at the lowest elevation, where, on the basis of density, it should be. There is no inclination for it to rise. This is quite opposite to the unstable condition of the atmosphere on a hot summer day, when the heated and expanded air near the earth's surface is like a cork held under water.

61. FROST AND FROST PROTECTION. The term "frost" may be applied either (a) to the white deposit of condensed water vapor in solid form (hoarfrost) or (b) to a temperature of 32° or below, even though there is no deposit of white frost. There are frosts of various degrees of severity, but it is the "killing frost," which may be defined as a temperature condition "of sufficient severity to be generally destructive to the staple products of the locality," that is of principal interest to geographers. When it is difficult by direct observation of destructive effects to determine the dates of the first killing frost in autumn and the last in spring, and thereby the length of the frost-free, or growing, season, the first and last dates on which a minimum temperature of 32° was recorded are accepted. Throughout most of the middle latitudes frosts are of chief significance in autumn and spring,

although in subtropical latitudes, such as California and Florida, midwinter frosts are critical because of the active growth of sensitive crops during that season (Fig. 23). On the poleward margins of the intermediate zones, on the other hand, in such regions as northern Canada and northern Eurasia, summer frosts not infrequently do serious damage to cereal crops. In tropical lowlands freezing temperatures are entirely absent.

62. *Conditions Favorable for Frost.* Ideal conditions for the occurrence of frost are those that are conducive to rapid and prolonged

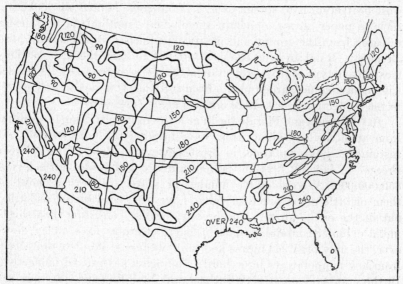

Fig. 23.—The average length of the growing season, *i.e.*, the number of days between the last killing frost in spring and the first killing frost in fall, throughout the United States is shown on the above map. Figures indicate number of frost-free days. (*After map by U. S. Weather Bureau.*)

surface cooling, *viz.*, (a) a preliminary importation of a mass of chilly polar air, (b) followed by clear, dry, calm nights, during which the surface air, by radiation and conduction, may be reduced below freezing. The original importation provides the necessary mass of cool air, the temperature of which is already relatively low, although still somewhat above freezing, while further rapid loss of heat by earth radiation during the following clear night is all that is necessary to reduce the temperature of the surface air below freezing. But even though the generally favorable conditions for frost occurrence described above may prevail over extensive areas, the destructive effects very often are local and patchy. This is a matter chiefly of surface configuration and air drainage (60).

63. *Frost Protection.* The problem of artificial protection from frost is of genuine significance only in regions of highly sensitive and valuable crops which occupy restricted areas. It is obviously quite impossible to protect such extensively grown crops as corn or small grains, even when Weather Bureau warnings are issued 12 to 24 hr. in advance of the anticipated freeze. The highly valuable citrus groves of California and Florida, however, occupying only restricted areas, present a somewhat different problem. For small-scale vegetable gardeners or fruit growers the simplest and most effective means of frost protection is to spread over the crop some nonmetallic covering such as paper, straw, or cloth, thereby intercepting the heat being radiated from the ground and plants. The purpose of the cover, quite obviously, is not to keep the cold out but to keep the heat in. This inexpensive type of frost protection is the one resorted to by the housewife in saving her garden plants from freezing. It is not so well suited to the protection of extensive orchard areas, however.

In California and Florida the huge losses in the citrus areas resulting from an occasional killing frost have inspired the most careful and sustained experimentation in frost-fighting methods. The "Great Freeze" of Jan. 19, 1922, in California resulted in a total citrus loss of $50,000,000. A considerable number of protective devices, most of them of little or no practical value, have been constructed and tried out in the citrus groves. The orchard heater, consisting of a sheet-metal cylinder containing about a gallon of crude oil, is today, however, the only practical means known of obtaining complete protection from low temperatures in orchards. Smudging has proved ineffective. In the cranberry areas of Wisconsin and New England, the bogs are usually flooded if killing frost seems probable. The water surface created by flooding cools more slowly than a land surface and thereby essens the frost hazard. Moreover, a protective cover of light fog is likely to develop over the flooded fields.

Horizontal Distribution of Temperature

64. Isothermal Maps. Temperature distribution over the earth is shown on Figs 24, 25, and Plate I by means of isotherms, *i.e.*, lines connecting places of the same temperature. Thus all points on the earth's surface through which any one isotherm passes have identical average temperatures. It would be entirely feasible to cover the world map with figures representing the temperatures of hundreds of stations, but such a map would be very cumbersome to use. Without scrutinizing each figure it would be difficult to determine, for instance, the regions of highest or lowest temperatures. But if lines are drawn on such a

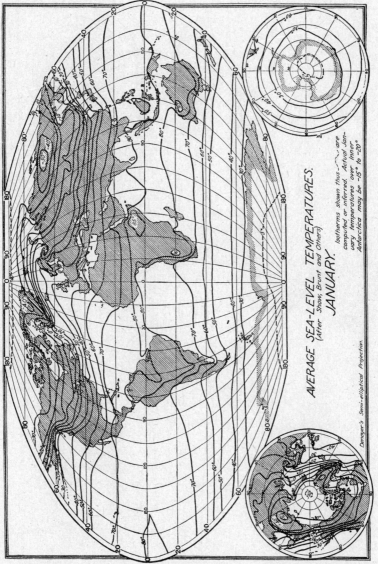

AVERAGE SEA-LEVEL TEMPERATURES.
(After Shaw, Brunt and Others)
JANUARY.

Isotherms shown thus ~~~~ are
computed or inferred. Actual January temperatures over Inner
Antarctica may be -15° to -20°

Denoyer's Semi-elliptical Projection

FIG. 24.

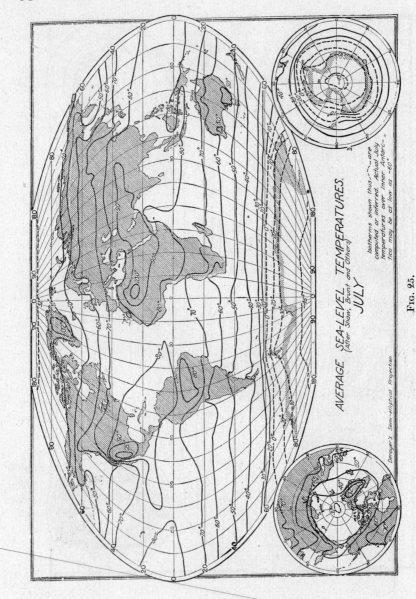

AVERAGE SEA-LEVEL TEMPERATURES.
(After Shaw, Brunt and Others)
JULY

Isotherms shown thus-·-·- are computed or inferred. Actual July temperatures over Inner Antarc- tica may be as low as -60°

Denoyer's Semi-elliptical Projection

FIG. 25.

map connecting places of the same average temperature, then one can see at a glance many of the significant facts of thermal distribution. On Figs 24 and 25 all temperatures have been reduced to sea level so that the effects of altitude are eliminated. If this were not done, the complications and details induced by mountains and other lesser relief forms would render the maps so confusing that the general world-wide effects of latitude and of land-and-water distribution would be difficult to perceive. These maps of sea-level isotherms are not so useful to agriculturists, engineers, and others who desire to put their data to practical use as are those showing *actual* surface temperatures (Plate I). Isotherms in general trend east-west, roughly following the parallels (Figs. 24, 25). This is not unexpected, since, except for differences in the transparency of the atmosphere, all places in the same latitude, or along the same parallel, receive identical amounts of solar energy. This east-west trend of isotherms indicates that latitude is the single greatest cause of temperature contrasts. On no parallel of latitude at any season are temperature differences so great as between poles and equator. With increasing distance above the earth's surface the isotherms become more parallel to the latitude circles.

65. *General Features of Temperature Distribution.* The highest average annual temperatures are in the low latitudes, where, for the year, the largest amounts of insolation are received, while the average lowest temperatures are in the vicinity of the poles, the regions of least annual insolation. Isotherms tend to be straighter and are also more widely spaced in the Southern Hemisphere, the surface of which is more homogeneous, in this case largely water. The greatest deviations from east-west courses are where the isotherms pass from continents to oceans or vice versa. That is caused by the contrasting heating and cooling properties of land and water surfaces and the effects of ocean currents. After latitude or sun, land and water are the next greatest control of temperature distribution. Cool ocean currents off the coasts of Peru and northern Chile, southern California, and southwestern Africa make themselves conspicuous through the *equatorward* bending of the isotherms. Similarly, warm currents in higher latitudes cause isotherms to bend *poleward*, this condition being most marked off the coast of northwestern Europe.

66. JANUARY AND JULY TEMPERATURES. For the earth in general, January and July represent the seasonal extremes of temperature. Following are some of the more significant features of temperature distribution as shown on the seasonal maps (Figs. 24, 25, Plate I).[1]

[1] The latest and probably the most reliable maps of Arctic temperatures are contained in "Klima des Kanadischen Archipels und Grönlands," Vol. II, Part K of

(a) From a comparison of the two maps it is obvious that there is a marked latitudinal shifting of the isotherms between July and January, following the latitudinal migration of sun's rays and insolation belts. (b) The migrations of isotherms are much greater over continents than over oceans because of the former's greater extremes of temperature. (c) The highest temperatures on both the January and July maps are over land areas, whereas the lowest temperatures in January emphatically are over Asia and North America, the largest land masses in the middle and higher latitudes. (d) In the Northern Hemisphere the January isotherms bend abruptly equatorward over the colder continents and poleward over the warmer oceans, whereas in July exactly the opposite conditions prevail. (e) No such seasonal contrasts

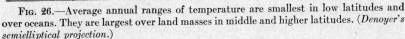

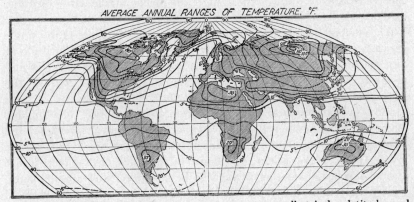

Fig. 26.—Average annual ranges of temperature are smallest in low latitudes and over oceans. They are largest over land masses in middle and higher latitudes. (*Denoyer's semielliptical projection.*)

between land and water as exist north of the equator are to be found in the Southern Hemisphere, for there large land masses are absent in the higher middle latitudes. (f) The lowest temperature on the January map is over northeastern Asia, the leeward side of the largest land mass in higher middle latitudes. The next lowest temperatures are over Greenland and North America.

67. *Annual Ranges of Temperature.* By the annual range of temperature is meant the difference between the average temperatures of the warmest and coldest months. The largest annual ranges of temperature are over the Northern Hemisphere continents which become alternately hot in summer and cold in winter (Fig. 26). Ranges are never large (a) near the equator, where insolation varies little; or

Handbuch der Klimatologie, edited by W. Köppen and R. Geiger. Gebrüder Borntraeger, Berlin, 1935.

(*b*) over large water bodies. For the latter reason ranges are everywhere small in the middle latitudes of the Southern Hemisphere. In general, they increase toward the higher latitudes but much more markedly over the continents than over the oceans.

68. AIR TEMPERATURE AND SENSIBLE TEMPERATURE. Correct *air temperature* can be obtained only by an accurate thermometer *properly exposed*. One of the principal items of correct exposure is to see that the instrument is *not* in the sun; otherwise it receives energy not only from the surrounding air but from the absorption of insolation as well. It also should be protected from direct radiation from the ground and adjacent buildings.

69. *Sensible temperature* refers to the sensation of temperature that the human body feels, as distinguished from actual air temperature which is recorded by a properly exposed thermometer. Unlike a thermometer that has no temperature of its own, the human body is a heat engine, generating energy at a relatively fixed rate when at rest. Anything, therefore, that affects the *rate of loss* of heat from the body affects physical comfort. Air temperature, of course, is an important factor, but so also are wind, humidity, and sunlight. Thus a *humid*, hot day is more uncomfortable than one of dry heat with the same temperature, since loss of heat by evaporation is retarded more when the air is humid. A *windy*, cold day feels uncomfortable because the loss of heat is speeded up by greater evaporation. A sunny day in winter feels less cold than it actually may be owing to the body's absorption of direct insolation. Cold air containing moisture particles is particularly penetrating because the skin becomes moist, and evaporation results, while further loss of heat results from contact with the cold water. The rate of heat loss by radiation is greater in dry than in humid air. Because of its sensitiveness to factors other than air temperature, the human body is not a very accurate thermometer.

Chapter IV. Atmospheric Pressure and Winds

70. IMPORTANCE OF PRESSURE AND WINDS AS CLIMATIC ELEMENTS AND CLIMATIC CONTROLS. Compared with temperature and precipitation, atmospheric pressure and winds are relatively insignificant as *elements* of weather and climate. To be sure, winds of high velocity may be dangerous to man's crops and structures, and there are, as well, certain physiological reactions to strong air movement, but the sum total of these direct effects of wind is not of first importance. Still less is human life directly affected by the slight changes in air pressure which occur at the earth's surface. Although imperceptible to our bodies, these pressure differences are the reason for the existence of winds. Therefore, while not directly of first importance as climatic elements, both pressure and winds are indirectly of outstanding significance in the effects that they have upon temperature and precipitation, the two genuinely important elements of weather and climate. The sequence of events might be as follows: A minor change in pressure (of little consequence directly) acts to change the velocity and direction of wind (also not of major importance directly), and this in turn brings about changes in temperature and precipitation, which together largely determine the character of weather and climate. Whether it is a south wind or a north wind is chiefly consequential because of the contrasting temperature conditions induced. An onshore wind as compared with an offshore one is climatically significant because of differences in moisture and temperature. It is chiefly as *controls* of temperature and precipitation, then, rather than as *elements* of weather and climate, that pressure and winds are worthy of attention. *The single most important function of wind is the transportation of water vapor from the oceans to the lands, where that water vapor condenses and falls as rain.* Because rainfall distribution over the earth is closely associated with the great pressure and wind systems, this chapter on pressure and winds precedes the one on moisture and precipitation. On the other hand, the discussion of atmospheric pressure logically follows the one on temperature, because many of the significant pressure differences and variations are induced by temperature.

71. RELATION OF AIR PRESSURE TO TEMPERATURE. A column of air 1 sq. in. in cross-sectional area extending from sea level to the top of the atmosphere weighs approximately 14.7 lb. This weight is balanced by a column of mercury nearly 30 in. tall having the same cross-sectional area. Thus it is customary to measure air pressure in terms of its equivalent weight as expressed in inches of a column of mercury— in other words, by a mercurial barometer. On all United States weather maps issued since January, 1940, pressure readings have been in millibars instead of inches. (The millibar is a force equal to 1,000 dynes per square centimeter.) One-tenth of an inch of mercury is approximately equal to 3.4 millibars, and sea-level atmospheric pressure may be expressed as 29.92 inches, 760 millimeters, or 1013.2 millibars.

RELATION OF PRESSURE IN INCHES TO PRESSURE IN MILLIBARS

Inches	Millibars	Inches	Millibars	Inches	Millibars
27.00	914.3	29.00	982.1	29.92	1,013.2
28.00	948.2	29.50	999.0	30.00	1,015.9
28.50	965.1	29.75	1,007.5	30.25	1,024.4

But the density and weight of a given volume of air vary with temperature. Thus when air is heated it expands and becomes less dense, so that a column of warm, light air weighs less than a column of cold, heavy air, both having the same height and cross-sectional area. In central Asia in January, when air temperature is very low and its density therefore high, the air pressure is nearly 1 in. of mercury greater than it is in summer. Changes in temperature produce changes in air density which set up vertical and horizontal movements resulting in changes in air pressure. Over a warm region air is heated, expands, and overflows aloft to adjacent regions where temperatures are lower (53). As a result of this horizontal transfer the weight of the air is reduced in the warm region and increased in the adjacent cooler one. It may be accepted as a general rule, therefore, that regions with high temperatures are *likely* to have air pressures lower than those of other regions where temperatures are not so high. *In other words, high temperature tends to produce low pressure, and low temperature is conducive to high pressure.* But although the *ultimate* cause of pressure differences is probably regional contrasts in temperature, it is not to be inferred that the aforementioned direct relationship is always obvious. On the contrary, there are numerous apparent exceptions.

Distribution of Atmospheric Pressure

72. VERTICAL DISTRIBUTION. Since air is very compressible it almost goes without saying that there is a rapid decrease in air weight or pressure with increasing altitude. The lower layers of the atmosphere are the densest because the weight of all the layers above rests upon them. For the first few thousand feet above sea level the rate of pressure decrease is in the neighborhood of 1 in. or 34 millibars of pressure for each 900 to 1,000 ft. With higher altitudes the air rapidly becomes much thinner and lighter, so that at an elevation of 18,000 ft. one-half the atmosphere by weight is below the observer, although the whole air mass extends to a height of several hundred miles. The pressure is again halved in the next 18,000 ft., and so on. The human body is not physiologically adjusted to the low pressures and associated small oxygen content of the air at high altitudes, and nausea, faintness, and nosebleed often result from a too rapid ascent. Oxygen tanks are a part of the normal equipment of aircraft operating at high altitudes.

73. HORIZONTAL DISTRIBUTION. *Average Conditions.* Just as temperature distribution is represented by *isotherms,* so atmospheric pressure distribution is represented by *isobars, i.e.,* lines connecting places having the same pressure (Figs. 29, 30). On the charts here shown, effects of elevation have been eliminated, all pressure readings having been reduced to sea level. Figure 27 is a very diagrammatic sketch of the arrangement of sea-level latitudinal pressure "belts"[1] as they might exist on an earth composed of either all land or all water. This arrangement is recognizable in the seasonal isobaric charts for January and July (Figs. 29, 30), particularly in the Southern Hemisphere where oceans predominate. North of the equator, where great land masses and oceans alternate, the pressure belts are so disrupted that they are not always easily recognizable. The more or less ideal arrangement shown in Fig. 27 is likewise relatively obvious on a map of world pressure for April or October, months in which the disturbing effects of temperature contrasts between continents and oceans are least prominent.

Following are the most noteworthy and characteristic features of average world-pressure conditions at sea level diagrammatically represented by Fig. 27. (a) There is an *equatorial belt of low pressure* (below 30 in.) in the general vicinity, but slightly to the north, of the geographic equator. It coincides rather closely with the belt of highest temperature and is largely the result of those thermal conditions.

---

[1] The term *belt,* as applied to distribution of atmospheric pressure and winds, is something of a misnomer but is used here for lack of a better name.

As proof of this causal relationship it may be pointed out that the lowest pressures within the belt coincide with the highest temperatures, both being over the land areas. (*b*) A series of connected high-pressure centers form two irregular belts of high pressure at approximately 30 to 40°N. and S. These are known as the *subtropical highs*. (*c*) From the subtropical highs pressure decreases poleward toward the troughs of low pressure located roughly in the vicinity of the Arctic and Antarctic circles. These are *subpolar troughs of low pressure*. In the Southern

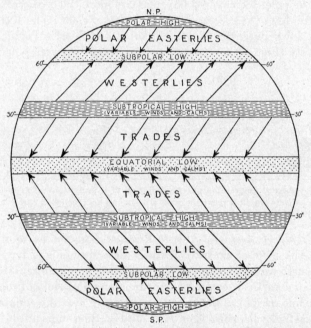

Fig. 27.—A very diagrammatic representation of pressure and wind arrangements as they might appear on an earth with a homogeneous surface.

Hemisphere the trough is much deeper and more continuous, and the pressure gradients steeper than in the Northern Hemisphere. (*d*) Beyond the subpolar lows, pressure appears to rise with increasing latitude, resulting in the *polar highs*, for which there are few data. Like the low pressure at the equator, the high pressures in the polar regions are, for the most part, directly thermally induced.

The character and arrangement of pressure features in the vicinity of the two poles are not entirely understood. In the Southern Hemisphere the symmetrical arrangement of land and water areas, with an elevated ice-covered continent at the pole and uninterrupted bordering ocean, appears to make for symmetrical pressure distribution as well. A permanent high over the Antarctic continent and a ring of low pressure surrounding it are the result. In the Northern Hemisphere, on the other hand, no such simple arrangement is evident.[1] At the North Pole is an ocean covered for most of the year by pack ice. Surrounding the Arctic Ocean are the land masses of Eurasia and North America with their great seasonal fluctuations of temperature and pressure, which in turn affect the inner polar area. During the cold seasons higher pressures exist over northern Eurasia and North America than at the pole. Ice-covered Greenland is more the center of a *permanent* Arctic high than is the immediate polar region. The Iceland and Aleutian lows over the North Atlantic and North Pacific Oceans respectively (Fig. 27) are portions of the fragmented subpolar trough.

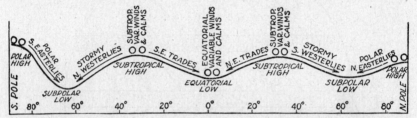

Fig. 28.—A very diagrammatic representation of a profile of surface pressure and wind belts as they might appear on an earth with a homogeneous surface. Compare with Fig. 39.

74. *Profile of Average Sea-level Pressure Distribution along a Meridian.* The general pressure features described above for a homogeneous earth are made clear in the very diagrammatic representation (Fig. 28) of a vertical section of pressure along a meridian from pole to pole. The line rises from the belt of low pressure near the equator to the subtropical highs at about 30 or 35°N. and S., then sinks until it reaches the subpolar lows in latitudes 60 to 70°, after which it rises again in the vicinity of the polar highs.

75. *Thermal and Dynamic Control of Average Sea-level Pressure Distribution.* Applying the general rule concerning the relationship between temperature and pressure (71) to the diagram below, it is evident that only the equatorial low and the polar highs appear to conform. Certainly the subtropical highs are not in regions of excessive cold, nor are the subpolar lows in regions of unusual heat. These are major exceptions to direct thermal control of pressure. It may be suggested at this point that these two pressure features owe their existence and location to dynamic forces associated with earth rotation

[1] The latest maps of Arctic pressures are contained in "Klima des Kanadischen Archipels und Grönlands," *op. cit.*

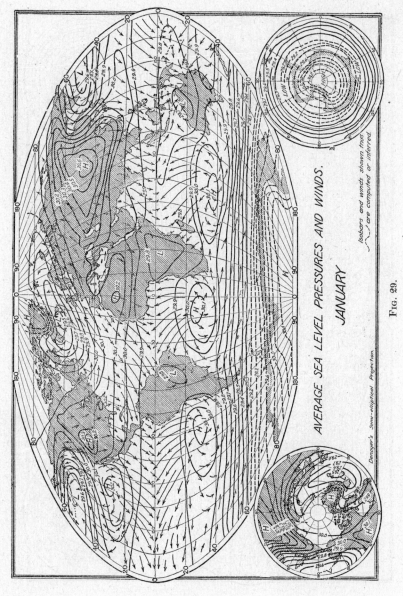

AVERAGE SEA LEVEL PRESSURES AND WINDS.
JANUARY

Isobars and winds shown thus
are computed or inferred.

Demoyer's Semi-elliptical Projection.

FIG. 29.

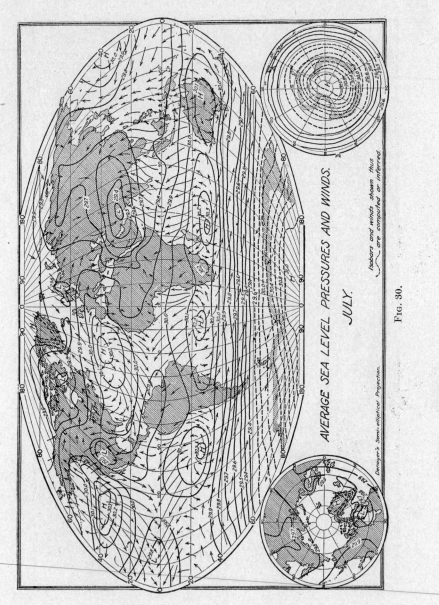

AVERAGE SEA LEVEL PRESSURES AND WINDS.

JULY.

Isobars and winds shown thus
are computed or inferred

Denoyer's Semi-elliptical Projection.

FIG. 30.

rather than to thermal forces or to a compromise between the two. A more complete explanation, however, must be postponed until greater familiarity with wind systems has been attained.

76. *Isobars for January and July* (Figs. 29, 30). The most noteworthy characteristics of pressure distribution in January and July, which represent the extreme seasons, are as follows: (*a*) Pressure "belts," like those of temperature, migrate north with the sun's rays in July and south in January, always lagging somewhat behind and usually not migrating so far as do the insolation belts. The latitudinal pressure migrations are greater over land masses than over the oceans, reflecting a similar situation with respect to temperature. (*b*) The

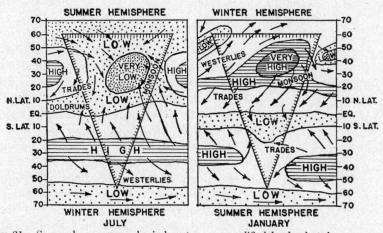

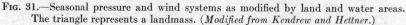

FIG. 31.—Seasonal pressure and wind systems as modified by land and water areas. The triangle represents a landmass. (*Modified from Kendrew and Hettner.*)

subtropical high-pressure belts are broken or fragmented into definite and discontinuous centers by the warm continents in summer. In winter, on the other hand, the cold land masses tend to strengthen the highs, making for greater continuity of the subtropical belts. (*c*) The middle-latitude continents, especially North America and Asia, become alternately sites of semipermanent high- and low-pressure centers in winter and summer respectively. The adjacent oceans likewise reverse their seasonal pressure conditions, but they are low when the continents are high and vice versa. These seasonal reversals of pressure have their origins in the temperature contrasts between land and water in the opposite seasons (Figs. 24, 25, Plate I). In general, pressure is higher in the colder hemisphere where the air is denser. The extraordinarily large and deep continental low-pressure center developed over Asia in July tends to wipe out the equatorial low which would normally prevail to the south of that land mass. Both North America and Asia in winter develop such strong and extensive continental highs that the normal subtropical belts of high pressure are merged with them and are thereby shifted 10+° too far northward. Like the trough of low pressure at the equator, and the polar highs, the seasonal lows and highs over the large middle-latitude continents are of direct thermal origin. As indicated in an earlier article (76), because of the disrupting effects of seasonal temperature contrasts over the great continents and oceans of the Northern Hemisphere, seasonal *centers* of low and high pressure often are more conspicuous north of the equator than are distinct pressure belts. In conjunction with the above discussion, see Fig. 31 and Art. 96.

Relation of Winds to Pressure

77. PRESSURE GRADIENT. Air that moves essentially parallel to the earth's surface is referred to as wind. Vertical air movements are more properly designated as currents, although the name is often applied to horizontal movements as well. Wind is usually caused by differences in air density, resulting in horizontal differences in air pressure. It represents nature's attempt to correct pressure inequalities. The rate and direction of change of pressure, as indicated by isobaric lines, are referred to as *pressure gradient*, or *barometric slope*, and it is this which indicates the velocity and general direction of air movements. Two very fundamental rules concerned with the relationships existing between pressure and winds are as follows: (*a*) The *direction* of air flow is from regions of greater to those of less density, *i.e.*, from high to low pressure or down the barometric slope, which may be represented by a line drawn at right angles to the isobars (Fig. 32).

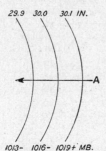

29.9 30.0 30.1 IN.

A

1013- 1016- 1019+ MB.

FIG. 32.—Gradient is represented by a line drawn at right angles to the isobars.

This follows the law of gravitation and is just as natural as the well-known fact that water runs downhill. (*b*) The *rate* of air flow, or velocity of the wind, is indicated by the steepness of the pressure gradient or the rate of pressure change. When the gradient is steep, air flow is rapid, and when it is weak, the wind is likewise weak. Just as the velocity of a river is determined largely by the slope of the land, or rate of change in elevation, so the velocity of wind is determined largely by the barometric slope, or the rate of change in air pressure. One, therefore, can determine the steepness of the pressure gradient, and consequently the relative velocity of air movement, by noting the spacing or closeness of the isobars. Closely spaced isobars, like those in the vicinity of the subpolar trough in the Southern Hemisphere (Figs. 29, 30), indicate relatively steep gradients, or marked pressure differences, and under these conditions winds of high velocity prevail. When isobars are far apart, gradients are weak, and winds are likewise. Calms prevail when pressure differences over extensive areas are almost, or quite, nil. At such times there is nearly an absence of isobaric lines on the pressure map.

APPROXIMATE RELATION OF WIND VELOCITY TO PRESSURE GRADIENT NEAR LONDON, ENGLAND[1]

Difference in Pressure per 15 Nautical Miles, Inches	Corresponding Wind Velocity, Miles per Hour
0.005	7.0
0.01	9.2
0.02	16.5
0.03	25.2

78. WIND DIRECTION AND VELOCITY. Winds are always named by the direction from which they come. Thus a wind from the south, blowing toward the north, is called a south wind. The wind vane points *toward* the source of the wind and so in a very general way toward the high-pressure area down the barometric slope of which the air is flowing. *Windward* refers to the direction from which a wind comes; *leeward*, that toward which it blows. Thus a windward coast is one along which the air is moving onshore, while a leeward coast has winds offshore. When a wind blows more frequently from one direction than from any other it is called a *prevailing wind*.

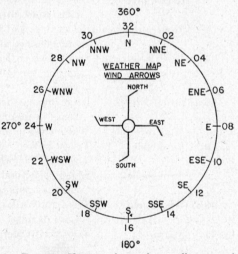

FIG. 33.—Here are shown the usually reported wind directions on a 32-point compass. (*From Haynes.*)

Wind direction is referred to directions on a 32-point compass and is expressed in terms of letter abbreviations of the directions, by

[1] Kendrew, W. G. "Climate." p. 73, University Press, Oxford, 1930. The nautical mile is 6,080 ft., or the length of 1′ of a great circle.

the number of the compass point, or by the number of degrees east of north (Fig. 33).

Wind velocity varies greatly with distance above the ground, and the variation is particularly rapid close to the ground. Wind is not a steady current but is made up of a succession of gusts and lulls of variable direction. Close to the earth the gustiness is caused by the irregularities of the surface which create eddies. Larger irregularities in the wind are caused by convectional currents. All forms of turbulence of the wind are important in the process of transporting heat, moisture, and dust into the upper air.

THE BEAUFORT SCALE OF WIND FORCE WITH VELOCITY EQUIVALENTS

Beaufort Number	General Description	Specifications for Use on Land	Miles per Hour
0	Calm	Smoke rises vertically	Less than 1
1	Light air	Wind direction shown by smoke drift but not by vanes	1 to 3
2	Slight breeze	Wind felt on face; leaves rustle; ordinary vane moved by wind	4 to 7
3	Gentle breeze	Leaves and twigs in constant motion; wind extends light flag	8 to 12
4	Moderate breeze	Raises dust and loose paper; small branches are moved	13 to 18
5	Fresh breeze	Small trees in leaf begin to sway; crested wavelets form on inland water	19 to 24
6	Strong breeze	Large branches in motion; whistling heard in telegraph wires	25 to 31
7	Moderate gale	Whole trees in motion	32 to 38
8	Fresh gale	Twigs broken off trees; progress generally impeded	39 to 46
9	Strong gale	Slight structural damage occurs; chimney pots removed	47 to 54
10	Whole gale	Trees uprooted; considerable structural damage	55 to 63
11	Storm	Very rarely experienced; widespread damage	64 to 75
12	Hurricane	....	Above 75

The Earth's Wind Systems

THE PLANETARY SYSTEM OF WINDS

79. A HYPOTHETICAL THERMALLY CONTROLLED ATMOSPHERIC CIRCULATION. The earth's wind systems are complicated. For that reason it is deemed advisable to approach their study by an analysis

that proceeds from the simple to the complex and in which the several complications are added one at a time.

First, let there be assumed a *nonrotating* planet having a *homogeneous level surface* (composed of either all land or all water) and with the rays of solar energy vertical at the equator (Fig. 34). On such a homogeneous nonrotating planet, with the vertical rays always at the equator, temperatures would diminish regularly from equator to poles. Atmospheric pressure, under thermal control, would then be highest at the poles, diminishing toward a permanent trough of low pressure at the equator. The heated air in the low latitudes would expand, rise, and overflow aloft, moving out toward the poles in the higher altitudes. In the polar regions it would sink to the earth, feeding the cool surface currents that would flow from the higher latitudes toward the equator. Under this situation it is obvious there would be two gigantic convectional circulations, one in each hemisphere, between the warm equatorial and

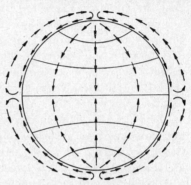

Fig. 34.—System of winds as it might develop on a homogeneous nonrotating earth with the maximum solar energy received at the equator.

the cold polar regions. That such a simple thermally induced air circulation does not exist is largely the result of (*a*) the earth's rotation on its axis and (*b*) the disrupting effects of land and water surfaces.

80. DIAGRAMMATIC REPRESENTATION OF SURFACE WINDS ON A ROTATING EARTH WITH A HOMOGENEOUS SURFACE. A closer approach to a correct representation of actual wind circulation, because it takes into consideration the effects of a rotating earth, is set forth in Figs. 27 and 28. A homogeneous surface is still assumed, however. Two fundamental differences are at once observable: (*a*) the rotating earth develops conditions of high pressure in the subtropics at about latitude 30 to 35°, and conditions of low pressure at about latitude 60 to 65°, which result in several different belts of winds between equator and poles; and (*b*) the deflective force of earth rotation causes winds to deviate from a north-south gradient direction.

If rain were to fall upon a land surface the configuration of which is represented by the very much idealized profile of pressure along a meridian (Fig. 28), it is fairly obvious that six distinct and separate streams of water would result. Each would originate at one of the four higher elevations and flow downslope to one of the three intervening depressions. In a similar way six great surface air movements, or winds, corresponding to the six streams of water, result from the idealized pressure distribution from pole to pole on a homogeneous earth represented in Fig. 28. Each stream of air originates in an area of high pressure and, acted upon by gravity, flows down the barometric slope toward an area of low pressure. Two of the great air streams originate on the equatorial sides of the subtropical high-pressure centers and, controlled by the gradient, move toward low pressure near the equator. These are the *trades*. Two others originate on the poleward sides of the subtropical highs and move poleward toward the subpolar troughs of low pressure. These are the *stormy westerlies*. Still another pair originates at the polar highs and flows equatorward toward the subpolar lows, where they meet the stormy westerlies from the lower latitudes. These high-latitude winds, about which relatively little is known, are sometimes designated as the *polar easterlies*. Both at the bottoms of the low-pressure troughs and at the crests of the high-pressure ridges, where pressure gradients are weak and variable, the wind systems are poorly developed, and calms and variable winds are characteristic. Thus between the trades, and at the bottom of the equatorial low-pressure trough, is the *equatorial belt of variable winds and calms*, or *doldrums*. At the tops of the subtropical highs, between the westerlies and the trades of either hemisphere, are the *subtropical belts of variable winds and calms*, sometimes called the *horse latitudes*. Still other regions having variable winds, but little calm, are to be found in the subpolar troughs of low pressure between the stormy westerlies and the polar easterlies. These regions of storm and variable winds have no general and accepted name.

81. DEFLECTION OF WINDS DUE TO EARTH ROTATION. If the earth's surface-air currents described above are represented on a map instead of on a profile, they may be shown very diagrammatically as in Fig. 27. It is immediately obvious that the surface winds do not, as might be expected, flow directly down the barometric slope (right angles to the isobars) but instead are always deflected into oblique courses. Thus the trades instead of flowing from north or south along the meridians are from the northeast and southeast. Similarly, the winds on the poleward sides of the subtropical highs (stormy westerlies) do not flow north or south but are southwesterlies and northwesterlies, while those originating at the polar highs are northeasterlies and southeasterlies. The cause for this bending of winds from the true gradient direction is the deflective force of the earth's rotation. This deflective force causes all winds in the Northern Hemisphere to be turned to the *right* and those of the Southern Hemisphere to the *left*.

This will not be apparent from looking at the winds on Fig. 35 unless it is kept in mind that one must face in the direction toward which the wind is traveling in order to appreciate the proper deflection. Only at the equator is the deflective force of earth rotation absent, and it increases with increasing latitude. At some distance above the earth's surface where friction is greatly reduced, deflective force causes the winds to blow nearly parallel to the isobars. The surface winds usually make an angle of 20 to 40° with the isobars, and it may be as low as 10° over the oceans.

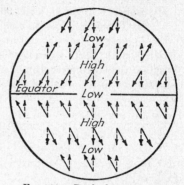

82. CIRCULATION ON A NONHOMO-GENEOUS EARTH. Admittedly the scheme of pressure and winds on a homogeneous rotating earth, represented by Figs. 27 and 28, is so much simplified that it does not accurately represent the true condition of surface winds. Nevertheless, it does provide a valuable *idealized framework* on which to hang the numerous modifications to be dealt with later. Chief of these modifications is the result of the fact that the earth is

FIG. 35.—Dashed arrows show wind direction as determined by pressure gradient alone and without the effects of earth rotation. Solid arrows show the deflected winds on a rotating earth.

not homogeneous but is composed of land and water areas that have a disrupting effect upon any truly zonal circulation. Such a zonal circulation of winds as that represented by Figs. 27 and 28 is best exemplified in the Southern Hemisphere with its more nearly uniform water cover. In the Northern Hemisphere with its great continents and oceans the belts of low and high pressure are broken down into isolated centers with distinct cyclonic and anticyclonic atmospheric circulations about them. During the winter at least six such distinct quasi-permanent centers may be observed: the Icelandic low, the Aleutian low, the Pacific high, the Bermuda or Açores high, the North American high, and the Asiatic high (see Figs. 29 and 30).

GENERAL CIRCULATION OF THE ATMOSPHERE[1]

83. NECESSITY FOR A GENERAL CIRCULATION. In the chapter on temperature (56) it was pointed out that there is an excess of solar radiation over earth radiation in the lower latitudes, while exactly the opposite is true in the higher latitudes, and still there is no change in the climates of the various latitudes. To maintain this equilibrium there is required a transfer, by some means, of the heat from the general region of excess in the lower latitudes to the region of deficiency in the middle and higher latitudes.

[1] See "Climate and Man." Yearbook of Agriculture, 1941, pp. 599–631.

This necessary transfer is brought about largely by the atmospheric circulation and to a less degree by the circulation of ocean waters.

Numerous and easily obtained observations of the surface winds permit speaking of their characteristics with considerable assurance. The upper-air currents, on the other hand, for which data are none too plentiful, are much less well known. With the somewhat fragmentary data available at the present time, students of air physics have deduced the following scheme of atmospheric circulation (Fig. 36).

84. Tropical Circulation. The expanded and rising warm air at the equator spreads out and overflows aloft, moving both to the north and to the south. Earth rotation causes these high-altitude winds to be deflected so that they become southwesterlies in the Northern Hemisphere and northwesterlies to the south of the equator. These winds are designated as the

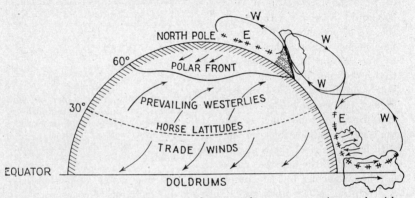

Fig. 36.—General zonal circulation of the atmosphere on a rotating earth with a homogeneous surface. (*After Rossby.*)

antitrades because they flow in a direction opposite to that of the surface trade winds below them. By the time that the antitrades reach subtropical latitudes (35±°N. or S.) deflection has caused them to become almost westerly currents so the air masses move farther poleward only with difficulty. As a result of this damming up of the poleward-moving air, high-pressure areas with settling currents result. These are the well-known subtropical highs. The descending currents in the vicinity of the subtropics are the feeders of the surface trades, which move toward the equator as northeast and southeast winds, becoming more easterly as the equator is approached. This completes the circulation between the equator and the subtropics.

85. High-latitude or Polar Circulation. Circulation in the middle and higher latitudes is less simple and less well understood. As air in the westerlies moves obliquely poleward from the subtropical highs its radius of rotation is constantly diminished (the diameter of the earth is smaller in the higher latitudes) and as a result its velocity of rotation is proportionally increased. With the increase in angular velocity of air flow there is an

accompanying increase in centrifugal force which tends to hold the air away from the polar areas. A very crude analogy is to be observed in the emptying of water from a circular lavatory basin. As the whirling water gets closer to the drain at the bottom of the basin where the radius of rotation is smaller, its angular velocity increases so much that the centrifugal force urges the water away from the center, so that a hollow core is developed. If these dynamic forces alone were operating, the polar areas should be regions of atmospheric deficiency and therefore low pressure. Such is actually the case at an elevation of about 6,000 ft. However, the constantly low surface temperatures in these high latitudes, especially over the ice caps of Antarctica and Greenland, induce shallow high-pressure centers. The resulting compromise between thermal and dynamic forces is to be observed in the existing system of surface pressure, *viz.*, polar highs surrounded by the subpolar troughs or centers of low pressure. As air in the westerlies moves poleward, finally leaving the earth's surface and ascending over the polar easterlies, it cools and settles over the polar areas to form the shallow polar highs. From polar highs, surface currents move downgradient as northeasterly and southeasterly currents to the subpolar low-pressure troughs located in latitudes 60 to 70°N. and S. At about latitude 60° this cold surface air reaches its equatorward limit of regular progress. Here it may, in part, be warmed sufficiently to ascend and return poleward in the general drift of high-altitude air from the lower latitudes (Fig. 36). In part, however, it continues to move farther equatorward in great surges or outbursts of cold air, in this way returning to the middle and lower latitudes some of the air that has been removed from those regions in the surface westerlies. In the Northern Hemisphere, owing to the less constant and symmetrical pressure arrangement, the polar wind system is much more complicated than it is in the Southern Hemisphere. It is probably true that the vast ice-covered plateau of Greenland plays a dominant role in the Arctic wind system.

86. MIDDLE-LATITUDE CIRCULATION. Both the tropical and the polar circulations thus far described conform in their general aspects to the thermally induced convectional system of air movement affirmed for a nonrotating earth heated at the equator (79); *i.e.*, their surface winds flow equatorward, and their high-altitude winds flow poleward. It is in the surface winds of middle latitudes that the direction of movement is opposite to that of the simple convectional system, for between latitudes 35 and 65° the stormy westerlies are blowing from lower to higher latitudes, *i.e.*, from warmer to colder regions. They have their origins in the descending air of the subtropical high-pressure belts as do the surface trades. Moving poleward, they meet the polar easterlies in the subpolar troughs of low pressure. The latter air masses being colder and denser, the warmer westerlies from lower latitudes are forced to ascend over the colder polar easterlies along a mildly inclined surface of discontinuity. This line of conflict between westerlies and polar easterlies is designated as the *polar front*. Above the surface westerlies the winds still appear to be westerly in direction but perhaps with a very slight amount of equatorward movement.

THE SURFACE WINDS AND THEIR CHARACTERISTICS

87. WIND BELTS, CENTERS OF ACTION, AND AIR MASSES. In
order to state the case simply and with the fewest complications, the
brief description of surface winds that follows is organized around
the well-known planetary system. These are the conditions as they
would prevail on a homogeneous earth, *e.g.*, one whose surface was all
water. In a general way latitudinal wind belts do exist, but on the
other hand such a concept obviously greatly simplifies what in reality
is a very complicated atmospheric circulation. In the relatively
homogeneous Southern Hemisphere, the belted arrangement of winds
is conspicuous. In the Northern Hemisphere with its great continents
and oceans, the average wind conditions for January and July (Figs.
29, 30) show monsoonal circulations of air around distinct pressure
centers. They are like the gear wheels of a great machine. However,
since these centers of spiraling circulations are disposed longitudinally,
the belted arrangement of winds is still fairly conspicuous, especially
over the oceans. It needs to be emphasized, however, that both wind
belts and wind spirals as they appear on annual or seasonal charts
are simply averages of what, on the daily weather maps, are seen to
be great irregularly moving masses of homogeneous air, associated with
traveling high- and low-pressure centers. It is this modern concept
of the atmosphere as composed of nonperiodic moving air masses, making contact with each other along fluctuating margins or fronts, that
comes closest to reality.

**88. THE DOLDRUMS, OR EQUATORIAL BELT OF VARIABLE WINDS
AND CALMS.** As the northeast and southeast trades converge toward
the equator, they rise above the earth's surface, leaving between them
at low elevations a condition of light and baffling breezes with much
calm (Fig. 37). This doldrum belt therefore occupies the axis or valley
of lowest pressure in the equatorial low-pressure trough where pressure
gradients are weak and variable, resulting in winds of the same
character. It needs to be emphasized that the nature of the winds is
the result of the character of the barometric gradients. The belt of
calms and variable winds is not clearly marked all round the equator,
nor does it exist at all times of the year. In places and upon occasions
it may be reduced to the vanishing point by the encroaching trades
or by monsoons, and then again it may expand to twice its normal
width. Its northern and southern margins may fluctuate several degrees
even within the period of a few days.

The principal air movement is vertical rather than horizontal,
ascending currents being indicated by the abundance of cumulus
clouds, numerous thunderstorms, and heavy convectional rainfall.

Because this is a region of converging air currents which escape by upward movement, the doldrums are inclined to be turbulent and stormy, with calms, squalls, and light winds alternating. Within the doldrums calms prevail 15 to 30 per cent of the time, and winds, chiefly light and gentle breezes, come from all points of the compass with about equal frequency (Fig. 37). Poor ventilation and sultry, oppressive weather are characteristic. These regions were rigorously avoided by sailing vessels. Owing to the fact that a sailing ship could very well be becalmed for days in the doldrums because of lack of wind, such boats often took longer routes and went far out of their courses in order to cross in the narrowest parts of the belt. Although the doldrums are usually spoken of as a belt, it would be incorrect to conceive of this condition of variable winds and calms as having definite northern and southern boundaries. Irregular in width but averaging perhaps 200 to 300 miles, it extends in places for as much as 10° or more away from the equator, whereas in other longitudes, especially where monsoons are well developed, as

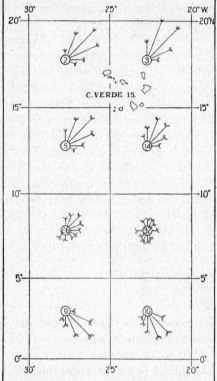

Fig. 37.—Northeast and southeast trades and doldrums over the Atlantic Ocean, June, 1922. The wind rose is given for each 5-degree square. Arrows fly with the wind. The length of the arrow is proportional to the frequency of winds from that direction. The number of feathers on the arrow indicates the average force of the wind on the Beaufort scale. The figure in the center gives the percentage of calms, light airs, and variable winds. (U. S. Hydrographic Office Pilot Chart.)

they are in the Indian Ocean, it may be wiped out entirely. Over the Atlantic Ocean in July doldrums lie between latitudes 11 and 3°N. and in January between 3°N. and 0°. Most of the doldrum belt probably lies between parallels 5°N. and 5°S.

In modern air-mass terminology the air of this doldrum region is designated as Equatorial (E). If two converging trade winds meet, and one is somewhat cooler and drier than the other, the warmer trade will be forced to ascend over the denser, cooler one along an inclined surface. Under this condition a belt of calms may be absent. The line or zone of convergence between the trades has been given the significant name "tropical front" (sometimes "equatorial" or "intertropical" front).

89. THE TRADE WINDS.   Moving obliquely downgradient from the subtropical centers of high pressure toward the equatorial low, roughly between latitudes 30 or 35 and 5 or 10° in each hemisphere over the oceans, are winds whose steadiness has earned for them the name *trade winds*. Over the North Atlantic in summer the approximate limits of the northeast trades are 35 and 11°N., in winter, 26 and 3°N. In parts of the low latitudes they reach, and even cross, the equator. Away from land masses trades blow rather constantly from an easterly direction (northeast in the Northern and southeast in the Southern Hemisphere). Over continents, and even adjacent to them, both steadiness and direction may be considerably modified. On the island of St. Helena, which lies in the heart of the southeast trades of the South Atlantic, the percentage of winds from various directions is as follows, according to Kendrew:[1]

	N.	N.E.	E.	S.E.	S.	S.W.	Calm
January	..	..	5	76	19	..	..
July	1	2	9	62	20	1	5

They are the most regular and steady winds of the earth, particularly over the oceans, their characteristic moderate to fresh breezes averaging 10 to 15 miles an hour. Calms are infrequent, usually prevailing less than 5 per cent of the time (Fig. 37). Over land masses and near their margins, the surface trades are much less conspicuous. They blow with greater strength and constancy in winter than in summer, for in the hot season the belt of subtropical highs is broken by the heated continents, resulting in a much less continuous belt of trades at that season. Especially over eastern and southern Asia, and to a degree over the waters south and east of the United States as well, summer monsoons tend to weaken or even eliminate the trades. In winter, on the other hand, outflowing continental winds tend to strengthen the trades. In general, except on their equatorward margins, they are regions of fine, clear weather with few storms. The most spectacular of these storms are the tropical hurricanes which infest their western poleward margins over the oceans in the late summer and early fall. As the trades move in toward the equator they are constantly being heated from below by the increasingly warmer earth's surface. The

[1] "Climate," p. 90, *op. cit.*

poleward portions of the trades lying on the flanks of the subtropical highs where there is a good deal of subsiding air are relatively dry, and fair weather is prevalent. Farther equatorward and closer to the equatorial zone of convergence where ascent of air rather than subsidence is characteristic, the trades become increasingly rainier.

Because of the steady nature of the trades, as well as their fine clear weather with few severe storms, they were thoroughfares for sailing vessels. Columbus in his first voyage to the New World sailed south from Spain to the Canary Islands and then westward in the trades. His journal of the voyage contains frequent remarks concerning the fine weather and the favorable winds experienced. One notation describes the weather as being like April in Andalusia. The almost constant following winds from the northeast worried the

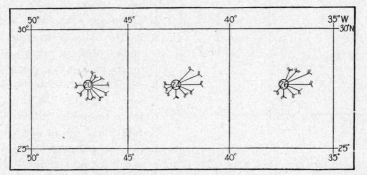

FIG. 38.—The subtropical "belt" of variable winds and calms, or horse latitudes, over the North Atlantic Ocean, June, 1922. For explanation of symbols see Fig. 37. (*U. S. Hydrographic Office Pilot Chart.*)

sailors, however, for they feared that the return trip to Spain might be impossible. Upon one occasion when a westerly wind was experienced, Columbus wrote: "This contrary wind was very necessary to me, because my people were much excited at the thought that in these seas no wind ever blew in the direction of Spain."

90. THE SUBTROPICAL BELTS OF VARIABLE WINDS AND CALMS, OR THE HORSE LATITUDES. Lying between the diverging trades and stormy westerlies over the oceans and occupying the crests of the high-pressure centers where pressure gradients are weak are areas of light, variable winds and calms (Fig. 38). All regions with such wind characteristics must of necessity have weak pressure gradients. Perhaps the horse latitudes are better thought of as transition conditions between trades and westerlies rather than as relatively distinct and more or less continuous wind belts. On the wind charts (Figs. 29, 30) the horse latitudes are the centers of the great subtropical "whirls" of

air, these whirls having opposite rotations in the Northern and Southern Hemispheres. Although the horse latitudes are like the doldrums in their preponderance of light and fickle winds, blowing from any and all points of the compass, they are totally unlike them in their general weather conditions. Because they are regions of settling air and diverging wind systems (compare with doldrums), the air is prevailingly dry, skies are clear, weather is fine much of the time, sunshine is abundant, and rainfall is relatively low. As a general rule the western margins of the subtropical whirls have much more

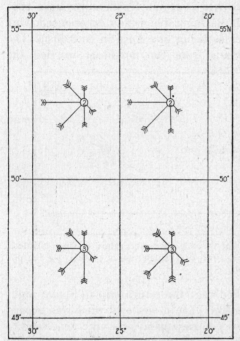

cloud and rainfall than the eastern sides. The centers, or "ridges," of subtropical high pressure lie in the vicinity of latitudes 30 to 40°N. and S. These are sometimes known as the Mediterranean latitudes because they correspond in location with that sea. The representative wind rose (Fig. 38) for these regions resembles that of the doldrums, calms prevailing 15 to 25 per cent of the time, and light and gentle breezes from all points of the compass the remainder.

91. THE STORMY WESTERLIES. Moving downgradient from the centers of subtropical high pressure to the subpolar lows (roughly 35 or 40 to 60 or 65°) are the stormy westerlies. Particularly is the poleward

FIG. 39.—The westerlies over the North Atlantic Ocean, January 1922. For explanation of symbols see Fig. 37. (*U. S. Hydrographic Office Pilot Chart.*)

boundary of this wind belt a fluctuating one, shifting with the seasons and over shorter periods of time as well. The westerlies are distinctive among the wind belts in that they are not uniformly either strong or weak but instead are composed of extremes. Spells of weather are one of their distinguishing characteristics. At times, and more especially in the winter, they blow with gale force, and upon other occasions mild breezes prevail. Although designated as *westerlies*, westerly being, to be sure, the direction of most frequent and strongest winds, air does blow from all points of the compass (Fig. 39). The variability of winds, in both direction and strength, so characteristic of the westerlies, is largely the result of the procession of storms (cyclones and anticyclones) which travels from west to east in these latitudes. These storms, with their local systems of converging and diverging winds, tend to break up and modify the general westerly air currents. Moreover, on the eastern sides of Asia, and to a lesser degree North America, continental wind systems called *monsoons* tend to disturb the westerlies, especially in summer (96). It is in the Southern Hemisphere, where in latitudes 40 to 65° land masses are largely absent, that the stormy westerlies can be observed in their least interrupted latitudinal development. Over these great expanses of ocean, winds of gale strength are common in summer as well as winter. These are the roaring forties of nautical jargon. In the vicinity of Cape Horn they are often so violent as to make east-west traffic around the Cape not only difficult but even dangerous. It is a wild region where gale follows gale with only brief intervening lulls; where raw chilly weather, cloudy skies, and mountainous seas prevail.

The westerlies of the Northern Hemisphere, where the great land masses with their seasonal pressure reversals cause the wind systems to be much more complex, are considerably less violent in summer than in winter. In the former season gentle to fresh breezes prevail, and winds come from a great variety of directions with almost equal frequency. But in winter they are like their counterparts in the Southern Hemisphere, being strong and boisterous with a greater prevalence of winds from westerly directions. The poleward margins of the westerlies near the subpolar troughs of low pressure are particularly subject to great surges of cold polar air in the winter season. The sinuous line of discontinuity, known as the polar front, which separates the cold, dry polar air from that warmer and more humid mass coming from the subtropics in the form of the westerlies is the zone of origin for a great many middle-latitude cyclones and anticyclones. It follows, therefore, that the poleward margins of the westerlies are much more subject to stormy, variable weather than are the subtropical margins. Since this polar front and the accompanying belt of storms migrate with the sun's rays, retreating poleward in summer and advancing equatorward in winter, it also follows that storm control of weather in the middle latitudes should be much more pronounced in the winter season.

92. THE POLAR WINDS. In the higher latitudes, beyond the belts of westerlies, meagerness of long-continued observations prevents one from speaking with great assurance regarding the wind systems.

The subpolar low-pressure troughs, relatively continuous in the Southern Hemisphere but existing as isolated centers (Iceland low and Aleutian low) north of the equator, are extremely wild and stormy areas, for they are the routes followed by a large number of the cyclonic storms of high latitudes. Great surges of cold polar air cause the outlines of the subpolar troughs to be extremely sinuous, almost completely interrupting their continuity both frequently and at numerous points. The inner polar areas of settling air and high pressure are probably quiet, relatively calm, and free from storms. The outflowing easterlies are, for the most part, moderate in velocity, although at times they are intensified to the point of becoming violent gales, blizzardlike in character. However, these blizzards appear to be more characteristic of the outer margins of the polar highs than they are of the inner, anticyclonic polar regions. As indicated previously (85), the surface wind system of the north polar region is much more complicated and complex than that of the Antarctic, owing to the proximity of great landmasses near to, but not at, the Pole and to the asymmetrical position of the Greenland Ice Cap. The permanent high pressure over Greenland is, for the year as a whole, the wind pole of the Northern Hemisphere, as the Antarctic high is for the Southern Hemisphere.

TERRESTRIAL MODIFICATIONS OF THE PLANETARY WIND SYSTEM

93. Thus far many of the general features of the wind system described have been those that would characterize any planet with an atmosphere, warmed at the equator and rotating from west to east. But the particular planet Earth has several characteristics peculiar to itself which modify the simpler planetary system. These terrestrial modifications result from (a) the inclination ($23\frac{1}{2}°$) and parallelism of the earth's axis, causing a uniform latitudinal shifting of the belts of solar energy during the course of a year; (b) a nonhomogeneous surface composed of both land and water areas, having contrasting temperature, pressure, and wind characteristics; and (c) land areas the surfaces of which are variable in configuration and altitude.

94. LATITUDINAL SHIFTING OF THE WIND BELTS. Consequent upon the parallelism and inclination of the earth's axis, during the period of revolution the sun's vertical ray shifts from $23\frac{1}{2}°$N. (summer solstice) to $23\frac{1}{2}°$S. (winter solstice), a total of $47°$. Of course it is not only the vertical ray that shifts but all the insolation belts as well, and along with them the temperature belts, which are largely sun controlled. Pressure and wind belts, in part thermally induced, likewise

may be expected to migrate latitudinally with the sun's rays. This north-south shifting of the wind belts is by no means so simple a thing as it may appear to be from the above description, for it varies in amount and rapidity of shift from one part of the earth to another. In general there is a lag of a month or possibly two behind the sun. Over the oceans and along coasts where the migration is more readily observable the total migration is not great, usually not much over 10 to 15°. Over continents, on the other hand, the total latitudinal shift is greater, and the lag is considerably less than over oceans. Then, again, surface wind systems are much confused over land masses owing to surface irregularities and greater seasonal variations in temperature, so that the migration is not very evident. Instead of a simple latitudinal migration, the seasonal changes in pressure and winds are often to be observed in terms of shifts in position and intensity of the great centers of action, which in turn result in a prevalence of different air masses in different seasons.

95. *Latitudes Covered by More than One Wind Belt.* This latitudinal shifting of the wind belts becomes climatically significant, especially in those regions lying in an intermediate position between two great wind systems or air masses of unlike weather conditions, as, for instance, between the westerlies on the one hand and the dry subsiding air of the subtropical highs on the other, or between the trades and the doldrums. Such a position assures the region of being encroached upon at the opposite seasons of the year by contrasting air masses and consequently of experiencing contrasting weather conditions. Ideally, three such transition regions should be present in each hemisphere, and there are evidences that they actually do exist, although in imperfect form and *certainly not as continuous latitudinal belts.*

a. Latitudes 5± to 15±° are intermediate in position between the humid doldrum air masses and the drier trades, the latter winds, often in modified form, prevailing at the time of low sun (winter), and the doldrums at the time of high sun (summer). One dry and one wet season should be the result. Even equatorward from latitudes 5° there is some encroachment by the trades, although regions very close to the equator usually do not experience a strong and persistent trade-wind influence. However, these winds are responsible for the less wet seasons of places near the equator.

b. Latitudes 30 to 40° are between the subtropical highs and the stormy westerlies. With the poleward migration of the sun's rays in summer the dry subtropical highs are shifted over these regions, whereas the westerlies with their cyclonic storms prevail in winter when the sun's vertical ray is in the opposite hemisphere.[1] It is evident that this arrangement should give rise to dry summers and wet winters. Monsoon winds definitely interrupt this migration along the eastern sides and interiors of the continents, so that it is chiefly present over the oceans and along western littorals.

c. Latitudes 60 to 70°, which mark the subpolar lows, are intermediate in position between stormy westerlies and winds of polar origin so that latitudinal shifting of winds should allow this region to experience both. The numerous cyclones which inhabit these latitudes tend to complicate and obscure any simple migration of wind belts. It is much more a region of alternating polar and modified tropical air masses. It is a fact, nevertheless, that in these higher latitudes there is a greater prevalence of cold polar air in winter and of warmer southwesterly currents in summer, suggesting a semblance of wind-belt and storm-belt migration.

96. MONSOON WINDS. This terrestrial system of winds is characterized by a tendency toward a reversal in prevailing wind direction between winter and summer. It is directly the result of the earth's surface being composed of great land and water areas which have unequal heating and cooling qualities. (It has been noted in an earlier article (87) that the effect of large land and water areas is to modify latitudinal wind belts, with the result that there are created semipermanent centers of high and low pressure with outblowing and inblowing winds.) If the earth's surface were composed of either all land or all water, monsoons could not exist. It needs to be recalled at this point that seasonal differences in temperature often give rise to seasonal contrasts in pressure, and of course contrasts in pressure give rise to changes in wind direction. The chain of events, then, is from temperature, through pressure, to winds. In winter, for example, the interior of Asia becomes excessively cold, resulting in the development of a great stationary continental anticyclone, or high-pressure, center. Over the warmer seas to the east and south of Asia temperatures are higher, and the pressures consequently lower. As a result of this arrangement of the pressure areas the surface gradient is *from* the continent *toward* the ocean, with cold surface winds moving out from Asia toward the surrounding seas. This prevailing land wind con-

---

[1] As the term trade wind is used here it is intended to include winds having the same general character as trades, even if not from a northeast or southeast direction. For example, winds over the Mediterranean Basin in summer are prevailingly northwest. Yet these are essentially trade winds in both origin and character, even though modified in direction. This concept, expressed specifically for the trades, applies to the other wind systems as well.

stitutes the *winter monsoon* (Fig. 40). (In the higher altitudes air is
flowing from the ocean toward the continent, and it is this transfer
of air from sea to land at higher elevations that creates the differences
in surface pressure.) The low-pressure goal of the Asiatic winter
monsoon lies south of the equator over the Indian Ocean and the hot
interior of Australia. The winter monsoon is not always from the same
direction in the various parts of eastern and southern Asia, for it
blows from the west and northwest in Japan and North China and from
the north and northeast in southern Asia, where it acts to strengthen
the normal trade winds of those latitudes. But although not always
from the same direction, it is, in almost all sections, a polar air mass of
continental origin bringing cold, dry air down to the very sea margins

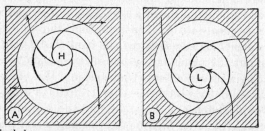

Fig. 40.—Shaded areas represent oceans; white areas are continents. In winter (*A*)
pressure is high over the cold continents, while in summer (*B*) it is low. The result is
an outflow of continental air in winter and an inflow of ocean air in summer. This is a
monsoon system. (*From Petterssen.*)

and beyond. This condition is not conducive to rainfall, so that winter
is characteristically the driest season in monsoon lands. Winter
monsoons, particularly those of middle latitudes, are liable to interruptions by the passage of cyclonic storms which bring some precipitation even in the cool season. The influence of passing cyclones and

PERCENTAGE OF WIND FREQUENCY IN NORTH CHINA
(Kendrew)[1]

	N.	N.E.	E.	S.E.	S.	S.W.	W.	N.W.
Winter	17	8	5	6	6	8	18	32
Summer	10	9	12	26	16	10	7	10

anticyclones is indicated by the table showing wind frequency in North
China. Although land winds predominate in winter (67 per cent from
west, northwest, and north), there are some from opposite directions:
and in summer, although sea winds are most numerous (63 per cent

[1] "Climate," p. 97, *op. cit.*

from northeast, east, southeast, and south), winds from the continent are by no means absent (Fig. 29).

Summer Monsoon. In summer the Asiatic continent becomes warmer than the adjacent oceans, and, as a consequence, a semi-permanent seasonal low-pressure center develops over that land mass. Higher pressure prevails over the cooler oceans, so that the gradient is *from* sea to land, and the winds are as well (Fig. 40). This equatorial maritime air mass moving in toward the heated continent is called the *summer monsoon.* Much of it originates in the trades south of the equator. Since it travels great distances over bodies of tropical water, it brings with it abundant supplies of water vapor which are conducive to rainfall. Summer, therefore, is characteristically the wet season in monsoon lands. The summer monsoon is not always a wind from the same direction throughout southeastern Asia, but at least it is from the sea and from tropical latitudes. Interruptions due to cyclonic storms are not infrequent. In monsoon regions continental-controlled winds tend to wipe out the planetary system of trades and westerlies, substituting in their places a terrestrial system. Hot, humid summers and relatively cold, dry winters are characteristic of most regions with continental wind systems in the middle latitudes. India, cut off as it is from the rest of Asia by high mountain ranges and plateaus, has a monsoon system of local origin, quite distinct from that of the rest of the continent (Figs. 41*A*, 41*B*). The following diagram will help to fix the chain of events described above for a monsoon region:

Winter—Asia cold—high pressure—surface winds toward the sea
Summer—Asia warm—low pressure—surface winds toward the land

Partly owing to the great size of the continent, the monsoon system of winds is most perfectly developed over eastern and southern Asia, although monsoons in modified form, or *monsoon tendencies*, are characteristic of other regions as well. Southeastern United States, northern Australia, Spain, and South Africa all are regions with monsoon tendencies. These land areas may not be always sufficiently powerful to cause a complete seasonal reversal of winds as does Asia, but at least they create partial monsoons (Figs. 42, 43*A*, 43*B*).

It is conspicuous that regions with strong monsoon tendencies usually are on the eastern sides of continents. This is especially true in the middle latitudes, since the western or windward coasts are so distinctly marine in character, with only small changes in temperature from summer to winter. It is, therefore, only on the more continental eastern, or leeward, sides that sufficiently large seasonal extremes of temperature can develop to produce a wind reversal.

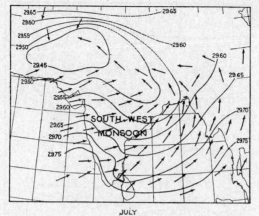

FIG. 41A.

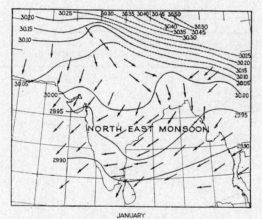

FIG. 41B.

FIGS. 41A and 41B.—Seasonal pressures and winds over India. The Indian monsoon is distinct and separate from that of eastern Asia.

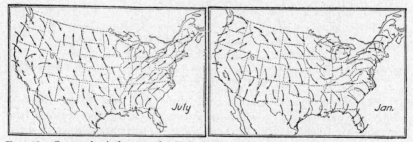

FIG. 42.—Seasonal winds over the United States. Note the monsoon tendency over eastern United States. (*After Ward.*)

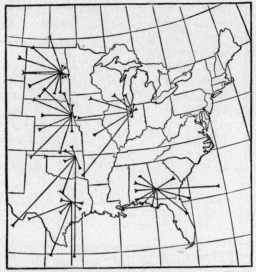

Fig. 43A.—Prevailing direction of upper winds in summer. They are more southwesterly in the warm season. (*U. S. Weather Bureau.*)

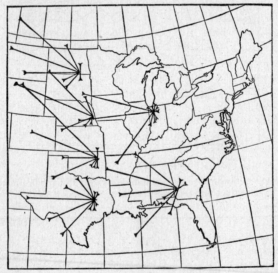

Fig. 43B.—Prevailing direction of upper winds in winter. They are more northwesterly in the cold season. (*U. S. Weather Bureau.*)

97. MINOR TERRESTRIAL WINDS. *Land and Sea Breezes.* Just as there are *seasonal* wind reversals (monsoons) resulting from seasonal temperature contrasts between land and water, so there are *diurnal,* or daily, monsoons resulting from similarly induced temperature contrasts within the 24-hr. period. These are called *land and sea breezes,* or *diurnal monsoons.*

Thus along coasts there is often a drift of cool, heavy air from land to water at night (corresponding to winter) and a reversed wind direction, sea to land, during the heat of the day (corresponding to summer). Usually the sea breeze begins between 11:00 and 12:00 A.M. and seldom lasts much later than 4:00 P.M. It is a shallow wind, penetrating only a short distance inland, usually not over 20 miles. Along tropical littorals the sea breeze is a remarkably important climatic phenomenon, causing them to be more livable and healthy places than they otherwise would be. The beginning of the sea breeze may cause a drop in temperature of 15 to 20° within $\frac{1}{4}$ to $\frac{1}{2}$ hr. At Joal, Senegambia (West Africa), the temperature at 12:30 P.M. on Apr. 14, 1893, was 100°F., with a land wind from the northeast and a relative humidity of 3 per cent. At 12:45 the wind direction was northwest, from the sea, temperature had dropped to 82°F., and the relative humidity had risen to 45 per cent (Hann). Coasts with well-developed sea breezes are inclined to have modified marine climates, with the daily temperature maxima much reduced.

98. *Mountain and Valley Breezes.* Like land and sea breezes, these local winds have a distinct diurnal periodicity. During the day the air of an enclosed valley or that adjacent to a slope receiving relatively vertical rays of the sun becomes heated so that active convectional ascent of the warm and expanded air takes place up the valleys and along the mountain slopes. This daytime updraft of warm air, or *valley breeze*, is indicated by the masses of cumulus clouds which collect about the peaks of mountains during summer days. They are the "visible tops of invisible ascending air currents." Daily summer afternoon rains are therefore common in mountains, and visibility, because of the cloud masses, is restricted during the warm hours of the day. After sundown, as the rapidly cooling slopes begin to chill the air layers next to them, the cooler, heavier air begins to slip down the mountainsides into the valleys. This is a reversal of the day current and is known as the *mountain breeze*. It is often very perceptible at the mouth of a gulch; and where there are marked constrictions in a valley that drains a large area, strong winds may result. Summer camps are sometimes pitched at the mouth of a valley in order to benefit from the cooling effect and ventilation provided by the mountain breeze.

99. *Diurnal variation in wind velocity* is another terrestrial modification of surface winds with a daily periodicity. It is very noticeable that calm nights and early mornings in the warmer months are often followed by windy middays, the maximum wind velocity corresponding with the time of greatest heat. By sunset there is usually a marked calming of the atmosphere again. The boisterous midday winds are associated with convectional overturning, or interchange of air between upper and lower strata which occurs at the time of greatest surface heating. Under those conditions the lower air, entangled with the fast-moving upper air as a result of the ascending and descending currents, is dragged along at a rapid rate. It is noticeable that cumulus clouds are often numerous during the windiest hours when convection is at a maximum, a coincidence that has gained them the name

of "wind clouds." During the night, when the lower air is colder and heavier, there is no tendency for it to rise. At that time interchanges between the upper and lower air are at a minimum so that the surface air is relatively undisturbed by the fast-moving currents aloft. It is at the time of maximum vertical convectional interchange that surface winds reach their highest diurnal velocities.

Ocean Drifts and Currents

The discussion of the movement of ocean waters is included within the climatic section of this book chiefly because ocean currents are one of the controls of climate, and a knowledge of their characteristic systems is useful in an understanding of world climates. It should be added also, as a further reason for their inclusion at this point, that the drift of ocean waters is climatically induced, winds, temperature, precipitation, and humidity contrasts being the principal direct or indirect motivating agents.

100. SCHEME OF SURFACE DRIFTS AND CURRENTS IN AN INDIVIDUAL OCEAN. Except in the polar seas, there is a tendency for all the other great oceans to exhibit general circulations of surface currents and drifts, which, in many of their broader aspects, greatly resemble each other (Fig. 44). Fundamentally surface ocean currents are related to the direction of the prevailing wind. The scheme of ocean currents as developed in the North Atlantic, which is reasonably representative of those of other seas as well, will be taken as an example for analysis.

The most conspicuous element of the North Atlantic circulation is probably the great, closed elliptical whirl about the subtropical Açores high. The trade winds on the equatorward sides of the subtropical highs in both hemispheres tend to drift the surface waters before them across the ocean. The deflective force of earth rotation, right in the Northern and left in the Southern Hemisphere, acts to make this a westward-flowing current, moving somewhat at an angle to the direction of the trades. This is the *Equatorial Current*. (There are really two equatorial currents, separated in the eastern part of the ocean by a minor countercurrent setting toward the east.) Checked in its westward progress by the South American continent, the Equatorial Current is divided, the larger part of it flowing northwestward, and the smaller part of it southwestward. Partly owing to deflection (earth rotation) and trend of the coast line, and partly because of the wind direction around the western end of the subtropical Açores high, the warm northward-moving current gradually is bent more and more to the east. A part of it enters the Caribbean Sea and passes through the Straits of Yucatán into the Gulf of Mexico. This water returns to the Atlantic through the Florida Strait, where it joins the major part of the warm-water drift. which has kept eastward of the West Indies, to form the *"Gulf Stream"* (better designated as the *Caribbean* or *Florida Current*) which parallels the Ameri-

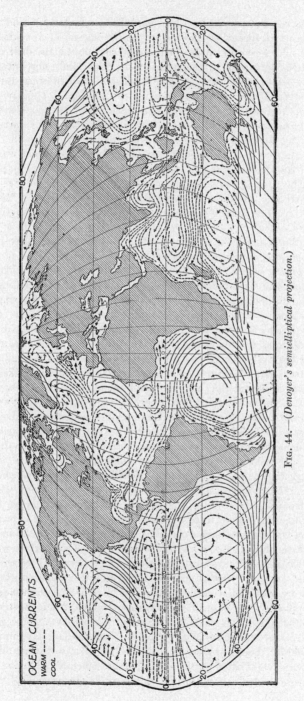

Fig. 44.—(Denoyer's semielliptical projection.)

OCEAN CURRENTS
WARM ------
COOL ———

can Atlantic seaboard. At about latitude 40°N. westerly winds and deflection cause the warm surface waters to turn slowly eastward across the ocean in the form of a west-wind drift. In the eastern Atlantic the drift divides, a part of it being carried by the subtropical anticyclone's northwesterly and northerly winds southward along the coast of southwestern Europe and northwestern Africa, until it joins again the Equatorial Current and thus completes the low-latitude circuit. This is the relatively cool *Canaries Current*. A considerable portion of the west-wind drift, however, is carried northeastward by the stormy southwesterlies along the northwest coast of Europe to form the *North Atlantic Drift*, its relatively warm waters washing the coasts of the British Isles and Norway, and eventually entering the Arctic Ocean. The Arctic, compensating for this receipt of warm water from the eastern Atlantic, produces an outward surge of cold waters, in the western Atlantic on either side of Greenland, the western branch being called the *Labrador Current*.

101. *Warm and Cool Currents.* If it is kept in mind that poleward-drifting surface waters, since they come from lower latitudes, are inclined to be *relatively* warm, while those from higher latitudes are likely to be cooler than the surrounding waters, the following generalizations may be made. In the lower latitudes (equatorward from 35 or 40°) warm ocean currents tend to parallel the eastern sides of continents, while cool ocean currents parallel the western sides of continents (Fig. 44). In the middle and higher latitudes the reverse is more often the case, warm ocean currents affecting the western sides of land masses, and cool ones the eastern sides. Along east coasts (western sides of oceans), therefore, there is likely to be a *convergence* of contrasting currents, while along west coasts they tend to *diverge*. It needs to be added that a part of the cool water along west coasts in lower latitudes (Peru and northern Chile, northwest and southwest Africa, southern California, and others) is the result of upwelling from depths along the coast. These regions occupy positions along the eastern margins of well-developed subtropical high-pressure centers and their associated wind whirls, which are conspicuous features over oceans in these latitudes. Along their coasts, paralleling equatorward-moving winds from the subtropical whirls, drive the surface waters toward lower latitudes. Owing to the deflective force of earth rotation, the ocean currents along these cool-water coasts have a component of movement away from the land. Colder water from below, therefore, rises to replace the surface water.

102. CLIMATIC SIGNIFICANCE OF OCEAN CURRENTS. *Temperature.* In order that an ocean current may have direct and marked effect upon the temperature of the adjacent land mass, it is obvious that the winds must be onshore. Such is the case in northwestern Europe, where westerly winds carry the effects of the warm North Atlantic Drift far into the continent. Parts of coastal Europe are 30 to 40° too warm in January as compared with the normal for their latitudes. In contrast, the warm waters paralleling the east coasts of the United States and Japan are much less effective as direct temperature controls, because the winter winds are prevailingly offshore.

Nevertheless, the relatively frequent east winds on the fronts of cyclonic storms create sporadic importations from off the mild waters and thereby tend to raise the normal winter temperature. Where cool ocean currents parallel coasts, temperatures along the adjacent littorals are likely to be markedly lowered. Thus the coast of Peru, which is paralleled by the cool Peru Current, is 10° cooler than the coast of Brazil in a similar latitude, where a warm current prevails.

It has been stated previously that there is a tendency for cool and warm ocean currents to converge along the western sides of oceans and to diverge along the eastern sides. Where contrasting currents *converge*, the effect is to squeeze the isotherms closer together, making for marked latitudinal temperature contrasts, steep temperature gradients, and advection fogs. This condition is found, for instance, along the east coasts of Asia and North America. Where contrasting currents *diverge* they tend to spread the isotherms, making for milder temperature gradients. This is the case in the eastern Atlantic. It must not be inferred, however, that ocean currents are the principal cause of these temperature-gradient phenomena on the opposite sides of oceans; at best they are only auxiliary causes cooperating with more powerful marine and continental influences.

103. *Fog and Precipitation.* Cool-water coasts in low latitudes often present the unusual situation of being characterized by both fog and aridity —an apparently contradictory combination. The fog is the result of warm air from over the ocean proper being chilled by blowing over the cool current lying alongshore and mixing with the cool air above it. It may then be drifted in over the land, but usually it is confined to a narrow coastal fringe. The aridity, on the other hand, is the result of a rapid increase in temperature, and consequent decrease in relative humidity, of air from over the cool ocean current which moves inland over the warmer tropical or subtropical land. Where a cold current parallels a tropical coast, therefore, dry climates prevail. In western Peru, desert conditions are carried to within 5° of the equator by the effects of the cool Peru Current. The cool Benguela Current has a similar effect upon the coast of southwestern Africa. In these regions, as along many other cool-water coasts, upwelling is an important item. Where warm currents lie offshore they tend somewhat to amplify the atmospheric humidity and to increase the rainfall.

104. *Indirect Climatic Effects of Ocean Currents.* Indirectly ocean currents may affect the general climatic character of an adjacent land area by their influence upon the routes of cyclonic storms. This indirect influence applies to leeward as well as to windward coasts. Cyclones are attracted by the relatively high temperatures and consequent low pressures associated with large masses of warm surface water. The location of one of the world's principal storm tracks, lying off the coast of northwest Europe, is associated in a cause-and-effect relationship with the warm waters of the North Atlantic Drift. It has been observed that when the "Gulf Stream" along the American South Atlantic Coast is stronger and warmer than usual, so that pressures in that vicinity are below normal, cyclonic storms in eastern United States

tend to travel more southerly routes, giving that part of the country abnormally cold and snowy winters. A weak "Gulf Stream" and associated
higher pressures, on the other hand, result in the storm tracks being shifted
farther poleward, and a milder, less snowy winter is the result. In this
instance there is the anomalous situation of an excess of warm water offshore
indirectly causing an abnormally cold and snowy winter, while a minimum
of warm water induces a milder one.

Chapter V. Atmospheric Moisture and Precipitation

105. IMPORTANCE OF WATER VAPOR. The proportions of most of the gaseous constituents that compose the atmosphere near sea level are relatively constant from place to place at the surface of the earth. One in particular, water vapor, is highly inconstant, varying from nearly zero up to a maximum of almost 5 per cent. This variability in the atmospheric content of water vapor, as to both place and time, is of outstanding importance for at least four reasons: (*a*) The amount of that gas in a given volume is an indication of the atmosphere's capacity for precipitation, one of the two most important climatic elements. (*b*) Water vapor is closely related to temperature phenomena through its absorptive effects on terrestrial radiation, regulating thereby the rate of heat loss from the earth. (*c*) The greater the amount of water vapor the larger the quantity of latent or potential energy stored up in the atmosphere for the production of storms. (*d*) The amount of water vapor is likewise an important factor affecting the human body's rate of cooling, *i.e.*, the sensible temperature.

106. SOURCES OF WATER VAPOR. Like all the other gases in the atmosphere, water vapor is invisible. The primary source of this important gas is the great oceans which cover approximately three-quarters of the earth's surface. By winds and diffusion methods, the water vapor evaporated from these bodies of water through the expenditure of solar energy is carried in over the continents. Less important, but nevertheless significant, sources of atmospheric moisture are the moist land surfaces, the vegetation cover, and the minor bodies of water. Plants give off more moisture to the air than does bare ground but not so much as does a freely exposed water surface. A constant turnover is forever in progress as regards the atmosphere's water vapor, additions being made through *evaporation* of water in its solid and liquid states, while some is being lost to the atmosphere by *condensation*. By the process of condensation, water vapor, a gas, is changed back into the liquid or solid state, while through evapora-

93

tion the liquid or solid water is converted into invisible gaseous water vapor. As winds carry the moisture in gas form from the oceans to the land, so rivers and glaciers deliver it again in liquid or solid form to the seas. Half the water vapor in the air lies below an altitude of 6,500 ft.

107. THE HYDROLOGIC CYCLE. Of the precipitation that falls upon the continents it is calculated that only about 30 per cent finds its way back to the sea through rivers and glaciers. It follows that

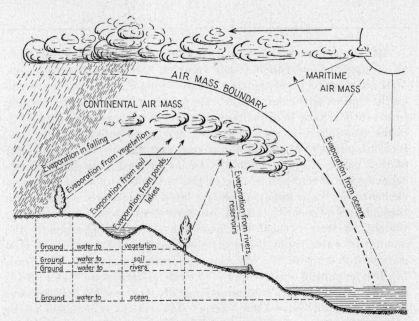

FIG. 45.—The hydrologic cycle correlated with the air-mass cycle. (*After Holzman; courtesy of George Jenkins and the Journal of Geography.*)

the remaining 70 per cent must be returned to the atmosphere by evaporation from the ground, from inland bodies of water, and from the vegetation cover. From these data some have concluded that the oceans contribute only 30 per cent of the moisture falling as land precipitation and that local evaporation from the lands must provide the other 70 per cent. Actually local evaporation is of very minor significance as a source of moisture for the precipitation of an area. It is coming to be recognized that a large proportion of that part of continental precipitation (70 per cent) evaporated from the land and not returned to the oceans by rivers and glaciers is actually carried back to the seas by the equatorward-moving dry polar-continental air masses (Fig. 45).

In the cycle of atmospheric exchange between land and sea, moist tropical maritime air masses carry oceanic moisture poleward into the middle-latitude continents, where it is cooled and precipitated. Conversely dry polar continental air masses carry much of the evaporated land moisture back again to the tropical oceans. The great surges of polar air moving southward over the United States are great invisible rivers evaporating and transporting land moisture in vapor form back to the Gulf of Mexico and the tropical Atlantic where it is precipitated.

108. LATENT ENERGY IN WATER VAPOR. It is common knowledge that energy is required in the form of heat to change ice (solid) into water (liquid) and water into vapor or steam (gas). The unit of heat energy, the calorie, is the amount of heat required to raise the temperature of a gram of water one degree centigrade. But it takes 79 calories to convert a gram of ice into a gram of water at freezing temperature and 607 calories to evaporate the gram of water at 32° and convert it into water vapor at the same temperature. Since energy is required to change the solid into a liquid, and likewise the liquid into a gas, it follows that water vapor contains more potential energy than liquid water, and water in turn more than ice. This stored-up energy in water vapor is known as *latent heat*, or *latent energy*. For the most part it is transformed sun energy, which has been employed in evaporating water, ice, or snow and converting them into water vapor. One reason why bodies of water heat slowly is that so much energy is consumed in evaporating at their surfaces. That evaporation requires heat is evident from the cool sensation experienced when the skin is moistened with water or, even better, with alcohol. In this case heat is subtracted from the skin to convert the liquid into a gas. If energy is consumed in the process of evaporation, then, conversely, energy should again be released during condensation. This released heat, known as the *latent heat of condensation*, is an important source of energy in the growth of storms and in the production of precipitation. On a night when condensation takes place, cooling is retarded by the liberation of so much latent heat.

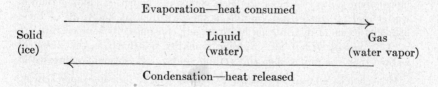

109. THE CONDITION OF THE ATMOSPHERE AS REGARDS MOISTURE. The capacity of the air for water vapor depends very largely upon its

temperature.[1] That the capacity advances at an increasing rate with higher temperatures is indicated by the following table. Thus by

MAXIMUM WATER-VAPOR CAPACITY OF 1 CU. FT. OF AIR AT VARYING TEMPERATURES

Temperature, Degrees Fahrenheit	Water Vapor, Grains	Difference between Successive 10° Intervals
30	1.9	
40	2.9	1.0
50	4.1	1.2
60	5.7	1.6
70	8.0	2.3
80	10.9	2.9
90	14.7	3.8
100	19.7	5.0

increasing the temperature of a cubic foot of air 10°, from 30 to 40°, the moisture capacity is advanced only 1 gr., while a similar 10° increase, from 90 to 100°, results in an increase of 5 gr. It is evident that the air on a hot summer day is able to contain much more moisture than is cold winter air and is likely, therefore, to have greater potentialities for abundant precipitation. Air over Madison, Wis., in July has a water-vapor capacity seven to eight times what it is in January. When a given mass of air contains all the water vapor that it is capable of retaining it is said to be *saturated*. The condition of the air as regards water vapor is spoken of as *humidity*. If air is completely dry, its humidity is zero.

110. *Absolute Humidity*. The total amount of water vapor that a given mass of air contains, expressed in weight of the water vapor per unit *volume* (as grains per cubic foot), is called its *absolute humidity* (vapor pressure). Since it expresses the actual water-vapor content of air, it is of some significance in gauging the atmosphere's possibilities for precipitation. Air over the north-central part of the United States in July has 3.5 to 5.5 times greater absolute humidity than has the January atmosphere. It is usually highest in the vicinity of the equator and decreases toward the poles, varying considerably, however, with distance from oceans and other more minor sources of moisture. It is commonly higher in summer than in winter and is usually greater during the day than at night, all of these principal items of distribution being largely controlled by temperature.

111. *Specific Humidity*. Specific humidity is defined as the *weight* of water vapor in a unit *weight* (not volume) of air. It is usually expressed in

[1] Although it is customary to speak of the *capacity of the air* for water vapor, actually the air itself has practically no effect in this respect. A cubic foot of space and a cubic foot of air at the same temperature can contain essentially the same amount of water vapor.

grams of water vapor per kilogram of air. As a mass of air rises or subsides its volume changes and hence its absolute and relative humidities, but specific humidity is not affected since the relative weights of water vapor and air have not been altered. Specific humidity therefore has much more value in identifying air masses as they move from place to place or as they rise and subside.

112. *Relative Humidity.*   Relative humidity is always expressed in the form of a ratio, fraction, or percentage. It represents the amount of water vapor actually in the air (absolute humidity) compared with what it could hold if saturated at that same temperature. As an illustration: Air at 70° can contain approximately 8 gr. of water vapor per cubic foot. If it actually contains only 6 gr. (its absolute humidity), then it is only three-fourths saturated, and its relative humidity is 75 per cent. Relative humidity can be altered either by changing the amount of water vapor or by varying the capacity of the air, *i.e.*, changing its temperature. The following table shows how air, which was saturated at 40°, acquires successively lower relative humidities simply by increasing its temperature, the water-vapor content remaining unchanged. Relative humidity is an important determinant of

Temperature, Degrees Fahrenheit	Absolute Humidity, Grains	Relative Humidity, Per Cent Saturated
40	2.9	100
50	2.9	71
60	2.9	51
70	2.9	36
80	2.9	27
90	2.9	19

the amount and rate of evaporation, and hence is a critical climatic factor in the rate of moisture and temperature loss by plants and animals, including human beings.

113. *Dew Point and Condensation.*   If air that is not saturated is sufficiently cooled, its capacity for moisture thereby being reduced, a temperature is eventually reached at which the mass of air is saturated, even though the amount of water vapor has not been altered. This critical temperature at which saturation is reached is called the *dew point*. If air is cooled below the dew point, then the excess of water vapor, over and above what the air can contain at that temperature, is given off in the form of minute particles of water (if above 32°) or ice (if below 32°) and *condensation* has taken place. For example, when the temperature of the air is 80° and the absolute humidity 8 grains of water vapor per cubic foot, then the relative humidity is 73 per cent (Table, p. 96). If this mass of air is gradually reduced in temperature so that its capacity for water vapor is lowered, it eventually reaches the dew point 70° and is therefore saturated at that

temperature. Further cooling below the saturation point leads to condensation, the amount of water vapor condensed being the difference between the capacity of air at the different temperatures. Thus a cubic foot of saturated air at 70°, if reduced to 60°, will result in 2.3 grains of water vapor being condensed, this being the difference between the capacities of a cubic foot of air at those two temperatures. An equivalent amount of cooling of saturated air at different temperatures does not, however, yield the same amount of condensed water vapor. If a cubic foot of saturated air at 90° has its temperature reduced 20° (to 70°), 6.7 grains of water vapor are condensed (Table, p. 96), but a further cooling of 20° (to 50°) releases only 3.9 grains, and the next 20° drop only 2.2 grains. It is obvious that warm summer air has greater potentialities for abundant precipitation than does cold winter air.

Condensation

114. The only method known whereby water vapor in the atmosphere can be converted into the liquid or solid state (condensation) is to reduce the temperature of the air *below the dew point*. By cooling the atmosphere its capacity for water vapor is lowered, and, if sufficiently reduced, condensation must result. The dew point of any mass of air is closely related to its relative humidity. When the relative humidity is high, and the air is close to saturation point, only a slight amount of cooling may be required before the dew point is reached and condensation begins. On the other hand, when relative humidity is low, as it usually is over the hot deserts, a large amount of cooling is required before dew point is reached. Condensation, therefore, depends upon two variables: (*a*) the amount of cooling and (*b*) the relative humidity of the air. If the dew point is not reached until the temperature falls below 32°, the condensed water vapor may be in the form of tiny ice crystals (white frost, snow, and some clouds); if condensation occurs above the freezing point, it will be in the liquid state (dew, fog, and most clouds).

In explaining the physical principles of condensation it is usually assumed that (*a*) water in the atmosphere is entirely in vapor form until saturation is reached, (*b*) liquid condensation droplets do not exist at temperatures below freezing, and (*c*) all condensation at temperatures below freezing is in the solid form. As far as the atmosphere is concerned all three assumptions are partly incorrect. Actually the formation of fog and some cloud is likely to begin before 100 per cent relative humidity is reached. Some smoke fogs over cities occur when air is only 90 per cent saturated. The formation of ice on aircraft clearly indicates that condensation droplets in liquid form exist in air at subfreezing temperatures. Moreover, these supercooled droplets not only exist in air at subfreezing temperatures but actually form when condensation occurs at temperatures below 32°.

All condensation in the free atmosphere occurs around hygroscopic nuclei. The most universal condensation nuclei are salt particles sprayed up from oceans, and those associated with the burning of sulphurous fuels such as coal and oil.

METHODS OF COOLING THE ATMOSPHERE, AND FORMS OF CONDENSATION RESULTING

115. DIRECT COOLING BY CONDUCTION AND RADIATION FROM THE OVER-LYING AIR TO A COLD EARTH. Since air is a poor conductor, and, moreover, since only a relatively small part of the whole atmosphere is ever in contact with the earth's surface, the processes here described are not capable of cooling sufficiently large masses of air to give rise to abundant condensation. They may, however, result in such minor forms as fog, white frost, and dew, all of which are usually confined to shallow air layers close to the earth's surface.

116. *Radiation and Conduction from Quiet Air over Cold Surfaces.* Ideal conditions for this type of cooling are a clear sky, little or no wind, a dry atmosphere, and relatively long nights. Under these conditions radiation of terrestrial energy proceeds very rapidly so that the earth's surface, which is a better radiator than air, soon becomes colder than the atmospheric layer resting upon it. The adjacent air layer in turn becomes chilled by radiation and conduction to the earth's cold surface. Clear skies and dry air are relatively essential to this process, since they permit a rapid loss of heat from the earth. Windy nights are not conducive to surface-air cooling, for under these conditions there is a constant "churning" of the lower air so that it does not remain long enough in contact with the earth's surface to be markedly cooled. Moreover, the cooling is distributed throughout a larger mass of air. It is a well-known fact that both dew and frost are much more likely to occur on nights that are clear and calm than on those when the sky is overcast and a wind is blowing. If the temperature of the surface air is reduced below the dew point, condensation takes place. This may be in the form of (a) *dew* (if dew point is above 32°) or (b) *white frost*[1] (if dew point is below 32°), both of which collect on cold objects close to the earth; or condensation may take place throughout a shallow layer of surface air producing (c) a *radiation,* or *lowland fog.* This last form of condensation is particularly noticeable in lowlands where, as a result of air drainage, the colder, heavier air has collected. Such fogs are therefore associated with temper-

---

[1] If the temperature drops below 32° but does not reach the dew point, no deposit of frost will occur. Nevertheless a frost has occurred, this type being called a dry freeze (61).

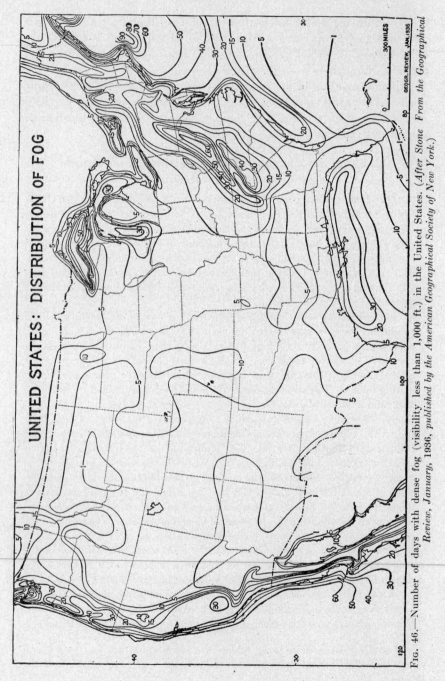

FIG. 46.—Number of days with dense fog (visibility less than 1,000 ft.) in the United States. (*After Stone   From the Geographical Review, January, 1936, published by the American Geographical Society of New York.*)

ature inversions. Thus it often happens that while the slopes and uplands of a region may be quite clear, the adjacent valleys are damp and foggy. From an elevation one may be able to perceive numerous "lakes" of fog occupying the surrounding depressions. This lowland variety is usually short-lived, being evaporated rather quickly by the sun the following morning. The famous London fogs are of this type, the chilled air collecting in the Thames lowland. Their darkness and persistence are the result of a "lid" of smoke and soot which prevents the penetration of sunlight which would evaporate the moisture particles. Ground fogs in the vicinity of landing fields are one of the greatest hazards to commercial aviation.

117. *Radiation and Conduction from Moving Air over Cold Surfaces.* Relatively widespread, dense, and persistent fogs are the principal form of condensation resulting from this type of cooling. Such a fog, since it occurs in *moving* air currents, is called an *advection fog* to distinguish it from the lowland or radiation type. There are several characteristic locations where these advection fogs occur. A common one is on the fronts of winter cyclonic storms where warm, humid air from lower latitudes blows poleward over a colder, and often snow-covered, surface. This type is associated in most people's minds with mild, thawing, winter weather. Dense advection fogs likewise develop over cool water bodies where warmer air from the land drifts over the chilly water. This variety is common along the margins of the oceans and the Great Lakes, especially in spring, when the waters are still relatively cold (Fig. 46). Similarly, fog may result when air from off a warm-water body drifts over a colder land surface or when air from off a warmer ocean passes over a cool current and mixes with the chilly air which lies above it. The dense fogs in the region of the Grand Banks off Newfoundland, where the warm North Atlantic Drift and the cool Labrador Current meet, are of this latter origin. Where cool ocean currents parallel tropical or subtropical coasts, as they do in southern California, southwestern Africa, and Peru, advection fogs are common. In such locations air from the warm ocean proper drifts over the cool coastal currents, and the resulting fog is then wafted in over the adjacent littoral. It is especially noticeable during the cooler hours of the day. Without doubt the mixing that takes place when warm and cool air masses intermingle is a cooling process supplementary to radiation and conduction.

118. COOLING RESULTING FROM EXPANSION OF THE AIR IN RISING CURRENTS (ADIABATIC COOLING). When air rises, no matter what the reason, it expands because there is less weight of air upon it at the higher altitudes. Thus if a mass of dry air at sea level, under an atmospheric pressure of approximately 30 in., rises to an altitude of 17,500 ft., the pressure upon it is reduced one-half, and consequently its volume is doubled. A cubic foot of air at sea level would then, if carried to that altitude, occupy 2 cu. ft. In making room for itself as ascent and gradual expansion take place, other air has to be displaced. As indi-

cated in a previous article (55), the work done in pushing aside the surrounding air requires energy, and this necessary energy is subtracted from the rising air mass in the form of heat, resulting in a lowering of its temperature. Conversely, when air descends from higher altitudes it is compressed by the denser air at lower levels. Work is done upon it, and its temperature consequently is raised (55). It is a truism, therefore, that rising air cools, while descending air is warmed. The rate of cooling or heating resulting from vertical movement of dry or non-saturated air is approximately $5\frac{1}{2}°$ per 1,000 ft. change in altitude. The rate of cooling of ascending air, therefore, is considerably more rapid than is the normal decrease of temperature (about 3.3° per 1,000 ft.) with increasing elevation (58). These two rates should be clearly distinguished as being very different things, for one represents the cooling of a rising and therefore moving mass of air, while the other represents the change in air temperature that would be recorded by a thermometer carried up through the atmosphere by a balloon or kite. Heated air continues to rise until it reaches air layers of its own temperature and density. *This process of cooling, by expansion of rising air currents, is the only one capable of reducing the temperature of great masses of air below the dew point.* It is the only one, therefore, which is capable of producing condensation on such a large scale that abundant precipitation results. There is no doubt that nearly all the earth's precipitation is the result of expansion and cooling in rising air currents. The direct result of cooling due to ascent is *clouds*, a form of condensation characteristic of air at altitudes usually well above the earth's surface, just as dew, white frost, and fog are forms characteristic of the surface air. Fog and cloud are identical except for differences in height above the ground. Not all clouds, to be sure, give rise to precipitation, but all precipitation has its origin in clouds and is the result of processes that are supplementary to those causing condensation.

The Formation of Clouds and Precipitation in Ascending Air Currents

119. STABILITY AND INSTABILITY. Since vertical movements of the atmosphere are the cause of practically all precipitation, the conditions which promote or hinder such movements are of prime importance. When air resists vertical movement and tends to remain in its original position it is said to be *stable*. Cold and dry air masses are usually stable in character. During a temperature inversion the cold heavy surface air has no tendency to rise. Stable air, therefore, is not conducive to precipitation. On the other hand when air has a tendency to move upward away from its original position, a condition

of *instability* prevails. When such is the case movement is prevalent and cloud and precipitation likely. Instability is characteristic of mild, humid air in which there is a rapid vertical decrease in temperature. Such a condition is common in the warm tropical air from the Gulf of Mexico which dominates the weather of eastern United States in the summer season. Many times air that is mildly stable is forced to rise over mountain barriers or over colder wedges of air. Upon reaching condensation level heat of condensation is added and the air then becomes unstable and so continues to rise, producing abundant rainfall. Such air is said to be *conditionally unstable*, *i.e.*, unstable after condensation has commenced.

120. STAGES IN THE COOLING OF A RISING AIR MASS.   As a mass of unsaturated air rises, no matter for what reason, it begins to cool at the normal rate of about 5.5° per 1,000 ft. of ascent. Until it has risen and cooled sufficiently for the saturation point to be approached, there are no condensed liquid or solid particles in the ascending air. All humidity is in vapor form. For this reason this first stage, without condensation, is called the *dry stage*.

Eventually the ascending and cooling air reaches the dew point, condensation begins, or is greatly accelerated, and the rising air enters the *cloud and rain stage*. The air still contains much moisture in vapor form, but some of it has been converted into liquid form. Here clouds, composed of minute water particles, begin to form. As condensation commences, heat of condensation is released into the rising air, so that cooling is at a slower rate.

It is possible for ascending air to pass somewhat beyond the condensation level, with a resulting formation of clouds, and still yield little or no precipitation. The first condensation takes place around almost innumerable hygroscopic dust nuclei, the individual condensed water particles being so small that they fall very slowly and are probably evaporated before they reach the earth's surface. Gray, overcast, cloudy days with no rain are consequently very common. However, if the air continues to ascend well above condensation level, more and more of these multitudes of condensation nuclei are left behind, literally strained out of the ascending air because of their greater density or weight, so that further condensation must take place around fewer nuclei. As a result of the drops forming around fewer nuclei, they grow large enough to overcome the force of the ascending air, fall, and eventually reach the earth. Growth in size of drops is further aided by (a) intense turbulence and (b) electrical attraction. There is some reason to believe that large-scale precipitatation is not released from a cloud until it builds up to such heights that ice crystals begin to form. The ice crystals seem to have the same function in releasing precipitation that condensation nuclei have in starting condensation.

When the ascending and cooling air finally reaches a temperature of 32°, some of the condensed liquid particles *already in the air* probably are changed into ice. That not all of them are frozen, but that some continue to exist in liquid form at temperatures well below freezing, is indicated by the fact that ice frequently collects on airplanes. As the air continues to rise above the freezing level, and cooling continues, much, although not necessarily all, of the subsequent condensation is in the solid form. In this stage, known as the *snow-and-ice stage*, water vapor in the form of a gas may pass directly into the solid form, molecule by molecule, and build a tiny ice crystal. Therefore clouds at these subfreezing temperatures commonly are composed of minute ice crystals, although supercooled liquid particles may be present as well. Snowflakes are simply agglomerations of these tiny ice crystals.

Fig. 47*A*.—Cumulus clouds. (*U. S. Weather Bureau Photograph.*)

Cloud Types

Four principal or pure cloud types are usually recognized, all the other numerous types that can be observed being modifications or combinations of these four.

121. *Cumulus.* These relatively fair-weather clouds are distinguished by their flat bases and their beautiful, towering, cauliflower tops (Figs. 47*A*). The flat bases mark condensation level. Cumulus clouds are the result of vertically ascending air currents and are usually associated with local surface heating on warm summer days. Of course convectional ascent does not take place over the entire heated surface, the rising currents being localized and having descending cooler currents between them. Thus separate and isolated cumuli occur with patches of blue sky between. Sometimes on hot, humid days when convection is exceedingly well developed the cumuli may extend to great heights and develop into thunderheads. These overgrown cumulus, or cumulo-nimbus, clouds are the sources of many local thunderstorms and a considerable part of the earth's rainfall (Fig. 47*B*).

122. *Cirrus.* These also are fair-weather clouds, although not infrequently they may be forerunners of an approaching storm. They occur at great altitudes (5 to 9 miles) where temperatures are usually well below freezing so that they are composed of minute ice crystals. Cirrus clouds

assume various forms, sometimes appearing like white ringlets, curls, or wisps of hair (Fig. 48). At other times they seem to form an unbroken thin

Fig. 47*B*.—Cumulo-nimbus cloud, or thunderhead. In such a cloud most of the earth's thunderstorms originate. (*U. S. Weather Bureau Photograph.*)

Fig. 48.—Cirrus clouds. (*U. S. Weather Bureau Photograph.*)

Fig. 49.—Stratus clouds. (*U. S. Weather Bureau Photograph.*)

veil of fibrous texture over the whole sky. In the latter case they produce halos around the moon or sun. Never are they thick enough to produce shadows, so that they always appear white.

123. *Stratus.* These low-lying sheets of cloud form a dull, gray sky of uniform color (Fig. 49). Often the gray ceiling stretches unbroken from horizon to horizon. They are relatively common in winter, producing gray, depressing days. A common method of their origin is mixture along the contact plane between two masses of air of different temperatures.

124. *Nimbus.* Thick, dark masses of cloud from which rain is falling are called nimbus. They often look like stratus clouds but differ from them in that they are sources of precipitation.

FORMS OF PRECIPITATION

125. *Rain,* which is the commonest form of precipitation is, as stated previously (120), the result of exaggerated condensation in rising air currents at temperatures usually above 32°, while *snow* forms at temperatures below freezing. *Sleet* is frozen rain and results when raindrops from a warmer air mass above fall through a cold surface layer of air. It is characteristic of the cooler seasons. *Glaze* is really not a form of precipitation but is the accumulation of a coating of ice on objects near the earth. Fortunately it is not of common occurrence, for the so-called *ice storm* which produces glaze is one of the most destructive of the cool-season types of weather. It occurs when rain, near or below the freezing point, strikes surface objects the temperatures of which are below 32°, and is immediately converted into ice. So great may become the weight of the ice accumulation that trees are often wrecked; telephone, telegraph, and electric wires broken; and their poles snapped off. *Hail,* although the heaviest and largest unit of precipitation existing in solid form, is exclusively the product of vigorous convection, occurring in thunderstorms, which in turn usually belong to the warm season. Hailstones are composed of concentric layers, or shells, of clear ice and of partially melted and refrozen snow, representing the successive vertical descents and ascents in the tumultuous convectional currents of a thunderstorm (170).

TYPES OF AIR ASCENT AND PRECIPITATION RESULTING

126. It already has been noted that rising air cools and that if the temperature of sufficiently large masses of humid air is reduced well below the dew point, abundant condensation and precipitation will result. It remains now to analyze the conditions under which large masses of air may be caused to ascend. Three classes of origin will be noted.

127. CONVECTIONAL PRECIPITATION. As a result of the heating of surface air it expands and is forced to rise by the cooler, heavier air above and around it. Ordinarily such rising air, since it cools at nearly double the rate of the normal vertical temperature decrease, will rise only a few thousand feet before its temperature has been reduced to the point where it is the same as that of the surrounding air. At that

point where the rising air reaches air strata of its own temperature and density, further ascent ceases. But if abundant condensation begins before this stage is reached, then heat of condensation is released, so that, with this added source of energy, the rising air will be forced to ascend much higher before reaching atmospheric strata of its own temperature. Thus on a hot summer afternoon, when surface heating is intense and condensation abundant, the towering cumulonimbus clouds resulting from convectional ascent may be several miles in vertical depth, and precipitation from them may be copious.[1] Convectional ascent is usually associated with the warm season of the year and the warm hours of the day. Since it is essentially a vertical movement of warm, humid air, cooling is rapid, and the rainfall resulting is likely to be in the form of heavy showers. Because a cumulo-nimbus cloud usually covers only a relatively small area, it quickly drifts by, so that the associated shower is not of long duration. Convectional rain, because it comes in the form of heavy showers, is less effective for crop growth, since much of it, instead of entering the soil, goes off in the form of surface drainage. This is a genuine menace to plowed fields, since soil removal through slope wash and gullying is likely to be serious. On the other hand, for the middle and higher latitudes, convectional rain, since it occurs in the warm season of the year when vegetation is active and crops are growing, comes at the most strategic time. Moreover, it provides the maximum rainfall with the minimum amount of cloudiness.

Of a somewhat different origin is rainfall resulting from the overrunning of warm and less dense air by colder, denser currents aloft. When this occurs atmospheric overturning is likely, the cool, heavy air sinking to the earth and forcing the warm air upward, often violently. Heavy downpours may result.

128. OROGRAPHIC PRECIPITATION.   Air also may be forced to rise when landform barriers, such as mountain ranges, plateau escarpments, or even high hills, lie athwart the paths of winds. Since water vapor is largely confined to the lower layers of atmosphere and rapidly decreases in amount upward, heavy orographic rainfall is the result of such forced ascent of air, associated with the blocking effect of landform obstacles. Witness, for example, the very abundant precipitation along the western or windward flanks of the Cascade Mountains in Washington and Oregon, along parts of the precipitous east coast of Brazil, which lies in the trades, or bordering the abrupt west coast of India, which the summer monsoon meets practically at right angles.

---

[1] Thunderstorms and their rainfall are dealt with in greater detail in the next chapter on storms.

The *leeward* sides of such mountain barriers, where the air is descending and warming, are characteristically drier (Fig. 50). This is called the *rain shadow*. The blocking effect of a mountain is normally felt at some distance out in front of the abrupt change in slope, the approaching wind riding up over a mass of stagnant air along its front. The belt of heaviest orographic rainfall along a mountain front usually is not far above the point where precipitation begins, although its elevation varies with the season, exposure, and latitude. In the Alps the mean elevation of the zone of maximum precipitation is approximately 6,500 ft.; in The Himalayas it is 4,000 ft. The most ideal condition for producing heavy orographic rainfall is when a high and relatively continuous mountain barrier lies close to a coast, and the winds from off a warm ocean meet the barrier at right angles. Orographic rains have less seasonal and daily periodicity than do those of convectional

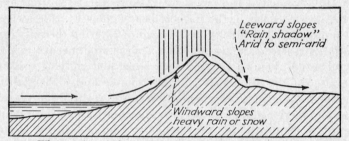

Fig. 50.—When moist winds are forced to ascend mountain barriers, heavy precipitation usually falls on the windward slopes; but leeward slopes where air is descending and warming are drier.

origin. In monsoon regions, very naturally, the maximum is at the time when air is moving from sea to land, usually high sun, or summer. In other regions the strength of the winds, the angle at which they meet the mountain barrier, or the contrast between land and water temperatures may determine the season of maximum orographic rainfall.

It seems likely that a considerable part of the excess precipitation associated with highlands is not the result of direct forced ascent of the prevailing winds, in other words, not simple orographic in type. Certainly of great importance are such indirect effects as (a) the production of convectional currents up mountain slopes exposed to strong insolational heating; (b) the "pinching" or "blocking" effect upon cyclonic storms; and (c) the providing of a "trigger" effect that gives the initial upthrust to conditionally unstable air masses. Sometimes only a slight amount of lifting is necessary to bring these air masses to condensation level, after which they become unstable and so continue to rise, yielding abundant rainfall. Thus highlands of less than 3,000-ft. elevation, although perhaps inducing no great amount of direct orographic precipitation, may by these indirect means become much rainier areas than the surrounding lowlands.

129. CYCLONIC PRECIPITATION.[1] In low-pressure storms (cyclones) of middle latitudes air from various directions, and consequently of different temperatures and densities, tends to converge toward a center (154). As a result of convergence and consequent lifting, plus the underrunning of warmer, lighter air masses from lower latitudes by colder, denser air currents from higher latitudes, large volumes of air are caused to ascend. Unlike convectional ascent, which involves direct vertical lifting, the warmer air in cyclones more often rises obliquely, and therefore slowly, along mildly inclined surfaces of cold, dense air, and cooling as a consequence is less rapid. As a result of the slower ascent and cooling, precipitation in cyclones is characteristically less violent than in thunderstorms and is inclined to be steadier and longer continued. The dull, gray, overcast skies and drizzly precipitation of the cooler months in middle latitudes, producing some of the most unpleasant weather of those seasons, are usually associated with cyclones. When overrunning of warm surface air by cooler currents aloft occurs in a cyclone, heavier downpours may occur. These storms are most numerous and best developed during the cool season. Where they dominate weather conditions, therefore, they tend to produce fall or winter maxima in precipitation curves. Most of the winter precipitation of lowlands in the middle latitudes is cyclonic in origin. In the tropics, as well as in the middle latitudes, cyclones are important generators of precipitation, although the storms of low latitudes are of a different origin, and their rainfall may be likewise. However, convergence of air and consequent ascent are characteristic of all low-pressure storms, whether in low or in middle latitudes.

130. IMPORTANT PRECIPITATION DATA. At least three items concerning precipitation of a region are of outstanding importance: (a) its total average amount, or depth, for the year (Plate II); (b) its seasonal periodicity; and (c) its dependability, both annual and seasonal (Fig. 79). Origin (convectional, orographic, cyclonic), and therefore general character, is also significant. It is the total average amount which usually receives the principal attention, although this practice cannot be defended. Geographically speaking, the fact that Omaha, Neb., receives 30 in. of rainfall annually is no more significant than the fact that 17.4 in. (58 per cent) falls during the months from May to

---

[1] Cyclones and their precipitation are considered in greater detail in the following chapter on storms.

August inclusive, and only 3.3 in. (11 per cent) falls during the period November to February inclusive. Time of occurrence therefore is coequal in importance with amount. Variability in the total amount of precipitation from year to year (its dependability) is hardly of less importance, especially for regions that are normally subhumid. It is a general rule that variability increases as the amount of rainfall decreases.

The average annual amount of rainfall and its characteristic seasonal periodicity at any place (rainfall regime) depend upon (a) accessibility to moisture-bearing winds, usually from the ocean; and (b) the existence of conditions, principally storms, favorable to the condensation of water vapor. Both conditions are essential. The accessibility of a region to moisture-bearing winds is related to (a) the general distribution of pressure and winds; (b) the character of surface configuration; and (c) the distance from oceans, the principal source of water vapor for the lands.

NOTE. Logically the preceding discussion of humidity and rainfall should be followed by an analysis of the distribution of precipitation over the earth. The discussion of rainfall distribution is omitted at this point, however, because that topic is adequately treated in later chapters (VII–XI) dealing with climatic types and their distribution over the earth.

Chapter VI. Storms and Their Associated Weather Types

131. Storms as Generators of Precipitation. It is a common misconception that air blowing in from the ocean over the land is the immediate and direct cause of rainfall. This is rarely the case except in a minor way, possibly as a result of frictional retardation of the lower air currents with a consequent overrunning and lifting of those aloft. There are plenty of illustrations on the daily weather maps, where air blows in from the sea over flattish land areas with no rainfall resulting. But this is not to say that the land or sea origin of air is of little consequence in affecting the probability of precipitation. On the contrary, it is significant and for the reason that air from over the sea is likely to have a more abundant supply of water vapor and so has greater potentialities for rain.

But actually to cause condensation on a large scale, with resulting precipitation, there is a further requirement than just abundant atmospheric moisture. That requirement is some method of causing a large volume of air to be lifted and consequently cooled. Except where orographic barriers are the cause for ascent, storms are the principal centers of rising air, with the result that storms of various types are the earth's principal generators of precipitation.

A large quantity of moisture in the air is meteorologically significant, not only as a potential reservoir for rainfall, as indicated above, but also because it creates an atmospheric environment conducive to the development and growth of storms. Tremendous amounts of latent energy (heat of condensation) are stored up in the atmosphere's water vapor, where it is available for the production and growth of storms (108). Dry air, therefore, has less potential *storm energy* than humid air. It is especially with rain-producing storms that this chapter deals.

Moving[1] Cyclones and Anticyclones

132. Classes of Cyclones and Anticyclones. The terms cyclone and anticyclone are applied to a variety of storms of contrast-

[1] This title is employed in order to distinguish the storms here described from the

ing types and characteristic locations. Thus there are (*a*) nonviolent cyclones and anticyclones of the intermediate zones, characteristic particularly of the cooler seasons. In fact they are so prevalent in the middle latitudes that the "prevailing" westerly winds are scarcely obvious on the daily weather maps. More commonly the surface winds appear to be converging and diverging circulations around distinct centers, these being respectively cyclones and anticyclones. It is analogous to a river's being so full of eddies and whirlpools that it is difficult to detect the direction of the main current. These characteristically mild storms of the middle latitudes stand out by contrast with (*b*) the smaller, but more intense, cyclones (hurricanes and typhoons) of tropical latitudes, the latter storms commonly being violent and destructive. In addition to these severe storms of the tropics there are, also, (*c*) in the low latitudes many weak, slow-moving cyclones which produce heavy rainfall but which are usually associated with only weak winds. This last type of cyclone likewise occurs in certain subtropical parts of the middle latitudes during the warm season. Each of the three types noted above is an important element of weather and climate in those parts of the earth where it is characteristic. At least the first type is important in producing temperature conditions and changes, but no doubt the chief climatic significance of moving cyclones as a class of storms is that within them great masses of air are forced to rise, resulting in precipitation.

MIDDLE-LATITUDE CYCLONES AND ANTICYCLONES[1]

GENERAL CHARACTERISTICS. APPEARANCE, SIZE, AND DIRECTION AND RATE OF MOVEMENT

133. Of principal importance in producing the frequent, erratic, and nonperiodic weather changes so characteristic of middle latitudes

---

stationary, semipermanent centers of high and low pressure, also designated as cyclones and anticyclones.

[1] The organization of the discussion on middle-latitude cyclones as it appears in this book is admittedly a compromise which the author has adopted largely because of the nature of the United States daily weather map. This publication as sent out by the district forecast centers still represents cyclones and anticyclones as pressure entities defined in terms of sea-level isobars. Air masses and fronts are not shown. Only the map that is made up in Washington, D. C., contains these data. Until such time as the published daily weather maps available to the country at large contain this information it is obviously unwise in a textbook of this type to adopt a kind of treatment of storms which the ordinary daily weather map is not able to illustrate. Sample copies of the daily weather map showing air masses and fronts, published at the Weather Bureau's office in Washington, may be obtained for teaching purposes.

are the moving cyclones and anticyclones which fill the westerly wind belt. In such regions the fickleness of the weather is proverbial, and it is in these parts of the world that weather-forecasting services are most necessary and best developed. No two storms are exactly alike, so that the generalizations concerning cyclones and anticyclones which follow must not be expected to fit any particular storm in all respects. Moreover, they differ somewhat from region to region.

134. NATURE AND LOCATION. Cyclones are low-pressure storms and commonly go by the name of *lows*, or *depressions*, while anticyclones are high-pressure areas and are called *highs*. The cyclone

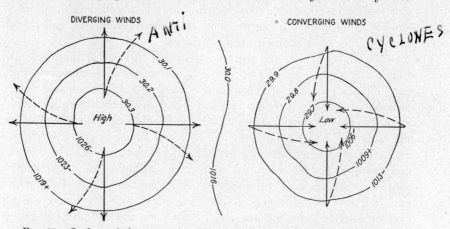

FIG. 51.—Surface wind systems in stationary cyclones and anticyclones diagrammatically represented. Solid arrows indicate direction of air flow on a nonrotating earth; dashed arrows, the deflected winds on a rotating earth. Pressure readings in inches and millibars.

must, therefore, be a mass of light air since surface pressures are low, while, conversely, the anticyclone, or high, is a mass of heavier air. Since these storms are prevalent throughout the westerly wind belts they are best known in those latitudes between parallels 35 and 65° in each hemisphere. Because cyclones and anticyclones are traveling storms within the westerlies, it is to be expected that they will be carried by those winds in general from west to east, much in the same way that a whirlpool in a river is carried downstream by the main current.

135. APPEARANCE. As one sees these storms on the published United States weather map they are represented by a series of closed, concentric isobars, roughly circular or oval in shape (Fig. 51, Plate III). In the cyclone the lowest pressure is at the center, and it *increases* toward the margins; while in the anticyclone pressure is highest at

the center and *decreases* outward. If the isobars in a low are imagined to be contours, then the cyclone resembles a circular or oval depression, while the high has the appearance of a dome-shaped hill. There is no definite amount of pressure that distinguishes lows from highs; it is entirely a relative thing. Normally there are several tenths of an inch pressure difference between the center and circumference of a low. Occasionally a large and particularly well-developed winter cyclone may show a difference of as much as 1 in. In highs the pressure difference between center and margins is usually in the neighborhood of $\frac{1}{2}$ in., although it may be double that in some instances. It is a general rule that both cyclones and anticyclones are less well developed, have smaller differences in pressure, weaker pressure gradients, and travel at lower speeds in summer than in winter.

136. SIZE. There are great variations in the size of these storms, but on the whole they spread over extensive areas, sometimes covering as much as one-third of the United States, or 1 million square miles, although most of them are smaller. They are *extensive* rather than *intensive*. Thus a normal cyclone with a vertical thickness of 6 to 7 miles probably will have a diameter one hundred times as great. Cyclones are inclined to be elliptical or egg-shaped in contour, with the narrow end toward the equator. The long axis, extending in a northeast-southwest direction, is commonly nearly twice the length of the short one (northwest-southeast), so that a typical well-developed winter cyclone might show long and short diameters of 1,200 and 650 miles respectively. Anticyclones are inclined to be somewhat larger, their diameters averaging roughly 25 per cent greater than those of lows.

137. DIRECTION AND RATE OF MOVEMENT. As noted in an earlier paragraph, lows and highs travel in a general west-to-east direction, carried along by the upper-air system of westerly winds in which they exist (Plate III). That is not to say, however, that storms always move due eastward. To be sure, they follow different routes, and there are some regions of concentration and others of divergence, but in spite of their vagaries in direction, as well as in rate of movement, their progress is, in general, eastward. The direction and rate of movement of cyclones are approximately those of the upper winds. It is easy to understand, therefore, why a weather forecaster in the middle latitudes bases his prediction upon weather conditions to the west, rather than to the east, of his station. Those storms to the east already have gone by; those to the west are approaching. There is a tendency for storms to follow certain general tracks, and a more detailed account of world-

wide storm movements, and the routes followed, will appear later in the chapter (161, 162).

Variability in rate of movement is characteristic, both as to season and as to individual storms. In the United States storms move eastward across the country at velocities averaging 20 miles an hour in summer and 30 miles an hour in winter, with the highs somewhat slower than the lows. In summer, when the whole atmospheric circulation is slowed down, storm speeds are reduced, and the contrasts between cyclones and anticyclones are less pronounced. As a consequence, warm-season weather is less changeable, and atmospheric disturbances are less violent. In the winter season a well-developed low characteristically requires 3 to 5 days for the transcontinental journey across the United States.

Just as temperature, pressure, and wind belts shift north and south. following the movements of the sun's rays, poleward in summer and equatorward in winter, so also do the storm tracks. This fact helps to explain the fewer and weaker storms over the lower middle latitudes in summer as compared with winter.

ORIGIN AND STRUCTURE OF CYCLONES AND ANTICYCLONES

AIR MASSES AND FRONTS

A comprehension of the nature and origin of air masses and fronts is necessary to an understanding of the characteristics of storms and the weather that is generated by them.

138. DEFINITIONS AND CHARACTERISTICS. An air mass is an extensive portion of the atmosphere whose temperature and humidity characteristics are relatively homogeneous horizontally. Such an air mass develops whenever the atmosphere remains in contact with an extensive and relatively uniform surface for a sufficiently long period that the properties of the air become similar to those of the surface on which it rests. Uniform areas of the earth's surface where air masses develop are called *source regions*. The snow-covered Arctic plains of Canada and Siberia in winter, large areas of tropical ocean, and the hot arid Sahara in summer are good examples of source regions. As a rule air masses do not remain long in their source regions but sooner or later move outward from them into other areas whose weather is thereby affected by the invading air mass. Air masses are able to travel great distances from their regions of origin and still maintain many of the properties attained at their sources. Because of their great size and the slowness with which they are modified it is easy to trace the movement of air masses from day to day.

When air masses having different temperature and humidity characteristics come together, they do not mix freely with each other but tend rather to remain separated with more or less distinct sloping boundary surfaces between them, the warmer and therefore less dense air mass being forced aloft over the wedge of colder air (Fig. 52). The sloping boundary surfaces separating contrasting air masses are called *surfaces of discontinuity* or *fronts*. Usually marked changes in temperature and humidity can be observed as one crosses a front. The location of fronts, both at the earth's surface and aloft, and the nature of

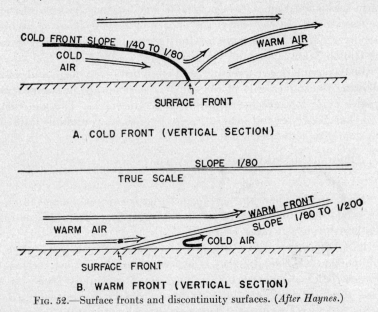

A. COLD FRONT (VERTICAL SECTION)

B. WARM FRONT (VERTICAL SECTION)

Fig. 52.—Surface fronts and discontinuity surfaces. (*After Haynes.*)

the contrasting air masses on either side of them, is of great importance in weather forecasting, for along such fronts a great many storms and associated weather changes originate. Whenever there is a convergent movement of air masses, such as characterizes low-pressure systems, frontal discontinuities are likely to be present.

The air-mass concept should be thought of as a further refinement of the earth's wind system. Certain air masses are relatively synonymous with a particular wind belt. For example, equatorial air masses are much the same as the doldrums. Polar air masses, which arrive from higher latitudes, in part are southward surges of the polar easterlies. It is recognized, however, that although belonging to the same general wind system there may be various types of polar air masses having markedly different characteristics, depending on the season of the year as well as the nature of the polar source region. Thus polar winds from off an open sea are strikingly different in temperature and humidity from polar winds from off a snow-covered continent. It is well to have in mind, therefore, that the discussion on air masses is largely supplementary to the treatment of the earth's wind systems in Chap. IV.

139. CLASSIFICATION OF AIR MASSES. Any classification of air masses must be based primarily upon the characteristics of their source regions. The latter fall naturally into two groups, those of high latitudes (*polar* and *subpolar*) and those of low latitudes (*equatorial, tropical,* and *subtropical*). It is largely in the high and the low latitudes that there are large areas of relatively homogeneous surface conditions and relatively light air movement. The middle latitudes are the scene of intense interaction between the polar and tropical air masses and generally lack the uniformity of conditions essential to a source region.

The air-mass classification may be further refined by dividing the *polar* (*P*) and *tropical* (*T*) source types, on the general basis of moisture and temperature differences, into *continental* (*C*) and *maritime* (*M*) subgroups. It is further necessary to take into consideration the particular season of the year, for some source regions differ markedly between winter and summer. Air masses are designated by the name or abbreviation of the source region. When they have become somewhat modified in thermal and moisture characteristics as a result of moving into other regions the letter *N* (neutralized) is prefixed. The letters *K* and *W* are sometimes added to the letters indicated above to show that the air mass is colder (*K*) or warmer (*W*) than the surface over which the air is moving.

For the Northern Hemisphere five general types of source regions may be distinguished: (*a*) the source regions of cold air, which include the polar areas and parts of the northern continents; (*b*) the source regions of tropical air which occupy the subtropical high-pressure belt and adjacent portions of the trades; (*c*) the regions of transition between polar and tropical air; (*d*) the equatorial regions; and (*e*) the monsoon region of transition between polar and equatorial air, with polar air dominant in winter and equatorial air in summer.

140. NORTH AMERICAN AIR MASSES. Unfortunately there is not available at the present time information that would make possible a treatment of the air masses that affect the weather and climate of each of the continents. Chief consideration is given here to the classification and discussion of North American air masses.

CLASSIFICATION OF IMPORTANT AMERICAN AIR MASSES BY GEOGRAPHICAL SOURCE REGIONS

Source by		Local source region	Corresponding air mass	Symbol	Season
Latitude	Nature				
Polar (P)	Continental (cP)	Alaska, Canada, and the Arctic	Polar Canadian (Polar continental)	Pc	Entire year
		Modified in Southern and Central U. S.	Transitional Polar Canadian	Npc	Entire year
	Maritime (mP)	North Pacific Ocean	Polar Pacific	Pp	Entire year
		Modified in Western and Central U. S.	Transitional Polar Pacific	Npp	Entire year
		Colder portions of the North Atlantic Ocean	Polar Atlantic	Pa	Entire year
		Modified over warmer portions of the North Atlantic Ocean	Transitional Polar Atlantic	Npa	Spring and Summer
Tropical (T)	Maritime (mT)	Gulf of Mexico and Caribbean Sea	Tropical Gulf	Tg	Entire year
		Modified over U. S. or the North Atlantic Ocean	Transitional tropical maritime	Ntm or Ntg	Entire year
		Sargasso Sea (Middle Atlantic)	Tropical Atlantic	Ta	Entire year
		Modified over U. S. or the North Atlantic Ocean	Transitional tropical maritime	Ntm or Nta	Entire year
		Southeastern Pacific Ocean	Tropical Pacific	Tp	Entire year
		Modified over Southwestern U. S. and Northeastern Pacific Ocean	Transitional tropical Pacific	Ntp	Entire year
	Upper-air subsidence	Upper levels of subtropical highs	Tropical Superior	Ts (or S)	Entire year

141. Pc (Polar Canadian, Polar Continental) Air Masses. The source region for the *winter Pc* air masses of North America is the ice-covered northern interior of Canada, Alaska, and the Arctic Ocean. Their characteristic properties are extreme coldness and low absolute and specific humidity. Severe winter cold waves are associated with rapid southward movement of *Pc* air. Marked stability and a large temperature inversion persist as long as the *Pc* air mass moves southward over a snow-covered surface. Rarely does it become genuinely unstable in the Mississippi Valley before reaching the Gulf of Mexico. Cloudless

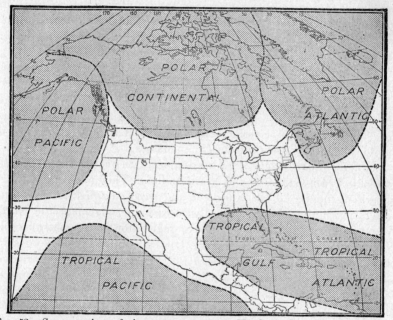

Fig. 53.—Source regions of air masses common to North America. (*After Transcontinental and Western Airways, Inc.*)

skies are a distinctive characteristic. Over northeastern United States and the Atlantic seaboard *Pc* air shows more cloudiness and has somewhat higher surface temperatures. This results from passage over the open water of the Great Lakes in winter and the presence of numerous highlands in the eastern part of the country (Fig. 53).

Source properties of American *Pc* air in *summer* are markedly different from those in winter. Long days cause the bare snow-free surface to become much warmed so that the air is heated from the ground instead of being chilled from beneath as in winter. A fairly low moisture content, moderately low temperatures, and absence of clouds are characteristic of *Pc* air in summer.

·142. *Pp* (*Polar Pacific*) *air masses* originate in the Arctic or sub-arctic but reach the west coast of the United States after having traveled for relatively long distances over the warm waters of the North Pacific. Thus while in its source regions *winter Pp* air resembles *Pc*, its sojourn over the North Pacific changes it from a cold, dry, stable mass to one which is relatively unstable and whose surface strata, at least, are milder and comparatively humid. On the Pacific Coast cloudy, showery conditions are commonly associated with onshore *Pp* air. Important modifications result as this air mass crosses the western mountains and reaches the interior of the country. There its moisture content is much lower and stability greater. The finest winter weather east of the Rockies prevails in the *Npp* (modified *Pp*) air masses—moderate winds, clear skies, and relatively mild temperatures (Fig. 53).

In *summer Pp* air is characterized by marked coolness and dryness. The cloud cover and showers characteristic of winter are definitely absent, for stability is relatively great. In general *Pp* air at Seattle is characterized by greater stability than is *Pc* air at inland stations. After they reach the interior of the country it is quite impossible in summer to distinguish *Pp* from *Pc* air masses.

143. *Pa* (*Polar Atlantic*) *air masses* originate over the cool Atlantic waters between Cape Cod and Newfoundland. They were originally *Pc* air which moved off the continent and were modified over the cold waters. Owing to the prevailing west-east air movement the North Atlantic is not an important source region for air masses affecting North America. This is especially true in winter. Seldom does its effect extend beyond the Appalachians. In *winter Pa* air is characteristically dry and stable aloft, while the surface layer is moderately unstable, moist, and chilly rather than cold. As compared with *Pp* air at Seattle the lower levels are colder, drier, and more stable. As *Pa* air comes onshore in winter it results in weather with surface temperatures near freezing, high relative humidity, low visibility, and frequently light flurries of fine mist (Fig. 53).

Pa air masses have their greatest influence upon American weather in late *spring* and early *summer*. At that time of year the North Atlantic waters are abnormally cold compared with the adjacent continent so that they become a source region of genuinely cold air for the whole coastal area east of the Appalachians and north of Cape Hatteras. *Pa* summer air is distinctly cool, relatively stable, and shows only thin and broken clouds from which precipitation never falls.

144. *Tg* (*Tropical Gulf*) and *Ta* (*Tropical Atlantic*) *air masses* have their origin over the warm waters of the Gulf of Mexico and the Caribbean Sea or over the Sargasso Sea of the Atlantic proper. *Tg*

and *Ta* air are so essentially similar that they are here discussed together and are referred to jointly as *Tg*. Marked warmth and high moisture content at lower levels are characteristic even in *winter*. Convective precipitation rarely occurs within a *Tg* air mass in the cool season, but along a warm front, where it is forced to ascend, precipitation may be extremely heavy. Combined with warmth and high humidity there is likely to be considerable cloudiness of the low stratus type, especially during the night and early morning. As the *Tg* air moves poleward, the ground strata are cooled by contact with progressively colder earth, and where air movement is slight dense fog frequently is the result. In rather strong air currents dense mist or fine drizzle is likely (Fig. 53).

Because of prevailing sea-to-land pressure gradients over eastern United States in *summer*, *Tg* air is able to extend much farther into the interior of the continent at that season than in winter. It is responsible for the oppressive humid heat which characterizes the summer weather of much of central and eastern United States. As it leaves its source region summer *Tg* air is somewhat warmer and more humid than it is in winter. Moving in over the continent and continuing northward over the warm land, there is a tendency for its surface layers to increase in temperature. Midday instability with numerous widely scattered local thunderstorms is characteristic of the air mass.

145. *Tp* (*Tropical Pacific*) *air masses* have their origin in the subtropical latitudes of the southeastern Pacific Ocean. Because of the relatively cool ocean surface in this source region *Tp* air in *winter* is only moderately warm, or even cool, at least near the ground. Water vapor content may be moderately high in the surface strata but certainly far from great considering that its source region is a tropical ocean. Clouds are absent until the *Tp* air has moved some distance northward from its source and surface cooling has resulted. On the other hand, heavy winter rains along the Pacific Coast and as far inland as the Great Basin or the southern Plateau may result when *Tp* air is foreced to overrun colder air masses. When cold air masses are absent *Tp* air may sweep poleward along the Pacific Coast as far as Seattle or beyond with little or no rain.

During *summer Tp* air masses play a very minor part in Pacific Coast weather, *Pp* air certainly dominating the situation as far south as southern California. It seems probable that in the Plateau and Rocky Mountain regions air of possible *Tp* origin may be responsible for the considerable cloudiness and widespread thunderstorms which develop there in the warm season. Recent studies seem to indicate that this air is more of *Tg* than of *Tp* origin, however.

146. *Ts* (*Tropical Superior*) *air masses* are present over southern and central United States at intermediate and upper levels throughout most of the year. On the western plains and especially in the Southwest *Ts* air may occur as a ground current. It is the warmest air mass to be observed, and this heat is associated with very low relative humidity. The hot dry weather which occurs over the western plains in summer and farther to the southwest even in winter is always associated with *Ts* air. Its origin is somewhat uncertain, but its most logical source appears to be the higher levels of the subtropical belt of high pressure, more specifically the Pacific anticyclone.

147. AIR MASSES OF EURASIA. The air masses that control the weather of Europe are in many respects similar to those of western North America. Thus Polar Atlantic air in western Europe is essentially similar to Polar Pacific air in western United States, and Tropical Atlantic air in Germany is not unlike Tropical Pacific in British Columbia. The contrasts in the relief of the two continents, however, permit the deeper entrance of the maritime air masses in Europe. Polar Continental air masses influence the weather and climate of eastern and central Europe chiefly but less frequently that of western Europe. The general west-to-east atmospheric circulation in these latitudes makes a reverse east-to-west movement of air masses relatively unusual. Dry, warm Tropical Continental air from the desert lands of northern Africa only occasionally affects the weather of central and western Europe, but it is a major control in the Mediterranean borderlands.

Eastern Asia in its air-mass characteristics resembles eastern North America. In winter, dry cold Polar Continental air from the Siberian anticyclone dominates the weather. Tropical maritime air plays a much less important role and rarely is felt north of the Yangtze Valley. When forced to overrun *Pc* air in cyclonic storms, it yields precipitation. In summer, on the other hand, tropical and equatorial maritime air masses pretty much dominate the weather of southern and eastern Asia, and Polar air is much less frequent than in winter.

148. CYCLONIC DEVELOPMENT AND STRUCTURE. By a large group of air physicists it is believed that the cyclone originates as a wave along a front separating two contrasting air masses. If this is true then those regions of the earth where large-scale air currents of different properties converge, and therefore numerous fronts develop, should be primary regions of cyclonic origin. Such a region of cyclo-genesis exists southeast of Greenland, which is the meeting place of intensely cold air masses from the Greenland Ice Cap and the mild ones coming from over the relatively warm waters of the North Atlantic Ocean. It

appears now that much of the world's weather is associated with storms that develop along the boundary surfaces separating unlike air masses. Where there are numerous fronts, therefore, storms should be numerous and weather changes frequent.

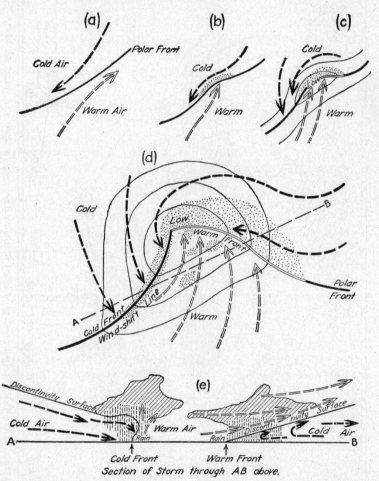

Fig. 54.—Growth and structure of a middle-latitude cyclone. (a), (b), and (c) Stages in the development of a cyclone. (d) The fully developed cyclone on a somewhat larger scale and in more detail. (e) A cross section of the same storm. (*Modified after Namias.*)

On the daily weather map a cyclonic storm is often first noted as a slight indentation along a front. It takes the form of a very shallow thrust of warm air into the mass of colder air. As the wave or indentation deepens the storm grows in size and intensity. Figure 54 illus-

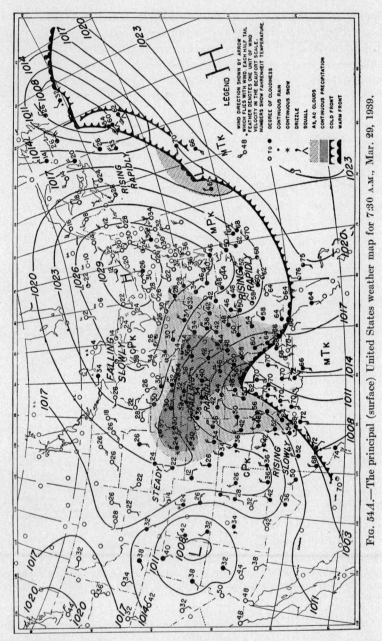

FIG. 54A.—The principal (surface) United States weather map for 7:30 A.M., Mar. 29, 1939.

trates a part of the life history of a cyclonic storm. It appears from this diagram that the storm is composed of two essentially different air masses (Fig. 54A). To the south and southeast is a poleward projection of warmer humid air being fed by southerly currents from tropical latitudes. Enveloping this projection of tropical air on its western, northern, and northeastern sides is colder, drier air, often of polar origin. In the wind system acquired by the developing storm the air movement is such as to cause the tropical air to advance over the cold air in one part and for the cold air to underrun retreating warm air in still another part. The lifting of the warmer air over the cold commonly leads to condensation and precipitation. That part of the front separating the two air masses which lies *ahead* of the advancing tongue of warm air is called the *warm front* (Fig. 52). Here the aggressive warm air currents leave the earth's surface and rise up over the retreating wedge of cold air along a surface of discontinuity. That part of the front lying *behind* the wedge of warm air is called the *cold front* (Fig. 52). Along this front the cold air is the aggressor, and it pushes in under the retreating warm air, forcing it to rise, often with vigor. The advance of the cold front is retarded by friction with the ground so that there is a tendency toward a piling up of the cold air in the foremost portion of the advancing current. This often leads to an overrunning by cold air aloft of warm air at the surface. Warm air is thereby entrapped below the overrunning cold air, under which conditions violent convectional overturning may occur (Fig. 54).

In normal cases the cold front advances more rapidly than the warm front so that it gradually catches up with and eventually overtakes the warm front. When contact between the cold air masses, one on the front and the other on the rear of the storm, has been made, and the intervening warm air has been lifted above the earth's surface, an *occlusion* is said to have taken place. Occlusions are normal developments in the life history of middle-latitude cyclones. In eastern United States the cold air mass behind the cold front is usually colder than that ahead of the warm front so that the resulting front has the aspects of a new cold front. Precipitation along occluded fronts results from continued lifting of the warm air, now everywhere above the earth's surface, as well as from the vertical displacement of the less dense of the two cold air masses.

Wind Systems in Cyclones and Anticyclones

Among laymen the terms cyclone and tornado often are used synonymously, but incorrectly, to represent any violent and destructive windstorm. While such is the nature of hurricanes and tornadoes, it is not the character of most intermediate-zone cyclones, which are a quite different type of storm. Occasionally there are winter cyclones and anticyclones accompanied by boisterous winds which produce blizzard conditions and raise heavy seas on the oceans and large lakes, but even these are not violently destructive. By far the larger number of lows and highs are accompanied by winds of only moderate velocity. It is the structure, or system, of winds in these middle-latitude storms that is distinctive, not their velocities.

149. WIND SYSTEM IN CYCLONES.   Seen in the ordinary two-dimension aspect as they appear on a United States weather map, where a cyclone is represented as a series of roughly concentric isobars with the lowest pressure at the center, air flow is from the circumference toward the center of the storm. In other words, it is a *converging* system of winds (Fig. 51). This convergence of surface air currents toward the center would of necessity result in the filling up and annihilation of the low pressure unless there was slow rising of air masses near the center and removal by outflow aloft. No doubt this actually happens. The updraft is not to be thought of as an uprush of vertically ascending air, such as takes place in a thunderstorm. More commonly it is a moderate lifting of air, usually along inclined planes of mild gradient, resulting from convergence of air masses of contrasting temperature, humidity, and density. Cloud types in cyclones usually are of the flattish sheet type, typical of conditions where warmer air is forced to ascend over a wedge of colder, denser air.

In well-developed cyclones, as they are observed on the United States daily weather map, the converging wind arrows ordinarily do not cross the isobars at right angles but instead make an angle of 20 to 40° with them. This results from earth rotation, through which winds receive a right-hand deflection (Northern Hemisphere) and consequently appear to spiral in toward the center of the storm in a counterclockwise whirl. But the simple inward-spiraling cyclonic wind system (Fig. 51) described above and observable on the weather map is a partial illusion. This comes about as a result of the fact that the weather map is a snapshot of atmospheric conditions at a particular instant so that the storms are shown as stationary phenomena, when in reality they usually are moving at the rate of several hundred miles a day. The *moving cyclone's* actual wind system is more accurately, although still very diagrammatically, represented by Fig. 55. In it convergence of air flow still is conspicuous, but the simple inspiraling system is considerably modified. Most significant is the fact that to the south, southeast, and possibly southwest of the storm center are southerly winds, usually of subtropical or tropical origin, while to the west, north, and northeast are colder air masses which had their origin in higher latitudes.

As a result of the converging system of air flow about a cyclonic center, winds on the front (east, or direction storm is traveling) of such a storm are from a general easterly direction, some of it northeasterly, more of it from the southeast and south. On the rear (west) of the storm, winds are, in general, westerly and especially from the northwest (Fig. 55). The easterly winds on the front of a low are likely to be both tropical and polar in origin, since the front separating the two air masses extends roughly eastward from the storm center. In central and eastern United States the southerly winds *south* and *west* of the front are from the Gulf and tropical Atlantic and so are warm and

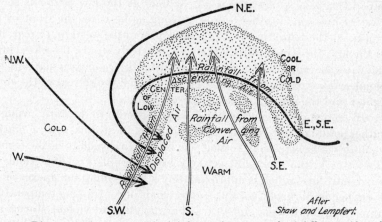

FIG. 55.—Diagrammatic representation of the wind system and rainfall areas (dotted) in a middle-latitude cyclone.

humid. On the other hand the northeast, east, or even southeast winds *north* and *east* of the line of discontinuity are of polar origin and consequently drier and colder. From wind direction alone it is unsafe to generalize as to whether an air mass is of polar or tropical origin, for the polar air on the front of a cyclone is not uncommonly observed as a southeast current. This is polar air that has been modified by a relatively long journey over middle latitudes and is returning poleward on the rear of a retreating anticyclone.

It is obvious that all these easterly winds on the front of a cyclone are opposite in direction to the general current of westerly winds in which they exist and likewise opposite to the direction of storm movement. Thus while the storm travels from west to east, the winds on its front blow from east to west. This characteristic of a cyclone, which in many respects is an eddy or whirlpool of air in the westerlies, finds a counterpart in the whirlpool of a river. The whirlpool of water is carried downstream by the major current just as the storm is carried eastward by the westerlies, but on its downstream side the water flows into the whirl in a direction opposite to that of the general current and likewise opposite to the downstream movement of the whirlpool itself. It is evident, then, that a cyclone is the meeting place of two very contrasting masses of air: a colder, drier, and heavier one arriving from higher latitudes on the poleward and rear sides of the storm; and a milder, more humid one from lower latitudes on the equatorward and front side.

150. WIND SHIFT WITH THE PASSING OF A CYCLONE.   When a cyclonic center approaches and passes by an observer, the latter will experience general easterly winds as long as the low center is to the west of him, or, in other words, as long as he is on the front of the storm. As the center passes by, leaving him in the western, or rear, half of the low, the winds shift to the west. Easterly winds, therefore, often indicate the approach of a cyclone with its accompanying rain and cloud, while westerly winds more often foretell the retreat of the storm center and the coming of clearing weather.

In many cyclones this shift from easterly to westerly winds is rather gradual and lacking in abruptness. In storms with a marked equatorward elongation, so that the isobars are roughly in the form of the letter V, the wind shift is likely to be abrupt (Fig. 66). Along the wind-shift line, which is approximately a line joining the apexes of the V-shaped isobars south of the center, winds of contrasting temperature, humidity, and density meet at a sharp angle, and violent storms and turbulent weather conditions often are the result. This wind-shift line is the cold front described in Art. 173b.

151. *Veering and Backing Winds.*   If the center of a cyclone passes to the north of the observer, so that he is in the southern quadrants of the storm, the succession of winds experienced will be southeast, south, southwest, and finally west and northwest (Figs. 51, 55). This is called a *veering wind shift.* On the other hand, if the storm center passes south of the observer, so that he is on the north side of the cyclone, he will experience in succession northeast, north, and finally northwest winds. This is known as a *backing wind shift.* The following note regarding *wind-barometer indications* associated with a passing cyclone appears on the United States daily weather map. "When the wind sets in from points between south and southeast and the barometer falls steadily, a storm is approaching from the west or northwest, and its center will pass near or north of the observer within 12 to 24 hr. with wind shifting to northwest by way of southwest and west. When the wind sets in from points between east and northeast and the barometer falls steadily, a storm is approaching from the south or southwest,

and its center will pass near or to the south or east of the observer within 12 to 24 hr. with wind shifting to northwest by way of north. The rapidity of the storm's approach and its intensity will be indicated by the rate and the amount of the fall in the barometer."

152. WIND SYSTEM OF AN ANTICYCLONE. The term anticyclone was invented to designate the outflowing, or diverging, system of winds about a center of high pressure (Fig. 51). Deflection due to earth rotation causes the outflow of air about a high to develop something of a clockwise whirl (Northern Hemisphere). Since surface air in the high is constantly spreading outward from the center, it follows that there must be a compensatory feeding in of air at higher elevations, and subsequent settling of it, in order to maintain the high. The wind systems about highs and lows, therefore, are opposite (a) in direction of gradient-induced flow, (b) in direction of spiral deflection, and (c) in vertical movement at the centers.

Anticyclonic wind systems are usually less well developed than those of cyclones so that no characteristic wind shift is forecast as they pass by. In general, however, winds on the front (east) of an advancing high are westerly, while those on the rear are easterly. Since lows and highs often alternate with one another as they move across the country, it is evident that the westerly winds on the front of a high and the rear of a low have a similar origin and are much alike in character. Pressure gradients are usually less steep and wind velocities lower in anticyclones than in cyclones. Weak pressure gradients are particularly conspicuous toward the centers of highs where there is much light wind and calm. The strongest winds are likely to be found on the front margins of advancing highs where there is a merging with the preceding low. In this location between the cyclonic and anticyclonic systems the isobars tend to become nearly parallel straight lines trending in a general north-south direction. A strong horizontal pressure gradient from west to east is thereby developed, which is a consequence of combined westerly-wind gradients and storm gradients, vigorous west and northwest winds being the result. Cold waves and blizzards over central and eastern North America are associated with these strong outpourings of cold air in the transition areas between the rears of lows and the fronts of highs.

PRECIPITATION IN CYCLONES AND ANTICYCLONES

153. CYCLONES AND ANTICYCLONES OPPOSITE IN PRECIPITATION CHARACTERISTICS. As a general rule, conditions in cyclones are conducive to condensation, so that commonly they are accompanied by large areas of cloud and often precipitation as well. Not every

cyclone, to be sure, is associated with rainfall, but on the other hand many of them are. Anticyclones, still maintaining their opposite nature in precipitation as well as in pressure and winds, are inclined to be fair-weather areas with clouds much less prevalent and rainfall meager. These differences are not unexpected, since in lows there is a general convergence of contrasting air currents toward the center of the storm with a consequent development of fronts. Lifting of the converging air masses, and subsequent cooling due to expansion, is the result. On the other hand, the slowly settling and warming air in anticyclones, as well as the diverging character of the surface air currents, is distinctly antagonistic to cloud and rainfall. The diverging nature of the anti-cyclone's air makes a conflict of contrasting air masses unlikely, so that active fronts are not to be expected.

154. CYCLONIC PRECIPITATION. Most of the cool-season precipitation of lowlands in the middle latitudes is cyclonic in origin. Winter snowfall on plains in these latitudes is almost exclusively from cyclonic storms. The fewer and weaker lows of the warmer months yield a smaller percentage of that period's rainfall, since in summer convection and thunderstorms are likely to be more dominant. Although cyclonic rain is the result of rising air, normally it does not rise because of local heating but rather because of forced ascent resulting from (a) a convergence of great masses of air toward a center, (b) the underrunning and lifting of warmer and lighter air masses by cooler heavier ones, and (c) the ascent of warm currents over colder ones (Fig. 55). Unlike conditions in a thunderstorm, where rapid vertical ascent is characteristic, the lifting of air in cyclones, as noted earlier (149), is more often a gliding of warm, moist air up a mild slope formed by the upper surface of a colder, denser mass of air. Cooling is slower in the latter case, and rainfall less heavy. Cyclonic precipitation, therefore, inclines toward being light or moderate in rate of fall, but because of the greater areal extent of the storm it is of relatively longer duration than that of thunderstorms. Dull, gray, uniformly overcast skies, with steady precipitation, are typical of cyclonic weather. It should be stressed that precipitation in any storm would be minor in amount and of short duration if it were not that new supplies of water vapor are constantly being imported by winds to any area where rain is falling.

Neither the expectancy of precipitation nor its nature and origin are the same in all parts of a low. In general, the front or eastern half is more cloudy and rainy than is the rear or western half, although the latter is not completely lacking in precipitation. Clouds and rain extend out much farther to the front of the center than to the rear. This is because the warm air currents, from which the precipitation is derived, are moving eastward. As a consequence they overrun the cold air along the warm front much farther to the east of the storm center than they do to the west. In well-developed winter lows snow is more common in the cooler northeastern part, whereas rain occurs more frequently in the warmer southeastern quadrant. Heavy snows over the eastern part of the United States usually arrive when storms travel the more southerly routes, so that the central and northern states are on the poleward sides of the cyclones.

155. REGIONS OF PRECIPITATION WITHIN A CYCLONE. Three general regions of precipitation within a low may be distinguished. As a general rule the rain areas are associated with vertical displacement of mild and humid marine air masses, often of tropical origin. The cold air masses act chiefly as barriers over which the warmer air is lifted, and only a small amount of precipitation is actually derived from the cold air itself (Fig. 55).

a. Rainfall from Converging Air (Nonfrontal). In the southeastern quadrant of the storm, in particular, the warm, humid, southerly (including southeasterly and southwesterly) currents are driven upward by their own convergence as they move toward the center of the low (Fig. 55). This section of the cyclone is not a region of prevailingly heavy cloud cover and persistent rain. Quite the contrary, for, although scattered showers are common and widespread, there also may be considerable broken sky and sunshine. During the warm season, the sultry, humid section to the south and southeast of the low center is a region of active convection, with cumulus clouds and local thunderstorms.

b. Warm-front Rain. To the north, northeast, and east of the storm center the warm, humid, southerly air masses meet the colder, drier air of polar origin. Because the latter is more dense, the warm air flows up over the gently inclined wedge of colder air just as it would flow over a mountain range and is lifted above the earth's surface (Fig. 52). As a result of rising over the wedge of cold air, the southerly currents are cooled by expansion, and widespread cloud and precipitation are the result (Figs. 54e, 55). Chilly, gray, overcast days with long-continued steady rain are typical of weather in this part of the storm. In the colder months this is also the region of heavy snowfall. Since the warm air is rising over the cold wedge along a gently inclined plane whose angle of slope is between 0.5 and 2°, its increase in elevation is slow, so that the resulting precipitation is likely to be only light or moderate in rate of fall, although, because of its long duration, the total amount may be considerable. It is not uncommon for warm-front rains to continue steadily for 24 hr. and more without letup. Such moderate rain is ideal in some respects, for it comes slowly enough for the ground to absorb most of it, and surface runoff and destructive slope wash and gullying are reduced to a minimum. Low evaporation under such conditions of weather likewise increases the effectiveness of the precipitation. In the warm seasons if the air ascending over the cold wedge is conditionally unstable, warm-front rainfall may be relatively heavy. Cool, overcast weather with rain is ideal for the growth of forage crops and pasture but less so for a crop like corn, which benefits from sunshine and higher temperatures. It needs to be kept in mind that it is not from the cold surface air that the rain is chiefly coming but rather from the southerly currents aloft which are rising over the cold northerly air. Precipitation falling through the cold surface air, however, has its temperature reduced so that it reaches the earth as a chilly rain, and the day is inclined to be dark and dismal.

   c. *Cold-front Rain.*   To the south and southwest of the storm center is still another region of forced ascent. Here the cold west and northwest currents of polar origin meet and underrun the warm southerly currents, forcing them upward, sometimes with much vigor (Figs. 52, 54e, 55). This cold-front rain belt is best developed in storms with a marked southward looping of the isobars, *i.e.*, a V-shaped cyclone, for under these conditions the contrasting air masses meet at a sharp angle with resulting vigorous overturning. In storms with more circular shape this is less likely to be the case. The name *squall line* has been derived from the fact that it may be a region of great atmospheric turbulence, with associated severe thunderstorms and squall winds. Because of the rapid lifting and overturning of the warm air along the cold front, the accompanying rain is likely to be in the form of heavy showers but not of long duration. This cloud and rain belt, therefore, usually is much narrower than that along the warm front to the north and east of the storm center.

   It should be stressed here that not all these three rainfall types or areas are present in each storm, nor are they always distinct from each other. There are numerous mergings, modifications, and intermediate conditions. Nevertheless, all three types are sufficiently common and distinct in cyclones to warrant their recognition.

TEMPERATURE IN CYCLONES AND ANTICYCLONES

   156. It is difficult to make significant generalizations regarding temperature contrasts between lows and highs. It is not true, as is sometimes stated to be the case, that, disregarding the season of the year, cyclones are always areas of high temperature and anticyclones of low. In themselves they are neither hot nor cold, but, depending upon the season as well as their own individual character (region of origin, path, velocity of movement), they may be either or both. An analysis of temperatures in cyclones and anticyclones actually resolves itself into a study of the air masses that comprise the storms.

   157. TEMPERATURES IN ANTICYCLONES.   Certainly in the winter season a vigorous, well-developed high, advancing rapidly toward central and eastern United States from northern Canada, progresses as a mass of cold, dry, Polar Continental air with clear skies. Such an anticyclone accounts for the *cold waves* and bitterest winter weather

(Figs. 56, 57A). This type of high is cold for two reasons: (a) because it advances southward from the Arctic regions as a mass of cold polar air accompanied by strong northwest winds and (b) because its dry, clear air provides ideal conditions for rapid terrestrial radiation during long winter nights. An anticyclone composed of Polar Pacific air brings less severe cold. Even in summer, a well-developed high approaching rapidly from higher latitudes gives low temperatures for

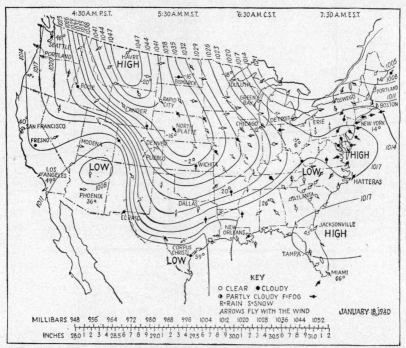

Fig. 56.—United States daily weather map. A great Polar Continental (Pc) air mass had advanced into the United States as a high-pressure system from the Arctic plains of Canada. St. Joseph, Mo., had a minimum temperature of 21° below zero, and Galveston, Tex., on the Gulf of Mexico, 15° above zero. Ten inches of snow fell at Birmingham, Ala., and at Atlanta, Ga. (Courtesy of U. S. Weather Bureau.)

the season, providing several days of clear, cool, delightful weather. It is not unusual in middle latitudes, then, for highs to have come to be associated with low temperatures for any particular season.

However, when in summer a large, relatively stagnant high, composed of tropical or subtropical air, spreads slowly over the south-central part of the country, excessively high temperatures, called *hot waves*, are likely to result over central and eastern United States (Fig. 57B). The same clear skies and dry air that make for rapid terrestrial radiation during the long winter nights are conducive to

maximum receipts of strong solar radiation during long summer days.
Moreover, as tropical air from this anticyclone moves northward over
the country, the south winds carry with them the heat absorbed in

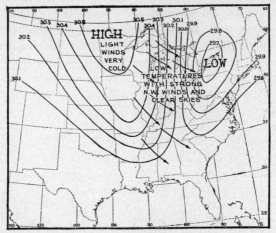

FIG. 57A.—A winter anticyclone advancing southeastward as a mass of cold polar air.

the lower latitudes. Clear, mild days in the cooler seasons likewise are
usually associated with these same large, stagnant highs over the

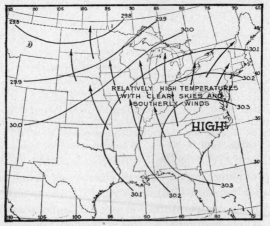

FIG. 57B.—A relatively stagnant anticyclone over southeastern United States producing
unseasonably warm weather over the central and eastern parts of the country.

south-central part of the country. In summary, then, it may be stated
that vigorous, moving highs arriving from higher latitudes are likely
to bring lower than normal temperatures, especially in winter; while

weak, stagnant highs, especially in summer, are associated with abnormally high temperatures.

158. TEMPERATURES IN CYCLONES. Well-developed cyclones, accompanied by an extensive cloud cover and precipitation, are likely to bring higher than average temperatures in winter, and somewhat lower than average temperatures in summer—just the opposite from those induced by the anticyclone. During the long winter nights the cloud cover and humid air of the cyclone tend to prevent rapid loss of earth heat, while these same conditions in summer, when days are long and sun stronger, tend to weaken incoming solar radiation.

159. *Temperature Contrasts within Different Parts of a Cyclone.* The foregoing general rule concerning lows and seasonal temperatures cannot be accepted too literally, however, for a cyclone, composed of unlike air masses, usually has marked temperature contrasts within its several parts or quadrants. Thus the south and southeast part (front) of a low, where relatively warm air masses and southerly winds prevail, is considerably warmer than the north and west portion (rear), where air movement is from cooler higher latitudes. The effect of these temperature importations is to cause the isotherms in cyclones to trend north-northeast by south-southwest instead of the usual east-west direction, the south winds on the front of the storm pushing them poleward, and the northwest winds on the rear pushing them equatorward (Fig. 58). To the east and north of the storm center, where the

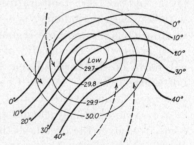

FIG. 58.—Characteristic arrangement of isotherms in a winter cyclone over central and eastern United States. The front is usually warmer than the rear.

air is of a modified polar character, being markedly colder than the tropical air to the south but not so severe as the fresh polar air to the west, isotherms more closely follow the parallels.

In general, the average rise of temperature above seasonal normal in front of a winter storm in eastern United States is not far from 10°, although it may reach 20 or 30°. Between the front and rear of a well-developed winter cyclone in eastern United States the temperatures may differ by as much as 30 to 40° or even more. If the temperature of the center of a low is taken as a standard, the average departures of the four quadrants of well-developed winter cyclones in eastern United States are as follows: northwest, −8.7°; northeast, −5.6°; southeast, +6.3°; southwest, +2.6° (Ward). Stations on the southern side of a passing low, therefore, experience a greater *change* in temperature than do those to the north of the center, even though the temperatures are not so low.

160. SUMMARY OF WEATHER CHANGES WITH THE PASSING OF A WELL-DEVELOPED CYCLONE AND A FOLLOWING ANTICYCLONE OVER EASTERN UNITED STATES.   The essence of cyclonic control in weather is its irregularity and undependability. Averages of the weather elements by days, months, or years give only a lifeless picture of the actual weather experienced, for such averages tend to mask the nonperiodic storm control. Rapid and marked weather changes are characteristic of regions and seasons where cyclones and anticyclones are numerous and well developed, as they are, for instance, over eastern United States in winter. Temperature changes with passing storms are especially marked in winter, when latitudinal temperature gradients are steepest and importations by winds consequently most severe. In summer, with the poleward migration of the storm belt, cyclones are fewer and weaker; temperature gradients milder; and sun control, with its daily periodicity, is more influential. In that season, then, weather changes are more regular and diurnal, and less marked.

It is incorrect to conceive of cyclonic control as identical in different parts of the earth. Even within the United States storms act differently over the Pacific Coast or the western plateaus from the way they do in eastern United States. Northwest winds on the rear of a cyclone obviously cannot import very low temperatures if they come from over the ocean, as they do in northwestern Europe or the Pacific Coast of the United States. Storms differ in character with the regions and the seasons, although they all conform to the same general laws. Following is a description of a series of weather changes during the passage of a well-developed cyclone and a following anticyclone over eastern United States (Plate III, Figs. 59, 60).

As the cyclone approaches from the west and the barometer falls, there is a gradual clouding up in front of the storm. Far out in front of the center the sky becomes covered with fine veils, or films, of cirrus and cirro-stratus clouds, which produce circles around the moon or sun. These distant heralds of the storm are associated with the warm-front discontinuity surface as much as 1,000 to 1,500 miles ahead of the surface warm front where the inclined wedge of cold air may be 3 to 4 miles thick. Contemporaneous with the appearance of the cirrus and cirro-stratus clouds the wind sets in from an easterly direction and continues easterly until the center of the storm or the surface cold front has passed. As the storm center approaches closer and the cold wedge becomes thinner the clouds gradually thicken, darken, and

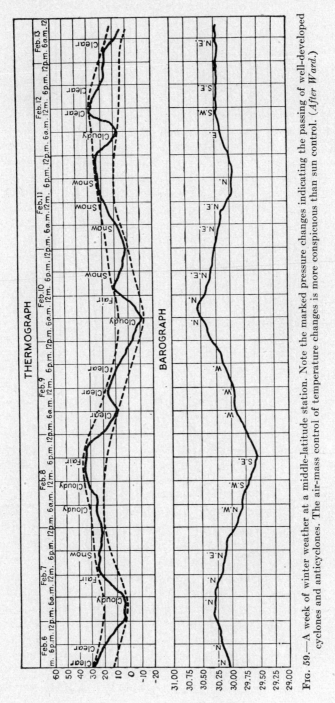

FIG. 59.—A week of winter weather at a middle-latitude station. Note the marked pressure changes indicating the passing of well-developed cyclones and anticyclones. The air-mass control of temperature changes is more conspicuous than sun control. (*After Ward.*)

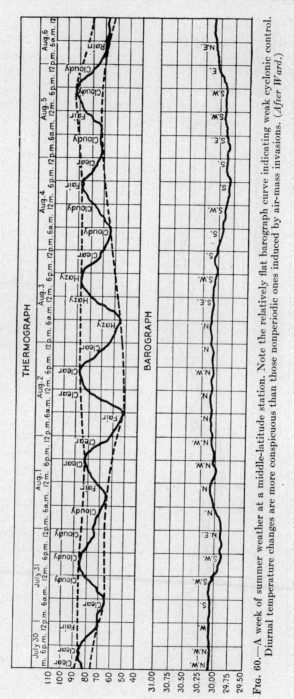

FIG. 60.—A week of summer weather at a middle-latitude station. Note the relatively flat barograph curve indicating weak cyclonic control. Diurnal temperature changes are more conspicuous than those nonperiodic ones induced by air-mass invasions. (*After Ward.*)

become lower in elevation. Precipitation usually begins out several hundred miles ahead of the surface warm front and continues until that front is passed. Temperature increases somewhat as the surface warm front draws nearer, but since the air on the front of the storm may be modified polar in character there is no abrupt temperature rise until the warm front at the surface passes. The passage of the warm front at the surface, with an associated shift from polar to tropical air, is marked by a number of weather phenomena, including (a) a slight wind shift, usually about 45°, the wind becoming more southerly as the warm air mass is entered; (b) a distinct rise in temperature; (c) a clearing in the weather conditions, and (d) a rapid increase in the amount of moisture in the air.

Within the warm air mass weather conditions may vary considerably depending on the nature of the air and the season of the year. In summer if the air is from the Gulf of Mexico hot sultry weather with local showers and thunderstorms is common. If the air is from a drier source the heat will be less oppressive but more desiccating. In winter this tropical air mass gives rise to mild weather and rapid thaws, often associated with fog.

The passage of the cold front at the surface with an accompanying shift from the warm to the cold air mass is frequently associated with strong turbulence, particularly if the cold front is well developed. In summer severe thunderstorms with strong squall winds are common. Other associated weather phenomena are (a) a marked rise in barometric pressure, (b) an abrupt drop in temperature heralding the arrival of the cold air, (c) well-marked shift in wind direction amounting to from 45 to 180° (southerly to westerly), (d) heavy rains at the front but fairly rapid clearing and improvement in the weather conditions following its passage, and (e) a marked decrease in both specific and relative humidity. The advancing anticyclone moving southeastward as a mass of cold polar air with northwest winds continues to reduce the temperature until its center has passed. Toward the center of the high, winds are light and calms are prevalent, and in winter extremely low temperatures are likely to prevail. As the anticyclone retreats the cycle is complete, winds again become easterly, and another approaching cyclone begins a new sequence.

Obviously there are considerable variations from the above description. These variations depend upon the nature of the air masses generating the storms as well as upon the routes the storms take with respect to the observer. For example, warm and cold fronts are often not well developed on the poleward side of a cyclone, for the warm air mass is lacking at the surface.

161. PATHS OF CYCLONIC STORMS. It was stated earlier that the origin of cyclonic storms appears to be associated with moving fronts bounding unlike air masses. If this is true then the middle latitudes, which are the meeting place of air masses from the tropics and from the polar regions, should be the part of the earth where cyclones are most numerous and most vigorous. That such is the case is demonstrated by the extremely variable weather of the middle latitudes.

All parts of the middle latitudes, and likewise the adjacent margins of the low and high latitudes, are affected by moving cyclones and anticyclones. In the low latitudes as well, there is increasing evidence for believing that cyclones play a relatively important role in weather.

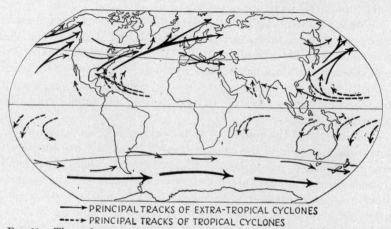

→ PRINCIPAL TRACKS OF EXTRA-TROPICAL CYCLONES
---→ PRINCIPAL TRACKS OF TROPICAL CYCLONES

FIG. 61.—The cyclone tracks here shown are highly simplified. (*From Petterssen.*)

All parts, however, are not affected to the same degree, for, although there is no rigid system of clearly defined *storm tracks*, there are, nevertheless, certain broad belts over which storms travel more frequently than elsewhere. These are the regions of most numerous and most active fronts.[1] Of course the effects of a storm are felt far beyond the path of its center. Figure 61 shows in a generalized way the principal cyclonic tracks of the world.

In the Southern Hemisphere, as a result of a very stable and intense anticyclone over the Antarctic Continent providing abundant supplies of cold polar air throughout the year, there is great year-round vigor of cyclonic storms, in summer as well as winter. Their centers appear to follow the subpolar low-pressure trough, but the poleward

[1] An attempt has been made to show the principal frontal zones of the Northern Hemisphere in winter and in summer. See Petterssen, Sverre. "Weather Analysis and Forecasting." pp. 269 and 271, McGraw-Hill Book Company, Inc., New York, 1940.

parts of all the Southern Hemisphere continents are affected by their northerly margins, especially in the low-sun season. The Cape Horn region of South America, extending as it does to nearly latitude 55°S., is a stormy area at all times of the year. Winter cyclones are likewise relatively numerous over the Pampa of Argentina.

162. *Northern Hemisphere Tracks.* The less vigorous (except in winter), and likewise less persistent, continental anticyclones forming over the Arctic and subarctic regions provide the principal southward

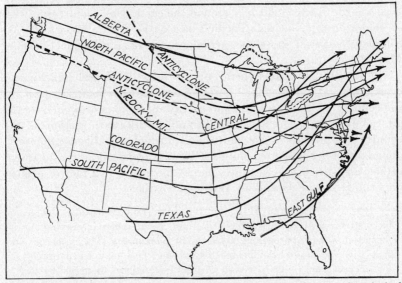

FIG. 62.—Solid lines show principal tracks of cyclones; broken lines are the principal tracks of anticyclones. Note how the cyclone tracks converge on the northeastern part of the United States. Anticyclones moving south from northern Canada (*Pc* air) bring severe cold in winter; those from the Pacific northwest (*Pp* air) bring only moderate cold.

gushes of cold polar air for the formation of Northern Hemisphere storms. The Arctic and subarctic anticyclones are relatively weak in summer, which accounts for the poleward migration of the storm tracks as well as for the general weakening of cyclonic control over the whole Northern Hemisphere in that season. In winter, on the other hand, when the Arctic and subarctic high-pressure centers are much better developed, and therefore are able to provide the necessary southward surges of cold air, storms are both numerous and vigorous. The principal concentration of cyclones is in the North Pacific (Aleutian low), northern United States and southern Canada, the North Atlantic (Iceland low), and northwestern Europe. A secondary

European track passes through the Mediterranean Basin. Middle and northern China and Japan are regions of relatively strong cyclonic influence in the Far East. The storm track of northwestern Europe is particularly well developed, cyclone following cyclone in rapid succession in that region during the winter. In the cold season there appears to be a tendency for storm tracks to dip southward over the continents, thereby avoiding the continental highs, and to swing poleward over the oceans, passing through the centers of the permanent lows and following the belt of marked temperature contrasts. Cyclones have been known to travel entirely around the earth. One such storm, with its center on the American Pacific Coast on Feb. 23, 1925, was traced completely around the globe, arriving again on the Pacific Coast on Mar. 19.

In the United States there appears to be a general bunching of cyclonic storm tracks in the northwestern and northeastern parts of the country, with a spreading and southward looping of them over the interior (Fig. 62). The northeastern and northwestern sections of the country in winter obviously must have much changeable weather with abundant cloud and precipitation. Most storms follow the northern rather than the southern routes across the country, a fact of utmost importance in understanding American weather.

163. THE WEATHER MAP AND WEATHER FORECASTING.[1]   People are by instinct weather forecasters, for there is an inherent craving for information about approaching atmospheric phenomena. The numerous current weather proverbs indicate this craving. One may learn roughly to foretell weather conditions, even without instruments or maps, by merely being observant of such local indicators as direction of wind, kinds of clouds, and rising or falling temperatures. However, a much more accurate job of forecasting can be done if one has access to certain instruments, particularly a barometer. The United States Weather Bureau's daily forecasts are based upon data from over 250 stations rather uniformly distributed off the airways and about 550 stations along the civil airways. By radio, teletype, telephone, and telegraph weather reports from these several hundred stations are relayed to forecast centers and to the central office at Washington, D. C., for analysis and charting. At more than 100 weather stations upperair weather observations are taken by means of pilot balloons, and at over 30 stations upper-air observations of temperature, pressure, and humidity are made by means of radiosondes. The latter are miniature radio transmitters which are carried up to heights of 50,000 to 75,000 ft. by balloons. Supplementing the weather reports from stations within the United States are others received from Canada, Mexico, Central America, Puerto Rico, and Panama and from ships at sea.

[1] See "Climate and Man." Yearbook of Agriculture, 1941, pp. 579–598.

In the United States complete weather observations are made four times a day at 6-hr. intervals, beginning at 1:30 A.M. eastern standard time. At most airway stations observations are made hourly. The whole atmosphere is the forecaster's laboratory, but this is too large for him to comprehend without first reproducing it on a miniature scale on a map. This is the weather map, sometimes called a synoptic chart (Figs. 54A, 56, Plate III). On this map are represented graphically the data obtained from simultaneous observations at the several hundred stations. At airway stations weather maps are made at 6-hr. intervals for 8 hr. following. The published United States Weather Maps are prepared from the 1:30 A.M. and the 7:30 A.M. observations.

On the maps prepared at the weather stations, there are represented in addition to the conditions of temperature, pressure, wind, cloudiness, and precipitation, the distribution of air masses and the fronts that bound them. Unfortunately, on the published weather maps sent out from the district forecast centers air-mass and frontal data are entirely lacking. Only on the Washington map are these to be found (Fig. 54A).

The techniques of weather forecasting do not properly belong in a book of this sort, and only a few of the most general types of comment are offered. Fundamentally it involves trying to picture the changes in storm centers and fronts during the subsequent forecast period. The concept of middle-latitude weather changes as resulting chiefly from the interaction of contrasting air masses has resulted in recent years in the application of new techniques in forecasting methods. No longer is weather viewed in simply a two-dimensional aspect as represented by surface isobars on the ordinary weather map. There is an increasing attempt to understand atmospheric conditions vertically as well as horizontally. To do this there are constructed maps of the various weather elements at different levels aloft as well as at the surface. Such maps are made possible by the data obtained from the ascent of radiosondes. Accurate weather forecasts for more than a few days, or at most a week in advance, are not yet practicable except in a very limited number of instances.

TROPICAL CYCLONES OF THE HURRICANE AND TYPHOON VARIETY

164. GENERAL CHARACTERISTICS. These often violent and destructive storms of the low latitudes in some respects resemble the middle-latitude cyclones, as, for instance, in the central area of low pressure, the cyclonic system of winds, and a relatively widespread area of cloud and rain. In other ways, however, the hurricane differs from its less intense counterpart of the middle and higher latitudes. Some of the more important features that distinguish it from the middle-latitude cyclone are as follows: (a) The isobars of the tropical storm are more symmetrical and more nearly circular. Pressure gradients also are usually steeper, so that winds are stronger. To be a genuine hurricane wind velocities in the storm must reach at least 75 miles an hour. (*b*) Rains are inclined to be more torrential and somewhat more evenly distributed about the center, although this latter characteristic is more common in nearly, or quite, stationary storms than in moving ones. The rear quadrants usually have less rain than the front ones. (*c*) Temperature distribution around the center is relatively similar in every direction. There are no surface cold fronts or surface warm fronts as in the middle-latitude low. (*d*) There are no sharp wind shifts, the winds developing a more perfect spiral whirl, with strong vertically ascending currents around the vortex, or core. (*e*)

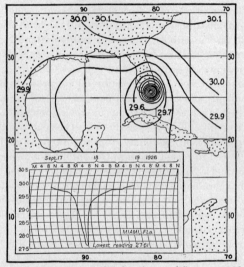

FIG. 63.—The West Indies hurricane of Sept. 8, 1926.

Tropical cyclones are most numerous in the warm season, rather than in winter. (*f*) Hurricanes have relatively calm, rainless centers, 5 to 30 miles in diameter. This is called the "eye" of the storm. (*g*) The tropical cyclone has no anticyclonic companion.

The hurricane type of storm varies greatly in size, but in general it is smaller and more intense than the low of middle latitudes. The total diameter of the whirl may be from 100 to 400 miles (Fig. 63). Wind velocities are not always violent, but on the other hand they may reach such destructive speeds as 90 to 130 miles per hour. Tremendous damage to shipping and coastal settlements, with accompanying loss of life, is by no means rare. A considerable part of the property destruction, and loss of life from drowning, is due to the great avalanches of sea water piled up and driven onshore by the gale winds and to the excessive rainfall and associated floods that accompany the storm. In the violent hurricane of Sept. 18, 1926, which devastated Miami, Fla., at least 114 lives were lost in the Miami district, and damage to buildings was estimated at nearly $75,000,000.

165. ORIGIN. Tropical hurricanes originate only over oceans, where there is abundant moisture and little frictional resistance to wind. Moreover, they are limited to tropical oceans and usually to those parts of tropical oceans where the trades are dying out and merging with the doldrums. No doubt the local heat and moisture of the doldrums are predisposing causes. But that alone is not sufficient, for hurricanes do not originate in the doldrums when that wind belt is at, or very close to, the equator, because in that latitude there is insufficient deflective force of earth rotation to set up the whirl. It is significant in this respect that they principally develop along the *poleward* margins of the doldrums and are most numerous in late summer and fall, when the "belt" of calms is at its greatest distance from the equator. In most cases the storms first tend to move westward as carried by the trades, then curve poleward around the western ends of the subtropical highs in the vicinity of latitudes 20 or 25° (Fig. 61). As soon as they move into the middle latitudes, or over land masses, they lose some of their intensity, spreading out and taking on the characteristics of well-developed extratropical cyclones. The sustaining energy of a hurricane is largely latent heat derived from the copious condensation which must of necessity accompany the heavy rainfall (108). Although *surface* fronts have not been observed in tropical hurricanes, there appears to be increasing agreement among meteorologists that these storms are of frontal origin. On several occasions upper-air observations in hurricanes have revealed the presence of contrasting air masses and above-surface fronts.

166. *Regions of Most Frequent Occurrence.* Tropical cyclones appear to occur over the warmer parts of all oceans, except possibly the South Atlantic, where the doldrums do not migrate south of the equator. There are at least six regions of general concentration, however (Fig. 61). These regions are (a) the China Seas, the so-called *typhoons* of that region affecting particularly the Philippines, southeastern China, and southern Japan; (b) the Arabian Sea and the Bay of Bengal, on either side of peninsular British India; (c) the Caribbean Sea, with the West Indies, Yucatán, and southeastern United States all feeling the effects of hurricanes; (d) the eastern north pacific in the region west of Mexico; (e) the south Indian Ocean east of Madagascar; and (f) the tropical waters to both the northeast and the northwest of Australia. The average number of severe tropical cyclones per year in each of the regions noted above is 22, 10, 5, 13, and 13, respectively.

WEAKER TROPICAL LOWS[1]

167. Besides the severe hurricane type of cyclone described in the previous section, there are, throughout those parts of the low latitudes where heat and humidity are abundant, many more weaker cyclones. These less vigorous cyclones have received little attention from students of weather and climate, probably because they are less severe and spectacular and do little damage. These shallow barometric depressions, here designated as *weak tropical lows* to distinguish them from the hurricane variety, may not be conspicuous on the weather map, often showing only as bulges in the general isobaric setup. Their wind systems commonly are not well developed, a definite cyclonic arrangement often being absent. Feeble winds and much calm seem to prevail. Westerly drift of these storms is evident in some parts of the tropics, but definite tracks are not conspicuous, stagnation and tangled paths being more common. Temperature effects are negligible. It is in the rainfall element that they become particularly conspicuous and significant, for frequently they are productive of beneficial rainfall, not always supplied in sufficient amount by the simple convectional showers typical of these regions. When these same weak disturbances remain nearly stationary over a limited area for several days, the rainfall may even become excessive, resulting in damaging floods. Without doubt too large a percentage of tropical rainfall has been ascribed to local convection resulting from surface heating, and too little to the effects of these weaker tropical lows which certainly are more numerous, as well as more beneficial, than are the better known hurricanes.

These cyclones of the humid tropics appear to originate as wavelike disturbances along tropical fronts. Most of them probably do not grow beyond this stage and so appear as only shallow depressions accompanied by showery rains. There is some evidence that hurricanes have their beginnings as weak tropical lows.

Weak cyclones of probable frontal origin, resembling those of the tropics, are not unknown in humid subtropical parts of middle latitudes as well, although there they are confined to the warm season. They are best known perhaps in the Yangtze Valley of China and over the southern half of Japan (Fig. 64). In the latter country they give rise to an unpleasant and depressing rainy season extending from about mid-June to mid-July, during which the sky is overcast much of the time and more or less rain falls nearly every day. The air is so damp

[1] Visher, Stephen S. Frequency of Tropical Cyclones, Especially Those of Minor Importance. *Monthly Weather Rev.*, Vol. 58, pp. 62–64, February, 1930

that walls and pavements remain wet, and furniture and clothes become moldy. These *Bai-u* rains (meaning plum rains) are highly important for the rice crop, for they come at the time of transplanting when the rice fields need to be soaked.

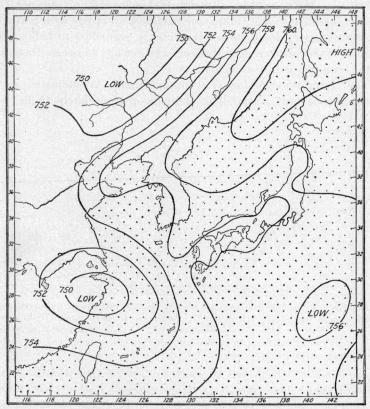

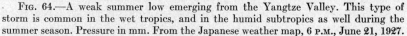

FIG. 64.—A weak summer low emerging from the Yangtze Valley. This type of storm is common in the wet tropics, and in the humid subtropics as well during the summer season. Pressure in mm. From the Japanese weather map, 6 P.M., June 21, 1927.

THUNDERSTORMS

168. GENERAL CHARACTERISTICS.   A thunderstorm is character-ized by a strong upward current of air. In fact it owes its origin to such a vertical updraft of moist air, for a thunderstorm is really an overgrown cumulo-nimbus cloud with all its attendant phenomena of lightning, thunder, and squall winds. This characteristic turbulence is very evident in the seethings and convulsions that one sees taking place in a great thunderhead cloud (Fig. 65). Rapid vertical upthrusts of air are commonly associated with high surface temperatures and

vigorous convectional overturning, so that it is not unexpected to find thunderstorms most prevalent in the warmer latitudes of the earth, in the warmer seasons of middle latitudes, and in the warmer hours of the day. It is obvious that heat, particularly humid heat, and thunderstorms are closely related, although high temperatures are not their only requirement. Some of them are so closely identified with particular regions within cyclonic storms that one is compelled to believe that there is a definite cause-and-effect relationship between them and certain conditions in the cyclone.

169. PRECIPITATION IN THUNDERSTORMS. As indicated in an earlier article (127), rainfall in thunderstorms is likely to be more

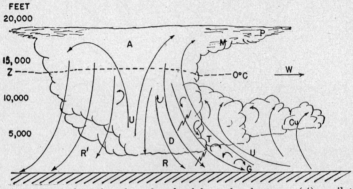

FIG. 65.—Vertical section through a local heat thunderstorm. (*A*) anvil top of cumulo-nimbus cloud; (*C*) roll cloud; (*Cu*) advance cumulus cloud; (*D*) descending air; (*G*) strong gusts; (*M*) mammato-cumulus; (*P*) protruding portion of anvil cloud; (*R*) primary rain or hail area; (*R'*) secondary rain; (*T*) severe turbulence; (*U*) updraft; (*W*) wind direction; (*w*) zero isotherm (centigrade) or freezing level. (*From Haynes.*)

vigorous while it lasts, but of shorter duration, than that associated with cyclones. One speaks of *thundershowers* rather than *thunder rains*. This downpour type of precipitation is related to (*a*) the more rapid vertical ascent of air in thunderstorms (at least 2,400 ft. a minute must often occur) than in most cyclones and (*b*) the higher temperature and, therefore, higher absolute humidity of the air in the summer season when thunderstorms are prevalent. The vigorous nature of convectional rainfall, together with the fact that in middle latitudes it is concentrated in the growing season, has important economic consequences.

170. *Hail.* Occasionally hail, the most destructive form of precipitation, is developed in very intense thunderstorms. Fortunately it occurs in only a few and usually falls in only restricted areas or belts within any particular storm. On first thought, it may appear peculiar that these relatively large globules of layered ice and snow should be

a form of precipitation almost confined to the warm season of the year. That is because they are associated with vigorous convectional systems such as are typical principally of the warmer season. When convection is most violent and air currents are ascending at a rate of 25 to 50 miles an hour, raindrops caught in these upward-surging currents are carried up into regions of extreme cold, so that on mixing with snow they freeze as globules of cloudy ice. Getting into descending currents they again fall to the rain levels and acquire a coating of clear ice from contact with raindrops. Again shot back up into higher altitudes, they acquire another layer of snowy ice, and this layering process may continue until the hailstones occasionally grow as large as golf balls and, in rare instances, even larger. When the strong upward-moving currents are temporarily halted, the hailstones fall to earth, often doing serious damage to crops, to structures such as greenhouses, and occasionally even killing livestock in the fields.

171. LIGHTNING, THUNDER, AND SQUALL WINDS. Three other common phenomena of thunderstorms need brief comment: *lightning*, *thunder*, and the *squall wind*. Lightning is the result of the disruption of raindrops, with consequent development of static electricity, in rapidly ascending air currents. Like hail, therefore, it is largely confined to vigorous convectional storms, which are most numerous in the warm season. As raindrops in the storm grow larger and larger, they eventually reach such a size that their limit of cohesion is passed, and they begin to break up, the larger portions of the drops remaining at lower levels of the cloud or falling to earth, while the smaller particles, carried off as spray at the top of the drop, are swept up into the cloud tops. The larger drops carry a positive electrical charge, the smaller ones a negative charge, while the earth itself is usually negative as well. Thus is created a situation in which a positive electrical charge lies between two negative ones. Eventually, as these charges grow to great size, an electrical discharge in the form of a lightning flash takes place, more commonly from cloud to cloud but occasionally from cloud to earth. Probably not more than 1 per cent of the lightning flashes go to the earth. In the United States 700 to 800 persons lose their lives each year as a result of lightning, and double as many are injured, while fire losses due to lightning amount to over $12,000,000 annually. Thunder is produced by the violent expansion of the air caused by the tremendous heat of the lightning. It is due wholly to an explosive type of expansion consequent upon an extremely sudden and great rise in temperature.

172. *The Thundersquall.* The thundersquall is the strong outrushing mass of cool air just in front of the thunderstorm (Fig. 65).

It is associated with the so-called squall cloud, an onrushing dark, gray, boiling arch or roll of cloud which is the forward projection of the lower portion of the storm cloud. The velocity of the squall wind at times attains hurricane violence, so that it may do serious damage. It should be carefully avoided by airplane pilots. The force of the squall is due in part to the cool air which has been brought down from aloft with the mass of falling rain. Being denser than the warm surface air, it spreads out in front of the storm, underrunning the warm air. In part its velocity is due also to the onrushing motion of the storm mass itself, so that forward and outward motions are combined.

173. CLASSES OF THUNDERSTORMS.   Two main groups of thunderstorms are here recognized: (a) the simple convectional, or heat, type and (b) the cyclonic squall-line type.[1]

a. Local, intra-air-mass, heat thunderstorms occur sporadically owing to local convection and are associated with weak barometric gradients and hot, relatively stagnant, humid air (Fig. 65). The heat, humidity, and slight air movement characteristic of the doldrums furnish ideal conditions for their development and growth. These local storms, many of them small and ephemeral, although not always so, are usually confined to late afternoon or evening on hot summer days with abundant humidity. An unstable condition results from overheating of the quiet, humid, surface air, so that convection and towering cumulus clouds are often the result. If the latter grow to cumulo-nimbus size, they may give rise to a thundershower. Such scattered, local storms may travel in almost any direction, although usually in the middle latitudes they move toward the east. Literally hundreds of these ephemeral thundershowers may dot central and eastern United States on a hot summer day. It is impossible to forecast the time or place of their occurrence. They are of great economic significance, for they produce a considerable part of the summer precipitation in the interiors of middle-latitude continents and probably a still larger part of that which falls in tropical latitudes.

Willis I. Milham gives the following excellent description of a local thunderstorm: "It has been a hot, sultry, oppressive day in summer. The air has been very quiet, perhaps alarmingly quiet, interrupted now and then by a gentle breeze from the south. The pressure has been gradually growing less. The sky is hazy; cirrus clouds are visible; here and there they thicken to cirro-stratus or cirro-cumulus. The temperature has risen very high, and the absolute humidity is very large, but owing to the high temperature the relative humidity has decreased somewhat. The combination of high moisture and temperature and but little wind has made the day intensely sultry and oppressive. In the early hours of the afternoon, amid the horizon haze

[1] There are varieties of cyclonic thunderstorms other than the one here discussed. In all cases they are probably due to the crossing of air currents of different temperatures and densities, resulting in atmospheric overturning.

and cirro-stratus clouds in the west, the big cumulus clouds, the thunder-heads, appear. Soon distant thunder is heard, the lightning flashes are visible, and the dark rain cloud beneath comes into view. As the thundershower approaches, the wind dies down or becomes a gentle breeze blowing directly toward the storm. The temperature perhaps drops a little as the sun is obscured by the clouds, but the sultriness and oppressiveness remain as before. The thundershower comes nearer, and the big cumulus clouds with sharp outlines rise like domes and turrets one above the other. Perhaps the loftiest summits are capped with a fleecy, cirrus-like veil which extends out beyond them. If seen from the side, the familiar anvil form of the cloud mass is noticed. Just beneath the thunderheads is the narrow, turbulent, blue-drab squall cloud. The patches of cloud are now falling, now rising, now moving hither and thither as if in the greatest commotion. Beyond the squall cloud is the dark rain cloud, half hidden from view by the curtain of rain. The thunderheads and squall clouds are now just passing overhead. The lightning flashes, the thunder rolls, big, pattering raindrops begin to fall or perhaps, instead of these, damage-causing hailstones. The gentle breeze has changed to the violent outrushing squall wind, blowing directly from the storm, and the temperature is dropping as if by magic. Soon the rain descends in torrents, shutting out everything from view. After a time, the wind dies down but continues from the west or northwest, the rain decreasing in intensity; the lightning flashes follow each other at longer intervals. An hour or two has passed; it is growing lighter in the west; the wind has died down; the rain has almost stopped. Soon the rain ceases entirely; the clouds break through and become fracto-stratus or cirriform; the temperature rises somewhat, but it is still cool and pleasant; the wind has become very light and has shifted back to the southwest or south. Now the domes and turrets of the retreating shower are visible in the east; perhaps a rainbow spans the sky; the roll of the thunder becomes more distant; the storm has passed, and all nature is refreshed."[1]

b. Cyclonic cold-front thunderstorms, which often are more severe than the local heat variety, are characteristically formed along the cold front of well-developed V-shaped summer cyclones (Fig. 66). The wind-shift line, previously discussed in Art. 150, marks the abrupt meeting place of warm, humid, southerly currents on the front and south of the cyclone, with the cooler, heavier, northwest winds on the rear. Thunderstorms may form a nearly continuous series of active centers hundreds of miles long, the individual storms strung out along the squall line like beads on a string. Usually, however, they are some distance apart. When the cool westerly winds strike the side of the warm southerly currents along the cold front they either underrun it like a blunt wedge or, owing to surface friction, overrun a portion of the warm air and entrap it (Fig. 54e). In either case violent overturning and upthrust take place with resulting turbulence and

[1] Milham, W. I. "Meteorology." pp. 321–322, The Macmillan Company, New York, 1934.

associated development of thunderstorms. Occasionally tornadoes, those most violent of all windstorms, likewise develop at or near the wind-shift

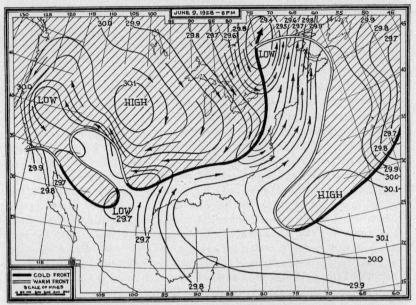

Fig. 66.—A V-shaped summer cyclone with a well-developed cold front and severe thunderstorms. Regions covered by air of polar origin are shaded; those covered by air of tropical origin are left unshaded. U. S. Weather Map, June 9, 1928, 8 P.M.

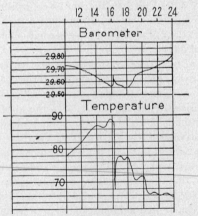

Fig. 67.—Record of pressure and temperature at the Naval Air Station, Anacostia. D. C., during the approach and passage of the squall-line storm shown in Fig. 66. Hours indicated at top.

line of V-shaped cyclones. Since the cold-front variety of thunderstorm is associated with a frontal zone, it must of necessity travel with the latter, and its approach and passage, therefore, can be forecast with a considerable degree of accuracy. In general, a cold-front storm can be distinguished from the local heat variety by the following criteria: (a) The former is commonly more severe although by no means always so. (b) It is not confined to any particular time of day, for its origin does not depend upon local surface heating. It may arrive, therefore, at any time of day or night. Local convectional storms, on the other hand, more commonly are concentrated in the warmer hours of the day. (c) The cold-front thunderstorm is usually followed by a shift of wind from southwest, south, or southeast to northwest (from a tropical to a polar air mass) and by a consequent drop in temperature (Fig. 67). The local heat thunderstorm gives only very temporary

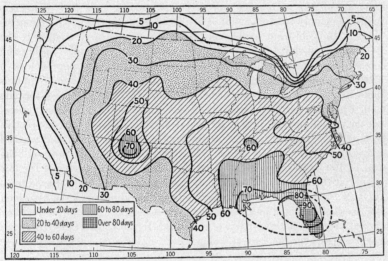

Fig. 68.—Average annual number of days with thunderstorms.

relief during the period of cloud cover and rain and is likely to be followed by the same kind of hot, humid weather that preceded it. Less frequently thunderstorms develop along warm fronts and occluded fronts, but ordinarily these are not so vigorous as the cold-front variety.

174. Distribution of Thunderstorms. Since in the doldrum belt, with its constantly high temperatures, stagnant air, and high humidity, are to be found the most ideal conditions for thunderstorm formation, it is not surprising that equatorial regions should have the maximum number of days with such phenomena. There is a general decrease in their frequency of occurrence from equator to poles but with many variations. In the region of the doldrums thunder is heard on 75 to 150 days a year, and there are a few places recording more than 200 such days. The low-latitude deserts, however, also in the tropics and likewise hot, have fewer than 5 days with thunder, rela-

tive humidity being too low for thunderstorm formation. In middle latitudes there is a marked excess of thunderstorms over land as compared
with sea. Thunder is rarely heard in the polar areas. Southeastern
United States is the most thundery area outside of the tropics, there
being 70 to 90 days a year with such storms over the central and
eastern littoral of the Gulf of Mexico. A portion of New Mexico has
over 70 (Fig. 68). The number decreases to the north and west, the
central tier of states having 50±, the northern tier 25 to 40, and the
Pacific Coast fewer than 5.

175. TORNADOES, the most violent and destructive of all storms, fortunately are of rare occurrence and very restricted in area, their diameters
usually being only 300 to 1,500 ft. They are closely associated with thunderstorms of the cold-front variety and characteristically occur slightly to the
east of the wind-shift line in well-developed V-shaped cyclones. Spring and
early summer witness their maximum development. The approach of a
tornado is usually heralded by dark and greenish masses of cumulo-nimbus
clouds in wild turmoil, from which descends the funnel-shaped tornado
cloud. Upper air currents carry the storm in a general northeasterly direction, the rate of movement averaging 25 to 40 miles an hour. The destructive
effects of tornadoes are of dual origin: (a) the high horizontal and vertical
wind velocities, the former estimated at 100 to 500 miles per hour and the
latter at 100 to 200; and (b) the explosive effect upon buildings of the low
pressure at the center of the storm. Tornadoes are sometimes referred to as
"twisters" because of the inward and upward spiraling masses of air which
comprise them. They appear to be typically American phenomena, for they
are relatively rare in other parts of the world. In the United States they are
most frequent over the central and southern states east of the Rockies.

Section B. Climatic Types and Their Distribution

176. In the four preceding chapters the individual elements out of which climates are composed have been analyzed, and their distributions over the earth's surface described. Variations in the amount, intensity, and seasonal distribution of these elements, as determined by the climatic controls, resulting in changeful combinations of the elements, are the reason for the existence of the variety of climates, the description of which is to follow (33).

177. CLASSIFICATION BY TEMPERATURE ZONES. Perhaps the broadest and most general classification of climates is the one devised by the ancient Greeks who divided each hemisphere into three broad belts, or zones. Thus in the low latitudes is the *winterless* tropical region where temperatures are high throughout the year. Similarly in the high latitudes, in the vicinity of the poles, are the *summerless* polar regions, where there is a general prevalence of low temperatures. Between these two extremes, which are the tropical and the polar parts of the earth, are broad intervening belts where seasonal contrasts in temperature are marked, one season usually being warm or hot, and the other cool or cold. These are the *intermediate,* or *middle, latitudes,* sometimes designated as the "temperate zones," although obviously that name is not well chosen.

178. CLIMATIC REGIONS AND CLIMATIC TYPES. This threefold classification of the earth's climates into tropical, middle-latitude, and polar types plainly does not take into consideration that other great climatic element, precipitation, since within both the low and the middle latitudes there are very wet as well as very dry climates. It is obvious that the geographer requires not only a more detailed and refined classification but likewise one in which both temperature and precipitation are considered when making the climatic subdivisions.

155

Such a subdivision of the land areas of the earth into climatic types and climatic regions is presented on Plate V.

Any portion of the earth's surface over which the climatic elements, and therefore the broad climatic characteristics, are similar (not necessarily identical) is called a climatic region. But it will be noted that not all the subdivisions on Plate V differ from one another climatically, for areas with similar climates are found in widely separated parts of the earth, although often in corresponding latitudinal and continental locations. This frequent duplication of climates in roughly corresponding positions on the continents suggests that there is order and system to the origin and distribution of the climatic elements. It likewise makes possible the classification of the numerous *climatic regions* into a relatively few principal *climatic types*. The degree of order and system to be observed in the latitudinal and continental arrangement of climatic types is associated with the distribution of solar energy and the planetary winds, these controls providing a rough framework for the climatic pattern of the earth. That there are numerous modifications of, or deviations from, any rigid scheme suggests the operation of other controls, some of which are not entirely understood. For the latter reason not all the facts of climatic distribution are at present explainable.

179. GENERAL SCHEME OF CLIMATIC CLASSIFICATION. In its broader aspects the general scheme or outline of climatic subdivision here employed follows the Köppen system.[1] In the low latitudes near the equator is a winterless region *A* with adequate rainfall. This is the humid tropics. Poleward from this belt, and extending beyond the tropics far into the intermediate latitudes, are the dry climates *B*,

---

[1] See, Köppen, W. "Grundriss der Klimakunde." Walter de Gruyter Company, Berlin, 1931. The particular value of Köppen's classification lies in the fact that it is a quantitative system, which uses numerical values for defining the boundaries of the climatic groups and types. Where exact definitions are given to the lines limiting the climatic types, the boundaries are subject to checking and revision as new data are available. The Köppen system has been so widely adopted that it is almost a world standard. Another valuable world classification of climates, likewise employing numerical values of temperature and rainfall for defining the boundaries of climatic types, is by C. Warren Thornthwaite (see references, p. 159). Both the Köppen and the Thornthwaite classifications, representing quantitative systems of comparative climatology, are particularly useful to professional geographers or to college students who are training to enter that field. It is the authors' belief, however, that in an introductory book in geography for college freshmen and sophomores, scarcely any of whom will become geographers, major emphasis should be placed upon the descriptive elements of a climate rather than upon the values employed to establish boundaries, especially since these values are still somewhat tentative. For this reason no attempt has been made to impress the student with the necessity of memorizing the specific Köppen formulas,

sometimes designated as the "death zones." The humid middle latitudes C and D, with their seasonal contrasts in temperature, are divided into two climatic groups, one in which the winters are short and mild (C), and the other in which they are severe and long (D). Finally in the higher latitudes are the summerless polar climates E. In more detail the outline of principal climatic types and their subdivisions appears below.

TYPES OF CLIMATE[1]

I. *Low Latitudes (The Tropics)*

Groups	*Types*
A. Tropical rainy climates	1. Tropical rainforest {*Af*, constantly wet) {*Am*, monsoon variety)
	2. Tropical savanna (*Aw*, wet and dry)
	3. Low-latitude dry climates
	a. Low-latitude desert (*BWh*, arid)
	b. Low-latitude steppe (*BSh*, semiarid)

II. *Middle Latitudes (Intermediate Zones)*

B. Dry climates	4. Middle-latitude dry climates
	a. Middle-latitude desert (*BWk*, arid)
	b. Middle-latitude steppe (*BSk*, semiarid)
C. Humid mesothermal climates	5. Mediterranean or dry-summer subtropical (*Cs*)
	6. Humid subtropical (*Cfa, Cwa*)
	7. Marine west coast (*Cfb*)
D. Humid microthermal climates	8. Humid continental climates:
	a. Humid continental with long summers (*Dfa, Dwa*)
	b. Humid continental with short summers (*Dfb, Dwb*)
	9. Subarctic (*Dfc, Dwc, Dwd*)

III. *High Latitudes (Polar Caps) or High Altitudes*

E. Polar climates	10. Tundra (*ET*)
	11. Ice cap (*EF*)

H. Undifferentiated highlands

---

the more important ones of which are given below for those who desire to use them. Definitions of other Köppen symbols are given in footnotes at the points where they may be useful.

A = temperature of coolest month over 64.4° (18°C.)
B = evaporation exceeds precipitation
C = coldest month between 64.4° (18°C.) and 26.6° (−3°C.)
D = temperature of coldest month under 26.6° (−3°C.); warmest month over 50° (10°C.)
E = temperature of warmest month under 50° (10°C.)

[1] Temperature and precipitation data for representative stations are included for each type of climate. It is expected that data for selected stations will be plotted on the coordinate-paper blocks provided in Plate IV. Supplementary climatic data can be found in Appendix A.

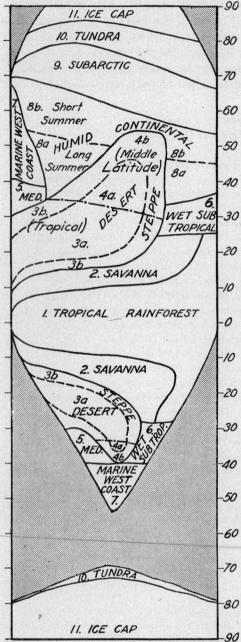

FIG. 69.—Arrangement of climatic types on a hypothetical land mass of moderately low and uniform elevation.

In order to facilitate shifting back and forth between the standard Köppen system of classification and the modified and simplified form of that scheme here employed, the corresponding Köppen symbols appear in parenthesis after each type of climate. Since the two classifications are *similar*, but not *identical*, the latter symbols indicate only somewhat comparable climates, and should not be understood to imply complete agreement.[1]

180. DISTRIBUTION OF CLIMATES ON AN IDEAL CONTINENT. In studying the text materials on types of climate to follow, constant reference should be made to Plate V, showing distribution of the types over the land areas of the earth. In conjunction with the analysis of actual distribution as exhibited on Plate V, careful attention likewise should be paid to Fig. 69. It is designed to show the typical positions and arrangements of the climatic types as they would appear on an idealized continent of low and

[1] One of Köppen's principal climatic types *Cw* is here omitted. It is felt that this climate is not sufficiently distinctive to warrant setting it apart, for the purpose of this classification, as a separate type.

uniform elevation, the shape of which roughly corresponds to that of the actual land masses. In other words, on this hypothetical continent one is able to see the climatic types as they probably would be, with the modifications and complications resulting from varying shapes, sizes, positions, and elevations of the land masses eliminated. The strong resemblances between Fig. 69 and Plate V are obvious.

REFERENCES FOR SECTION B

Ackerman, Edward A. The Köppen Classification of Climates in North America. *Geog. Rev.*, Vol. 31, pp. 105–111, 1941.

"Atlas of American Agriculture." Part 2, Climate. 3 sections: Frost and the Growing Season; Temperature, Sunshine and Wind; Precipitation and Humidity. Government Printing Office, Washington, D. C. Contains excellent and detailed maps of the climatic elements.

Brooks, C. F., Connor, A. J., *et al.* "Climatic Maps of North America." Harvard University Press, Cambridge, Mass., 1936.

"Climate and Man." Yearbook of Agriculture, 1941. Government Printing Office, Washington, D. C. Contains an abundance of climatic data on foreign countries as well as on the United States.

Hann, Julius. "Handbook of Climatology." Part 1, English translation by Robert De C. Ward. The Macmillan Company, New York, 1903. 4th rev. German ed. by Karl Knoch, J. Engelhorn's Nachfolger, Stuttgart, 1932.

James, Preston E. "An Outline of Geography." Ginn and Company, Boston, 1935. Contains a brief but relatively complete presentation of the Köppen classification.

Kendrew, W. G. "Climate." University Press, Oxford, 1930. A particularly good treatment of the climatic elements.

———. "Climates of the Continents." University Press, Oxford, 1927.

Köppen, W. "Grundriss der Klimakunde." Walter de Gruyter & Company, Berlin, 1931. Contains a relatively complete analysis of the Köppen scheme of climatic classification.

——— and Geiger, R. "Handbuch der Klimatologie." Gebrüder Borntraeger, Berlin, 1930 and later. 5 vols.; not completed. Vol. I covers the field of general climatology; the other four are on regions. Those parts dealing with the United States, Mexico, West Indies, Central America, Australia, New Zealand, and parts of eastern Africa are in English; the other parts are in German. Vol. I, Part C, 1936, contains Köppen's latest analysis of his system of climates. The most complete and up-to-date compendium of information on general and regional climatology. Contains abundant climatic data.

Miller, A. Austin. "Climatology." Methuen & Co., Ltd., London, 1931.

Thornthwaite, C. Warren. The Climates of North America According to a New Classification. *Geog. Rev.*, Vol. 21, pp. 633–655, 1931.

———. The Climates of the Earth. *Geog. Rev.*, Vol. 23, pp. 433–440, 1933. A new and original method of climatic classification.

United States Weather Bureau, *Bull. W.* Summary of the Climatological Data of the United States by Sections. Government Printing Office, Washington, D. C. Contains the most detailed and complete climatic data of the United States.

Ward, Robert De C. "Climates of the United States." Ginn and Company, Boston, 1925.

Chapter VII. The Tropical Rainy Climates (A)[1]

181. LOCATION AND BOUNDARIES. The humid tropics comprise a somewhat interrupted and irregular "belt" 20 to 40° wide, around the earth and straddling the equator (Fig. 69, Plate V). This region is distinguished from all other humid regions of the earth by reason of the fact that it is constantly warm; in other words, *it lacks a winter*. In the humid tropics summer heat is a less important factor than a season of coolness, during which there is some relief from high temperatures. As a consequence, the poleward boundary of the tropical rainy climates, except where they come in contact with the dry climates, is according to Köppen, approximately the isotherm of 64° for the *coolest month*.[2] Stated in a different way, within this climatic group there is no month with an average temperature of less than 64°. This temperature was selected because it was found to coincide reasonably well with the poleward limit of certain plants which grow only in the warmest regions and cannot tolerate marked seasonal changes in temperature. The chief interruptions of the belt of humid tropical climates over the continents are caused by mountains and plateaus, these elevated lands, even though near the equator, having temperatures too low to permit them to be classed as typically tropical.

Normally the tropical rainy climates extend farthest poleward along the eastern or windward sides of the continents (Fig. 69). Here tropical maritime air masses (trades) come onshore from off warm waters and provide atmospheric conditions conducive to thunderstorm and cyclonic precipitation. East-coast rainfall is especially heavy where the tropical air masses are forced to ascend highland barriers. Hurricanes are likewise prevalent along certain of the tropical east coasts.

---

[1] Unfortunately there is insufficient information concerning air masses and their characteristics in the various parts of the world to permit a consistent use of air masses in explaining the distribution of climatic types.

[2] Upland savannas (201), therefore, could not be included if the Köppen definition were strictly applied.

On these windward sides of the land masses, therefore, the humid tropical climates extend poleward until they meet the humid subtropical climates of the middle latitudes. In the interior, and toward the western sides of the continents, however, the humid tropics are bounded by the dry *B* climates. As the trades sweep farther inland, their aridity increases, so that in the continental interiors semiarid and arid conditions are brought somewhat closer to the equator. Where cool equatorward-moving ocean currents parallel the west coasts in low latitudes (103) they may carry the dry climates to within a few degrees of the equator, notably constricting the breadth of the humid tropical belt.

182. PRECIPITATION. Rainfall is relatively abundant, rarely lower than 30 in., and usually it is well over that amount (Plate II). Much of the precipitation is convectional in origin, the heavy showers often being accompanied by severe thunder and lightning. Cyclonic rains associated with weak tropical lows are likewise important. Unlike the uniform temperature conditions, rainfall is more variable in amount and in both seasonal and areal distribution. The two principal climatic types within the humid tropics are distinguished from each other on the basis of their seasonal distribution of precipitation, one type, tropical rainforest, having ample rainfall throughout the year, while in the other, savanna, there is a distinctly wet and a distinctly dry season.

1. Tropical Rainforest Climate (*Af* and *Am*)[1]

183. LOCATION. (*a*) Uniformly high temperatures and (*b*) heavy precipitation distributed throughout the year, so that there is no marked dry season, are the two most distinguishing characteristics of the *Af* or tropical rainforest climate. When typically located it is found astride the equator and extending out 5 or 10° on either side. This latitudinal spread may be increased to 15 or even 25° along the windward margins of the continents.

TEMPERATURE

184. ANNUAL AND SEASONAL TEMPERATURE. Lying as it commonly does athwart the equator and consequently in the belt of maximum insolation, it is to be expected that temperatures will be uniformly high, the yearly averages usually lying between 77 and 80°+ (see data, pp. 167, 169). Since the sun's noon rays are never far from a vertical position, and days and nights vary little in length from one

---

[1] In the Köppen symbols *f* = moist (*feucht*) throughout the year, no month with less than 2.4 in. of rain; *m* = monsoon variety, with heavy annual rainfall but a short dry season.

part of the year to another, not only are the annual temperatures high, but there is likewise little seasonal variation (Fig. 70). The annual temperature range, or difference between the warmest and coolest months, is usually less than 5°. Thus Belém and Iquitos in the Amazon Valley have annual ranges of 3° and 4.3° respectively, Coquilhatville in central Africa 2+°, and Singapore in southern Malaya 3.2°. Over the oceans in these low latitudes ranges are even less, Jaluit in the Marshall Islands in mid-Pacific recording only 0.8° difference between the extreme months. It becomes evident from the very small temperature ranges that it is not the excessively high monthly averages but rather the *uniformity* and *monotony* of this constant succession of hot months, with no relief, that characterizes the tropical rainforest climate. Thus the average July temperatures of many American cities, such as Charleston, with 81.6°; Galveston, 83.3°; and Montgomery, 81.6°, may equal, or even exceed by a few degrees, those of the hottest months at stations near the equator. The hottest month at Belém (Amazon Basin) is only 79.7°, and at Akassa (Niger Delta) 79.9°.

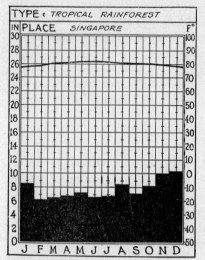

FIG. 70.—Average monthly temperatures and precipitation for a representative tropical rainforest station. Monthly temperatures are much more uniform than monthly precipitation.

185. DAILY TEMPERATURES. The daily or diurnal range of temperature (difference between the warmest and coolest hours of the day) is usually 10 to 25°, or several times greater than the annual range. For example, at Bolobo in the Belgian Congo, the average daily range is 16°, while the annual range is only 2°. During the afternoons the thermometer ordinarily rises to temperatures varying from 85 to 93° and at night sinks to 70 or 75° (Figs. 71, 72, 73). It is commonly said, therefore, that night is the winter of the tropics. Even the extremes of temperature are never very great, the average of the daily maxima at Belém being only 91.4°, and the average of the daily minima 68°. The highest temperature ever recorded at Santarem (Amazon Basin) is 96.3°, while the lowest is only 65.3°. This absolute maximum of 96.3° may be compared with 103° for Chicago and 108° for St. Louis. Although the day temperatures may not be excessively high, the heat,

together with slight air movement, intense light, and high relative and absolute humidity, produces an atmospheric condition with low cooling power. It is oppressive and sultry so that one's vitality and energy are sapped. *Sensible temperatures* are, therefore, excessively high, although the thermometer readings may not indicate abnormal heat.

Even the nights give little relief from the oppressive heat. Rapid nocturnal cooling is not to be expected in regions of such excessive

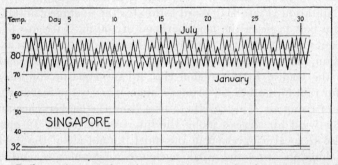

FIG. 71.—Daily maximum and minimum temperatures for the extreme months at a representative tropical rainforest station. The thinner line is July.

humidity and abundant cloudiness. The periods of less rainfall and clearest skies have the lowest night temperatures, the thermometer on rare occasions falling below 60°.

186. DAILY MARCH OF TEMPERATURE. Figures 71, 72, and 73 show the daily march of temperature for the extreme months at repre-

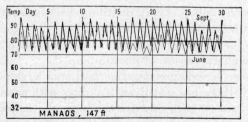

FIG. 72.—Daily maximum and minimum temperatures for the extreme months at a representative tropical rainforest station in the Amazon Valley. (*Courtesy of Mark Jefferson and the Geographical Review.*)

sentative stations within tropical rainforest climate. The graphs illustrate a temperature regime in which sun is almost completely in control. There is a marked diurnal regularity and periodicity about the changes, temperatures rising to about the same height each day and falling to about the same level each night, so that one 24-hr. period almost duplicates every other. Irregular invasions of heat and cold, of the type so common in the middle latitudes, are practically unknown.

PRECIPITATION

187. AMOUNT AND SEASONAL DISTRIBUTION. Rainfall is both heavy and distributed throughout the year, there being no distinctly dry season (Figs. 70, 77; see data, pp. 167, 168). Taken as a whole, tropical rainforest climate is coincident with the world's heaviest belt of precipitation (Plate II). Ward estimates the average rainfall of the doldrum belt to be in the neighborhood of 100 in., with less over the continents and more over the oceans. Because of the abundant precipitation, surface ocean waters in the doldrums are less salty than they are in the trades. In this region close to the equator conditions are ideal for rain formation. Of primary importance is the fact that it is a region of rising air. This results in part from the convergence and rise of trade-wind air masses along the intertropical front. In part it is due also to local convection in the quiet, humid air of the doldrums. Both thunderstorms and weak cyclones are numerous, and only a small amount of lifting of the unstable air is required to produce abundant rainfall. Cloudiness, much of it cumulus in character, is relatively high in the doldrums, averaging in the neighborhood of 58 per cent. At Manaus, in the Amazon Valley, cloudiness varies between 6/10 and 7/10 for each month. At Belém it is 4/10 in the driest month and 8/10 in the rainiest.[1]

Although it is true that there is no genuinely dry season in the tropical rainforest climate, it should not be inferred, on the other hand, that the rainfall is evenly distributed throughout the year. By comparison with the rainiest periods there are others that are less wet, but they are far from being dry. There is no distinctive seasonal rainfall regime characteristic of the rainforest type of climate.

In the rainier periods precipitation falls on a large majority of the days, although there are usually a few days with none. Fewer rainy days and less rain on each day are characteristic features of the less wet seasons. At Belém in the Amazon Valley with 94 in. of rain, March (13.9 in.) has six and one-half times more rain than November, but even November has 10 rainy days although March has 28. Precipitation varies much more from year to year than does temperature, although these variations are seldom enough to injure crops. Even the driest years are still relatively wet.

188. NATURE OF THE RAINFALL. Much of the rainfall is convectional in origin, falling in hard showers from towering cumulo-

[1] Cloudiness is here expressed in terms of the part of the total sky covered.

nimbus clouds. The maximum usually occurs during the warmer hours of the day, when local heating, and therefore convectional ascent, are at a maximum. Early mornings are often relatively clear, but as the sun climbs toward the zenith and temperature increases, cumulus clouds begin to appear, growing in number and size with the heat of the day, until by afternoon ominous thunderheads are common. Several thunderstorms, accompanied by thunder and lightning, in a single afternoon are not unusual, and the rain may continue on into the evening, although there is a tendency for the skies to become clearer as the heat wanes. The cloud cover and downpour of rain accompanying the storm temporarily cool the air, but with its passing and the reappearance of the sun, the usual oppressive conditions are reestablished. Within the doldrum belt thunderstorms reach their maximum development for any latitude of the earth, there being on the average 75 to 150 days with such storms during the course of a year. These paroxysms of nature, with their fierce lightning, crashing thunder, and deluges of rainfall, are awesome spectacles. One traveler[1] writes as follows concerning the heavy convectional showers in the tropical rainforest climate:

"The force of the downpour is another factor in the oecology of the forest. In the wet season thunderstorms of great violence are frequent, and the rain descends with a suddenness and volume unknown outside the tropics. The sun is shining, the forest glitters with a million lights, birds are on the move, and insects hum and dance from leaf to leaf. All at once a shadow is drawn over the sun, and all activity of bird and beast ceases as the sound of rushing rain rapidly approaches. An avalanche of water then crashes down, blotting out surrounding objects and, as it seems, sweeping the very breath from the nostrils, bewildering and benumbing the senses. Every twig and leaf is bent and battered, and in a few seconds streams pour down the paths and the world seems changed into a thundering cataract. Then, as suddenly as it came, the storm passes, and the sun blazes out again before the roar of the storm sweeping over the treetops has died away in the distance. Even before the leaves have ceased to drip, or the land-crabs, tempted forth by the teeming water, have scuttled to cover again, the life of the forest is resumed. It is almost incredible how some fragile forms escape destruction under such terrific bombardments. . . . "

Weak tropical cyclones, probably of frontal origin, are likewise important rain bringers. Cyclonic rain is less intense but of longer duration and falls from more uniformly overcast gray skies. These cyclonic storms appear to be most numerous at the periods of heaviest rainfall.

[1] Haviland, Maude D. "Forest Steppe and Tundra." p. 39, University Press, Cambridge, Mass., 1926.

189. Winds. The feeble temperature gradients beget only weak pressure gradients, so that air movement is prevailingly slight. The whole region is poorly ventilated, and this, in conjunction with high temperatures and excessive humidity, makes for physical discomfort. Temporary relief may be brought by the strong squall winds associated with thunderstorms. Occasionally the trades advance far enough equatorward, especially in the drier season, to bring spells of desiccating weather. This wind, known as the *harmattan* along the Guinea Coast of Africa, is usually described as a cool wind, especially at night, probably owing to its great evaporation.

Sea breezes are important climatic phenomena along coasts in the low latitudes. The importation of cooler air from the sea during the heat of the day is a great boon to residents along the littoral, causing tropical coasts to be much more livable than are the interiors.

Daily Weather

190. Daily Weather Largely Sun Controlled. (Figs. 71, 72, 73.) The following description by an eye witness, of daily weather conditions in the Amazon Valley, may serve to synthesize and vivify the previous description:

"The heat increased rapidly toward two o'clock (92° and 93° Fahr.), by which time every voice of bird or mammal was hushed; only in the trees was heard at intervals the harsh whir of a cicada. The leaves, which were so moist and fresh in early morning, now became lax and drooping; the flowers shed their petals. Our neighbours, the Indian and Mulatto inhabitants of the open palm-thatched huts, as we returned home fatigued with our ramble, were either asleep in their hammocks or seated on mats in the shade, too languid even to talk. On most days in June and July a heavy shower would fall some time in the afternoon, producing a most welcome coolness. The approach of the rain-clouds was after a uniform fashion very interesting to observe. First, the cool sea-breeze, which commenced to blow about 10 o'clock, and which had increased in force with the increasing power of the sun, would flag and finally die away. The heat and electric tension of the atmosphere would then become almost insupportable. Languor and uneasiness would seize on every one; even the denizens of the forest betraying it by their motions. White clouds would appear in the east and gather into cumuli, with an increasing blackness along their lower portions. The whole eastern horizon would become almost suddenly black, and this would spread upwards, the sun at length becoming obscured. Then the rush of a mighty wind is heard through the forest, swaying the tree-tops; a vivid flash of lightning bursts forth, then a crash of thunder, and down streams the deluging rain. Such storms soon cease, leaving bluish-black motionless clouds in the sky until night. Meantime all nature is refreshed; but heaps of flower-petals and fallen leaves are seen under the trees. Toward evening life revives again, and the ringing uproar is resumed from bush and tree. The following morning the sun again rises in a cloudless sky, and so the cycle is completed; spring, summer, and autumn, as it were, in one tropical day.

The days are more or less like this throughout the year in this country. . . . It is never either spring, summer, or autumn, but each day is a combination of all three. With the day and night always of equal length, the atmospheric disturbances of each day neutralising themselves before each succeeding morn; with the sun in its course proceeding midway across the sky, and the daily temperature the same within two or three degrees throughout the year—how grand in its perfect equilibrium and simplicity is the march of Nature under the equator!"[1]

191. REPRESENTATIVE REGIONS. The Amazon Valley in South America, the Congo Basin and Guinea Coast in Africa, and large parts of the East Indies are the three largest areas with tropical rainforest climate (Plate V). Of the two large interior regions, the Amazon and Congo Basins, the former possesses the more severe rainforest climate, having, on the whole, heavier rainfall. The trades find free entrance into the Amazon Valley through the opening between the Brazilian and the Guiana Highlands, and likewise by way of the Orinoco Valley, carrying with them enormous supplies of moisture which are precipitated as rain in the interior. Unlike the Amazon Valley, which is extremely low, the Congo Basin averages 1,000 to 1,600 ft. in elevation. Moreover, it is shut off from the sea on the east by a relatively high plateau, which prevents entrance of the trade winds. As a result the rainfall is 10 to 20 in. less than in the Amazon Valley.

CLIMATIC DATA FOR REPRESENTATIVE TROPICAL RAINFOREST STATIONS
Singapore, Straits Settlements (Malaya)

	J	F	M	A	M	J	J	A	S	O	N	D	Yr.	Range
Temp.	78.3	79.0	80.2	80.8	81.5	81.1	81.0	80.6	80.4	80.1	79.3	78.6	80.1	3.2
Precip.	8.5	6.1	6.5	6.9	7.2	6.7	6.8	8.5	7.1	8.2	10.0	10.4	92.9	

Belém, Amazon Valley

	J	F	M	A	M	J	J	A	S	O	N	D	Yr.	Range
Temp.	77.7	77.0	77.5	77.7	78.4	78.3	78.1	78.3	78.6	79.0	79.7	79.0	78.3	2.7
Precip.	10.3	12.6	13.3	13.2	9.3	5.7	4.9	4.3	3.2	2.5	2.3	5.1	86.7	

Nouvelle Anvers, Belgian Congo

	J	F	M	A	M	J	J	A	S	O	N	D	Yr.	Range
Temp.	79.2	80.1	79.2	78.1	79.2	78.4	76.5	76.3	77.0	77.4	77.9	78.1	78.1	3.8
Precip.	4.1	3.5	4.1	5.6	6.2	6.1	6.3	6.3	6.3	6.6	2.6	9.3	66.9	

MODIFIED RAINFOREST TYPES

192. THE EASTERN LITTORALS (1t). Smaller areas of tropical rainforest climate are to be found in parts of eastern Brazil, the eastern lowland of Central America, the west coast of Colombia, and eastern Madagascar. In three of the above-named regions, where the location is on the eastern or windward side of a land mass, the tropical rain-

[1] Bates, Henry Walter. "The Naturalist on the River Amazon." pp. 31–32, John Murray, London, 1910.

forest climate extends poleward farther than it ordinarily does. This results from the unusually abundant rainfall characteristic of these windward littorals. *Af* climates 20° ± away from the equator have certain slight modifications of typical Amazon Valley conditions. Marine location and onshore winds slightly modify the heat while the trade winds make for better ventilation. As a result the climate is not

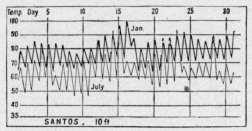

Fig. 73.—Daily maximum and minimum temperatures for a tropical rainforest station on the east coast of Brazil, 24° south of the equator. (*Courtesy of Mark Jefferson and the Geographical Review.*)

quite so oppressive (Fig. 73). Because of their closer proximity to the middle latitudes, invasions of modified polar air masses are occasionally felt, resulting in more variable temperature condition.

Climatic Data for Belize, British Honduras, a Representative 1t Station

	J	F	M	A	M	J	J	A	S	O	N	D	Yr.	Range
Temp.	74.8	76.8	79.2	79.2	81.9	82.4	82.6	82.6	82.0	79.3	76.1	73.6	79.3	9
Precip.	5.1	2.6	1.6	1.5	4.1	9.1	9.6	8.5	9.4	11.0	10.2	6.3	79.0	

193. Monsoon Littorals (1m). Regions with the symbol 1*m* are under the influence of monsoons or strong monsoon tendencies. Characteristically they are coastal locations backed by mountains or by plateau escarpments. Rainfall is very heavy, a considerable part of it being orographic rain from the onshore summer monsoon. It differs from the typical rainforest climate in that precipitation is not so well distributed throughout the year, there being at least a short dry season. In annual rainfall distribution, therefore, this subtype somewhat resembles the savanna regime, although the total amount is much heavier and the dry period commonly is not so long. The maximum precipitation usually occurs at the time of high sun, which is the period of the onshore monsoon. In spite of a distinct dry season, variable in length, the precipitation is so heavy that the ground remains sufficiently damp throughout the year to support a relatively dense, semideciduous forest. Temperatures usually reach a maximum during the period of clearer skies just before the season of heaviest rainfall and cloud, even though the latter is the period of highest sun (see data for Calicut). This subtype is best developed in the monsoon lands of tropical southeastern Asia and on the western Guinea Coast of Africa.

Climatic Data for Calicut, India, a Representative 1m *Station*

	J	F	M	A	M	J	J	A	S	O	N	D	Yr.	Range
Temp.	77.8	79.8	81.6	83.6	83.1	78.5	76.7	77.4	78.3	79.1	79.5	78.3	79.5	6.9
Precip.	0.3	0.2	0.6	3.2	9.5	35.0	29.8	15.3	8.4	10.3	4.9	1.1	118.6	

2. Savanna Climate (Aw)[1]

Savanna climate differs in two principal respects from tropical rainforest climate: (a) It usually has less precipitation; and (b) rainfall is unevenly distributed throughout the year, there being a distinctly wet and a distinctly dry season (Plate II, Fig. 77). These climatic contrasts result in the dense forest cover, typical of areas near the equator, being replaced by lighter, more open, tropical forests and tall grass in the savanna regions.

194. LOCATION AND BOUNDARIES. On Fig. 69, showing the distribution and characteristic locations of types of climate on an ideal continent, savanna areas lie on the poleward and interior sides of the tropical rainforest climate and between it and the dry climates. In a general way the characteristic latitudinal location of the savannas is about 5+ to 15°±, and they extend still farther poleward along the windward, or eastern, side of the continent. This places them between the humid and relatively unstable rising air masses of the doldrums and equatorial margins of the trades on one hand, and the drier and more stable settling air masses of the subtropical high-pressure cells and poleward margins of the trades on the other. With the northward and southward movements of the sun's rays these transition regions are encroached upon by both air masses or wind systems during the course of a year.

It becomes evident from a scrutiny of Plate V that many, if not most, of the large savanna areas do occupy the characteristic location described above and shown in Fig. 69. The Llanos of the Orinoco Valley (Colombia and Venezuela) and adjacent parts of the Guiana Highlands in northern South America, the Campos of Brazil, the Sudan and Veld of northern and southern Africa, respectively, and the tropical grasslands of northern Australia are all thus situated. In position, therefore, these savanna regions are often intermediate between the constantly wet and the constantly dry climates and are like each on their opposite margins. Not only are they intermediate in

---

[1] In the Köppen symbols w = dry season in winter or low-sun period; at least one month with less than 2.4 in. of rain.

position, but they are likewise transitional in their wind, temperature, rainfall, and vegetation characteristics. On the rainforest or equatorward margins of the savannas rainfall is heavy, the dry season short, and temperature and vegetation closely resemble those of the rainforest. But as one travels poleward or interior toward the dry climates, the rainy season becomes shorter, temperature ranges are somewhat larger, and trees give way more and more to grasses.

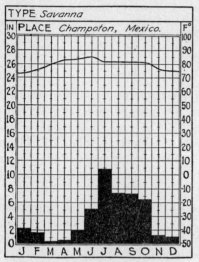

FIG. 74.—Average monthly temperatures and precipitation for a representative savanna station.

TEMPERATURE

195. THE TEMPERATURE ELEMENTS in savanna and tropical rainforest are not greatly unlike. Constantly high temperatures are still the rule, for the noon sun is never far from a vertical position, and days and nights change little in length from one part of the year to another. In general, however, yearly ranges are somewhat greater (although still small) than in typical rainforest regions, usually over 5° but seldom exceeding 15° (Fig. 74). These larger ranges may result from the fact that the high-sun months are slightly hotter and the

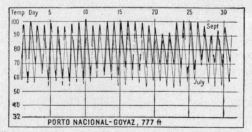

FIG. 75.—Daily maximum and minimum temperatures for the extreme months at a representative savanna station in Brazil. (*Courtesy of Mark Jefferson and the Geographical Review.*)

low-sun months are slightly cooler than is typical for regions nearer the equator.

It is significant that the hottest month or months many times do not coincide with the time of highest sun but usually precede it somewhat and thus occur before the height of the rainy period, when the more persistent cloud cover and heavier precipitation tend to lower the temperature. Thus March, April, and possibly May, are likely to

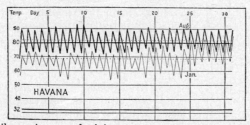

Fig. 76.—Daily maximum and minimum temperatures for the extreme months at a representative savanna station with a marine location. (*Courtesy of Mark Jefferson and the Geographical Review.*)

be hotter than June or July, which are the rainiest periods for Northern Hemisphere savannas.

CLIMATIC DATA FOR REPRESENTATIVE SAVANNA STATIONS

Timbo, French West Africa (10°40′N.)

	J	F	M	A	M	J	J	A	S	O	N	D	Yr.	Range
Temp.	72	76	81	80	77	73	72	72	72	73	72	71	74	9.7
Precip.	0.0	0.0	1.0	2.4	6.4	9.0	12.4	14.7	10.2	6.7	1.3	0.0	64.1	

Calcutta, India

	J	F	M	A	M	J	J	A	S	O	N	D	Yr.	Range
Temp.	65	70	79	85	86	85	83	82	83	80	72	65	78	21
Precip.	0.4	1.1	1.4	2.0	5.0	11.2	12.1	11.5	9.0	4.3	0.5	0.2	58.8	

Cuiabá, Brazil (10°S.)

	J	F	M	A	M	J	J	A	S	O	N	D	Yr.	Range
Temp.	81	81	81	80	78	75	76	78	82	82	82	81	80	6.6
Precip.	9.8	8.3	8.3	4.0	2.1	0.3	0.2	1.1	2.0	4.5	5.9	8.1	54.6	

PRECIPITATION

196. AMOUNT OF RAINFALL. Since temperatures are not greatly different within the tropics, rainfall becomes the more critical element in setting apart the several climatic types of the low latitudes. Characteristically, the total amount of rainfall of the savanna is less than that of the tropical rainforest climate, 40 to 60 in. being more typical of the former. But since the savanna type usually occupies transitional belts between the constantly wet and the constantly dry climates, it naturally follows that there will be considerable contrast between the amount of rainfall on its two margins.

197. RAINFALL REGIME. It is the seasonal distribution rather than the amount of precipitation, however, which chiefly distinguishes the two climates of the humid tropics, for the savanna type has a distinctly wet and a distinctly dry season. This contrast between the two types is principally due to their latitudinal locations, for although tropical rainforest is almost constantly within the doldrum belt of unstable rising air and heavy rains, savannas are on the margins of the doldrums and, therefore, in an intermediate position between them and the dry settling air masses of the subtropical high-pressure cells and the poleward margins of the trades.

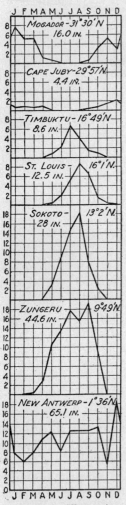

Fig. 77.—Illustrating rainfall regimes in the low latitudes; Africa north of the equator. Stations are arranged according to latitude with Nouvelle Anvers (New Antwerp) closest to the equator.

NOTE. Although in the planetary system of winds *three* wind belts, doldrums, trades, and horse latitudes, are recognized as belonging to the tropics, only *two* general air masses with contrasting humidity and precipitation characteristics are so designated. These are the *tropical* and the *equatorial*. There is no distinct line of separation between the source regions of these two air masses, but usually it is drawn somewhere between latitudes 10 and 20, where the anticyclonic divergence and subsidence vanishes and where there is a distinct change in humidity, cloudiness, and precipitation. So drawn the line passes through the trades so as to include their equatorward portions with the doldrums to form the humid equatorial air masses, and their poleward margins with the subtropical anticyclones to form the drier tropical air masses where subsidence is prevalent.

The Sudan of northern Africa may be used as a concrete example to clarify further the mechanics of the savanna rainfall regime. As the sun's rays move northward from the equator after the spring equinox, their thermal effects cause pressure and wind belts to shift in the same direction, although lagging a month or two behind in time. As the equatorial air masses (doldrums and equatorial margins of trades) with heavy rains gradually creep northward, thunderstorms begin to appear in March or April over the Sudan, and the rainfall continues to increase in amount until July or even August, when the doldrums have reached their maximum northward migration. With the southward retreat of the equatorial air masses, following the sun, the rains decline in amount, until by October or November the dry settling tropical air masses (subtropical anticyclone and poleward margins of trades) are prevailing over the Sudan, and drought grips the land. The length of the wet and the dry seasons is variable, depending upon distance from the equator.

There is no abrupt boundary between the constantly wet and the wet-and-dry climates, but a very gradual transition from one to the other (Fig. 77). Thus on the equatorward margins of the savannas the rainy season persists for almost the entire year. In such locations there even may be a slight depression at the crest of the precipitation curve, this falling off of the rains occurring in the short interval of time between the northward and southward migrations of the doldrums (Fig. 77, Zungeru). The farther poleward one travels in the Sudan the shorter is the period of doldrum control and the longer that of the drier settling air masses, so that the dry season increases in length while the wet period shrinks. For the sake of emphasis it bears repeating that the rainy season in the savannas closely coincides with the period of high sun and the presence of unstable rising equatorial air masses, whereas the dry season is identified with the period of low sun and drier settling tropical air masses. Most emphatically, rainfall follows the sun. This rule holds for either hemisphere, although one should keep in mind that December to February is the period of high sun (summer) south of the equator and June to August the period of low sun (winter). It is obvious, therefore, that when a Northern Hemisphere savanna is having its rainy season, a similar region south of the equator is experiencing drought, and vice versa.

198. MONSOON SAVANNAS.   In certain parts of southern and southeastern Asia, particularly in British India, Burma, and French Indo-China, are savanna lands that do not have the characteristic location with respect to wind belts described above. Here, instead of lying between latitudinally migrating wet and dry air masses, the savannas are under the influence of monsoon winds and so experience nearly a complete reversal of wind direction within the year. In monsoon savannas the wet and dry seasons usually coincide with the periods of onshore and offshore winds respectively. During the low-sun or dry period relatively stable continental air masses prevail. In the opposite season, at the time of high sun, there is an importation of warm humid air from over great expanses of tropical ocean. This is the rainy season. The onshore monsoon is effective in producing a wet season, chiefly because it transports a tremendous amount of water vapor in over the land, so that a reservoir of moisture is created, in which thunderstorms, tropical lows, and hurricanes may readily produce rainfall. Where the onshore monsoon is forced to ascend over

coastal mountains, rainfall is usually so abundant that, in spite of seasonal periodicity, monsoonal rainforest climate (1*m*), instead of savanna climate, is the result. Where coasts are less elevated, or the region has an interior location so that rainfall is lower, savanna climate is more likely to prevail.

199. SEASONAL WEATHER. During its *rainy* season the weather of savanna climate closely resembles that of tropical rainforest at its worst. This period usually is ushered in and out by violent thunderstorms and severe squall winds, which in Africa are called tornadoes. In these transition periods the weather is very trying, "violent short deluges of rain and intensely hot sunshine alternating." During the height of the rains violent thunderstorms appear to be less frequent than they are at the transition periods, while on the other hand heavy, long-continued, and more general rains reach their maximum at that time. These latter probably originate in weak tropical lows.

In the low-sun, or *dry*, season the weather is like that of the deserts. The humidity becomes very low so that the skin is parched and cracked. In spite of the aridity, the dry season is welcomed after the humid, oppressive heat of the rainy period. An occasional shower may occur during the months of drought, the number depending upon which margin of the savannas is being considered. On the dry margin the period of absolute drought may be of several months' duration, while on the rainy margin, where it makes contact with tropical rainforest climate, there may be no month absolutely without rain. *The fact should never be lost sight of that none of these boundaries is sharp, there being very gradual transitions from one type to another.* During the dry season the savanna landscape is parched and brown, the trees lose their leaves, the rivers become low, the soil cracks, and all nature appears dormant. Smoke from grass fires and dust fill the air, so that visibility is usually low.

The following quotation is a description of the seasonal weather and related landscape changes in a savanna region. It should be emphasized, in order to avoid confusion, that the region described is Zambezia, Africa, which is *south* of the equator. As a result of Southern Hemisphere location, the months included within the several seasons are exactly opposite from what they are in regions north of the equator.

"The winter months, or dry season, extend, with a slight variation, from April to November. They are, as I have said, pleasant and healthy in the extreme. Now the traveller and hunter of big game make their appearance; the deciduous trees are leafless; the grasses dry, yellow, and ready for the chance spark or deliberate act which, with the aid of a steady breeze, will turn vast expanses of golden grasslands into so many hideous, bare deserts of heat-tremulous black. All nature seems to be at a standstill, hibernating. The rivers are low. Where, but a few short months since, wide, watery expanses rushed headlong toward the sea . . . there now remain but tranquil, placid channels, flowing smilingly at the bottom of steep, cliff-like banks. . . .

"With October the heat becomes very great. Vast belts of electrically charged, yellowish clouds, with cumulus, rounded extremities, begin to gather and at the close of day are seen to be flickering in their murky centres with a menacing tremor of constant lightning. This may go on for a week or more, and then Nature arises like a strong man in anger and looses the long pent-up voice of the thunder and the irresistible torrents of the early rains. The first manifestation may come at evening and is a soul-moving display of natural force. . . .

"After such a disturbance as the one I have just described, rain is fairly continuous for some time, and the effect of this copious irrigation makes itself felt in every branch of animal and vegetable life. Within a few days the change is startling; the paths and roadways choke themselves with a rich clothing of newly sprung grasses, whilst the trees, the extremities of whose twigs and branches have been visibly swelling, now leap into leaf and blossom. The mosses, which for months past have looked like dry, bedraggled, colourless rags, regain once more their vivid, tender green. Now the forest throws off its puritanical greyness and, with an activity and rapidity beyond belief, decks itself in flowers of a thousand gorgeous shades of colour, from chrome-yellow and purple to grateful mauve.

"The birds now put on their finest feathers, the animals appear in their brightest hues. Colour and warmth run riot in the brilliantly clear air now washed clean from the mist and smoke which for so many months have obscured it. The clear verdant green of rapid-springing grasses and opening fronds clothes the landscape, and the distant peaks of the mountains lose their pale, bluey-grey haziness and stand boldly out in the light of the sun. The months succeed each other, bringing with them new and strange beauties, for summer is now at its height, and trees and flowers at their most perfect period. . . . April comes, and suddenly Nature holds her hand. The swollen rivers and inundated plains shake themselves free from the redundant waters. The grasses have now reached a formidable height. The rains now cease, and the land begins to dry up. Rich greens turn to copper, and brown, and yellow, and little by little, with the advent of May, the winter returns with its sober greyness."[1]

200. RAINFALL RELIABILITY. Not only is savanna rainfall less in total amount, and more periodic in its distribution throughout the year, as compared with tropical rainforest, but it is likewise less reliable, there being wider fluctuation in the amounts from year to year. One year may bring such an abundance of rain as to flood the

[1] Maugham, R. C. F. "Zambezia." pp. 383–388, John Murray, London, 1910.

fields, rot the crops, and increase the depredations of injurious insects and fungi, while the following year may witness even more severe losses from drought. In northern Australia the average rainfall variation from the normal is as much as 25 per cent (Fig. 79).

UPLAND SAVANNA (Cw)[1]

201. In tropical latitudes on several continents, but especially Africa and South America, there are extensive upland areas, possessed

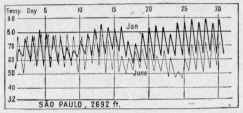

FIG. 78.—Daily maximum and minimum temperatures for the extreme months at an upland savanna station on the Brazilian Plateau. (*Courtesy of Mark Jefferson and the Geographical Review.*)

of many of the normal savanna characteristics but differing chiefly in their lower temperatures (Fig. 78). These are included within the general savanna type but on Plate V are set apart from the more standard lowland variety by a light stippling. (For climatic modifications imposed by altitude, see Chap. XI.)

[1] According to the Köppen classification, *Cw* climates appear in two characteristic locations: (*a*) tropical-savanna uplands, where because of altitude the temperature is lowered below that of the surrounding lowlands (*Aw*); and (*b*) mild subtropical monsoon lands such as exist in southern China. It is the first group that is here being classified as the subtype *upland savanna*. The other group is included within the humid subtropical climates of the middle latitudes.

Chapter VIII. The Dry Climates (*B*)

---

202. DEFINITION AND BOUNDARIES OF DRY CLIMATES. The essential feature of a dry climate is that potential evaporation shall exceed precipitation.[1] As a result of rainfall deficiency there is no surplus of water with which to maintain a constant ground-water supply, so that permanent streams cannot originate within such areas. It may be possible, however, for streams to cross them, as do the Nile and the Colorado, for instance, provided they have their sources in more humid regions.

If the above definition of a dry climate, *viz.*, one in which potential evaporation exceeds precipitation, is accepted, then, since evaporation varies greatly in different parts of the earth, it follows that no specific amount of rainfall can be used to bound dry climates over the world as a whole. Potential evaporation is greater in warm than in cold regions, so that while 25 in. of precipitation may be effective in producing a humid landscape with forests in cool northwestern Europe, the same amount falling in the hot tropics results in semiarid conditions. If a large amount of the annual precipitation comes in the warmer months when evaporation is higher, more is lost through evaporation and less is available for plant growth.

203. DESERT AND STEPPE. Two subdivisions of dry climates are commonly recognized: (*a*) the arid, or desert, type and (*b*) the semiarid, or steppe, type. In general, the steppe is a transitional belt surrounding the real desert and separating it from the humid climates beyond. The boundary between arid and semiarid climates is a relatively arbitrary one, but by Köppen it is defined as one-half the amount separating steppe from humid climates. For example, if in a particular region 19 in. of rainfall marks the outer, or humid, boundary of dry climates in general, then $9\frac{1}{2}$ in. may be taken as the boundary between steppe and desert for that same region.

---

[1] Rate of evaporation may be measured by freely exposing to the weather an open vessel containing water and noting the drop in the level of the water surface.

177

204. TEMPERATURE. Since dry climates exist in a wide variety of latitudes and continental locations, few significant general comments on their annual temperatures can be made. On the whole, however, because of characteristic interior and leeward locations on the continents, they tend to be severe for their latitude, having relatively extreme seasonal temperatures and consequently large annual ranges.

More marked, however, are the large daily ranges, clear, cloudless skies, and relatively low humidity permitting an abundance of solar energy to reach the earth by day but likewise allowing a rapid loss of

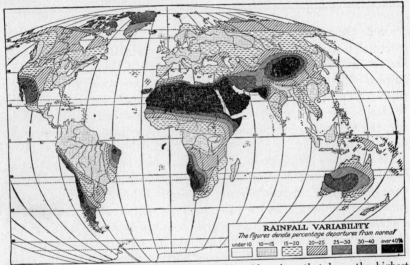

FIG. 79.—In general it is the dry and subhumid regions that have the highest rainfall variability. (*After Edwin Biel. Courtesy of the American Geographical Society of New York.*)

earth energy at night. Large diurnal ranges in deserts also are associated with the meager vegetation cover, which permits the barren surface to become intensely heated by day. It is a physical law that the higher the temperature of a body the more rapid is its loss of heat by radiation and consequently the more rapid its reduction in temperature.[1] Deserts, therefore, not only acquire, but likewise lose, heat rapidly. In humid regions with a greater amount of vegetation, more of the solar radiation is absorbed by the plant cover or is used to evaporate moisture, so that extreme temperatures, like those of deserts, are less likely. Where vegetation is abundant, water vapor is likely to be also, so that night cooling is retarded.

[1] The amount of heat radiated by a body is directly proportional to the fourth power of its absolute temperature.

205. PRECIPITATION AND HUMIDITY. Rainfall in the dry climates is always meager. In addition it is extremely variable from year to year so that the average is not to be depended upon (Fig. 79). It is a general rule, worthy of memorization, that dependability of precipitation usually decreases with decreasing amount. Two handicaps, therefore, (a) meagerness and (b) unreliability of rainfall, seem to go together. No part of the earth, so far as is known, is absolutely rainless, although at Arica, in northern Chile, the average yearly rainfall over a period of 17 years was only 0.02 in. During the whole 17 years there were only three showers heavy enough to be measured.

Relative humidity is (with a few exceptions) low in the dry climates, 12 to 30 per cent being usual for midday hours. Conversely, evaporation is extremely high. Absolute humidity, on the other hand, is by no means always low, for hot desert air usually contains a considerable quantity of water vapor, even though it may be far from being saturated. The amount of sunshine is great, and cloudiness small. Direct as well as reflected sunlight from the bare, light-colored earth is blinding in its intensity.

206. WINDS. Dry regions are inclined to be windy places, there being little friction of the moving air with the lowly and sparse vegetation cover. In this respect they are like the oceans. Moreover, the rapid daytime heating of the lower air over deserts leads to convectional overturning, this interchange of lower and upper air tending to accelerate the horizontal surface currents during warm hours when convection is at a maximum (99). "In the desert the wind is almost the only element of life and movement in the domain of death and immobility. A journey in the desert is a continuous strife against the wind charged with sand and, in moments of crisis, a painful physical struggle." (Gautier.) Nights are inclined to be much quieter. Because of the strong and persistent winds, desert air is often murky with fine dust which fills the eyes, nose, and throat, causing serious discomfort. Much of this dust is carried beyond the desert margins to form the loess deposits of bordering regions. The heavier, wind-driven rock particles, traveling close to the surface, are the principal tool of the wind in sculpturing desert landforms.

In the classification of climates here employed, two great divisions of dry climates, based upon temperature contrasts, are recognized: (a) the dry climates of the low latitudes, or the *hot* steppes and deserts; and (b) the dry climates of the middle latitudes, or the *cold* (in winter) steppes and deserts.[1] Not infrequently the low- and middle-latitude

[1] Köppen uses the mean annual isotherm of 64.4° (18°C.) as the boundary between the two principal latitudinal subdivisions of dry climates. For North America at least,

dry climates are continuous with each other, the latter occupying the far interiors of the middle-latitude continents, and the former the interiors and western (leeward) margins of land masses in the latitudes of the subtropical highs and where cool ocean currents parallel the coasts.

3. Low-latitude Dry Climates (*BWh* and *BSh*)[1]

207. LOCATION. The heart of the tropical dry climates (Fig. 69) is in the vicinity of latitudes 20 or 25°N. and S., with the average positions of their extreme margins at approximately $15\pm$ and $30\pm$. They are fairly coincident with the dry settling and warming tropical air masses of the subtropical highs. Subsidence and drought are by no means confined to the centers of the anticyclonic cells, for these same characteristics extend out onto the equatorward slopes of the highs into the trade winds. Ordinarily the dry climates do not extend to the eastern margins of the continents, humid climates characteristically taking their places on these more windward margins. Here the subtropical highs are less well developed and subsidence not conspicuous. Tropical hurricanes add to the rainfall of some of these east coasts. Along west coasts in these latitudes, on the other hand, dry climates extend down to the sea margins and even far beyond over the oceans (Plate II). Here to the drought-producing effects of strong anticyclonic control are added those of cool ocean currents which characteristically parallel tropical west coasts. These cool ocean currents tend to intensify the aridity and frequently cause steppe and desert conditions to be carried 5 to 10° farther equatorward than normal. It appears to be a general rule, then, that humid tropical climates extend unusually far poleward along the eastern (windward) sides of the continents (eastern Brazil, eastern Central America, eastern Madagascar), while dry climates are carried equatorward beyond their normal latitudes along the western littorals (western Peru, western Angola in southwestern Africa).

3a. LOW-LATITUDE DESERT (*BWh*)

208. The low-latitude deserts probably are the most nearly rainless regions on the earth. Next to the deserts of snow and ice on the polar ice caps, they are also the most hostile to life. Since they occupy regions of

---

the January isotherm of 32° is a much better boundary between the hot and the cold dry climates.

[1] In the Köppen symbols, W = desert (Wüste); S = steppe; h = hot (heiss), annual temperature over 64.4° (18°C.).

warm, dry, settling and diverging air currents, conditions are unfavorable to the development of convectional showers. This same divergence is opposed to the development of fronts and cyclonic storms. Too far equatorward to be reached by the greatest equatorward advance of middle-latitude fronts and cyclones on the poleward side, too far poleward to be affected by doldrum convection and fronts advancing from the low latitudes, and too far interior from eastern littorals to be affected by the onshore winds and the hurricanes, these low-latitude deserts are outside the realms of the usual rain-bringing winds and storms. Some of the extensive low-latitude deserts, particularly Sahara and the Australian desert, are important source regions for tropical continental air masses.

PRECIPITATION AND HUMIDITY

209. ANNUAL RAINFALL. Although no exact amount of rainfall can be accepted as defining the outer, or humid, margins of the hot deserts (202), the figure usually lies somewhere between 10 and 20 in. Over much of the Sahara precipitation is under 5 in., a condition true, as well, of large parts of the other low-latitude deserts, *viz.*, Kalahari in South Africa, Atacama-Peruvian desert in western South America, Australian desert, Thar in northwestern British India, and Sonora in northwestern Mexico and southwestern United States. At Cairo, Egypt, the annual rainfall averages 1.2; at Lima, Peru, 2; William Creek, Australia, 5.4; Yuma, Ariz., 3.3; and Port Nolloth in southwestern Africa, 2.3 in. In parts of northern Chile rain may not fall for 5 or 10 years in succession. However, averages are of little value in giving a correct impression of desert rainfall, for not only is it small in amount, but it is likewise erratic and uncertain in its time of fall. Over most of the low-latitude deserts the rainfall variability shows a 40+ per cent departure from the normal (Fig. 79). It is, therefore, almost impossible to speak of a *typical* rainfall curve, or an *average* annual rainfall, for desert stations. As an illustration: At Iquique in northern Chile, during a period of 4 years, no rain fell. Then on the fifth year one shower gave 0.6 in., which made the "average" annual rainfall for the 5-year period 0.12 in. On another occasion 2.5 in. of rain fell in a single shower.

210. DESERT DOWNPOURS. General, widespread rains are almost unknown over large parts of the hot deserts, most of the precipitation coming in violent convectional showers which cover no very extensive area. Seven single storms brought nearly one-quarter of the total rain (30.7 in.) that fell at Helwan in the Egyptian Sahara in the 20-year period 1904–1924. These sudden and heavy downpours may be disastrous in their effects, causing more damage than they do good. The wadies, entirely without water during most of the year, may become torrents of muddy water filled with much debris after one of these flooding rains. Settlements suffer; roads, bridges, and railways may be injured; and irrigation systems are often clogged with debris after a serious desert flood. Because of the violence of tropical desert rains and the sparseness of the vegetation cover, temporary local runoff is excessive, and consequently less of the total fall becomes effective for vegetation or for the crops of the oasis farmer. This "dash" character of hot-desert showers, plus their local nature and their erratic seasonal distribution, makes them of little direct use for agriculture, so that no immediate dependence is placed upon them as a source of water. Much of the precipitation that reaches the earth is quickly evaporated by the hot, dry, desert air, but some sinks in to replenish the underground water which appears at the surface in the form of springs or artesian flows. On the *poleward* margins of low-latitude deserts there are occasional widespread rains of a less violent nature. These are usually associated with the fronts of middle-latitude cyclones and are largely confined to the low-sun period.

211. CLOUDINESS AND SUNSHINE. Skies are prevailingly clear in the low-latitude deserts so that sunshine is abundant. In the Sonora desert of the United States and Mexico 75 ± per cent of the possible sunshine is experienced in winter, and 90 ± per cent in the other seasons. Over much of the Sahara December and January have a cloudiness of only 1/10, while from June to October it drops to about 1/30. The pitiless glare of sunlight in the tropical deserts is such an essential characteristic of their landscapes that the occasional dark or rainy day, being so unusual, is said to be depressing. Strong surface heating, due to the intense insolation and the nearly bare ground, must give rise to vigorous convectional currents, but the whole mass of air is too warm and has too low a relative humidity, to allow these rising air currents, except infrequently, to reach condensation level and produce "thunderheads." Dark cumulo-nimbus clouds do form occasionally, sometimes accompanied by thunder and lightning, but the streamers of rain that can be seen descending from them usually are evaporated in the arid atmosphere before they reach the earth. But even though the air may be *physiologically dry* and have unusual evaporating power there is usually a moderate amount of moisture in the atmosphere. Thus the air at Yuma, Ariz., contains nearly as much moisture in July, and double as much in January, as does that at Madison, Wis., in the same months although the relative humidity is only two-thirds to one-half as great in either season.

212. *Evaporation,* due to the high temperature and low relative humidity, is excessive, often being twenty or more times the precipitation. At Yuma the average evaporation during the hot months is 55 in., while the average rainfall during the same period is not quite 1 in. Relative humidities as low as 2 per cent, with temperatures of over 100°, have been recorded in the Egyptian Sahara. It was the excessively dry air which allowed the Egyptians to mummify their dead.

TEMPERATURE

213. ANNUAL AND DIURNAL TEMPERATURES. Annual ranges of temperature in the low-latitude deserts are larger than in any other type of climate within the tropics, 20 to 30° being usual (Fig. 80). Aswân, in the Sahara, has mean temperatures of 61° in January and 95° in July, resulting in an annual range of 34°. Such ranges, which even exceed those of some middle-latitude climates, reflect not only the clear skies, bare earth, and low humidity but also the higher latitudes of the deserts, and their somewhat greater extremes of insolation, as compared with most of the humid tropics. It should be emphasized that it is the excessive "summer" heat, rather than the "winter" cold, which leads to the marked differences between the seasons. Daily ranges average 25 to 45° and in rare instances even reach 60 or 70°. The same conditions that make for relatively large temperature differences between the extreme months are likewise conducive to

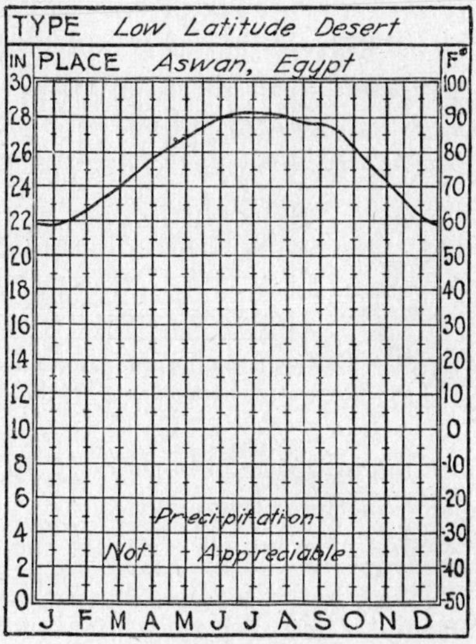

FIG. 80.—Average monthly temperatures at a representative station in a low-latitude desert.

wide differences within the 24 hr. On Dec. 25, 1878, at Bir Milrha, south of Tripoli in the Sahara, a minimum temperature of 31° and a maximum of 99° were recorded on the same day.

214. SEASONAL TEMPERATURES. During the high-sun period scorching, desiccating heat prevails. Hot-month temperatures average between 85 and 95° (Yuma 91°; Timbuktu 94.5°; Nullagine, Australia, 89.8°), and midday readings of 105 to 110° are common at this season. At Yuma, in 1914, the daily maxima exceeded 100° for 80 consecutive

days, except for one day (Fig. 81). At this time of the year, although
the lower night temperatures are a distinct relief by contrast with
the days, they are by no means cool. At Phoenix, Ariz., the midsummer
daily maxima usually exceed 100°, and the minima are close to 75 or
76°. At Azizia, 25 miles south of Tripoli, 136.4° has been recorded,
this being the highest air temperature in the shade ever registered under
standard conditions. The highest official air temperature ever recorded
in the United States is 134°, in Death Valley in the California
desert.

During the period of low sun the days still are warm, with the daily
maxima usually averaging 60 to 70° and occasionally reaching 80°
(Fig. 81). Nights are distinctly chilly at this season, with the average

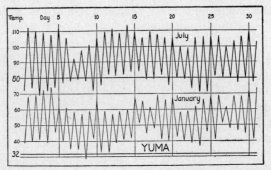

Fig. 81.—Daily maximum and minimum temperatures for the extreme months at a
representative station in a low-latitude desert. Compare with Figs. 71, 72.

minima in the neighborhood of 40° ±. Occasional light frosts are experienced in these tropical deserts.

Sun very much controls the weather in tropical deserts so that
succeeding days are very similar (see Fig. 81). On their poleward
margins there are occasional invasions of polar air with associated
fronts that bring "spells of weather" especially in winter. Figure 81
showing the daily march of temperature clearly reveals these non-
diurnal oscillations of the temperature belt.

CLIMATIC DATA FOR REPRESENTATIVE STATIONS IN LOW-LATITUDE DESERTS
Jacobabad, India

	J	F	M	A	M	J	J	A	S	O	N	D	Yr.	Range
Temp.	57	62	75	86	92	98	95	92	89	79	68	59	79	41
Precip.	0.3	0.3	0.3	0.2	0.1	0.2	1.0	1.1	0.3	0.0	0.1	0.1	4.0	

William Creek, Australia

	J	F	M	A	M	J	J	A	S	O	N	D	Yr.	Range
Temp.	83	83	76	67	59	54	52	56	62	70	77	81	68	30.5
Precip.	0.5	0.4	0.8	0.4	0.4	0.7	0.3	0.3	0.4	0.3	0.4	0.3	5.4	

The Cool Western Littorals (BWn)[1]

215. TEMPERATURE. The usual characteristics of tropical deserts —high temperatures, low relative humidity, and little cloud—are modified to a considerable degree along the littorals (usually western) of several of the low-latitude deserts, where cool ocean currents parallel the coasts (Fig. 82). The presence of cool currents is especially marked along the desert coasts of Peru and northern Chile and the Kalahari in southwestern Africa, but their influence is also felt along the Atlantic coasts of the Moroccan Sahara, Somaliland in eastern Africa, northwestern Mexico, and a number of other places as well. The land margins adjacent to the cool waters are themselves unusually cool, with temperatures 10° or more lower than normal for the latitude. Thus Callao, on the Peruvian coast, has an annual temperature of only

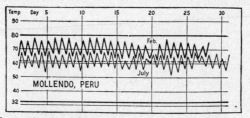

FIG. 82.—Daily maximum and minimum temperatures for the extreme months at a coastal station in a low-latitude desert paralleled by a cool ocean current. Note the relatively low temperatures and the small daily ranges. (*Courtesy of Mark Jefferson and the Geographical Review.*)

67°, and Mollendo 65°, while Bahia on the east coast of Brazil, in a similar latitude, averages 77°. The hottest month at Callao is only 71° (similar to July at Madison, Wis.), while the coldest is 62.5°. This annual range of only 8.5° is extraordinarily small for a desert, but it needs to be emphasized that it is principally the result of the unusually cool summer.

216. PRECIPITATION AND FOG. Rainfall along these cool coasts is extremely low (2.3 in. at Port Nolloth in southwestern Africa, 1.18 in. at Callao), and the drought conditions may extend to within a few degrees of the equator. As the cool ocean air drifts in over the warmer land its temperature is markedly increased, and its relative humidity lowered, so that precipitation is made less likely (see data, p. 186). Peculiarly enough, however, in spite of the fact that precipitation is very low, fog and even mist are characteristic phenomena over the cool ocean current and the adjacent land margins. The foggiest belt is several miles offshore, and the condition is brought to the land by

[1] In the Köppen symbol n = frequent mist and fog (*Nebel*).

winds from the sea. As the cool, foggy air moves in over the warmer land, the fog is quickly evaporated and rarely extends far inland. At Swakopmund (Southwest Africa) fog is recorded on 150 days in the year. Sea breezes along these coasts, intensified by the cool ocean water offshore, are extraordinarily strong.

In Peru the heavy fog, or "wet mist," is sufficient to make for a meager showing of vegetation on the coastal hills. Darwin, in his book "The Voyage of the Beagle," describes these Peruvian mists as follows:

"A dull heavy bank of clouds constantly hung over the land, so that during the first sixteen days I had only one view of the Cordillera behind Lima. It is almost become a proverb that rain never falls in the lower part of Peru. Yet this can hardly be considered correct; for during almost every day of our visit there was a thick drizzling mist which was sufficient to make the streets muddy and one's clothes damp; this the people are pleased to call 'Peruvian dew.'"

CLIMATIC DATA FOR A REPRESENTATIVE DESERT STATION ON A COOL-WATER COAST

Lima, Peru

	J	F	M	A	M	J	J	A	S	O	N	D	Yr.	Range
Temp.	71	73	73	70	66	62	61	61	61	62	66	70	66	12.8
Precip.	0.0	0.0	0.0	0.0	0.0	0.2	0.3	0.5	0.5	0.1	0.0	0.0	1.8	

3b. LOW-LATITUDE STEPPE (BSh)

217. LOCATION.   It is again necessary to emphasize the fact that low-latitude steppe climates characteristically surround the low-latitude deserts, except possibly on their western sides (Fig. 69), and are, therefore, transition belts between them and the humid climates both to the north and to the south. Because they are less at the heart, and more on the margins of the dry, settling tropical air masses associated with subtropical highs and trades, and are, therefore, one step closer to the humid climates than are the deserts, the steppe lands are encroached upon for a short period of the year by rain-bearing winds and their associated storms. It is this brief period of seasonal rains which causes them, although still a dry climate, to be semiarid rather than arid.

PRECIPITATION AND HUMIDITY

218. PRECIPITATION MEAGER AND ERRATIC.   Rainfall in the steppes, like that in the deserts, is not only meager but also variable and undependable (Fig. 79). This characteristic is perhaps even more dangerous in the semiarid than in the arid lands, for in the latter precipitation is never enough to tempt settlers to make agricultural conquest other than at oases, while occasional humid years in the

steppe may be sufficiently wet to lure inexperienced persons to attempt it. But humid years are invariably followed by dry ones, and with these comes disaster to settlers who have ventured too far beyond the safety line. Only where irrigation water supplements the normal rainfall is agriculture safe, so that the grazing of animals becomes a more widespread form of land use.

219. *Steppes with Low-sun Rainfall.*[1] Those belts of steppe lying on the poleward sides of tropical deserts, and usually in fairly close proximity to Mediterranean climate, have nearly all their rain in the cool seasons. Like the Mediterranean climates on whose margins they lie, they receive their rain from fronts associated with middle-latitude cyclones which because of sun migration characteristically travel more equatorward routes in winter than in summer. During most of the year, however, these steppes are dominated by dry settling air masses associated with the subtropical anticyclones. Because rainfall is concentrated in the cool season, evaporation is less, and consequently the small amount that falls is relatively effective for plant growth. Moreover variability is not so great as in those steppes having a high-sun rainfall maximum. In steppe lands with a low-sun rainfall *spells of weather* associated with the air masses and fronts of passing cyclonic storms are not unusual in the winter season. Not only cloud and rainfall, but changes in temperature as well, are involved. In spite of winter being the rainiest season, it is nevertheless prevailingly sunny, the precipitation coming in showers of rather short duration. Occasional gray, overcast days with rain do occur, however.

CLIMATIC DATA FOR A REPRESENTATIVE LOW-LATITUDE STEPPE STATION
WITH LOW-SUN RAINFALL
Bengasi, Tripoli

	J	F	M	A	M	J	J	A	S	O	N	D	Yr.	Range
Temp.	55	57	63	66	72	75	78	79	78	75	66	59	69	24
Precip.	3.7	1.8	0.7	0.1	0.1	0.0	0.0	0.0	0.1	0.3	2.1	3.1	11.9	

220. *Steppes with High-sun Rainfall.*[2] Those tropical steppe lands lying on the equatorward margins of the deserts, and therefore between them and the savannas, are likely to have a very brief period of relatively heavy rains at the time of high sun, when the unstable equatorial air masses are farthest poleward. Rainfall periodicity is like that of the savannas except that the dry season is longer and the total precipitation less. Since the rainfall arrives in the hot season less of it is effective for vegetation, and consequently these steppes bordering the savannas usually are characterized by a greater total rainfall than are their poleward counterparts described above (219). Rainfall variability is also greater. Temperatures are not greatly different from those of the adjacent desert.

[1] Köppen subtype *BShs*, in which *s* stands for summer drought.
[2] Köppen subtype *BShw*, in which *w* stands for winter drought.

CLIMATIC DATA FOR A REPRESENTATIVE LOW-LATITUDE STEPPE STATION
WITH HIGH-SUN RAINFALL
Kayes, French West Africa

	J	F	M	A	M	J	J	A	S	O	N	D	Yr.	Range
Temp.	77	81	89	94	96	91	84	82	82	85	83	77	85	19.2
Precip.	0.0	0.0	0.0	0.0	0.6	3.9	8.3	8.3	5.6	1.9	0.3	0.2	29.1	

4. Middle-latitude Dry Climates (*BWk* and *BSk*)[1]

221. LOCATION. The middle-latitude steppes and deserts are not primarily the result of location within particular wind belts or along cool-water coasts, as are those of low latitudes. Dry climates in the middle latitudes usually are found in the deep interiors of the great continents, far from the oceans, which are the principal sources of the atmosphere's water vapor (Fig. 69, Plate V). Asia, the greatest land mass in middle latitudes, has the largest area of dry climates, and North America is next in order. Further intensifying the aridity of these deep interiors is the fact that they are largely surrounded by mountain barriers that block the entrance of humid maritime air masses. Where high mountains closely parallel a coast as in western North America, arid climates approach close to the sea.

Although tropical deserts characteristically extend down to the ocean margins on the leeward (western) sides of continents, the leeward (eastern) sides of land masses in the westerlies are far from dry. Witness, for example, eastern North America and Asia. This shifting of middle-latitude dry climates interior from the leeward coasts is associated with the presence of monsoons and cyclonic storms along the eastern sides of land masses in the westerlies. Owing to an unusual combination of circumstances, dry climates do reach the east coast in Patagonia (Argentina), but this is the exception. There the land mass is so narrow that all of it lies in the rain shadow of the Andes, where descending currents make for drought conditions. This same small land mass precludes monsoon development. The cool Falkland Current lying offshore likewise induces aridity, while the principal frontal zones are to the north and south of the area in question. Moreover, those storms that do cross the high Andes temporarily are so disrupted that they are unable to bring much rain to the Patagonian uplands. With the exception of South America, none of the other Southern Hemisphere continents extends into sufficiently high latitudes to permit the development of very extensive middle-latitude steppes and deserts.

[1] In the Köppen symbol k = cold (*kalt*): average annual temperature below 64.4° (18°C.).

222. TEMPERATURE. Although dry continental climates of middle latitudes duplicate the arid and semiarid climates of the tropics in their meager and undependable rainfall, they differ from them in having a season of severe cold, which is of course absent in the low latitudes (Fig. 83). On the other hand, they are like the *humid* continental climates of comparable latitudes in their temperature and weather characteristics, but they are unlike them in that they receive less rainfall.

The interior locations of most middle-latitude dry climates assure them of having relatively severe seasonal temperatures and consequently large annual ranges. Because they have such a wide latitudinal spread (15 or 20° in both North America and Asia) it is difficult to speak of *typical* temperature conditions, for they are very different on their equatorward and poleward margins. Yet for any given latitude temperatures are severe. Summers are inclined to be warm or even hot, and winters are correspondingly cold. Tehran, Iran, at 36°N. ranges from 34° in January to 85° in July, whereas for Urga, Mongolia, at 48°N. the comparable figures are −16 and 63°. Diurnal ranges are inclined to be large and for the same reasons as noted in the discussion on tropical steppes and deserts (Figs. 83, 84).

223. PRECIPITATION. Locational reasons for the aridity of middle-latitude dry climates have been given in Art. 221. An additional reason for winter drought in these regions is the well-developed winter anticyclones that cover all but their subtropical margins. In winter, therefore, they become source regions for dry, cold, continental air masses. Unlike the dry climates of the tropics, those of middle latitudes receive a portion of their precipitation in the form of snow, although the amount is characteristically small, and the winter snow cover is not deep.

Seasonal Distribution. It is not easy to generalize concerning seasonal distribution of precipitation in the dry climates of middle latitudes. In the more interior and continental locations, however, summer is usually the period of maximum precipitation (see data for Urga and Williston). This is related to the higher temperatures, greater absolute humidity, and inblowing system of monsoonal winds in summer. Most of interior Asia, and the Great Plains region of the United States, are dry lands with a distinct summer maximum in their precipitation curves. Urga, Mongolia, for example, receives 84 per cent of its 7.6 in. of rainfall in the three summer months.

On the other hand, those dry climates which occupy subtropical latitudes and lie on the interior margins of Mediterranean climate, are likely to have dry summers and wetter winters (see data for Fallon,

Nev., and Quetta, Baluchistan). This is the typical Mediterranean regime of rainfall and is particularly characteristic of west margins of continents in the lower middle latitudes. The dry lands of southwestern Asia—Anatolia, Iran, Mesopotamia—most perfectly represent this subtropical type with winter precipitation. In the Great Basin of the United States it is present in less ideal form (see climatic data, p. 191).

224. THE WEATHER ELEMENT. The weather element in middle-latitude dry climates is much stronger than it is in those of the tropics (Fig. 84). This is to be expected, because the middle latitudes are open to invasion by air masses from both the tropics and the polar regions, and cyclones and fronts are therefore better developed. Over larger parts of the middle-latitude dry climates, where the winter continental anticyclones are strong, weather of that season is inclined to be clear, cold, and relatively calm. The occasional passage of well-developed fronts may be accompanied by strong winds and snow. On the North American Plains this weather type is the famous blizzard. Low temperatures, high wind velocity, and blinding wind-driven snow make such storms dangerous to human beings as well as to livestock. Summers are hot and windy, but the irregular weather changes associated with cyclones and their fronts are less striking.

4a. MIDDLE-LATITUDE DESERTS (BWk)[1]

225. Because of their generally lower temperature, and therefore reduced evaporation rate, the humid boundaries of the middle-latitude deserts have lower rainfalls than those of tropical deserts. This does not mean that they are necessarily more arid. In fact the opposite is probably true, for some precipitation, no doubt, falls in middle-latitude deserts every year, so that they are not so completely rainless as are certain of their tropical counterparts. Characteristically, this subtype of the middle-latitude dry climates occupies the low-altitude basinlike areas in the continental interiors. Tarim, the Gobi, Dzungaria, Russian Turkistan, and central Iran are all of them surrounded, in part at least, by highland rims. Such is likewise the case with the principal desert area in the United States, where it practically coincides with the Great Basin. As a result, these are regions of rain shadow with descending currents, so that excessive aridity is developed. A further consequence of enclosure, when combined with low elevation, is the excessively high summer temperatures, with warm-month averages in some instances even approaching those of tropical deserts. At Lukchun, in the Turfan depression of Central Asia, the July average is 90°, while the daily maxima for that month often rise to 110° and

[1] See footnote on p. 188 for interpretation of symbol.

more, although this is an extreme case. At this same station, where 118° has been recorded, the January mean is only 13°.

Patagonia, in the Argentine, does not correspond in some respects to the description given above for middle-latitude deserts. Being a narrow land mass, with cool waters offshore, temperatures are more marine than continental, summer temperatures being unusually low. Winters are likewise mild, considering the latitude. Thus Santa Cruz at 50°S. has a January (hottest month) temperature of only 59°, while July is 35°.

CLIMATIC DATA FOR REPRESENTATIVE STATIONS IN MIDDLE-LATITUDE DESERTS

Santa Cruz, Argentina

	J	F	M	A	M	J	J	A	S	O	N	D	Yr.	Range
Temp.	59	58	55	48	41	35	35	38	44	49	53	56	47.5	24
Precip.	0.6	0.4	0.3	0.6	0.6	0.5	0.7	0.4	0.2	0.4	0.5	0.9	6.1	

Lukchun, Chinese Turkistan (−56 Ft.)

	J	F	M	A	M	J	J	A	S	O	N	D	Yr.	Range
Temp.	13	27	46	66	75	85	90	85	74	56	33	18	56	77
Precip.	No data.

Fallon, Nev. (3,965 Ft.)

	J	F	M	A	M	J	J	A	S	O	N	D	Yr.	Range
Temp.	31	36	41	50	56	65	74	72	61	51	40	32	50.6	42.7
Precip.	0.6	0.5	0.5	0.4	0.6	0.3	0.1	0.2	0.3	0.4	0.3	0.6	4.7	

4b. MIDDLE-LATITUDE STEPPES (BSk)

226. Middle-latitude steppes, like their counterparts the semiarid lands of the tropics, occupy transitional, or intermediate, positions between deserts and the humid climates (Figs. 83, 84). The general characteristics of these continental steppes have already been analyzed. Because of the greater precipitation than in deserts, the steppes are somewhat better fitted for human settlement, but this, together with the unreliable nature of the rainfall, also makes them regions of greater economic catastrophe (Figs. 79, 85). A succession of humid years may tempt settlers to push the agricultural frontier toward the desert, but here also drought years are sure to follow, with consequent crop failure and ensuing disaster. Over a considerable part of the American semiarid country, in 30 to 40 per

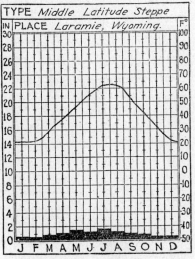

FIG. 83.—Average monthly temperatures and precipitation for a middle-latitude steppe station.

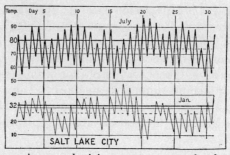

Fig. 84.—Daily maximum and minimum temperatures for the extreme months at a representative middle-latitude steppe station. (*Courtesy of Mark Jefferson and the Geographical Review.*)

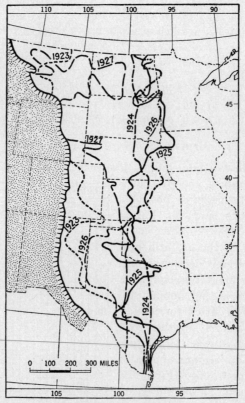

Fig. 85.—Fluctuations in the boundary separating dry and humid climates, over a period of five years, for the region between the Mississippi River and the Rocky Mountains. (*After H. M. Kendall.*)

cent of the years, rainfall is less than 85 per cent of the average. During the period 1871–1920, at Ogden, Utah, whose average annual precipitation is 15.2 in., there was one year with rainfall as high as 25 in. and another as low as 6.5.

A unique feature of the North American steppe lands east of the Rocky Mountains, from Alberta to Colorado, is the frequency and strength of chinook winds. Rapid changes in temperature over short periods of time and large variations in the mean winter temperatures of different years are the result.

CLIMATIC DATA FOR REPRESENTATIVE STATIONS IN MIDDLE-LATITUDE STEPPES

Williston, N. D.

	J	F	M	A	M	J	J	A	S	O	N	D	Yr.	Range
Temp.	6	8	22	43	53	63	69	67	56	44	27	14	39.2	62.7
Precip.	0.5	0.4	0.9	1.1	2.1	3.2	1.7	1.7	1.0	0.7	0.6	0.5	14.4	

Quetta, Baluchistan (5,500 Ft.)

	J	F	M	A	M	J	J	A	S	O	N	D	Yr.	Range
Temp.	40	41	51	60	67	74	78	75	67	56	47	42	58.1	38.2
Precip.	2.1	2.1	1.8	1.1	0.3	0.2	0.5	0.6	0.1	0.1	0.3	0.8	10.0	

Urga, Mongolia (3,800 Ft.)

	J	F	M	A	M	J	J	A	S	O	N	D	Yr.	Range
Temp.	−16	−4	13	34	48	58	63	59	48	30	8	−17	28	79
Precip.	0.0	0.1	0.0	0.0	0.3	1.7	2.6	2.1	0.5	0.1	0.1	0.1	7.6	

Chapter IX. The Humid
Mesothermal[1] Climates (C)

227. Lacking the constant heat of the tropics and the constant cold of the polar caps, middle-latitude climates are characterized by a very definite seasonal rhythm in temperature conditions. Thus temperature becomes coequal with rainfall in determining the various types of middle-latitude climates. In the tropics seasons are designated as wet and dry; in the middle latitudes they are called winter and summer, and the dormant season for plant growth is one of low temperatures rather than drought. In the intermediate zones the changeableness of the weather is a striking characteristic. This results from the fact that the middle latitudes are the natural region of conflict for contrasting air masses expelled from the tropical and polar source regions. Fronts are therefore numerous, and large numbers of cyclones and anticyclones travel across these intermediate latitudes. The science of weather forecasting is best developed and most useful in the intermediate zones where irregular and nonperiodic weather changes are the rule.

In general, the mesothermal climates lie either on the equatorward margins of the middle latitudes or else in marine locations farther poleward. Both of the subtropical types are intermediate in position and character between the tropical climates on their equatorward sides and the more severe ones interior and poleward. Only one of the three mesothermal climates, the marine west-coast type, extends into the higher middle latitudes, and this is possible because it characteristically lies along the windward sides of the continents where the westerlies bring oceanic conditions onshore (Fig. 69).

5. Mediterranean or Dry-summer Subtropical Climate (Cs)[2]

228. GENERAL FEATURES. In its simplest form this climate is characterized by three principal features: (a) a concentration of the

---

[1] Meso-, from Gr. *Mesos*, middle. Mesothermal, therefore, refers to "middle," or moderate, temperatures.

[2] In the Köppen symbol, s = dry season in summer of the respective hemisphere.

modest amount of precipitation in the winter season, summers being nearly or completely dry; (*b*) warm to hot summers and unusually mild winters; and (*c*) a high percentage of the possible sunshine for the year and especially in summer. Quite deservedly this climate with its bright, sunny weather, blue skies, few rainy days, and mild winters, and its usual association with abundant flowers and fruit, has acquired a glamorous reputation. It has the unique distinction of being the only one of the earth's humid climates having drought in summer with a strong rainfall maximum in winter. The Mediterranean type is strongly marked in its climatic characteristics, these being duplicated with notable similarity in the five regions where it occurs, *viz.*, the borderlands of the Mediterranean Sea, central and coastal southern California, central Chile, the southern tip of South Africa, and parts of southern Australia.

229. LOCATION. Mediterranean climates characteristically are located on the tropical margins of the middle latitudes (lats. 30–40°) along the western sides of continents. Lying thus on the poleward slopes of the subtropical highs, they are intermediate in location between the dry centers of those anticyclonic cells on the one hand, and the rain bringing fronts and cyclones of the westerlies on the other. With the north-south shifting of wind belts during the course of the year, these Mediterranean latitudes at one season are joined to the dry tropics, and at the other season to the humid middle latitudes. Tropical constancy, therefore, characterizes them in summer, and middle-latitude changeability in winter. Emphatically, this is a transition type between the low-latitude steppes and deserts and the cool, humid, marine west-coast climates farther poleward.

As previously stated, Mediterranean climates are usually confined to the western sides of continents, roughly between latitudes 30 and 40° (Fig. 69, Plate V). In both central Chile and California, mountains terminate the type abruptly on the land side, steppe and desert prevailing interior from the mountains. In South Africa and south-western Australia the farthest poleward extent of these continents carries them barely to Mediterranean latitudes, so that the dry-summer subtropical climates occupy southern and southwestern extremities rather than distinctly west-coast locations. Only in the region of the Mediterranean Basin, which is an important route of winter cyclones, does this type of climate extend far inland, perhaps for 2,000 miles or more, the extensive development there being responsible for the climate's name. It is the relative warmth of the Mediterranean Sea in winter, and the resulting low-pressure trough coincident with it, that makes the Mediterranean Basin a region of air-mass convergence with a resulting development of fronts and cyclones (Fig. 61). Interiors and eastern margins of continents, with their tendencies toward monsoon systems, are not conducive to the development of Mediterranean climates, more especially their characteristic rainfall regime.

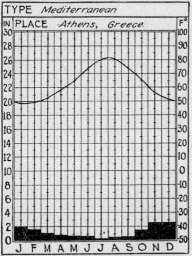

FIG. 86.—Average monthly temperatures and precipitation for a representative station with Mediterranean climate.

TEMPERATURE

230. MILD WINTERS. Both because of its latitudinal location and because of its characteristic position on the continents, Mediterranean climate is assured of a temperature regime in which cold weather is largely absent (Fig. 86). Usually the winter months have average temperatures of between 40 and 50°, and the summer months between 70 and 80°, so that mean annual ranges of 20 to 30°+ are common. These are relatively small for the middle latitudes but are larger than those of most tropical climates, except possibly the low-latitude steppes and deserts.

231. MARINE LOCATIONS (*Csb*).[1] Littoral locations are likely to have somewhat modified Mediterranean conditions. Summers are unusually cool, owing partly to the general marine location, but this condition many times is accentuated by the cool ocean currents offshore (Fig. 87; see data for Santa Monica, p. 199). Thus Mogador, on the Atlantic coast of Morocco, has a hot-month temperature of only 68.5°, while San Francisco records only 59.2°, and Valparaiso, Chile, 66°. Fogs are frequent, as they are along the desert coasts

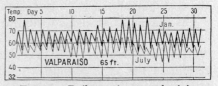

FIG. 87.—Daily maximum and minimum temperatures for the extreme months at a representative dry-summer subtropical station with coastal location in Chile (*Csb*). (*Courtesy of Mark Jefferson and the Geographical Review.*)

---

[1] In the Köppen symbols *Csb* and *Csa*, letter *b* indicates cool summers with the temperature of the warmest month under 71.6° (22°C.) but with at least 4 months over 50° (10°C.). The letter *a* indicates hot summers with the temperature of the warmest month over 71.6° (22°C.).

somewhat farther equatorward. Winters are unusually mild, frost being practically unknown. Thus the average cool-month temperature at Valparaiso, Chile, is 55°; Perth, Australia, 55°; and San Francisco 49.9°. In such marine locations the annual temperature range is uncommonly small, approximately 9° at San Francisco and 11° at Valparaiso. Daily ranges are likewise small (Fig. 88).

232. INTERIOR LOCATIONS (*Csa*).[1] Interior from the coast a short distance, however, Mediterranean climate has a more continental temperature regime (see data for Red Bluff, p. 199). Winters, of course, are still mild, for the latitude is distinctly subtropical, and in most regions mountains or bodies of water protect against severe importations of low temperatures from higher latitudes. Redlands, an interior station in California, has a January temperature of 50.9°, which is only slightly cooler than coastal stations in similar latitudes. Summers, however, are distinctly hotter than marine locations (July at Redlands 76.8°; Santa Monica, on the coast, 65.9°) so that annual ranges may be $15 \pm °$ greater.

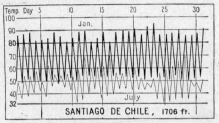

FIG. 88.—Daily maximum and minimum temperatures for the extreme months at a representative dry-summer subtropical station located interior from the coast in Chile (*Csa*). (*Courtesy of Mark Jefferson and the Geographical Review.*)

233. SUMMER TEMPERATURES. Except along coasts, summer temperatures in Mediterranean climates have many resemblances to those of tropical steppes and deserts slightly farther equatorward. Thus, Red Bluff in the Sacramento Valley has a July temperature of 81.5°, which is distinctly tropical in nature and approximately 16° higher than the July average at Santa Monica, Calif., farther south but situated on a cool-water coast. Stations in Mediterranean Europe have average hot-month temperatures approximating 75°; those of North Africa are in the neighborhood of 80°. Summer days, quite obviously, are likely to be excessively warm (Figs. 88, 89). On the other hand, they are not sultry, for relative humidity is low. Dry heat like that of the steppes and deserts is the rule, and oppressive, muggy weather is almost unknown. The averages of the daily maxima of cities in the Great Valley of California are usually between 85 and 95°+. Sacramento in 1931 had 27 days in July and 16 days in August with maxima over 90°; while the respective figures for Red Bluff were 30 and 30 days. Sacramento has recorded a temperature as high as

[1] For an interpretation of the Köppen symbols see footnote on p. 196.

114°, and Red Bluff 115°. The clear skies, dry atmosphere, and nearly vertical sun are ideal for rapid and strong diurnal heating.

However, these same conditions that give rise to high midday temperatures with a blazing sun are at the same time conducive to rapid nocturnal cooling, so that there is marked contrast between day and night. This feature is typical of most dry climates. At Sacramento, in the Great Valley, hot, clear, summer days, with afternoon temperatures of 85 to 95°, are followed by nights when the thermometer sinks to between 55 and 60°. The daily range for this same city in July, 1931, was 36.6°, a figure thoroughly characteristic of deserts. The relatively cool nights, following hot glaring days, are much appreciated by the inhabitants of Mediterranean climates (Figs. 88, 89). A light overcoat may feel distinctly comfortable when motoring on a summer

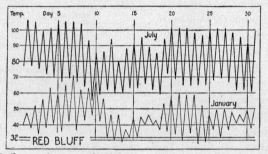

Fig. 89.—Daily maximum and minimum temperatures for the extreme months at a representative dry-summer subtropical station located interior from the coast in California (*Csa*).

night. One 24-hr. period is much like another in summer, for sun is in control.

234. WINTER TEMPERATURES. It is for the characteristically mild bright winters, with delightful living temperatures, that Mediterranean climates are justly famed. Peoples of the higher latitudes seek them out as winter playgrounds and health resorts. Even interior locations have average cold-month temperatures 10 to 20° above freezing. Thus Sacramento has an average January temperature of 46°, Marseille 43°, and Rome 44°. In southern California, in January, midday temperatures rise to between 55 and 65° and at night drop to 40° ± (Figs. 87, 88, 89).

The growing season is not quite the whole year, for frosts occasionally do occur during the three winter months. To say that the growing season is 9 ± months does not, however, adequately describe the situation, for while freezing temperatures are by no means unknown during mid-winter months, they occur on only relatively few nights, and rarely are they severe. During a period of 41 years at Los Angeles, there were 28 in which no killing frost occurred, or, in other words, the growing season was 12 months in length. In 1931 at Red Bluff, Calif., there were 10 nights, and at Sacramento 7, when the temperature dropped below 32°. The lowest temperature ever recorded at Los Angeles is 28°, at Napoli (Naples) 30°, and at Sacramento 19°. Even on the very occasional nights when temperatures do slip a few degrees below freezing, the following day sees them well above 32° again. Never does the thermometer stay below the freezing point for the

TEMPERATURES FOR SELECTED MEDITERRANEAN CITIES
(Kendrew)[1]

	Av. Annual Minimum	Absolute Minimum	Av. Annual Maximum	Absolute Maximum
Valencia	31	19	99	109
Napoli (Naples)	30	24	94	99
Athēnai (Athens)	29	20	100	105

entire day. Such frosts as do occur are usually the result of local surface cooling, following an importation of polar air, the low temperatures being confined to a shallow layer of surface atmosphere and particularly to depressions in which the cool dense air has collected. For this reason such sensitive crops as citrus are characteristically planted on slopes. Occasionally fires must be lighted among the citrus trees in order to prevent serious damage from freezing. Upon first thought it may seem odd that in Mediterranean climates, where frosts are neither frequent nor severe, unusual losses should result from low temperatures. But it is this infrequency and the small degree of frost that make it so treacherous, since the mild winters tempt farmers to grow types of crops, such as out-of-season vegetables and citrus, that are particularly sensitive to cold.

CLIMATIC DATA FOR REPRESENTATIVE MEDITERRANEAN STATIONS
Red Bluff, Calif. (Interior)

	J	F	M	A	M	J	J	A	S	O	N	D	Yr.	Range
Temp.	45	50	54	59	67	75	82	80	73	64	54	46	62.3	36.3
Precip.	4.6	3.9	3.2	1.7	1.1	0.5	0.0	0.1	0.8	1.3	2.9	4.3	24.3	

Santa Monica, Calif. (Coast)

	J	F	M	A	M	J	J	A	S	O	N	D	Yr.	Range
Temp.	53	53	55	58	60	63	66	66	65	62	58	55	59.5	13.6
Precip.	3.5	3.0	2.9	0.5	0.5	0.0	0.0	0.0	0.1	0.6	1.4	2.3	14.78	

Perth, Australia (Coast)

	J	F	M	A	M	J	J	A	S	O	N	D	Yr.	Range
Temp.	74	74	71	67	61	57	55	56	58	61	66	71	64	19
Precip.	0.3	0.5	0.7	1.6	4.9	6.9	6.5	5.7	3.3	2.1	0.8	0.6	33.9	

[1] "The Climates of the Continents." p. 246, University Press, Oxford, 1927.

PRECIPITATION

235. AMOUNT AND DISTRIBUTION. Rainfall is generally less than moderate, 15 to 25 in. being a fair average. More characteristic than the amount of rain, however, is its distribution over the year, for there is a pronounced maximum during the cooler months, summer being nearly, if not absolutely, dry (Fig. 86). If the relatively modest amount of rain typical of Mediterranean climate fell during the hot summers when evaporation is high, semiarid conditions would be the result. But coming as it does in the cooler seasons, much less is evaporated, and more, therefore, is available for vegetation. As a result, Mediterranean climate is more correctly described as subhumid than as semiarid. The name *dry-summer subtropical* is useful, therefore, in distinguishing this climate from its wetter counterpart, the *humid subtropical* climate located on the eastern sides of continents in similar latitudes.

Seventy-eight per cent of Los Angeles' precipitation falls during the period December to March inclusive, and less than 2 per cent during June to September inclusive. The rainfall regime, therefore, is alternately that of the deserts in summer and of the cyclonic westerlies in winter when rain is relatively abundant. This seasonal alternation of drought and rain results from a latitudinal shifting of wind and rain belts with the sun's rays, poleward in summer, bringing Mediterranean latitudes under the influence of drought-producing controls (subsiding air in the subtropical highs, or onshore winds from over cool ocean currents), and equatorward in winter when the westerlies with their rain-bringing cyclones prevail. Rainfall therefore is chiefly of frontal origin.

Lying as they do between steppe and desert on their equatorward sides and the rainy marine west-coast climate farther poleward, Mediterranean climates show a gradual increase in rainfall from their equatorward to their poleward margins. This is well illustrated by three California cities, arranged in order from south to north. San Diego, farthest south, has only 9.6 in. of rain, Los Angeles 15.6 in., and San Francisco 23.3 in. Precipitation also tends to increase from the interiors toward the coasts, except where elevations may modify the rule. A snow cover is absent at low elevations, and even snowfall is rare. Over Mediterranean central and southern California (excluding the mountains) annual snowfall averages less than 1 in., and there is none at all along the coast from San Luis Obispo southward. In all Mediterranean regions snow is so rare that it is a matter for comment when it does fall.

236. WINTER RAINFALL AND CLOUDINESS. But although winter is the rainy season, it is by no means dismal and gloomy as are the west-coast regions farther poleward at that season. Since Mediterranean latitudes usually are on the equatorward sides of the storm centers, and far removed from most of them, they experience a less persistent cloud cover, and sunshine is abundant even in winter. To be sure, winters are considerably cloudier than summers, but still they are bright and sunny. In interior Mediterranean California, mid-summer months have over 90 per cent of the possible sunshine, but in winter this is reduced to 50 per cent or less, although farther south in the vicinity of Los Angeles it reaches 60 to 70+ per cent. Dull gray days with persistent long-continued rain are by no means rare, but showery conditions with a broken sky are more common. After the rain the sun seems to shine more brilliantly than ever in the washed and dust-free atmosphere.

237. SUMMER DROUGHT AND SUNSHINE. Summers in the dry-summer subtropics are periods of brilliant sunshine, extremely meager precipitation, nearly cloudless skies, and desertlike relative humidity. Thus Sacramento has no rain at all in July and August, and in those months the percentage of the possible sunshine received is 95 and 96 respectively. Afternoon relative humidity is in the neighborhood of only 30 to 40 per cent. Los Angeles has, on the average, only one rainy day during the three summer months; San Bernardino has two; and Red Bluff three. The low rainfall, dry heat, abundant sunshine, and excessive evaporation, characteristic of interior Mediterranean summers, are ideal for out-of-doors drying of fruits on a large scale. In spite of the summer heat thunderstorms are rare, except possibly in the mountains or hills, two to four a year being the usual number in southern California. The dry settling air of these regions in summer or the onshore winds from over cool ocean currents are scarcely conducive to the formation of cumulus clouds.

Coastal regions, especially if paralleled by cool ocean currents, are characterized by high relative humidity and much fog. Rarely does it remain foggy for the entire day, the mists usually being burned off by the ascending sun after 9:00 or 10:00 A.M. Nights, however, may be damp and unpleasant. The coast of California is one of the foggiest areas in the United States, parts of the littoral having 40+ days with dense fog per year. These coastal sections with their cool, humid, and less sunny summers are really a subtype of general Mediterranean climate.

238. DEPENDABILITY OF PRECIPITATION. Like most subhumid climates, this one suffers from a rainfall that is none too reliable,

although it fluctuates less than a summer-maximum regime having the same amount (Fig. 79). At San Bernardino, Calif., where the annual rainfall averages 16.06 in., during a 48-year period it has been as low as 5.46 and as high as 37.08. In 5 of the 48 years it has been below 10 in. The somewhat precarious, as well as subhumid, character of the precipitation compels a relatively great dependence upon irrigation.

SEASONAL WEATHER

239. SUMMER. Daily weather is less fickle in the subtropical climates than it is farther poleward, where moving cyclones and anticyclones are more numerous and better developed. A typical *summer* day in the Mediterranean type is almost a replica of one in a low-latitude desert. Moreover, one day is much like another. Drought, brilliant sunshine, low relative humidity, high daytime temperatures, and marked nocturnal cooling are repeated day after day with only minor variations. Along seacoasts, and for a short distance inland, the daily sea breeze is often a marked phenomenon, greatly meliorating the desert heat. Regions with Mediterranean climates are famous for their well-developed sea breezes, the cool water offshore and the excessive heating of the dry land under intense insolation providing ideal conditions for strong daytime indrafts of air.

In *autumn* winds become less regular and uniform. As the cyclonic belt creeps equatorward, following the sun's rays, an occasional low with its associated cloud cover and rain makes itself felt. The dry and dusty land begins to assume new life under the influence of increasing precipitation. Temperatures are still relatively high. As sun control loses something of its summer dominance, daily weather becomes more uncertain, and "spells of weather" become more frequent.

Winter witnesses an increase in the frequency and strength of cyclones, and it is in that season that irregular, nonperiodic weather changes are most marked. Rainy days, brought by lows the centers of which are often well poleward from Mediterranean latitudes, are sandwiched in between delightfully sunny ones, in which the days are comfortably mild, even though the nights may be chilly with occasional frosts.

Spring is a delightful season of the Mediterranean year: fresh and yet warm. On the whole it is cooler than autumn. This is the harvest period for many grains. Passing cyclones gradually become fewer as summer approaches, but nonperiodic weather changes are still significant.

6. Humid Subtropical Climate (*Cfa, Cwa*)[1]

240. Three principal differences distinguish the humid subtropical from the dry-summer subtropical climates: (*a*) The former is characteristically located on the eastern rather than on the western sides of continents; (*b*) it has a more abundant precipitation; and (*c*) this precipitation is either well distributed throughout the year or else concentrated in the warm season. Even where the warm-season maximum is not emphatic, summer is still humid and usually has adequate rainfall for crops.

241. LOCATION. In latitudinal position the two subtropical climates are similar, both of them being on the equatorward margins of the intermediate zones but with the wet phase extending somewhat farther equatorward. Characteristically it extends from latitude $25° \pm$, poleward to 35 or 40° (Fig. 69, Plate V).

Since they are in similar latitudes, one might reasonably expect these two subtropical climates to experience a similar rainfall regime. It is chiefly the tendency toward a monsoon system of winds on the more continental leeward sides of middle-latitude land masses that there interferes with a normal latitudinal shifting of wind and storm belts, such as takes place along subtropical western littorals. The western, or windward, side of a continent in middle latitudes is too marine in character to create a genuine monsoon. Where land masses are large, and consequently seasonal differences in temperature comparatively great, as in Asia and North America, monsoon tendencies are relatively well developed. The stronger the monsoon tendency the greater the concentration of precipitation in the warm season.

Since warm ocean currents parallel the subtropical *eastern* coasts, while cool waters are more common along *western* littorals in similar latitudes, there is additional reason for the former having more abundant rainfall, especially in summer.

Lying as they do on the equatorward margins of the middle latitudes, and just beyond the poleward margins of the tropics, the humid subtropical, like the dry-summer subtropical, climate is a transitional type. But here the similarity in location ends, for while Mediterranean climate is characteristically bordered by low-latitude steppe and desert on its equatorward side, humid subtropical climate is terminated by humid tropical types, *viz.*, savanna and tropical rainforest. This contrast has a marked effect upon the kinds of importations from

---

[1] In the Köppen symbols, f = humid throughout the year; w = dry season in winter of the respective hemisphere; and a = temperature of warmest month over 71.6° (22°C.).

the low latitudes in the two types, parching dry heat accompanied by dust in. the one case, and humid sultry heat in the other. On their poleward sides they likewise make contact with contrasting types, for while Mediterranean generally merges into the mild rainy marine west-coast climate, humid subtropical not infrequently makes contact with severe continental climate. This is particularly true of North America and Asia, where there are extensive land masses in the higher middle latitudes. On their landward or western margins humid subtropical climates gradually merge into dry types characteristic of the continental interiors (Fig. 69).

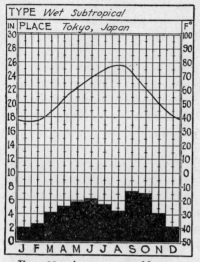

FIG. 90.—Average monthly temperatures and precipitation for a representative station in the humid, or wet, subtropics.

TEMPERATURE

242. TEMPERATURES LIKE THOSE OF THE MEDITERRANEAN TYPE. In temperature characteristics the humid subtropics are similar to Mediterranean climate but there is somewhat less contrast between coastal and interior locations (Fig. 90). This similarity is not unexpected since the two types roughly correspond in their latitudinal locations. Because warm, instead of cool, ocean currents wash the subtropical eastern coasts of continents, there can be no distinctly cool littorals such as are characteristic of some Mediterranean coasts. Cool, foggy stations, like San Francisco or Mogador, are absent.

243. SUMMER. Average hot-month temperatures of 75 to 80° are characteristic. Along the immediate coasts, especially of the smaller Southern Hemisphere land masses, they are as often below as above 75°. But everywhere summers are distinctly warm to hot, and this is particularly true of North America and Asia. Thus hot-month temperatures average 81.6° at Charleston, S. C.; 80.4° at Shanghai, China; 77.1° at Brisbane, Australia; 76.6° at Durban, South Africa; and 73.6° at Buenos Aires, Argentina.

Not only the air temperature, but also the absolute and relative humidity are high. The high humidity in conjunction with the high temperatures produces a sultry, oppressive condition with low cooling power. Sensible temperatures, therefore, are commonly higher in the humid- than the dry-summer subtropics, even when the thermometer registers the same. Summer heat in the American Gulf States, where Tropical Gulf air prevails, closely resembles that of the tropical rain-forest climate. At New Orleans during June, July, and August the average temperatures are 2 to 3° higher than they are at Belém in the Amazon Valley, while the amount of rainfall is nearly the same. In

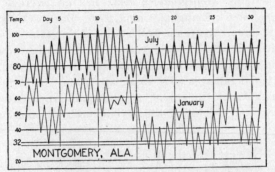

FIG. 91.—Daily maximum and minimum temperatures for the extreme months at a representative humid subtropical station. Note the greater irregularity in winter, the season of maximum storm control.

the humid subtropics of Japan and China Europeans and Americans frequently quit their usual places of residence during summer and go to high-altitude stations as they do in the genuine tropics. The average of the daily maxima in July throughout most of the American cotton belt is between 90 and 100°, while the highest temperatures ever observed are usually between 100 and 110° (Figs. 91, 92, 93).

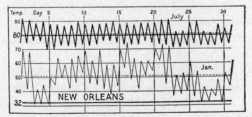

FIG. 92.—Daily maximum and minimum temperatures for the extreme months at a representative station in the humid subtropics. Note the greater irregularity in winter. (*Courtesy of Mark Jefferson and the Geographical Review.*)

244. *Night Temperatures.* Not only are the days hot and sultry, but the nights are oppressive as well, the humid atmosphere with more cloud preventing the same rapid loss of heat that takes place in the drier air and clearer skies of Mediterranean climates. The sultry nights are an additional item of resemblance to the wet tropics. The slower night cooling results in relatively small diurnal ranges, usually only one-half to two-thirds as great as those in the dry-summer sub-tropics (compare Fig. 89 with Figs. 91 and 92). Since the sun is very much in control of the daily weather, one day in summer is much like another in the humid subtropics.

245. WINTER. Winters are, of course, relatively mild in sub-tropical latitudes, cool-month temperatures usually averaging between 40 and 55°. Thus Montgomery, Ala., has an average cool-month temperature of 48.6°; Shanghai, China, 37.6°; Buenos Aires, Argentina, 50.2°; and Sydney, Australia, 52.3°. Annual ranges are usually small, although there is considerable variation, depending upon the size of the continent and the latitudinal location of the station. At Buenos Aires the annual range is only 23.4°, at Sydney 19.3°, but at Mont-gomery it is 33°, and it is 42.8° at Shanghai. Apparently the larger the land mass and the better the development of monsoon winds the

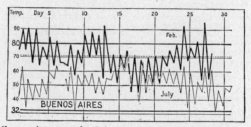

FIG. 93.—Daily maximum and minimum temperatures for the extreme months at a representative humid subtropical station in Argentina. (*Courtesy of Mark Jefferson and the Geographical Review.*)

colder are the winters and the larger the annual ranges. In eastern Asia the strong monsoonal outpouring of cold Polar Continental air in winter from the large land mass to the rear results in the lowest *average* winter temperatures in those latitudes for any part of the world.

The midday temperatures in winter are likely to be pleasantly warm, the thermometer usually rising to 55 or 60°. On winter nights temperatures of 35 to 45° are to be expected. These certainly are not low, but combined with a characteristically high humidity they are likely to produce a sensible temperature which is distinctly chilly and uncomfortable. Summer is so much the dominant season that little thought is given to the heating systems in homes, and as a result they are likely to be inefficient and ineffective. Consequently one is often more uncomfortable indoors than he is in colder regions farther pole-ward where adequate provision is made for winter heating.

246. *Minimum Temperatures and Frost.* It is to be expected that the growing season, or period between killing frosts, will be long. It is

usually at least seven months and from that up to nearly, if not quite, the entire year. Even though freezing temperatures may be *expected* during a period of several months, they actually occur on only a relatively few nights of the winter season. As in the Mediterranean climates, so too in these, the long growing season and infrequent severe frosts make them ideal regions for sensitive crops and for those

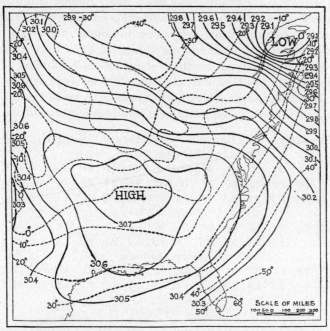

Fig. 94.—Weather controls giving rise to killing frosts in the American humid subtropics. A well-developed anticyclone advancing from the northwest as a mass of Polar Continental air produced minimum temperatures of 20° at New Orleans and 8° at Memphis. The isotherm of 20° fairly well parallels the Gulf and South Atlantic Coasts. (*U. S. Daily Weather Map, Feb. 9, 1933, 8 a. m., E.S.T.*)

requiring a long maturing period. In sections of the Southern Hemisphere humid subtropics frost does not occur every winter and usually is light when it does come. Thus the *average* lowest winter temperature at Brisbane, Australia, is 37.4°, and at Sydney 39.2°. The lowest temperature *ever recorded* at Buenos Aires is 23°; at Montevideo, Uruguay, 20.3°; and at Brisbane, Australia, 32°.

One of the distinguishing features of the South Atlantic and Gulf States of the United States, a region where the *average winter temperatures* are relatively high, is the unusually *low winter minima*, even lower than those of China. Thus while southeastern China has lower *average* winter temperatures, the American humid subtropics have severer *cold spells* and consequently lower minima. Severe killing frosts are of annual occurrence, and temperatures as low as 10° have been recorded along the ocean margins of all the Gulf States (Fig. 94). No other part of the world near sea level in these latitudes experiences such low winter minima. This is due to the open nature of the North American continent east of the Rocky Mountains which permits the surges of cold Polar Continental air to move rapidly southward into subtropical latitudes. In the Mediterranean region of California, mountain barriers prevent such severe invasions of cold air, so that there the absolute minima are much higher. Thus while commercial citrus production extends north to about 38° in California, it is confined to regions south of latitude 30 or 31° in southeastern United States. In China the more hilly and mountainous surface configuration prevents such unrestricted latitudinal importations of cold air.

CLIMATIC DATA FOR REPRESENTATIVE HUMID SUBTROPICAL STATIONS

Charleston, S. C.

	J	F	M	A	M	J	J	A	S	O	N	D	Yr.	Range
Temp.	50	52	58	65	73	79	82	81	77	68	58	51	66.1	31.4
Precip.	3.0	3.1	3.3	2.4	3.3	5.1	6.2	6.5	5.2	3.7	2.5	3.2	47.3	

Shanghai, China

	J	F	M	A	M	J	J	A	S	O	N	D	Yr.	Range
Temp.	38	39	46	56	66	73	80	80	73	63	52	42	49	42.8
Precip.	2.8	2.0	3.9	4.4	3.3	6.6	7.4	4.7	3.9	3.7	1.7	1.3	45.8	

Sydney, Australia

	J	F	M	A	M	J	J	A	S	O	N	D	Yr.	Range
Temp.	72	71	69	65	59	54	52	55	59	62	67	70	63	20
Precip.	3.6	4.4	4.9	5.4	5.1	4.8	5.0	3.0	2.9	2.9	2.8	2.8	47.7	

PRECIPITATION

247. AMOUNT AND DISTRIBUTION. Rainfall is relatively abundant (30 to 65 in.) within the humid subtropics, but still there are considerable differences within the several regions. On the landward frontiers of this type, where it makes contact with steppe climates, rainfall reaches the lowest totals. In general there is no marked drought season as there is in the dry-summer subtropics, although summer usually has more precipitation than winter. In the Southern Hemisphere where the monsoon tendency is weak the seasonal accent is less marked. China, having the best developed monsoons, with the fewest cyclonic interruptions in winter, likewise has the greatest rainfall contrasts between summer and winter.[1]

248. WARM-SEASON RAINFALL. A considerable part of the summer rainfall at low elevations originates in convectional storms,

[1] Parts of the Chinese humid subtropics have genuinely dry winters. These are Köppen's *Cw* areas.

many of them accompanied by thunder and lightning. In fact the American humid subtropics are the most thundery part of the United States, a large portion of that area having over 60 electrical storms a year, while a small part of Florida has over 90. These storms are mostly of local origin, resulting from strong surface heating of the potentially unstable Tropical Gulf air masses. The normal high temperatures and high humidity of the *Tg* air provide an ideal environment for vigorous development of local convection.

In addition to the thunderstorm rain, falling from cumulus clouds, a considerable part is also obtained from weak cyclonic storms and, in the late summer and early fall, from tropical hurricanes as well. In the weak shallow lows rain often falls steadily from gray overcast skies and is general over larger areas than is true of thunderstorm precipitation. Hurricane rainfall is largely confined to the American and Asiatic humid subtropics, giving parts of both those regions late-summer maxima in their precipitation curves. Not only are the heavy late-summer and early-autumn hurricane rains occasionally disastrous to ripening crops and the cause of serious floods, but the accompanying violent winds may play havoc with coastwise shipping and port cities. In the Swatow typhoon of August, 1922, 40,000 Chinese are estimated to have perished, chiefly by drowning.

In spite of the abundant summer rainfall characteristic of the humid subtropics, sunshine is relatively abundant, although much less so than is true of summers in Mediterranean climates. Montgomery, Ala., receives 73 per cent of the possible sunshine in June and 62 per cent in July.

249. COOL-SEASON RAINFALL. In winter the ground is cooler than the poleward moving tropical air masses so that the latter are chilled at the base and made more stable. As a consequence local convection is unlikely. Only as the tropical maritime air masses are forced to rise over relief barriers or over masses of cold air does precipitation usually occur. Winter rainfall over lowlands is chiefly frontal or cyclonic in origin. It is, therefore, usually associated with a general and persistent cloud cover extending over wide areas, from which precipitation may fall steadily during 12 to 36 hr. On the whole it is less violent, but of longer duration, than are the summer thundershowers. Because of the more numerous cyclones, winters are cloudier than summers. At Shanghai, China, in an average January, only 2 in. of rain falls, but there are 12 rainy days, whereas the 6 in. of August precipitation fall on only 11 days. Each rainy day in August, therefore, accounts for three times as much precipitation as a rainy day in January. Montgomery, Ala., which has 73 per cent of the possible sunshine in

June, receives only 49 per cent in January and 44 per cent in December. Gray overcast days with rain are unpleasantly chilly. Snow falls occasionally when a vigorous winter cyclone swings well equatorward, but it rarely stays on the ground for more than a day or two. On the northern margins of the American Gulf States snow falls on 5 to 15 days a year, and the ground may be covered for an equally long period.

SEASONAL WEATHER

250. Irregular nonperiodic weather changes are usually less marked in the humid subtropics than they are farther poleward, where the conflict between air masses is more marked and fronts more numerous. In *summer* when the frontal belt or storm belt is farthest poleward, and the sun is largely in control, irregular weather changes are at a minimum (Figs. 91, 92). Weak cyclones may bring some gray days with general widespread rains. Humid, sultry days with frequent thundershowers, each day much like the others, are the rule. The thermometer rises to about the same height each day and sinks to similar minima each night. *Late summer and fall* are the dreaded hurricane season, and, although these storms are not numerous, their severity more than makes up for their infrequency. Sunny, autumn days furnish delightful weather, although the equatorward advancing cyclonic belt gradually produces more gray cloudy days and unseasonable temperature importations as winter closes in. In *winter* the belt of fronts is farthest equatorward, so that irregular weather changes are most frequent and extreme at that time. The arrival of tropical air masses may push the day temperatures to well above 60 or even 70°, whereas the subsequent northwest winds of polar origin may reduce the temperature as much as 30° within 24 hr., resulting occasionally in severe freezes. Bright, sunny, winter days are distinctly pleasant and exhilarating out of doors. *Spring* again sees the retreat of the cyclonic belt and the gradual reestablishment of regular diurnal sun control.

7. Marine West-coast Climate (*Cfb*)[1]

251. LOCATION. These mild, marine climates characteristically occupy positions on the western or windward sides of middle-latitude continents, poleward from about 40°, where the onshore westerly winds import to them conditions from the oceans (Fig. 69, Plate V). In their general atmospheric characteristics, therefore, they are like the seas from which the imported air is arriving. Where land areas are relatively narrow, as, for instance, in the case of islands, such as

[1] See footnotes on pp. 196 and 203 for interpretation of individual letters in the Köppen symbol.

Tasmania, New Zealand, and Great Britain, or where the continent extends for only a short distance into the belt of westerlies, as do Australia and Africa, marine west-coast climate may not be limited to the western littoral. Distinct east-coast position on large continents is unlikely, however (in spite of the proximity of oceans), by reason of the severe temperatures resulting from leeward location and the monsoon wind systems with associated continental air masses.

On its equatorward margins this climate characteristically makes contact with the Mediterranean type. On its poleward side marine west-coast climate extends far into the higher middle latitudes, where it is eventually terminated by either the subarctic or the tundra type. The far poleward extension of this mild climate is the result of a prevalence of mild maritime air masses. Warm ocean currents, which parallel the west coasts of continents in middle latitudes, tend to accentuate the normal tempering effects of the ocean proper.

The depth to which the marine west-coast climates extend into the interiors of continents is determined largely by surface configuration. Where mountains closely parallel the west coasts, as in North and South America and Scandinavia, oceanic conditions are confined to relatively narrow strips of territory seaward from the highlands. But where extensive lowlands prevail, as in parts of western Europe, the

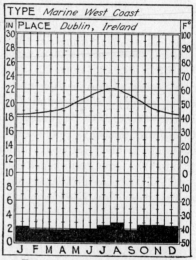

Fig. 95.—Average monthly temperatures and precipitation for a representative station in marine west-coast climate.

effects of the sea are carried well inland. On their land sides marine west-coast climates are characteristically bordered by severe continental types, either dry or humid.

Temperature

252. Summer. Although there are good and sufficient grounds for objecting to the use of the word "temperate" as applied to many middle-latitude climates, it is entirely suitable for the particular one under discussion (Fig. 95). Summers are moderately cool and, while more or less ideal for human efficiency and comfort, are somewhat too low for the best growth of many cereal crops. The characteristically cool

summer should be emphasized as one of the principal contrasts between
this third of the triumvirate of mild mesothermal climates, on
the one hand, and the two subtropical types, on the other. Seattle,
Wash., has a mean July temperature of only 64°; Dublin, Ireland,
60.1°, and Paris 65.5°. Night cooling is not rapid in these
humid, cloudy, marine climates, considerably less so than is characteristic of Mediterranean summers. The average of the daily minima in

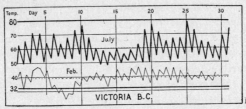

FIG. 96.—Daily maximum and minimum temperatures for the extreme months at a
representative marine west-coast station. (*Courtesy of Mark Jefferson and the Geographical Review.*)

July is only 54.6° at Seattle and 51.4° at Bellingham, Wash., while the
daily maxima are 73.1 and 71.6°, respectively, so that the normal
diurnal range is in the neighborhood of only 20° (Figs. 96, 97, 98).
Occasional hot days may occur when the effects of a tropical continental air mass are felt. Under such conditions both Seattle and
Bellingham have experienced a temperature as high as 96°, and Paris
100°. Severe and prolonged hot waves, however, are very few (see
temperature data, p. 215).

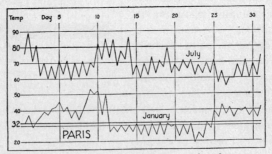

FIG. 97.—Daily maximum and minimum temperatures for the extreme months at a
representative marine west-coast station.

253. WINTER. Winters, on the whole, are more abnormally
mild for the latitude than the summers are cool. This is particularly
the case with western Europe, where a great mass of warm water,
known as the North Atlantic Drift, lies offshore. Thus the most
marine parts of western Europe are 20 to 30° too warm for their
latitudes in January. In winter isotherms tend to parallel these coasts

rather than follow the lines of latitude, indicating the dominance of land-and-water control. The decrease in temperature is much more rapid from the coast toward the interior than it is going poleward. Thus Paris is 7° colder in January than Brest, which is 310 miles nearer the ocean. January averages of 35 to 50° in western Europe are matched by others of 0 to −40° in the continental climates of interior Asia in similar latitudes.

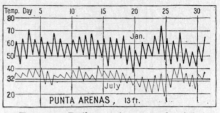

FIG. 98.—Daily maximum and minimum temperatures for the extreme months at a cool marine station in extreme southern Chile. The average temperature of the warmest month at Magallanes (Punta Arenas) is about 50°, but since its average annual temperature is above 32° it is scarcely genuine tundra. (*Courtesy of Mark Jefferson and the Geographical Review.*)

254. *Winter Minima and Frosts.* The average cold-month temperature at London is 39°; at Seattle, 40°; at Valentia, Ireland, 45°; and at Valdivia, Chile, 46°. Annual ranges are small: 14.7° at Valentia, 23° at London, 13.5° at Valdivia, and 24° at Seattle. For Seattle the average of the January daily minima is 35.4°, so that on a majority of nights frost is absent. At Paris frost occurs on about one-half of the nights in the three winter months, whereas in London the thermometer remains above the freezing point on more January nights than it goes below. At Seattle the thermometer has fallen as low as 3°, and at London to 9°. The prevailingly cloudy skies and humid atmosphere in winter tend to retard nocturnal cooling, thereby reducing the diurnal range of temperature (Figs. 96, 97, 98).

Frosts are more frequent, as well as more severe, and the frost-free season is shorter than in Mediterranean climates. Nevertheless the growing season is unusually long for the latitude, 180 to 210 days being characteristic of the American North Pacific Coast region. Seattle has only 4 months when temperatures below freezing are to be expected. However, winter is usually severe enough to produce a dormant season for plant life, which is not true for the dry-summer subtropics farther equatorward. During unusually cold spells temperatures may remain constantly below freezing for a period of several days. Midday temperatures of normal winter days are relatively high, however, the average of the daily maxima for January at Seattle being 44.5°, and the daily range less than 10°. On the whole, the day-to-day temperature changes are much less regular in winter than in summer, the former season being more completely controlled by the succession of cyclones and anticyclones.

255. Cold Spells. Unusual cold spells in these marine climates characteristically are caused by importations of cold polar continental air from the anticyclonic interiors. But such invasions of polar con-

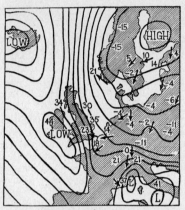

tinental air are infrequent for they are opposed to the general westerly air movement of the middle latitudes. The American North Pacific Coast is further protected against invasions of cold continental air by mountain barriers. Northeasterly, and not northwesterly, winds bring the coldest weather to the American North Pacific Coast and to western Europe (Fig. 99). During the unusual cold spell in Europe in February, 1929, the influence of the continental high persisted for several weeks. During that spell temperatures in eastern Kent, England, remained continuously below freezing for 226 hr., the Thames was frozen over in many parts, and practically the whole of

FIG. 99.—Weather controls suitable for producing severe cold in western Europe. Pressure gradient is from northeast to southwest so that Polar Continental air has spread over much of western and central Europe. (*After Kendrew.*)

the British Isles was frost-bound for 5 weeks (Kendrew). On the continent at this same time German coastal cities recorded temperatures below zero, while the Rhine was frozen throughout almost its entire course.

PRECIPITATION

256. AMOUNT. These are humid climates with adequate rainfall at all seasons (Fig. 95). The total amount, however, varies greatly from region to region, depending in a large measure upon the character of the relief. Where lowlands predominate, as they do in parts of western Europe, rainfall is only moderate, usually 20 to 40 in. But, on the other hand, where west coasts are elevated and bordered by mountain ranges, as is the case in Norway, Chile, and western North America, precipitation may be excessive, even reaching such totals as 100 to 150 in. Compensating for this contrast in amount is a further contrast in regional distribution, for where lowlands exist, moderate rainfall prevails well into the interior of the continent; but where coastal mountains intercept the rain-bearing winds, precipitation is confined pretty much to the littoral. East of the mountains drought conditions may prevail. There is no doubt that an *extensive* distribution of *moderate* rains is economically more desirable than the concentration of large and unusable quantities on a mountainous coast. Unfortunately, Europe is the only one of the three continents extending well

CLIMATIC DATA FOR REPRESENTATIVE MARINE WEST-COAST STATIONS

Valentia, Ireland

	J	F	M	A	M	J	J	A	S	O	N	D	Yr.	Range
Temp.	44	44	45	48	52	57	59	59	57	52	48	45	50.8	15
Precip.	5.5	5.2	4.5	3.7	3.2	3.2	3.8	4.8	4.1	5.6	5.5	6.6	55.6	

Seattle, Wash.

	J	F	M	A	M	J	J	A	S	O	N	D	Yr.	Range
Temp.	40	42	45	50	55	60	64	64	59	52	46	42	51.4	24
Precip.	4.9	3.8	3.1	2.4	1.8	1.3	0.6	0.7	1.7	2.8	4.8	5.5	33.4	

Paris, France

	J	F	M	A	M	J	J	A	S	O	N	D	Yr.	Range
Temp.	37	39	43	51	56	62	66	64	59	51	43	37	50.5	27
Precip.	1.5	1.2	1.6	1.7	2.1	2.3	2.2	2.2	2.0	2.3	1.8	1.7	22.6	

Hokitika, New Zealand

	J	F	M	A	M	J	J	A	S	O	N	D	Yr.	Range
Temp.	60	61	59	55	50	47	45	46	50	53	55	58	53	16
Precip.	9.8	7.3	9.7	9.2	9.8	9.7	9.0	9.4	9.2	11.8	10.6	10.6	116.1	

into the westerlies where the windward side of the land mass is freely open to the entrance of the rain-bearing winds. The precipitation of these marine west coasts has a high degree of reliability, and droughts are of rare occurrence.

257. ANNUAL DISTRIBUTION. With respect to annual distribution of precipitation, the thing to be emphasized is *adequate rainfall at all seasons*, rather than a particular season of marked deficiency. There is no dormant period for vegetation because of lack of rain. In some very marine locations winter may have slightly more precipitation than summer. This condition is most marked along the North American Pacific Coast (see data for Seattle) where cool, stable Polar Pacific air masses prevail throughout the summer, resulting in a greatly reduced rainfall at that season.

In spite of the fact that winter is characteristically a wet season, snowfall is not abundant, temperatures being too high on the lowlands for much snow. "Snow is sufficiently rare in most of northwest Europe to be a topic of conversation when it lies more than a few days. . . . " (Kendrew.) Paris has, on the average, 14 snowy days during the year; in the Puget Sound Lowland there are some 10 to 15 such days, and the duration of snow cover is approximately the same length. The snow that falls is wet and heavy, reflecting the relatively high winter temperatures. Upon the ground, it quickly turns to slush, making for unpleasant conditions underfoot. Where mountains border these west coasts, receiving abundant orographic and cyclonic winter precipitation, snowfall is extremely heavy. On the western slopes of the Cascade Range 300 to 400 in. of snow falls on the average each year. Snowfall is likewise heavy on the western slopes of the British Columbia Coast Ranges, the Scandinavian Highlands, the mountains of southern New Zealand, and the southern Andes. In each of these regions the mountain snowfields have in the past given rise to numerous valley glaciers, which in turn have been responsible for the characteristically irregular, fiorded coasts.

258. ORIGIN OF PRECIPITATION. Over lowlands precipitation is chiefly frontal or cyclonic in origin, falling as steady long-continued rain, often only drizzle, from a gray, leaden sky. It is in winter that these storms reach their maximum development, and it is at that time of year that cloudy, rainy days are most numerous. In spite of the fact that cyclones are weaker and less numerous in the warm seasons, because the absolute humidity is higher, and the entrance of lows into the continents is facilitated by lower pressures, summer rain may be nearly, if not quite, as great, although it falls in sharper showers on fewer days. Thus at London July has 13 rainy days with 2.4 in. of rain, whereas in January the respective figures are 15 and 1.9. Summers, therefore, are usually brighter and sunnier than winters. The cool marine air masses are not conducive to thunderstorm formation. The North American Pacific Coast records only two to four thunderstorms a year.

A distinguishing feature of the precipitation of these marine climates is the relatively small amount of rain that falls, considering the large number of cloudy, rainy days. Thus although Paris has only 22.6 in. of precipitation, it is spread out over 188 rainy days (average 0.12 in. for each rainy day). Seattle, with 33.4 in. of precipitation, has 151 rainy days; London has 24.5 in. and 164 rainy days; while Sumburgh Head, on the Shetland Islands, has 36.7 in. spread out over 260 rainy days. London has had 72 rainy days in succession. Where coasts are precipitous, abundant rains of direct or indirect orographic origin supplement those from cyclones and the few convectional storms.

259. CLOUDINESS AND SUNSHINE. Marine west-coast climate is one of the cloudiest climates of the earth. The American North Pacific Coast region has the highest cloudiness and least sunshine of any part of the United States, the mean annual cloudiness of that region being 60 to 70 per cent. Over wide areas of western Europe cloudiness is greater than 70 per cent, the sun sometimes being hidden for several weeks in succession. Winter, the season of maximum cyclones, is much darker and gloomier than summer. Seattle, which has only 22 per cent of the possible sunshine in November, and 21 per cent in December, has 65 per cent in July and 60 per cent in August,

so that summers there are relatively bright and pleasant. Valentia, Ireland, has only 17 per cent of the possible sunshine in December but in May 43 per cent. But even though summers are sunnier than winters, they are still much cloudier than those of Mediterranean climates. Fog and mist are characteristic weather elements of the marine west-coast climate. The American North Pacific Coast has over 40 days with dense fog during the year; Bergen, Norway, has 37.7; and Fanö, Denmark, 53.6.

SEASONAL WEATHER

260. NONPERIODIC WEATHER ELEMENT WELL DEVELOPED.   Since cyclonic storms are both numerous and vigorous, it is to be expected that the nonperiodic weather element will dominate. *Winter*, in spite of its mild temperatures, is a stormy period. In coastal locations gales are numerous as one storm follows another in rapid succession. The high seas generated by winter winds are strong enough to make navigation difficult, and unusually severe storms may do serious damage to shipping. The fog and mist make for poor visibility and add to the difficulties of navigation. Precipitation is relatively abundant and very frequent, most of it being in the form of rain rather than snow. Long periods of dark, gloomy, dripping weather are characteristic, so that winters are depressing and hard to endure. Between the frequent cyclones there are occasional sunny days with crisper weather, but these are the exception rather than the rule. Night frosts are not unusual, especially when skies are clear, but ordinarily they are not severe. A pushing westward of Polar Continental air masses now and then leads to a succession of clear days in which temperatures may remain continuously below freezing.

As the days lengthen with the advance of *spring*, cyclones become fewer and sunshine more abundant. The air is still cool, but the sun is warm, and in western Europe spring is acclaimed the most delightful season. *Summer* temperatures are pleasant for physical well-being, and where sunny days are numerous, as they are in the American Pacific Northwest, a more charming summer climate would be hard to find. More especially in the higher middle latitudes, or in very exposed marine locations, chilly, gray, overcast days are numerous even in summer. Rain is still relatively abundant, but it falls on fewer days than in winter. *Autumn* witnesses the equatorward swing of the storm belt again and, as a consequence, a rapid pickup in cloudiness and precipitation.

Chapter X. The Humid Microthermal[1] Climates (*D*)

261. LOCATION. Colder winters, longer frost seasons, and larger annual ranges of temperature distinguish the severe microthermal climates from the mesothermal types. This greater severity results primarily from locational differences, with respect to both (*a*) latitude and (*b*) positions on the continents, for microthermal climates lie poleward from the subtropical types and occupy more interior and leeward locations on the great land masses than does the marine west-coast climate (Fig. 69, Plate V). Emphatically, microthermal climates are land controlled and are, therefore, distinctly continental in their characteristics. It is because they are land controlled, being associated with large continents in higher middle latitudes, that they are confined exclusively to the Northern Hemisphere. Only Eurasia and North America are able to produce them. Of the Southern Hemisphere continents, South America alone extends sufficiently far poleward to permit of severe climates, but the narrowness of that land mass south of latitude 35° prevents genuinely severe conditions in spite of the latitude. Microthermal climates are excluded from the western, or windward, coasts because of the dominance there of maritime air masses. They occupy, instead, the interiors of land masses and commonly extend down to tidewater on their leeward or eastern sides, where, in spite of proximity to the sea, modified continental conditions likewise prevail. Unlike the mesothermal climates, those of the microthermal group differ substantially only in degree, and that chiefly in one element, temperature. For this reason the general aspects of microthermal climates as a group are discussed before the individual types of climate are analyzed.

262. TEMPERATURE. Because of wide latitudinal spread, there are marked temperature contrasts within those regions classed as microthermal. However, for any particular latitude, these climates

[1] Micro-, from Gr. *Mikros*, small. Microthermal, therefore, refers to "small," or low, temperatures.

are sure to have relatively severe seasons, so that annual ranges are large. Of the two extreme seasons, it is the winter cold, rather than the summer heat, which is most characteristic and distinctive. Nevertheless, summers are warm for the latitude. Not only are the seasons extreme, but they are likewise variable in temperature from one year to another. In marine climates, for instance, one winter is likely to be much like another, but wide departures from the normal seasonal temperature are characteristic of severe continental climates—in extreme instances as much as 30°.

263. *Effects of a Snow Cover upon Temperature.* Only in the microthermal, polar, and highland climates is the snow cover of sufficiently long duration to have a marked effect upon cool-season temperatures. Once a region is overlain by such a white snow mantle, the ground itself ceases to have much influence upon air temperature. Sunlight falling upon snow is largely reflected so that little of the solar energy is effective in heating the ground or the atmosphere. Moreover, although loss of energy by earth radiation goes on very rapidly from the top of a snow surface, the low conductivity of snow tends greatly to retard the flow of heat from the ground below to replace that which is being lost. Observations made at Leningrad, after a fall of 20 in. of loose, dry snow, showed a temperature of $-39°$ at the top of the snow surface, whereas the ground underneath recorded only 27°, a difference of 66°. Obviously, the effect of a snow cover is markedly to reduce winter temperatures. As spring advances it acts to retard the warming of the air, for the reason that much of the solar energy is expended in melting the snow and ice. On the other hand, the snow cover tends to keep the ground warmer and prevents deep freezing.

264. PRECIPITATION. Although winters are not without precipitation, summer is normally the season of maximum. This seasonal distribution is related to the following conditions: (a) The absolute humidity or reservoir of water vapor in the atmosphere is much less over the continents during the cold winter than it is in summer when temperatures are much higher. During winter the settling air in the continental seasonal anticyclone is likewise conducive to low absolute humidity. (b) These same continental anticyclones, which develop over the colder parts of the land masses in winter, are areas of diverging air currents, a condition that is antagonistic to the development of fronts and cyclones. In summer, although cyclones may be fewer and weaker, they can, nevertheless, penetrate deeper into the continents. This applies particularly to the more severe microthermal climates, such as the subarctic, where the winter anticyclone is best developed. (c) Convection is at a maximum during the warm summer months, and

it is convectional storms which bring most of the warm-season rain. (*d*) Consequent upon the seasonal extremes of temperatures, and hence of pressure, a tendency toward a monsoon system of winds is developed, which leads to a strong inflow of tropical maritime air with high rainfall potentialities in summer and to an outflow of dry, cold, Polar Continental air in winter. No such reversal of winds is experienced along marine west coasts in similar latitudes where seasonal temperature extremes are not well developed. In severe climates with short frost-free seasons it is highly important that rainfall be concentrated in the warm growing season.

Two principal types of climate are included within the microthermal group, *viz.*, (*a*) humid continental climate, including both long-summer and short-summer phases, and (*b*) subarctic climate. The first type, which is an important agricultural climate, characteristically lies on the equatorward margins of the subarctic type, the latter occupying such high latitudes that agriculture ceases to be of great importance.

8. Humid Continental Climates (*Dfa, Dfb, Dwa, Dwb*)[1]

265. *Location.* Depending upon the presence or absence of mountain barriers, marine climates of the west coasts change abruptly or gradually into the more severe continental climates of the interiors (Plate V). In North America, where mountain chains parallel the west coasts, the change is sudden and abrupt; on the west European lowlands, on the other hand, it is very gradual. A further contrast distinguishes the two great Northern Hemisphere continents as regards arrangement of climates. In North America, arid and semiarid conditions separate marine west coasts from the continental climates farther east. This results from the abrupt halting of the moisture-bearing winds from the west by mountain barriers, so that to the leeward of the highlands it is dry. A humid marine climate, therefore, passes over directly into a dry continental one. In Eurasia, on the other hand, where, except in Scandinavia, the absence of high mountains permits the deep entrance of marine air into the land mass, humid continental climate lies *both* to the east and to the west of the dry interior. Consequently this type is to be found both in central and eastern Europe, as well as in eastern Asia (Plate V).

In North America the humid continental climates lie poleward of latitude 35 or 40°. On their equatorward margins they pass over into

---

[1] The individual letters included in these symbols have been defined in footnotes in earlier chapters.

the humid subtropical type and on their poleward sides make contact with subarctic climate. This same arrangement is repeated in eastern Asia. In Europe, on the other hand, Mediterranean replaces humid subtropical climate on the southern frontier (Plate V).

TEMPERATURE

266. SEASONS SEVERE. Warm to hot summers and cold winters are characteristic of the humid continental climate, so that annual ranges are large (Figs. 100, 103). The monsoonal winds tend only to emphasize further the normal seasonal severity. In general the rigorousness of the climate increases from south to north and likewise from coasts toward the interior. Westerly winds and winter monsoons tend to carry continental air masses down to the eastern littorals, but there is some maritime air of cyclonic or summer-monsoon origin which acts to meliorate conditions slightly, with the result that east coasts have *modified* continental climates. For example, at New York City and Omaha, Neb., in similar latitudes, but the former on the Atlantic Seaboard and the latter deep in the interior, the July temperatures are 73.9 and 76.8° respectively, while their January temperatures are 30.9 and 21.8°. The annual range, consequently, is 43.0° at New York and 55.0° at Omaha. The higher atmospheric humidity of the air along the seaboard causes the summer heat to be more oppressive and sultry, and the winter cold more raw and penetrating, than are the drier extremes of the interior. The degree of marine modification is greatest where coasts are deeply indented, as, for example, in extreme eastern Canada.

267. SEASONAL GRADIENTS. Summer and winter in the continental climates present marked contrasts in latitudinal temperature gradients. In the warm season the few isotherms that cross eastern United States are spaced far apart so that one does not experience marked temperature changes in going from north to south, the rate of change being in the neighborhood of 1° for every degree of latitude, or approximately 70 miles. These same weak summer gradients are characteristic of eastern Asia. In winter, on the other hand, temperature changes very rapidly from north to south in eastern United States, the rate being 2.5° for each degree of latitude. Between Harbin, Manchuria, and Hankow, China, there is only 13.4° difference in July, but there is 41.8° in January. Between St. Louis and Winnipeg the January contrast amounts to 34.5°; the July contrast to only 12.9°. Obviously, there is much more reason for northerners to go south to escape winter cold than for southerners to go north to escape

summer heat. The growing season varies greatly in length from north to south in the continental climates, approaching 200 days on the low-latitude margins and decreasing to 100 ± days on the subarctic side.

PRECIPITATION

268. AMOUNT AND DISTRIBUTION. Rainfall decreases (*a*) from the seaward margins toward the interiors and (*b*) usually toward the higher latitudes as well. Thus along their interior margins the humid continental climates make contact with dry climates, and these interior sectors are definitely subhumid. The regions of the prairies, to be found in both interior Eurasia and North America, illustrate this drier sub-type. For reasons previously stated (264), these land-controlled climates are likely to receive their most abundant precipitation in the warm season, although winters are not necessarily dry. More especially it is (*a*) the deep continental interiors and (*b*) the regions of marked monsoonal tendencies, in which summers are emphatically rainier than winters. At Peiping in North China, a station typical of regions having well-developed monsoons, December and January each have only 0.1 in. of precipitation, while July and August have 9.4 and 6.3 in. respectively. Omaha, Neb., typical of an interior regime in North America, has 0.7 in. in January and 4.7 in June. Over much of the United States *east* of the Mississippi, however, the discrepancy between winter and summer precipitation is not so marked. New York City, which receives 3.3 in. in each of the three winter months, has only slightly more, 4.1 and 4.3 in., in July and August respectively. Its total for the year, however, is 42.5 in.

269. *Early-summer Maximum.* In the more subhumid interior locations the period of maximum rainfall, more often than not, is in early summer and late spring, rather than at the time of greatest heat. This is the case in the Danube Basin and in the western prairie region of the United States. At Beograd (Belgrade), Yugoslavia, June is the wettest month, and May has more precipitation than July. At Omaha, June likewise receives the maximum amount. Lacking a forest mantle, the shallow snow cover of these subhumid lands melts rapidly with the advance of spring, and the dry earth warms quickly under the strong insolation. By May or June, therefore, the lower air has become relatively warm although the upper layers, in which there is a greater seasonal temperature lag, are still cool. Atmospheric instability, and consequently convectional overturning, is therefore greatest in early summer when there is a maximum temperature contrast between lower and upper air. Later in the summer, even though surface temperatures are higher, there is less vertical contrast.

The economic importance to agricultural production of having the year's rainfall relatively concentrated in the early part of the growing season cannot be overestimated. In microthermal climates with only modest precipitation, where relatively long and severe winters definitely limit the season of plant growth, it is highly essential that the periods of sufficient warmth and sufficient rainfall coincide. It bears restating for the sake of emphasis that coequal in importance with *quantity* of rainfall is the matter of its *distribution* throughout the year.

270. WINTER PRECIPITATION. Cool-season precipitation is largely frontal in origin. Tropical Gulf air masses moving northward in winter usually do not get very far into the continent before being forced to ascend over cold polar air masses. Sometimes this happens even before Tg air reaches the northern Gulf Coast, and rarely does the tropical air advance at the ground farther than Iowa and the southern shores of the Great Lakes. A portion of the winter precipitation is in the form of snow, and a permanent snow cover, varying from a few weeks to several months in duration, is typical. Owing to the fact that (a) it takes 5 to 15 in. of snow to equal 1 in. of rain and (b) snow tends to remain on the ground whereas rain does not, the total less precipitation of winter may be more conspicuous and impressive than summer's greater amount. This contrast is further accentuated by the fact that the cyclonic winter precipitation is continuous over longer periods of time than are the sharper convectional showers of summer. In those parts of northeastern United States and Canada where winter cyclones are particularly numerous and well developed (Great Lakes region, St. Lawrence Valley, New England, and the Canadian Maritime Provinces) snow becomes excessively deep. Thus northern New England and New York have more than 7 ft. of snowfall during an average winter, and the snow cover remains on the ground for more than 4 months. In parts of the Adirondack Mountains 150 in. or more of snow falls annually. Over the American Great Plains, on the other hand, it amounts to only 20 to 30 in.

271. SUMMER PRECIPITATION. Summer rains, more convectional in origin, often fall in sharp showers from cumulo-nimbus clouds and frequently are accompanied by thunder and lightning. The warm humid Tg air that enters deep into the North American continent in summer provides ideal conditions for convectional development over eastern and central United States. In Hungary 61 per cent of the rain in June falls on days with thunderstorms (Kendrew). A considerable percentage of the thunderstorms of continental climates are of the simple heat variety resulting from excessive surface heating. A smaller

number are storms associated with the fronts of cyclones. Drizzly cyclonic rains falling from gray overcast skies are not absent, to be sure, but this type of weather is less frequent in summer than in the cooler seasons. On the whole, cyclonic weather is most typical of the poleward margins of the continental climates.

SEASONAL WEATHER

272. NONPERIODIC WEATHER CHANGES CHARACTERISTIC. In no other types of climate are rapid and marked nonperiodic weather changes so characteristic as in the humid continental, for it is in these regions that the conflict between polar and tropical air masses reaches a maximum development. It is in the cold season, when the sun has retreated farthest south, and with it the storm belt, that the continental climates experience the strongest nonperiodic control of weather. At that season the diurnal sun control is usually subordinate, and weather conditions are dominated by moving cyclones and anticyclones associated with rapidly shifting polar and tropical air masses and the fronts that develop along their boundaries. The daily rise and fall of temperatures with the sun many times are obscured by the larger nonperiodic oscillations caused by invasions of polar and tropical air masses (Figs. 101, 102).

In the deep interiors and higher middle latitudes of the continents the effects of the winter continental anticyclone are more pronounced and the weather drier, colder and somewhat less fickle. In summer air masses are more stagnant, fronts fewer, and weather more regular and sun controlled.

273. SPECIAL WEATHER TYPES. The usual cycle of weather changes with the passage of a cyclone, followed by an anticyclone, has been described in an earlier part of this book (160). There are, however, certain special weather types, which, because of their frequency or severity, have gained particular recognition as well as distinguishing names. Among these are the *blizzard*, the *cold wave*, the *hot wave*, and *Indian summer*.

A genuine *blizzard* is "a gale of wind, zero cold, and drifting powdery snow." Actually, there may be no precipitation falling at the time, yet the air is filled to a height of several hundred feet by swirling masses of dry, finely pulverized snow, whipped up from the freshly fallen cover. It is the combination of wind, cold, and blinding snow that makes these storms dangerous to both man and beast who may be caught out in them. The genuine blizzard, although extremely rare in the eastern states, occurs occasionally in the Middle West but is most truly representative of the western prairie and plains states. Under the name of *buran*, the blizzard is also known to the prairie lands of Russia and Siberia. On the weather map this storm type is associated with unusually steep pressure gradients on the rear of a well-developed cold front in fresh Polar Continental air.

Not every sharp drop in temperature is a *cold wave*, for to be an authentic one (*a*) the thermometer must fall a certain number of degrees within 24 hr., and (*b*) it must drop below a certain fixed minimum. In northern United States for a genuine winter cold wave the temperature must fall 20° within 24 hr. and must at least reach a minimum of zero. This weather type is associated with strong importations of cold, Polar Continental air following a cold front (Fig. 56). The sharp *drop* in temperature, which is the *cold wave*, occurs when the wind shifts from a southerly to a northwesterly direction. The lowest temperatures, however, may not be reached during the blowing of the strong northwest wind but, rather, a day or two later in the calm air of the following anticyclone, when radiation and conduction produce the maximum surface cooling in the *Pc* air mass.

Summer in continental climates has some of the aspects of tropical weather. Sun is largely in control, and regular diurnal variations in weather are marked. Cumulus clouds and afternoon thunderstorms tend to replace the sullen, gray skies and long-continued spells of precipitation characteristic of winter. Air-mass or cyclonic control of weather is not absent, however.

Spells of unusually hot weather or summer *hot waves*, with maximum temperatures of over 90° on several successive days, are caused by long-continued importation by southerly winds of tropical or superior air masses. The arrangement of storm areas on the weather map for such an invasion of warm air is nearly opposite to that for cold waves. Hot waves occur on the northern flanks of stagnant anticyclones centered over the Gulf States (Fig. 57*B*). Squall-line thunderstorms are associated with the cold fronts of V-shaped lows in which there is a distinct wind-shift line (173, Fig. 66). Preceded by days with south winds and high temperatures, the heat wave is broken when the eastward-advancing squall line, with its general turbulence and thunderstorms, is reached, and the wind shifts to northwest. The delightfully cool winds on the rear of such a storm bring the summer cool waves.

Spring and fall, the transition seasons, witness a more even struggle between storm and sun control. At times the one and then the other is in the ascendancy, so that there is something of an oscillation between summer and winter conditions. Mild, warm days in April and early May, with regular diurnal rise and fall of the thermometer, resembling summer, may be followed by a reestablishment of winter conditions as a passing cyclone lays down a snow cover, and the following anticyclone drops the temperatures to an unseasonable frost. Continental climates are famous for their fickleness of spring weather.

Autumn brings some of the loveliest days of the entire year but likewise some of the rawest, gloomiest weather. Bright, clear weather with warm midday temperatures and crisp, frosty nights come with anticyclonic control. A reestablishment of hot-wave gradients in October and November, after severe frost and perhaps even snow have been experienced, causes a temporary return of summer conditions. The result is those much cherished spells of warm weather with hazy, smoky atmosphere, known as *Indian summer*. But well-developed cyclonic storms of this season may also bring those raw, gray days with chilly rain, and occasionally a temporary snowy winter landscape may be produced as early as October.

8a. HUMID CONTINENTAL CLIMATE WITH LONG SUMMERS
(*Dfa* and *Dwa*)

274. LOCATION. This long-summer phase of humid continental climates is sometimes designated as *corn-belt climate*, because much of the world's commercial maize crop is grown in regions having its imprint. It is also occasionally called the *oak-hickory climate* because of its reasonably strong regional coincidence with that hardwood-forest association.

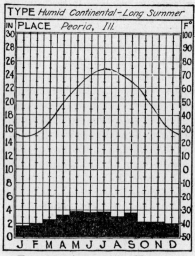

FIG. 100.—Average monthly temperatures and precipitation for a representative station in humid continental climate with long summer.

Because this is the mild phase of humid continental climates, it is to be expected that, characteristically, it will be located on the southern margins of the general microthermal group. On its poleward side is the more severe short-summer phase of continental climate, while to the south is one or the other of the subtropical types (Fig. 69, Plate V). It is obvious, by reason of the latitudinal location, that long-summer humid continental climate is the mildest and most equable of all those included within the microthermal group.

In the United States this subtype includes a tier of states, extending from central Kansas and Nebraska on the west to the Atlantic Seaboard and including, besides those states mentioned, Iowa, Missouri, Illinois, southern Wisconsin and Michigan, Indiana, Ohio, Pennsylvania, southern New York, and the coast states from southern New England to about Maryland. The American corn belt lies within its borders. In Europe the long-summer phase prevails chiefly in the south-central portions of that continent—the Danube and Balkan states, and the Po Valley of Italy. It is on the plains of the Danube and the Po

Valley that much of Europe's maize crop is grown. The third principal region, in eastern Asia, includes North China and southern Manchuria, most of Chosen (Korea), and northern Japan. This Asiatic segment is where the monsoon regime of winds and rainfall is particularly well developed.

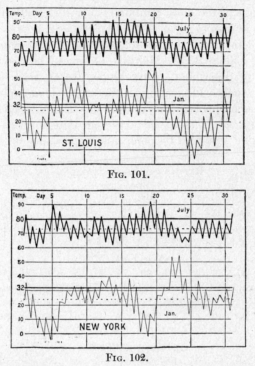

Fig. 101.

Fig. 102.

Figs. 101, 102.—Daily maximum and minimum temperatures for extreme months at representative stations in humid continental climate with long summer. Note the stronger storm or air-mass control in winter. (*Courtesy of Mark Jefferson and the Geographical Review.*)

TEMPERATURE

275. Summers are characteristically long and hot. July at St. Louis (78.6°), or Peiping, China (78.8°), is subtropical, or even tropical, in its heat, resembling very much conditions in the Amazon Valley. Typical American corn-belt cities have average July temperatures in the neighborhood of 75°. Not only are summers hot, but they are inclined to be relatively humid as well, so that a summer month contains a large number of sultry, oppressive days when the inhabitants experience great physical discomfort. At Urbana, Ill., in the heart of the corn belt, where the average July temperature is 74.8°, the

mean of the daily maxima is 85.7°. Nights, too, are often uncomfortably warm. Summers are relatively long, the period between killing frosts being in the neighborhood of 150 to 200 days.

276. WINTERS are likely to be relatively cold but with numerous spells of mild, disagreeable, rainy weather sandwiched in between the periods of cold. The average January temperature at Urbana is 25.6°, and the average of the daily minima is only 17.5°, although 25° below zero has been known to occur (Figs. 101, 102). St. Louis has an average January temperature of 31.8°; Bucureşti (Bucharest), Rumania, 25.5°; and Peiping, China, 23.5°. Monthly averages, however, are not of great value for describing winter temperatures, since the latter are composed of such wide variants. Since the long-summer phase is bounded by such opposite temperature conditions on its northern and southern frontiers, it is to be expected that marked temperature contrasts can be produced by polar and tropical air-mass invasions.

CLIMATIC DATA FOR REPRESENTATIVE STATIONS IN THE LONG-SUMMER
SUBTYPE
Peoria, Ill.

	J	F	M	A	M	J	J	A	S	O	N	D	Yr.	Range
Temp.	24	28	40	51	62	71	75	73	65	53	39	28	50.8	51.6
Precip.	1.8	2.0	2.7	3.3	3.9	3.8	3.8	3.2	3.8	2.4	2.4	2.0	34.9	

New York City

	J	F	M	A	M	J	J	A	S	O	N	D	Yr.	Range
Temp.	31	31	39	49	60	69	74	72	67	56	44	34	52.1	43.0
Precip.	3.3	3.3	3.4	3.3	3.4	3.4	4.1	4.3	3.4	3.4	3.4	3.3	42.0	

Bucureşti (Bucharest), Rumania

	J	F	M	A	M	J	J	A	S	O	N	D	Yr.	Range
Temp.	26	29	40	52	61	68	73	71	64	54	41	30	50.7	47.5
Precip.	1.2	1.1	1.7	2.0	2.5	3.3	2.8	1.9	1.5	1.5	1.9	1.7	23.0	

Peiping, China

	J	F	M	A	M	J	J	A	S	O	N	D	Yr.	Range
Temp.	24	29	41	57	68	76	79	77	68	55	39	27	53	55
Precip.	0.1	0.2	0.2	0.6	1.4	3.0	9.4	6.3	2.6	0.6	0.3	0.1	24.9	

PRECIPITATION

277. AMOUNT. In terms of the total amount of precipitation, most of the world regions possessing humid continental climate with long summers suffer from too little, rather than too much, rainfall. Thus parts of the North China Plain, the Danube Lowlands of Europe, and the western portion of this climatic region in the United States are all subhumid in character, with grass as the prevailing type of natural vegetation. It is chiefly northern Japan, Chosen, and the eastern and central portions of the American region that are fortunate in having more than 30 in. of precipitation. Occasional crop failures as a result of drought are characteristic of the subhumid portions.

This is especially true in North China where, because of the very dense population, drought years are likewise famine years.

278. ANNUAL DISTRIBUTION. Summer rains predominate, the warm-season maximum being particularly marked in the more sub-humid portions or where monsoons prevail (Fig. 100). This is fortunate, for in regions with severe winters, and where precipitation is none too bountiful, it is especially necessary for rainfall to be concentrated in the growing season for crops. The warm summertime convectional rains have the advantage of permitting a maximum of sunshine and heat along with an abundance of rain. Such a condition is ideal for the corn crop. At Peoria, Ill., though there is a distinct concentration of rainfall in the warm months, it is this same season that has the largest amount of sunshine. For example, July has 3.77 in. of precipitation, falling on 10 rainy days, and 75 per cent of the possible sunshine. January, with only 1.8 in. of precipitation and 9 rainy days, has only 47 per cent of the possible sunshine. Days with thunderstorms are numerous, averaging 40 to 60 a year in the American corn belt.

Winter precipitation is usually less than that of summer. Only in Japan, Chosen, parts of central Europe, and central and eastern United States can winters be classed as distinctly humid. North China represents the opposite extreme, for at Peiping the combined precipitation of the three winter months is only 0.4 in., as compared with 18.7 in. for the three summer months. This reflects the well-developed system of monsoon winds which dominates eastern Asia. The western margins of the American corn belt also have a relatively marked winter minimum in precipitation, with only 2 to 4 in. during December to February inclusive.

A portion of the winter precipitation falls as snow, although it is usually less than one-half the season's total. Over the American corn belt snow falls on 20 to 30 days of the year, the total amounting to 10 to 40 in. The number of days with snow cover varies from 10± on the southern margin to 60+ on the poleward side.

8b. HUMID CONTINENTAL CLIMATE WITH SHORT SUMMERS (Dfb and Dwb)

279. LOCATION. This more severe phase of humid continental climate lies on the poleward side of the long-summer subtype and between it and subarctic climate (Fig. 69). It is sometimes designated as the "spring-wheat" type, since that important commercial crop reaches its most specialized development in the subhumid parts of the short-summer phase. This is scarcely the case in the more humid parts, however. In North America the type is found in general east

of the 100th meridian and includes the northern tier of states in the United States and portions of southern Canada as well (Plate V). In Eurasia it includes most of Poland, eastern Germany, the small Baltic states, and a large part of the central Russian plain between latitudes 50 and 60°+. Beyond the Urals it extends on into Siberia as a narrower strip in the vicinity of latitude 55°. In much of European Russia and Siberia it is terminated on the south by steppe climate. The third large representative area is in northeastern Asia, more especially central and northern Manchuria (Manchukuo) and southeastern Siberia.

TEMPERATURE

280. TEMPERATURES RELATIVELY EXTREME. Because of its characteristic location in higher latitudes, temperatures are some-

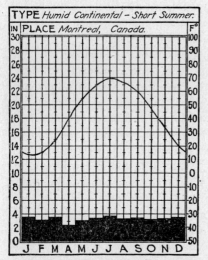

FIG. 103.—Average monthly temperatures and precipitation at a station in the humid continental climate with short summers. The absence of a marked summer maximum in precipitation results from the very abundant winter snowfall, Montreal being located on the principal winter storm tracks.

what lower than in the long-summer phase farther south (Fig. 103). This is much more emphatically the case with winter than with summer, for while the hot months are only 5 to 10° cooler, average winter temperatures are 10 to 30° lower. It is the severer winters, then, that chiefly account for the larger annual ranges. Summers are usually warm for a few months, the average July temperatures being a few degrees above or below 70° (St. Paul 72°; Montreal 69°; Moskva (Moscow) 66°; Barnaul, Siberia, 67°; Harbin, Manchuria, 72°). But the climate is handicapped by reason of the relatively short duration of summer. Thus, while Indianapolis (long-summer phase) has 7 months the average temperatures of which are over 50°, St. Paul and Winnipeg have only 5. Frost comes early and remains late, so that the growing season is only 3+ to 5 months in length, which is insufficient for a number of crops. Offsetting somewhat the two handicaps of shorter and cooler summers is the advantage of the longer days that prevail in the higher latitudes. Thus at the time of the

Northern Hemisphere summer solstice, Winnipeg has a daily period of insolation which is more than one hour longer than that of St. Louis.

Midday temperatures in July are likely to be warm to hot, especially when the sun is shining. Overcast days, on the other hand, are inclined to be chilly. It is not unusual to experience summer days with temperatures of 90° and above (Fig. 104). Hot waves, similar in origin to those in the regions farther south, do occur, but they are usually not quite so severe or so long. There are, on the other hand, more spells of cool, cloudy weather than in the long-summer phase, for, in the United States at least, this climatic type is closer to the tracks

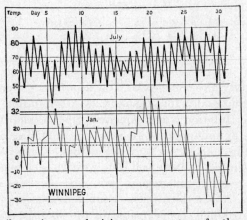

Fig. 104.—Daily maximum and minimum temperatures for the extreme months at a representative station in humid continental climate with short summers. (*Courtesy of Mark Jefferson and the Geographical Review.*)

of summer cyclones. It is these cool spells that draw down the general summer average.

Winter is the dominant season. At Barnaul the January average is −2.2°; Harbin, Manchuria, −1.7°; Bismarck, N. D., 7.8°. But these averages are composed of very unlike temperature elements, since the succession of cyclones and anticyclones brings much subzero weather as well as some that is distinctly above freezing (Fig. 104). Winters differ greatly from year to year in the continental climates. January, 1914, at Bismarck had only one day with temperatures below −10°, as compared with 14 the previous year. Large storm-controlled temperature fluctuations within a short period of time are likewise characteristic, changes of 40° within 24 hr. being relatively common. These temperature fluctuations and variations are associated with advances and retreats of polar and tropical air masses.

CLIMATIC DATA FOR REPRESENTATIVE STATIONS IN THE SHORT-SUMMER
SUBTYPE

Madison, Wis.

	J	F	M	A	M	J	J	A	S	O	N	D	Yr.	Range
Temp.	17	20	31	46	58	67	72	70	62	50	35	23	45.8	55.5
Precip.	1.5	1.5	2.1	2.6	3.7	3.9	3.8	3.2	3.6	2.4	1.8	1.6	31.6	

Montreal, Canada

	J	F	M	A	M	J	J	A	S	O	N	D	Yr.	Range
Temp.	13	15	25	41	55	65	69	67	59	47	33	19	42	56
Precip.	3.7	3.2	3.7	2.4	3.1	3.5	3.8	3.4	3.5	3.3	3.4	3.7	40.7	

Moskva (Moscow), U.S.S.R.

	J	F	M	A	M	J	J	A	S	O	N	D	Yr.	Range
Temp.	12	15	23	38	53	62	66	63	52	40	28	17	39.0	53.8
Precip.	1.1	1.0	1.2	1.5	1.9	2.0	2.8	2.9	2.2	1.4	1.6	1.5	21.1	

Harbin, Manchuria

	J	F	M	A	M	J	J	A	S	O	N	D	Yr.	Range
Temp.	−2	5	24	42	56	66	72	69	58	40	21	3	37.9	73.8
Precip.	0.1	0.2	0.4	0.9	1.7	3.8	4.5	4.1	1.8	1.3	0.3	0.2	19.3	

PRECIPITATION

281. AMOUNT AND SEASONAL DISTRIBUTION. Generalization is
difficult concerning any total amount of precipitation characteristic
of this climate. Interior North America, Siberia, and Manchuria are
representative of subhumid sections where rainfall is commonly less
than 25 or 30 in. and in parts even less than 20 in. Eastern Canada
and eastern United States, and the western portions of Europe's
short-summer continental region, are representative of the more
humid sections. It is in the former, or subhumid, group, that precipitation is more strikingly concentrated in the short period of warmth,
winters being relatively dry. Thus Bismarck with only 17.4 in. of
precipitation has 3.4 in. in June, the rainiest month, and only 0.5 in.
in each of the two driest months, January and February. In those
regions with more abundant annual precipitation previously noted,
especially eastern North America, winters are much less dry. In New
England and the Maritime Provinces of Canada, where tracks of
cyclones converge, winters have nearly, if not quite, as much precipitation as summers. For example, at Quebec, which has a total of 40.7 in.,
July has 4.3 and January 3.4 in., while Portland, Me., has slightly
more precipitation in January (3.9 in.) than in July (3.4 in.). See
Fig. 103.

282. SNOWFALL. Because of the lower winter temperatures,
much more of the cool-season precipitation is in the form of snow than
is true of the long-summer phase to the south. In northern Minnesota
there are 60 to 80 days with snowfall, the total amount being 40 to
60 in., while there is a continuous snow cover for over 120 days. A
similar situation with respect to duration of snow cover holds for

northern New England, while the total snowfall there amounts to more than 80 in. The actual amount of snow is much less along the drier interior margins of this type, but owing to the low temperatures, the number of days with snow cover may be quite as long.

9. Subarctic Climates (Taiga; *Dfc, Dwc, Dwd*)[1]

283. LOCATION. This is the extreme in continental climates, subarctic having the largest annual temperature ranges. It is found only in the higher middle latitudes (50 or 55 to 65°) of the great Northern Hemisphere continents (Fig. 69, Plate V). On its poleward side it makes contact with tundra, one of the polar climates. This northern boundary is approximately the isotherm of 50° for the warmest month (usually July), which is critical because it closely coincides with the poleward limit of tree growth. Subarctic climate, on its southern margin, usually makes contact with the short-summer phase of humid continental climate or, in places, with middle-latitude steppes and deserts. The Eurasian subarctic area extends from Sweden and Finland in Europe, across the whole of the continent to the coast of Siberia. It widens toward the Pacific, or leeward, side as continentality increases. In North America the subarctic belt stretches from Alaska on the Pacific, across Canada to Labrador and Newfoundland on the Atlantic.

TEMPERATURE

284. SUMMER. Long, bitterly cold winters, very short summers, and brief springs and autumns are characteristic (Fig. 105). Since the isotherm of 50° for the warmest month has been accepted as the poleward boundary of this type of climate, at least one month must have an average temperature of 50° or above. At Yakutsk, Siberia, nearly 62°N., representing the extreme in subarctic climates, July, the warmest month, has an average temperature of 66°, which is higher than the same month at London or Berlin and 9° higher than July at San Francisco. Midsummer daily maxima of 80° are common at Yakutsk, and the thermometer occasionally reaches 90°. The absolute maximum is 102°. At this same station, however, June and August have mean temperatures of only 59 and 59.5° respectively. It needs to be emphasized that, at Yakutsk, there are only three months in which the mean temperatures exceed 50°, for both May and September have averages in the low forties. At Fort Vermilion, at 58°27′N. in Canada, another representative subarctic station, July is cooler than

---

[1] In the Köppen symbols, c = cool summers with only 1 to 3 months above 50° (10°C.); d = cold winters with the temperature of the coldest month below −36.4° (−38°C.).

it is at Yakutsk, having an average temperature of only 60°, while June and August are 54.9 and 58.6° respectively. The mean of the daily maxima in July is 74.3°; and of the minima, 45.7°. Temperatures over 90° have been recorded at Fort Vermilion in both June and July. Subarctic summer days, then, are pleasantly warm and occasionally even hot (Figs. 106, 107; Canadian data from Koeppe).

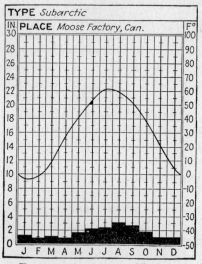

TYPE *Subarctic*

PLACE *Moose Factory, Can.*

Fig. 105.—Average monthly temperatures and precipitation for a representative subarctic station.

285. *Long Summer Days.* Somewhat compensating for the short and none too warm summers are the unusually long days in these higher latitudes. Thus, although the intensity of sunlight is not so great, the large number of hours during which the sun shines is an offsetting factor. Moreover, the short nights do not permit a long period of cooling. For example, at latitude 55°N. June days average 17.3 hr. of possible sunshine; latitude 60°N., 18.8 hr.; and latitude 65°N., 22.1 hr. Moreover, since twilight continues when the sun is as much as 18° below the horizon, it is evident that in summer the hours of darkness are very much limited. In the more northerly portions of the subarctic lands, at the time of the summer solstice, one can read a paper out of doors even at midnight.

286. *Growing Season.* Unfortunately, the subarctic lands have very short periods that are entirely without frost. The growing season in the Mackenzie Valley of Canada varies from about 50 to 75 days, and many stations must expect freezing temperatures in July and August in at least half of the years. A shift of wind to the north at any time brings with it the chill of the ice-laden Arctic. Thus while it is the occasional midwinter frosts which are dangerous in the subtropical climates, it is, on the other hand, the midsummer frosts which are of peculiar significance in this subarctic type. The characteristic coolness, shortness, and precariousness of the growing season are the most serious handicaps of the subarctic climates for agricultural development.

287. WINTER follows on the heels of summer with only a very brief intervening autumn season. Frosts may arrive in late August, and ice

begins to form on pools in September. By the middle of October navigation for small craft is made difficult on the subarctic lakes of Canada. At Verkhoyansk, Siberia, the mean temperature drops 40° from October to November. Subarctic Siberia holds the records for minimum temperatures at low elevations, even lower than those of polar climates. Verkhoyansk, in the northeastern part, boasts an average January temperature of 59° below zero, while an absolute minimum of −90° was recorded in February, 1892. This, of course, is an extreme case. At Yakutsk, however, where July has an average temperature of 66°, the January mean drops to approximately −46°, producing an annual range of 112°. For seven months at Yakutsk the average temperatures are below freezing, and during five months they are below zero. No other type of climate can show such contrasts between summer and winter temperatures.

Concerning the Siberian winter, Hann writes:

"It is not possible to describe the terrible cold one has to endure; one has to experience it to appreciate it. The quicksilver freezes solid and can be cut and hammered like lead; iron becomes brittle, and the hatchet breaks like glass; wood, depending upon the degree of moisture in it, becomes harder than iron and withstands the ax so that only completely dry wood can be split. Every step in the dry snow can be heard for long distances; the bursting of the ice cover and the frozen ground sound like the cannonading of distant batteries."

Subarctic winters in North America are not quite so severe as are those of Siberia. This comes about in part as a result of Asia's being a broader land mass. Representative stations such as Churchill, Dawson, and Fort Good Hope show average January temperatures of −20.2, −22.4, and −31.6° respectively. At Dawson, in the Yukon, at 64°3'N., the thermometer, on an average January night, falls to approximately −29° and rises to nearly −16° during the warmest hours of the day (Figs. 106, 107).

The excessive and long-continued cold of the subarctic winters causes large parts of taiga regions to be permanently frozen down to great depths. Over extensive areas of the subarctic lands only the upper few feet thaw out during the short summers. The depth to which frost penetrates and the depth of the summer thaw vary greatly from one part of the subarctic lands to another. Cleveland Abbe notes the case of a mine in the Klondike (Yukon) which passed out of the permanently frozen zone at a depth of 220 ft.

Just as long days are characteristic of subarctic summers, so long nights are characteristic of the winters. For example, on Dec. 21 all places on the 60°N. parallel can receive a maximum of only 5.7 hr. of sunshine, while on latitude 65°N. the maximum is only 3.3 hr. These

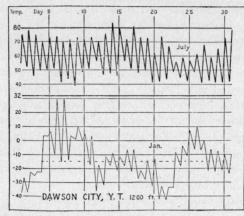

Fig. 106.—Daily maximum and minimum temperatures for extreme months at a representative subarctic station in Canada. (*Courtesy of Mark Jefferson and the Geographical Review.*)

long daily periods of darkness are not only depressing and hard to bear, but they are, in a considerable measure, responsible for the low winter temperatures.

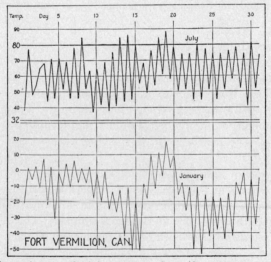

Fig. 107.—Daily maximum and minimum temperatures for extreme months at a representative subarctic station.

Spring, like autumn, is a short and inconspicuous season. At Yakutsk there is a difference of 25° between the mean temperatures of

April and May, and 18° between May and June. The average April temperature at Yakutsk is like that of Madison, Wis., in January, while May is only 4 to 5° lower than April at Madison.

CLIMATIC DATA FOR REPRESENTATIVE SUBARCTIC STATIONS

Fort Vermilion, Alberta, Canada (58°27′N.)

	J	F	M	A	M	J	J	A	S	O	N	D	Yr.	Range
T.	−14	−6	8	30	47	55	60	57	46	32	10	−4	26.7	74.3
R.	0.6	0.3	0.5	0.7	1.0	1.9	2.1	2.1	1.4	0.7	0.5	0.4	12.3	

Moose Factory, Canada (51°16′N.)

	J	F	M	A	M	J	J	A	S	O	N	D	Yr.	Range
T.	−4	−2	10	28	42	54	61	59	51	39	22	5	30.4	65.6
R.	1.3	0.9	1.1	1.0	1.8	2.2	2.4	3.3	2.9	1.8	1.1	1.1	21.0	

Yakutsk, Siberia, U.S.S.R.

	J	F	M	A	M	J	J	A	S	O	N	D	Yr.	Range
T.	−46	−35	−10	16	41	59	66	60	42	16	−21	−41	12	112
R.	0.9	0.2	0.4	0.6	1.1	2.1	1.7	2.6	1.2	1.4	0.6	0.9	13.7	

PRECIPITATION AND HUMIDITY

288. AMOUNT. Precipitation in subarctic climates is usually meager (Fig. 105). Over much of the Siberian taiga it is no more than 15 in., while most of subarctic Canada receives less than 20, and parts receive less than 15 in. It is principally along the oceanic margins in both Eurasia and North America that rainfall exceeds 20 in. In most middle-latitude climates these small amounts, characteristic of the taiga, would be classed as semiarid, but where such low temperatures and, therefore, low evaporation rates prevail, and where the ground is frozen so much of the year, the precipitation is sufficient for forest growth.

289. ANNUAL DISTRIBUTION. Precipitation is concentrated in the warmer months. At Yakutsk, where the total annual rainfall is 13.7 in., August is the wettest month with 2.6 in., and February the driest with 0.2 in. At Dawson in the Yukon the total is 12.49 in., with 1.54 in July and 0.83 in January (0.71 in. in February and 0.53 in March). It is over east-central Siberia, in particular, that winters are especially dry, the three winter months there having only 10 per cent of the annual precipitation, while the three summer months have 58 per cent. This is the region of most intense cold and highest winter pressures.

Over lowlands the meager winter precipitation, practically all of it in the form of snow, is cyclonic in origin. The few fronts that cross these areas yield sufficient precipitation, in the form of relatively dry, hard, snow, so that a permanent snow cover, lasting 5 to 7 months, is common. Because of the shelter provided by the forest, little melting or evaporation occurs, so that the winter snows accumulate to a depth of 2 to 3 ft. in the taiga. This same protection of the forest leads to slow melting of the snow cover in spring. In eastern Siberia, winter precipitation is so meager that sleighing is sometimes difficult.

Summer, the season of maximum surface heating, steepest vertical temperature gradients, and highest humidity, provides conditions that are relatively most favorable for rainfall. Warm-season precipitation is both convectional and cyclonic in origin. Thunderstorms are not numerous, however, the total number in the Mackenzie Valley of Canada being in the neighborhood of 5 to 10 a year. They are associated with the hottest spells, when convection is at a maximum. Fort Vermilion, in the Mackenzie Valley, has on the average 5.3 rainy days in June, 9.1 in July, and 7.5 in August. Comparable data for Dawson, in the Yukon, are 11.7, 10.3, and 10.9 (Koeppe).

Chapter XI. Polar Climates and Highland Climates

Polar Climates (*E*)

290. As the tropics are characterized by lack of a cool season, so the polar regions are wanting in a period of warmth. It is the prevalence of monotonous heat that typifies the low latitudes. In the high latitudes monotonous and long-continued cold is the greatest handicap. Certain explorers to the contrary, the polar areas cannot be made to appear warm by noting that occasional days with temperatures over 80° have been experienced beyond the Arctic Circle. "One swallow does not make a summer," nor do a few warm days determine the general climatic character of a region.

291. PHENOMENA OF LIGHT AND DARKNESS. A distinctive feature of the polar climates is their peculiarities with respect to periods of light and darkness. At the poles the sun is out of sight entirely for approximately six months, while for an equal period it is constantly above the horizon, although never very high in the heavens, so that insolation is weak. At the Arctic and Antarctic Circles, which lie near the equatorward margins of polar climates, the daily period of sunlight varies from 24 hr. at the time of the summer solstice to a complete lack of sunlight at the winter solstice. At points between the poles and the $66\frac{1}{2}°$ parallels the lengths of the periods of sunlight, and absence of sunlight, are intermediate in character between the two extremes noted.

292. LOCATIONS AND BOUNDARIES. Polar climates are largely confined to the high latitudes of the earth. Somewhat similar conditions can be found at high altitudes in a great variety of latitudes. But these latter regions of continuous cold usually are very isolated and fragmentary and in this book are included within the group designated as highland climates.

The poleward limit of forest is usually accepted as marking the boundary separating the cold climates from those of the intermediate latitudes. In continental locations this vegetation boundary approximately coincides with the isotherm of 50° for the *warmest month*, so that this seasonal isotherm is commonly employed in defining the outer margins of the polar climates.[1] It is significant that, while for the boundary of the humid tropics a *cool-month* isotherm is employed, a *warm-month* isotherm serves in the same way for polar climates. It suggests that while a period of coolness is of critical importance for plants and animals in the low latitudes, a period of warmth is much more significant in high latitudes. In the Southern Hemisphere the only conspicuous land area possessed of polar climates is the ice-covered Antarctic Continent. In the Northern Hemisphere it is the Arctic Sea borderlands of Eurasia and North America, together with extensive island groups north of both continents and ice-covered Greenland, which are included.

293. ARCTIC AND ANTARCTIC. Since the Arctic is almost a land-locked sea, while the Antarctic is a seagirt land, certain important climatic differences are to be expected between the two regions. As a consequence of its single land mass being centered at the Pole and surrounded on all sides by extensive oceans of uniform temperature, the Antarctic shows much greater uniformity and simplicity in its climate than does the Arctic. Wind and pressure systems are symmetrically developed about the South Pole, and there is little change in these elements throughout the year, whereas lack of symmetry and seasonal variations in these controls are characteristic of the north polar regions.

294. TEMPERATURE AND PRECIPITATION. Polar climates claim the distinction of having the lowest *mean annual*, as well as the lowest *summer*, temperatures for any part of the earth. In spite of the long duration of sunshine in summer, temperatures remain low, the rays being too oblique to be genuinely effective. Moreover, much of the solar energy is reflected by the snow and ice or is consumed in melting the snow cover and evaporating the water, so that neither the land surface nor the air adjacent to it becomes warm. Winters are bitterly cold, but there is some doubt as to whether the thermometer ever sinks as low in the polar regions as it does in the subarctic climate of northeastern Siberia. In spite of the cool summers, winter cold is sufficiently severe to develop large annual ranges.

Precipitation is meager throughout the high latitudes. Over large parts of the land areas it is less than 10 in. But in spite of its meagerness, the low evaporation permits of some runoff, part of it in the form

---

[1] In order to exclude certain cool marine climates which are not distinctly polar in nature, the definition should further stipulate a mean annual temperature of 32° or below.

of glaciers. It is because of the low evaporation and the small amount of melting that great permanent snow and ice fields several thousand feet thick have been able to accumulate on Greenland and the Antarctic Continent, and this in spite of the low precipitation. A dearth of polar precipitation does not seem unusual when one considers the prevailingly low absolute humidity which must accompany the low temperatures. The reservoir of water vapor is small at all times. Moreover, in these latitudes there is a general settling of the cold upper-air masses which creates a condition unfavorable to condensation. Precipitation is usually heavier in the warmer months when the moisture supply is most abundant.

295. TUNDRA AND ICE CAPS. Polar climates are usually subdivided into two types, with the *warmest-month* isotherm of 32° serving as the boundary between them. Where the average temperatures of all months are below freezing, the growth of vegetation is impossible, and a permanent snow-and-ice cover prevails. These are the *ice-cap climates*. Where one or more of the warm-season months has an average temperature above 32° (but not over 50°) so that the ground is free from snow for a short period, and a meager and lowly vegetation cover is possible, the climate is designated as *tundra*.

10. Tundra Climate (*ET*)[1]

296. LOCATION. Tundra climate is transitional in character between the ice caps, or regions of perpetual snow and ice, on the one hand, and middle-latitude climates, usually subarctic, on the other (Fig. 69, Plate V). Its accepted equatorward and poleward boundaries are the warmest month isotherms of 50 and 32°, respectively, which, as indicated previously, are reasonably coincident with important vegetation boundaries.

Tundra climate over land areas is almost exclusively confined to the Northern Hemisphere. In the Antarctic, ocean prevails in those latitudes where the tundra would normally develop. Only the most northerly fringes of the Antarctic continent, and certain small Antarctic islands, have sufficiently warm summers for them to be included. The most extensive tundra areas are the Arctic Sea margins of both North America and Eurasia. Most of the Arctic archipelago of the former continent, as well as the coastal fringe of Greenland, is likewise included.

TEMPERATURE

297. SUMMER. Long bitterly cold winters and very short cool summers are the rule (Fig. 108). By the definition of boundaries for

[1] *ET*, warmest month below 50° (10°C.) but above 32° (0°C.).

tundra climate, previously stated, the average temperature of the warmest month can be no lower than 32° and no higher than 50°. The cool character of the summer is therefore relatively fixed. Raw and

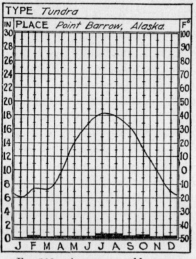

FIG. 108.—Average monthly temperatures and precipitation for a representative tundra station.

chilly, the warmest months of the tundra resemble March and April in southern Wisconsin and are like January in the American cotton belt. Usually only 2 to 4 months have average temperatures above freezing, and killing frost is likely to occur at any time. Along coasts, where water, ice, and land are in close proximity, fog is very prevalent. These fogs may last for days at a time and are extraordinarily depressing. Under the influence of unusually long summer days, the snow cover begins to disappear in May, and the lakes are usually rid of their ice cover in June. Because of the permanently frozen subsoil, subsurface drainage is deficient, and bog and swamp prevalent. Myriads of mosquitoes and black flies make life almost unbearable for man and beast alike during the summer period of wet earth.

At Ponds Inlet, Canada, a tundra station at 72°43′N., where the average July temperature is 42.4°, the thermometer in that month rises to about 49° during the warmest hours of the day and, on the average, sinks to 35 or 36° at night. Daily ranges in summer are relatively small, for the sun is above the horizon for all or a greater part of the 24-hr. period. On most July nights no frost occurs, but on the other hand it is not unusual for the thermometer to slip a few degrees below freezing (Fig. 109). Warm days occur now and then, Ponds Inlet having recorded, on at least one occasion, a temperature of 77°.

298. WINTER. While summer temperatures are not greatly different from one tundra region to another, there are greater variations in the winters. Thus along the Arctic coasts of Siberia, average January and February temperatures are in the neighborhood of −35 or −40°, and it is appreciably colder farther inland. At this season winds in general are from the bitterly cold subarctic region to the south, and these importations serve only further to intensify the severity of tem-

peratures in the tundra. Along the Arctic borderlands of North America winters are not quite so severe. A coastal station in Labrador shows a January mean of $-7.6°$; Ponds Inlet in Canada records an average of $-28.4°$ for January, $-29.7°$ for February, and even $-24.4°$ for March (Fig. 108). At the latter station 5 months, November to

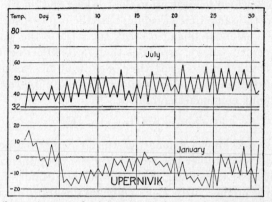

FIG. 109.—Daily maximum and minimum temperatures for the extreme months at a representative tundra station in Greenland.

March inclusive, have average temperatures below zero, while 9 are below freezing.

CLIMATIC DATA FOR REPRESENTATIVE TUNDRA STATIONS
Sagastyr, Siberia, U.S.S.R. (73°N., 124°E.)

	J	F	M	A	M	J	J	A	S	O	N	D	Yr.	Range
Temp.	−34	−36	−30	−7	15	32	41	38	33	6	−16	−28	1	77
Precip.	0.1	0.1	0.0	0.0	0.2	0.4	0.3	1.4	0.4	0.1	0.1	0.2	3.3	

Upernivik, Western Greenland (73°N., 56°W.)

	J	F	M	A	M	J	J	A	S	O	N	D	Yr.	Range
Temp.	−7	−10	−6	6	25	35	41	41	33	25	14	1	16.5	60.6
Precip.	0.4	0.4	0.6	0.6	0.6	0.6	1.0	1.1	1.0	1.1	1.1	0.5	9.2	

PRECIPITATION

299. AMOUNT AND DISTRIBUTION. Over most of the tundra lands precipitation is not over 10 or 12 in. (Fig. 108). In portions of eastern Arctic Canada, particularly Labrador peninsula, it is somewhat greater. Low summer temperatures and winter anticyclonic conditions are, in general, not conducive to abundant condensation, while convectional effects are largely absent. Summer and autumn, the warmest seasons, are likewise the periods of maximum precipitation throughout the tundra as a whole. In the more marine locations, where cyclones are greater in number, fall and winter may show larger totals than summer. Precipitation is principally cyclonic in origin. Much of that which falls in the warm season is in the form of rain, with occasional wet snows.

The meager winter snowfall is usually dry and powdery in character so that it forms a very compact cover. It is only this very compact snow, 2 in. of which may equal an inch of rain, that the Eskimos use in constructing their igloos. The actual amount of dry sandlike snow that falls is not easy to measure, since it is often accompanied by strong blizzard winds which heap it up in depressions and on the lee sides of hills, while at the same time sweeping bare the exposed surfaces. There are no forests, as in the taiga, to break the force of the wind and hold the snow cover. Stefansson estimates that 75 to 90 per cent of the surfaces of the Arctic lands is nearly free of snow at all seasons. Both as a result of the small amount of snow and as a result of its strong tendency to drift, sledging commonly is difficult.

11. Ice-cap Climate (EF)[1]

This least well known among the world's climatic types is characteristically developed over the great permanent continental ice sheets of Antarctica and Greenland and over the perpetually frozen ocean in the vicinity of the North Pole. Only fragmentary data have been obtained from these deserts of snow and ice where the average temperature of no month rises above freezing.

300. TEMPERATURE. The mean annual temperature of interior Greenland has been calculated to be −25.6°; that of the South Pole −22 to −31°; that of the North Pole −8.9°. These, without doubt, are the lowest annual temperatures for any portion of the earth. Observed temperatures for the *warmest* months in the neighborhood of the South Pole, at the time of continuous insolation, were −8.7° (December) and −18.8° (January). A temperature of −58° has been recorded in the Antarctic Continent in this season. Unquestionably, therefore, Antarctica has the distinction of being the earth's coldest spot in summer. While the North Pole and interior Greenland are certainly below freezing in July and August, they are far from being as cold as the South Polar plateau at the time of continuous day. To be sure, the figures given above are for interior portions of Antarctica and hence represent extreme conditions. Along the margins of that continent warm-month temperatures are considerably milder (McMurdo Sound 25°, Little America 21°).

During the period when the sun is constantly below the horizon, excessively cold weather prevails, although exact and reliable data are not available. On the Antarctic plateau the average winter-month temperatures are probably in the neighborhood of 35 to 45° below zero. It is not impossible that in some of the wind-protected depressions

[1] *EF*, warmest month below 32° (0°C.).

of that region, cold-month and minimum temperatures are as low as those of subarctic northeastern Siberia.

The inner portions of the ice caps, where permanent anticyclones with settling air prevail, are probably regions relatively free from storms and violent winds. Certain of their marginal areas, however, where there is a precipitous descent of cold air from the inland-ice plateau, are characterized by furious gales. But these regions of excessive storminess appear to be local rather than widespread. It is likely that storminess increases from the centers toward the circumferences of the ice caps.

CLIMATIC DATA FOR A REPRESENTATIVE ICE-CAP STATION
Little America, Antarctic Continent (79°S., 164°W.)

	J	F	M	A	M	J	J	A	S	O	N	D	Yr.	Range
Temp.	22	(9)	(−7)	−24	−27	−29	−34	−34	−29	−14	8.6	24	−11.3	58
Precip.	No data.													

301. PRECIPITATION. If little is known about the temperatures of the ice-cap climates, still less is known concerning their precipitation. There is no doubt that it is meager, and probably all of it falls as snow, most of it in the form of dry, hard, sandlike particles which are readily driven before the wind. The origin of the precipitation over the ice caps is not well understood. In such regions, although melting is practically absent, there is some loss by evaporation as well as through glaciers moving out to the sea. Enough precipitation must be accounted for to offset these losses. No doubt a portion of the inland snow has its origin in the cyclonic storms that pass along the margins of the ice plateaus. It may, in part, result from condensation in the form of fine ice particles or as hoarfrost within the descending air of the polar anticyclones as it reaches the intensely cold ice surface. The rate of deposit is exceedingly slow, no doubt, but since it is seasonally continuous, the total amount may be considerable.

12. Highland Climates (*H*)

302. ALTITUDE AND EXPOSURE AS CLIMATIC CONTROLS. Next to the distribution of land and water, elevation above sea level is the most important control causing differences in climate in similar latitudes. The climatic effects of such elevated land masses as mountains and plateaus are expressed through the two factors (*a*) *altitude* and (*b*) *exposure*.

It needs to be emphasized, however, that there is no such thing as a *highland type of climate* in the same sense that there is a savanna or a Mediterranean type. Almost endless varieties of local climates exist within a mountain mass, the atmospheric conditions varying markedly with altitude and exposure and of course with latitude as well. The enclosed valley or plateau is very different climatically from the exposed peak; windward slopes contrast markedly with those having leeward positions, while flanks inclined toward the sun are dissimilar to those oppositely inclined. And each of these in turn is different at various *altitudes* and *latitudes*. Above an elevation of 5,000 or 6,000 ft. marked differences in temperature are conspicuous between sunshine and shade, wind and calm. Representative temperature and rainfall curves for highland climates scarcely can be said to exist, and only the most flexible generalizations are broadly applicable. On Plate V, which emphasizes a relatively small number of simple types of climate, no attempt has been made to show the varieties of climate within great mountain masses. Instead most of the *high* mountain and plateau areas in low and middle latitudes have been included within one general group, *highland climates*. In contrast, regions of *moderate* elevation and relief, especially where there is considerable land utilization, have been included within the general climatic type characteristic of the surrounding lower lands, even though they may represent a modified form of the lowland climate. Up to an altitude of about 4,000 or 5,000 ft. the peculiarities of altitude climate are not prominent, but above 6,000 ft. they are usually very noticeable (*cf.* Plates V and VII).

303. ATMOSPHERIC PRESSURE IN MOUNTAINS. At low elevations the minor changes in air pressure from day to day, or from season to season, are directly imperceptible to the human body. However, the very rapid decrease in the atmosphere's weight with increasing elevation and the very low pressures that prevail in high mountains and plateaus cause this element to be a genuinely important one in highland climates. At an elevation above sea level of about 17,500 ft., pressure is reduced to approximately one-half its sea-level value. The highest human habitations are found below this level, although there are said to be settlements in Tibet and the Bolivian Andes the elevations of which approach it. Physiological effects (faintness, headache, nosebleed, nausea, weakness) of decreased pressure aloft are experienced by most people at altitudes above 12,000 to 15,000 ft. Sleeplessness is common, and exertion is difficult. Usually mountain sickness is a temporary inconvenience that passes away after a week or so of residence at high altitudes. Some persons, however, never become acclimated to the reduced pressure.

TEMPERATURE AND INSOLATION

304. INSOLATION. Intensity of sunlight increases aloft in the cleaner, drier, thinner air of mountains. This is to be expected, since

dust, moisture, and other principal scattering and absorbing elements of solar radiation in the atmosphere are much more abundant at lower elevations. On a clear day probably three-fourths of the insolation penetrates to 6,000 ft., but only one-half to sea level. The great relative intensity of the sun's rays attracts the attention of nearly all persons going to high elevations. This intensity of insolation causes soil temperatures to be relatively high as compared with the cooler air temperatures.

Insolation not only is more intense in the higher altitudes, but it also is proportionally richer in the shorter wave lengths of energy, or the violet and ultraviolet rays. One therefore burns and tans quickly in mountain sunlight. The greater therapeutic quality of this short-wave radiation is one reason for establishing many sanatoriums in the higher altitudes.

305. AIR TEMPERATURE. Probably of most fundamental importance among the climatic changes resulting from increased elevation is the decrease in air temperature (about 3.3° per 1,000 ft.), and this in spite of the increased intensity of insolation. Quito, Ecuador, on the equator, at an elevation of 9,350 ft. has an average annual temperature of 54.7°, which is 25° lower than that of the adjacent Amazon Lowland. But although the clear, rare air at that elevation, which is incapable of absorbing and retaining much energy, remains chilly, the sun is intensely strong. It is a climate of *cool shade and hot sun*. Viscount Bryce has the following to say concerning his experience on the Bolivian plateau: "The keen air which this elevation gives has a fine bracing quality, yet there are disadvantages. One is never warm except when actually in the sunlight. . . . The inhabitants get accustomed to these conditions and shiver in their ponchos, but the traveler is rather wretched after sunset and feels how natural was Sun worship in such a country."

CLIMATIC DATA FOR A HIGHLAND STATION IN THE TROPICS
Quito, Ecuador (9,350 Ft.)

	J	F	M	A	M	J	J	A	S	O	N	D	Yr.	Range
Temp.	54.5	55.0	54.5	54.5	54.7	55.0	54.9	54.9	55.0	54.7	54.3	54.7	54.7	0.7
Precip.	3.2	3.9	4.8	7.0	4.6	1.5	1.1	2.2	2.6	3.9	4.0	3.6	42.3	

Vertical temperature gradients along mountain slopes are many times steeper than the most severe winter horizontal gradients on lowlands. In the low latitudes, by a railroad trip of only a few hours, one can be transported from tropical to polar climates. This fact of steep vertical temperature gradients in mountains is particularly significant in the low latitudes, where, as a result of the prevailingly high temperatures of the lowlands, people look with favor upon elevated regions where they are able to escape the oppressive heat.

Largely because of their lower temperatures, elevations in the tropics commonly become the centers of concentration for white population. In tropical Latin America, for instance, the capital cities of Venezuela, Colombia, Bolivia, and five of the Central American republics are on highlands. In British India, the so-called "hill stations" of the sub-Himalayas, such as Darjeeling, Simla, Murree, and Naini Tal, at elevations of 6,500 to 7,500 ft., become havens for white residents from the lowlands during the long, hot season.

306. *Temperature Zones on Tropical Highlands.* As a consequence of the steep temperature gradients that characterize mountains, several zones of climate, with characteristic vegetation covers and crops, may be recognized. In the mountainous parts of tropical Latin America, four such zones commonly are delimited, *viz.*, the *tierra caliente* (hot lands), *tierra templada* (temperate lands), *tierra fría* (cool lands), and the cold *paramos*, or *puna*. Quite naturally these altitudinal belts are not defined by identical elevations throughout the entire tropics. In general the bounding elevations become lower with increasing distance from the equator. The lowest zone, or *caliente*, normally extends from sea level to 2,000 to 3,000 ft. (annual temperature roughly 83 to 75°). Where precipitation is abundant it is characterized by a luxuriant vegetation cover of trees or of trees and tall grass and by such crops as rubber, bananas, and cacao. The *tierra templada* lies above the *caliente* and extends up to 6,000 or 6,500 ft. (temperature roughly 75 to 65°). Within this climatic belt is produced a great variety of crops, among them coffee, maize, tea, cotton, and rice. *Tierra fría*, lying above the *templada*, prevails up to 10,000 to 11,500 ft. (temperature 65 to 54°). There middle-latitude crops such as wheat, barley, apples, and potatoes are at home, and the pastoral industries frequently are well developed. At still higher elevations are the cool or cold paramos, in which the raising of crops is relatively unimportant, although grazing may still persist. Trees are not uncommon in lower parts of the paramos, but its higher elevations are the zone of alpine meadows. Above heights of 14,000 to 15,000 ft. the zone of perpetual snow is usually encountered. Local trade of considerable importance, fostered by this temperature zonation of products, is carried on between the inhabitants at various altitudes.

307. *Seasonal Temperatures.* The lower temperatures at elevated sites have led to the statement that mountains in the tropics enjoy perpetual spring. Quito's annual temperature of 54.7°, for instance, is not greatly unlike the May average at Madison, Wis. However, the great variety of elevations within a tropical mountain mass obviously results in all gradations of temperature.

But although the thermometer stands lower on a tropical mountain than it does on an adjacent lowland, both locations have a similar *uniformity* in monthly and daily temperatures. Small seasonal ranges, and the same monotonous repetition of daily weather, belong alike to tropical highlands and plains (Fig. 110). At Quito, for instance, the temperature difference between the warmest and coolest months is only 0.7°, which is even smaller than that of the Amazon Lowlands in the same latitude. Mexico City at 7,474 ft. has an *average annual temperature* 17° below that for Veracruz on the coast, yet their *annual ranges* are almost identical—11.5 and 11° respectively. One climatologist has stated the situation tersely by saying: "The pitch changes; the tune remains the same."

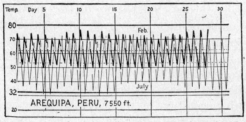

FIG. 110.—Daily maximum and minimum temperatures for a highland station in the tropics. (*Courtesy of Mark Jefferson and the Geographical Review.*)

308. *Middle-latitude Highlands.* While within the tropics mountains and plateaus may be climatically desirable because of their lower temperatures, this same characteristic causes highlands in the middle latitudes to be climatically inferior to lowlands. The difference lies in the fact that tropical lowlands have an *excess* of heat, so that any reduction of temperature with altitude usually is counted as an advantage, for human comfort as well as for the greater variety of products that can be grown. In the middle latitudes, on the other hand, even the lowlands usually are none too warm, so that reduction of temperature with altitude, causing a cooler summer and shorter growing season, materially decreases the opportunities for agricultural production. In other words, there are fewer *utilizable* temperature zones in middle-latitude highlands.

CLIMATIC DATA FOR A REPRESENTATIVE ALTITUDE STATION IN MIDDLE
LATITUDES

Longs Peak, Colo. (8,956 *Ft.*)

	J	F	M	A	M	J	J	A	S	O	N	D	Yr.	Range
Temp.	23	22	26	33	41	51	55	55	48	39	31	24	37	33
Precip.	0.7	1.2	2.0	2.7	2.4	1.6	3.6	2.2	1.7	1.7	0.9	0.9	21.6	

PRECIPITATION

309. INCREASED PRECIPITATION IN MOUNTAINS. Precipitation increases with altitude up to a certain elevation (usually 4,000 to 7,000 ft.), a zone of maximum above which it begins to decline. Thus on a rainfall map mountains are conspicuous as "islands" of heavier precipitation (Plate II). This fact is admirably illustrated by the Pacific Coast mountains of the United States or The Himalayas in Asia. The reasons for the increased precipitation in highlands has been discussed in an earlier section of this book (128). Above an elevation of 6,000 or 7,000 ft. the lower temperature, and hence lower absolute humidity of the air, usually causes a falling off in the amount of precipitation.

It is especially in dry climates, no matter in what latitude, that the heavier rainfall of highlands is of such critical importance. In regions of drought, mountains, besides being "islands" of heavier precipitation, are islands of heavier vegetation cover and more abundant agricultural production as well. In both arid and semiarid lands, highlands are likely to bear a cover of forest in contrast to the meager grass and shrub vegetation of the surrounding drier lowlands. The Black Hills of western South Dakota are "black" because their dark-green forests present such a color contrast with the tawny-hued steppes surrounding them. Not only are settlements attracted to the humid slopes and to the well-watered mountain valleys, but streams, descending from the rainier highlands, carry the influence of highland climate far out on the dry lowlands. Thus the Yemen Highlands in southern Arabia, and the adjacent lowlands watered by its rivers, are a garden spot and the principal center of settlement in that otherwise largely desert country. In eastern North Africa the Ethiopian (Abyssinian) Highlands are a similar "culture island," while the Nile floods have their origin in this same mountain knot. The waters of the Colorado River, with its principal sources in the Rocky Mountains, make possible the agricultural utilization of the dry Imperial Valley of southern California, over 700 miles distant. From the Andes come the 50 or more small streams that, crossing the Peruvian Desert, nourish the parallel irrigated strips of that otherwise waste land.

WINDS

310. On exposed mountain slopes and summits, where ground friction is small, winds are usually strong. Mountain valleys, on the other hand, are particularly well protected against violent winds. Owing to the great variety of relief and exposure in highlands, there are also a number of local winds

characteristic of such areas. The diurnal reversal of wind direction, upslope by day and downslope by night, has been discussed previously under the head of *mountain and valley winds* (98).

311. *Foehn*, or *Chinook*. Still another local vertical wind, characteristic of mountains, is the cyclonic-induced *foehn*, which in the United States and Canada is known as the *chinook*. It is a relatively warm, dry wind which descends a mountain front when a cyclonic storm causes air to cross the range from the opposite side of the divide (Fig. 111). For example, as a well-developed low travels southeastward down the Great Plains, paralleling the Rocky Mountain front, air is induced to ascend over the Rockies from the western side and descend their eastern slopes. The relatively high temperature and aridity of the chinook originate as follows: As the air

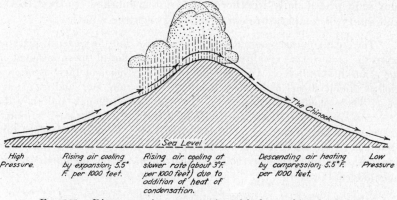

| High Pressure. | Rising air cooling by expansion; 5.5° F. per 1000 feet. | Rising air cooling at slower rate (about 3°F. per 1000 feet) due to addition of heat of condensation. | Descending air heating by compression; 5.5°F. per 1000 feet. | Low Pressure |

Fig. 111.—Diagrammatic representation of foehn or chinook winds.

ascends on the western side of the Rockies, condensation occurs, so that the rising air reaches the top of the divide with much of its moisture gone *but still retaining a relatively high temperature* as a result of liberation of heat of condensation during ascent. As this air descends on the side of the mountain toward the cyclone, it is further heated by compression and made relatively drier, so that it arrives at the eastern base of the Rockies as a mild, arid wind. The warmth of the chinook, therefore, is of dual origin: (a) heat of condensation and (b) heat resulting from compression. Usually its temperature is not over 40° in winter, but this appears very warm, by contrast at least, after a period of anticyclonic weather with intense cold. If snow lies on the ground, it vanishes as if by magic before the warm blast of the chinook. A rise in temperature of 40° within 24 hr. is not unusual. At Kipp, Mont., there is the extraordinary record of a 34° rise within an interval of 7 min. The genuine chinook country is the High Plains at the eastern foot of the Rockies from southern Colorado northward to the limits of settlement in Canada. The milder winters of this western portion of the plains, as compared with regions farther east, are associated with the prevalence of these local mountain winds. Here the snow cover is less persistent, so that grazing can go on throughout the winter. Foehn winds are by no means confined to the eastern Rocky Mountain foothill country but, on the contrary, are found in almost all mountain areas where cyclonic storms are prevalent. No doubt the region where they are best known is the Swiss valleys on the northern side of the Alps.

DAILY WEATHER

312. In highlands the weather changes within the 24-hr. period are likely to be greater than they are on adjacent lowlands. Violent changes from hot sun to cool shade, from chill wind to calm; at one period gusts of rain or possibly snow, and then again intense sunlight—such is the erratic nature of the daily weather. Even within the tropics, the complex sequence of daily weather stands out in marked contrast to the uniformity of temperature conditions between the months.

"The night and early mornings are cold and raw, but the powerful sunshine raises the temperature rapidly, and by noon it feels hot in the sun, though in the shade it is still cool. About midday clouds gather and there is often a violent thunderstorm in the afternoon with heavy rain, hail, and frequently snow. These clouds and storms are essentially convectional, and they die away after the heat of the day which caused them. . . . The early mornings are fine, and the air at these great altitudes (Quito, Ecuador) is remarkably clear; but in the afternoons the clouds hang low over the gloomy landscape, and hail, snow, and rain chill the air, so that the mountains are almost invariably hidden."[1]

[1] Kendrew, "The Climates of the Continents," p. 320.

SECTION C. PROCESSES CONCERNED WITH THE ORIGIN OF LANDFORMS

313. The earth upon which man lives is characterized by great and often pleasing variety in its surface features. High lands and low, level expanses and steep slopes, plains, plateaus, hill lands, and mountains are arranged in endless combinations which furnish the stage upon which the play of human life is enacted. Because there are so many kinds of landforms, it may sometimes seem that they are distributed over the earth without order and that an understanding of their nature and arrangement is beyond the ability of the beginning student. Such is not the case. It is quite as possible to understand the meaning of earth features and to perceive them in their interrelationships as it is to reach an understanding of the major climatic types of the world.

The study of climates in the preceding chapters was approached through a consideration of the elements and processes of the atmosphere. In the same manner, the study of landforms may be approached through a brief survey of the materials of which they are composed and the processes by which they originate. Although the student of geography is interested primarily in the shapes and patterns of the surface features of the land and in their human utility as elements of the regional equipment, a clear understanding of them is best reached through at least a brief survey of the *substances* of which they are made, of the *agents* that are involved in their origin, and of the *processes* by which they originate or by which their shaping is accomplished. It is the object of Sec. C (Chaps. XII, XIII) of this book to furnish that brief survey, reserving for Sec. D the details of interpretative description relating to the appearance of landforms produced by the work of the various agents.

REFERENCES FOR SECTION C

Agar, W. M., Flint, R. F., and Longwell, C. R. "Geology from Original Sources." Henry Holt and Company, Inc., New York, 1929.

Branson, E. B., and Tarr, W. A. "Introductory Geology." McGraw-Hill Book Company, Inc., New York, 1935.

Cleland, H. F. "Geology: Physical and Historical." American Book Company, New York, 1925.

Cornish, Vaughan. "Ocean Waves and Kindred Geophysical Phenomena." Cambridge University Press, London, 1934.

Cotton, C. A. "Geomorphology of New Zealand." Part I, Systematic. Dominion Museum, Wellington, 1926.

Daly, R. A. "Our Mobile Earth." Charles Scribner's Sons, New York, 1926.

Davis, W. M. "Die erklärande Beschreibung der Landformen." B. G. Teubner, Leipzig, 1912.

———. "Geographical Essays." Ginn and Company, Boston, 1909.

Emmons, W. H., Thiel, G. A., Stauffer, C. R., and Allison, I. S. "Geology." McGraw-Hill Book Company, Inc., New York, 1932.

Heck, N. H. "Earthquakes." Princeton University Press, Princeton, N. J., 1936.

Johnson, D. W. "Shore Processes and Shoreline Development." John Wiley & Sons, Inc., New York, 1919.

Johnstone, James. "An Introduction to Oceanography." University Press of Liverpool, Liverpool, 1923.

Lobeck, A. K. "Geomorphology: An Introduction to the Study of Landscapes," McGraw-Hill Book Company, Inc., New York, 1939. Notable for its excellent diagrammatic illustrations.

Longwell, C. R., Knopf, A., and Flint, R. F. "A Text Book of Geology." Part I, Physical Geology. John Wiley & Sons, Inc., New York, 1932.

Loomis, F. B. "Fieldbook of Common Rocks and Minerals." 6th ed., G. P. Putnam's Sons, New York, 1931.

Marmer, H. A. "The Sea." D. Appleton-Century Company, Inc., New York, 1930.

Martonne, Emmanuel de. "A Shorter Physical Geography." Alfred A. Knopf, New York, 1927.

Milne, John. "Earthquakes and Other Earth Movements." 7th ed., The Blakiston Company, Philadelphia, 1939.

Passarge, S. "Die Grundlagen der Landschaftskunde." L. Friederichsen & Co., Hamburg, 1920.

Salisbury, R. D. "Physiography." Henry Holt and Company, Inc., New York, 1919.

Supan, Alexander. "Grundzüge der physischen Erdkunde." Walter de Gruyter & Company, Berlin, 1930.

Tarr, R. S., and Martin, Lawrence. "College Physiography." The Macmillan Company, New York, 1928.

Thwaites, F. T. "Outlines of Glacial Geology." Edwards Bros., Inc., Ann Arbor, Mich., 1934.

Tolman, C. F. "Ground Water." McGraw-Hill Book Company, Inc., New York, 1937.

Woolbridge, S. W., and Morgan, R. S. "Outlines of Geomorphology." Longmans, Green and Company, London, 1937.

Worcester, P. G. "A Textbook of Geomorphology." D. Van Nostrand Company, Inc., New York, 1939.

Wright, W. B. "The Quaternary Ice Age." Macmillan & Company, Ltd., London, 1937.

Chapter XII. Earth Materials and the Tectonic Processes

Earth Materials

314. IMPORTANT EARTH ELEMENTS. The earth's crust (lithosphere) is composed mainly of rocks. Rocks are aggregations of minerals, and minerals are chemical elements or combinations of them. It is probable that the entire list of 92 chemical elements is present in the earth, but many of them are extremely rare. Some others are more common but still do not make up a great part of the lithosphere. Of them all only eight are abundant.

Oxygen is the most abundant of these. In an array of combinations with other elements it comprises about 46 per cent of the known crust of the earth. *Silicon* is next most abundant, for it combines with other elements so commonly that it makes up nearly 28 per cent of the total mass. Six other elements together make up 24 per cent of the total. They are, in the order of their abundance, *aluminum, iron, calcium, potassium, sodium,* and *magnesium.* The remaining 2 per cent of the earth's crust includes a long list of elements some of which, though small in amount, are of critical importance in human affairs. In this group are such as radium, platinum, gold, silver, and various of the semiprecious minerals.

315. MINERALS are sometimes composed of single chemical elements, such as pure copper or gold. More commonly they are combinations of two or more elements in chemical union. A given mineral always includes the same constituent elements in the same proportion, and in most cases it has its own distinctive crystalline form. In such minerals the elements are united in molecules which are very different from any of the constituent elements. Thus iron, a metallic element, may unite with oxygen, a gas, and water, a liquid, to form a soft brown earthy mineral, limonite, which is familiar as iron rust. The list of known minerals is a long one containing many hundreds of names, but, as in the case of the elements, a few of the many are so much more common than the others that they make up the bulk of the lithosphere.

Of these, *quartz*, a hard glassy mineral which is a combination of silicon and oxygen, is most important. It is the substance of common sand. Also important are the *feldspars*, a group of light-colored minerals including combinations of silica, aluminum, and oxygen with various other elements such as sodium, calcium, or potassium. The decomposed fragments of the feldspars, together with some fine sands and other substances, make up the bulk of ordinary clays. A third group is the *ferromagnesian minerals*, dark heavy combinations of silica with iron, magnesium, and other elements. Some minerals include several chemical elements which are combined in an extremely complicated manner.

316. ROCKS. Minerals, singly or in association, make up the rocks of the earth's crust. In rocks the component minerals exist separately and not in chemical combination. Moreover, the component minerals in various specimens of the same class of rock are not necessarily identical in kind or amount. They are locked together in an almost infinite array of physical combinations the patterns of which depend upon various things, especially the nature and proportions of the component minerals, their peculiarities of crystalline structure, and the history of the rock since its origin. It is clear that, since there are hundreds of minerals that may be combined in a great variety of ways and proportions and then subsequently changed by events in the history of the rock, the total number of different kinds of rock is very large. The many kinds can be grouped, according to their origin, into three general classes: (*a*) igneous, (*b*) sedimentary, and (*c*) metamorphic rocks.

317. IGNEOUS ROCKS are those which have been solidified from a molten state (Fig. 113). Even though they all are alike in that respect, they still are of great variety and may be grouped in different ways, such as (*a*) extrusive or intrusive, (*b*) coarsely or finely crystalline, and (*c*) acid or basic, according to the chemical nature of their predominant minerals. Although there are some notable exceptions to the rule, it is generally true that the igneous rocks are compact, of low porosity, and resistant to erosion as compared with those of sedimentary origin.

CLASSES OF IGNEOUS ROCKS. *Extrusive* rocks are solidified from molten materials poured out upon the earth's surface. Such are the products of a volcano of which lava, pumice, and finely divided rock particles called ash are examples. Some molten rocks, however, are pushed from within the earth toward the surface but, never reaching it, are left to cool slowly deep underground. These are called *intrusive*, although later they may be widely exposed by the removal of the covering layers. Granite is a rock of that class.

Extrusive rocks ordinarily are cooled quickly, giving little time for the collection of molecules of similar sorts into crystals of appreciable size. Such are, therefore, finely crystalline, or they may have no crystals at all and are then classed as volcanic glass. Intrusive rocks, when introduced in giant masses well below the surface, may have their cooling and solidification delayed for thousands of years. During that time minerals of like nature come together in the liquid and build up a coarse, interlocking crystalline structure.

Igneous rocks are called *acidic rocks* if their minerals are predominantly quartz, or others high in silica, and if they are light in color and have only minor amounts of the ferromagnesian minerals. Granite is such a rock, and commonly it has crystals so coarse as to be plainly visible. Others, in which the principal minerals are of the dark, heavy, ferromagnesian groups, and in which quartz is less abundant, are said to be *basic rocks*. Gabbro and basalt are examples of basic rocks.

The significance to the student of geography of these major distinctions between classes of igneous rocks lies in the differences in landforms produced by and developed in them, in the qualities they impart to some soils derived from them, in their relation to the origin of mineral ores, and in their comparative qualities for structural and other human uses. For example, the acidic rocks, being high in quartz, do not readily decompose and are therefore good structural materials and they also are likely to resist erosion and form conspicuous relief features. The ferromagnesian minerals, on the contrary, decompose more readily, and rocks composed of them are not commonly used in building. Neither are they so commonly the cause of prominent surface features.

318. SEDIMENTARY ROCKS are principally such as have been deposited as sediments. Some are the deposits of wind and streams on the land, but more largely they are put down in bodies of water such as lakes or, especially, the sea. They may be derived from materials that are rolled about by waves, like sand or gravel; or, like clay, are suspended in the water; or, like lime, are carried in dissolved form. Usually the sediments are deposited somewhat according to their size or weight and therefore accumulate in beds of similar nature which cover considerable areas. The process of deposition of most sedimentary rocks appears not to have been perfectly continuous for lengths of time sufficient for the building of great thicknesses but to have been interrupted. The interruptions are marked by changes, often slight, in the kind or quality of deposit which results in the formation of distinct layers, or *strata*, which are separated by planes of weakness called bedding planes (329, Fig. 112). Hardened sediments often are

called *stratified rock*. The principal place of deposition for sediments is the nearly level floor of the shallow seas near present or former shorelines. The normal attitude of most sedimentary strata is, therefore, practically horizontal, and when such rocks are found in positions greatly inclined from horizontal it is an indication that there has been a disturbance of the materials after their deposition. The processes by which ocean-bottom sediments become elevated to form part of the continental surface are reserved for future consideration. Here it may be noted merely that such is the fact and that the soft ocean

FIG. 112.—Stratified rock. An exposure of thin-bedded sedimentary rock grading upward into regolith and soil. (*Wisconsin Geological Survey Photograph.*)

sediments become consolidated into rock by compression, resulting from the great weight of the overlying accumulations, or by the cementing action of infiltering chemical materials. The principal classes of sedimentary rocks are (*a*) sandstone, (*b*) shale, and (*c*) limestone. However, the distinction between them is not always sharp since the materials often were intermingled as sediments or are graded from sands into muds or from muds into limy deposits, with increase in distance from the shoreline. Thus, there are sandy or shaly limestones, limy sandstones, etc. The classes of sedimentary rock differ considerably in their relations to landforms, soil origin, and other aspects *of regional character,*

319. *Sandstone* is comprised mainly of sand, coarse or fine, most of which was washed by the waves of ancient seas and deposited in shallow waters along their shores. The hardening of the sands into rock is accomplished by infiltered clay or lime, or sometimes silica or iron, deposited from solution. These act as cements, attaching the sand grains together, in some instances firmly, in others poorly. Some sandstones are well cemented and are in comparatively thick beds (massive sandstone) while others are so poorly cemented or so thinly bedded that they disintegrate readily upon exposure. Because of their composition, most sandstones are comparatively porous and permeable to water, but the silica of which they are composed is relatively insoluble. Therefore, massive sandstones often stand in cliffs or ridges while less resistant rocks are wasted away.

Closely allied to the sandstones are rocks called *conglomerate*. These are composed of coarse gravels, pebbles, or boulders which are imbedded in, and held together by, a ground-mass usually of sandstone, much after the manner of man-made concrete.

320. *Shale* is consolidated mud (clay or silt). It may contain lime that acts as a cement, or it may be hardened as a result of compression by the great weight of overlying rocks. Usually, shale is a relatively nonresistant rock which disintegrates easily upon exposure at the surface, and because it yields readily to the attacks of the elements it often gives rise to lowlands and to clay soils. However, it is comprised of fine grains and has small pore spaces. It is, therefore, a compact insoluble rock and does not readily permit the movement of water underground.

321. *Limestone* is a rock produced by the compacting of limy sediments, derived from chemical precipitates of lime in sea water or from the fragments of shells. In some places are found thick deposits of nearly pure limestone (calcium carbonate). More commonly they contain admixtures of other materials, especially sand or clay. Bodies of dense siliceous material also are found in limestones and are recognized as bands or masses of *chert*, or *flint*. Some limestones are compact and hard, others soft and porous. The latter are called chalk and are exemplified in the ranges of hills in southern England and the famous chalk cliffs of Dover. Some limestones are ridge makers, whereas others give rise to lowlands. The different classes of features to which they give rise depend largely upon differences in climate and in the composition of the limestones concerned. Unlike most rocks, pure limestones are readily soluble in ground water and through long-continued solution sometimes develop interior cavities or even great caverns, such as the Mammoth Cave of Kentucky. It is because of their solubility that limestones in regions of humid climate commonly, but not always,

give rise to lowlands, while those in regions of dry climates commonly stand out as features of striking relief. A closely related rock, called *dolomite*, which is calcium-magnesium carbonate, is much less soluble than limestone and commonly is a ridge maker, even in regions of humid climate (389).

322. *Less Abundant Sediments.* Not all sediments are of marine origin. Some appear to have been deposited in shallow coastal bays or marshes. Among these are organic deposits such as coal, iron-bearing sediments such as bog iron ore (limonite), and other forms of iron deposits. Some clearly have been deposited by streams or the wind, and still others are rocks believed to have resulted from deposits in the evaporating waters of interior basins or coastal lagoons in arid climates. Such are rock salt and gypsum.

323. METAMORPHIC ROCKS are derived from rocks of any other sort by processes of change. The commonest causes of change are pressure, heat, and the cementing action of percolating waters underground. In some metamorphic rocks the change appears to have been produced in a relatively short time (geologically speaking) by means of the great pressures exerted in the warping and bending of rocks in the progress of mountain building or by the great heat resulting from the introduction of molten lavas into older rocks or by both at once. Other rocks appear to have been changed by the extremely slow processes carried on through the alteration or replacement of minerals by underground waters.

Metamorphism in some rocks has involved a change so great as to produce minerals not present in the parent rock. Some of the valuable mineral ores are formed in that way. In others the changes are mainly those of form produced by recementation, by recrystallization, or rearrangement of the crystals.

324. *Common Metamorphic Rocks.* Metamorphism affects both igneous and sedimentary rocks and so generally that nearly every common rock has a well-known metamorphic equivalent. Granite, for example, may be metamorphosed into a *gneiss* or *schist*. A sandstone metamorphosed becomes a *quartzite*, a rock of extreme hardness and resistance to erosion. A shale subjected to great pressure has its particles flattened and arranged parallel so that the rock readily splits or cleaves. It is called *slate*, a rock of considerable economic value. A pure limestone, under similar processes, becomes recrystallized, sometimes takes on a translucent or waxy appearance, and is called *marble*. Bituminous coal becomes anthracite when metamorphosed or, if the process is carried far enough, *graphite*, the substance used in pencil leads.

In several parts of the earth are vast areas of rocks of great age. Some, doubtless, originally were igneous, others sedimentary. Whatever their original nature, they have been subjected, during the long progress of geological time, to deformative processes. In some regions these processes have been repeated on a vast scale more than once. As a result the rocks of these regions generally are metamorphosed to a high degree and have been largely recrystallized. Regions of that kind are sometimes broadly characterized as "areas of ancient crystalline rocks" (Fig. 176).

325. ROCK AND MANTLE ROCK. Over most of the land surface of the earth the solid rock of the earth's crust is buried underneath a covering layer, thin or thick, of disintegrated and decomposed rock fragments. This material is named *regolith* but is sometimes called mantle rock (Fig. 112). Not everywhere is the regolith sufficiently thick to cover the underlying rock. On steep slopes almost everywhere, and in some regions over large areas generally, the bare and solid rock may be seen. These exposures are briefly described as *outcrops*. Through the nature and attitude of the rocks displayed in widely scattered outcrops geologists are able to form intelligent opinions as to the kind, distribution, and extent of the rocks buried underneath the regolith.

326. LITHIC REGIONS. The rocks that underlie a region are associated in many significant ways with other of its natural and cultural features. For example, there is in some places a close relationship between the underlying rocks and the soil, since the regolith is the parent material of the soil and in some places is the principal constituent of the soil itself. The nature and structure of rocks often are reflected in the details of relief features and in the kinds and distribution of mineral resources. In many regions the rocks are of such different kinds, and change from one kind to another within such short distances, that they may be described only as regions of complex rocks. However, there are certain large regions in each of which a single class of rocks, such as recent sediments, older and more altered sediments, igneous rocks, or ancient crystalline rocks, is so widespread that it imparts at least some degree of fundamental unity to the region in which it is dominant. The larger of the world regions of rock similarity are worthy of consideration in connection with matters to be noted later. They are shown in Plate VI, which is entitled "Lithic Regions."

THE SURFACE-MOLDING FORCES

327. THE ORIGIN OF LANDFORMS. The major subdivisions of the earth's relief features are the great depressions which contain the

oceans and the broad elevations which are the continental platforms. Upon the bottoms of the ocean depressions there are features of a smaller order of size about which comparatively little is known because they are covered by water. Upon the tops of the continental platforms also are other features of a smaller order of size about which a great deal is known and with which people have daily and intimate concern. They are the high mountain masses, the broad plateaus, rough hill regions, and extended plains. Of a still smaller order of magnitude are the local features, hill or gully, dale or plain, which are a part of the immediate environment of every community.

Landforms, whether large or small, result from the interaction of certain forces with the materials of the earth's surface through longer or shorter periods of time. Some of the *forces* may be described as geologic, some as climatic, and still others as biologic. They accomplish their various kinds of work by means of *processes* of whose operation at least the rudiments must be understood. The forces work by means of these processes upon an earth crust made up of rocks of different kinds and degrees of resistance, arranged in different positions and attitudes with respect to each other and the surface of the earth.

328. THE TIME ELEMENT IN PHYSICAL GEOGRAPHY. The student of landforms and the processes by means of which they have evolved must adopt a different conception of time from that employed in considering the events of human history. Although some of the processes of nature are sudden and violent, accomplishing notable results in a short space of time, such are the exception rather than the rule. Most of the common landforms have been produced by the slow and long-continued operation of forces and processes still at work. Explanation of the fact that they are able to produce so little effect within a lifetime or within the span of human history requires merely the use of a different time scale for their measurement.

It is estimated by geologists that the age of the earth may possibly be $1\frac{1}{2}$ billions of years. Of this vast span of time the record of the first two-thirds is vague and nearly lost in antiquity. It is like that long period in human development before man learned how to make any written record of his doings. More is known of the latest one-third of earth history (around 500 million years). But even that time is so long that it dwarfs human history to a moment by comparison. However, most of the present landforms of the earth trace their origins to events in that time and especially in the later or more recent periods of that time. It is not desirable to enter here upon a study of the periods of time into which geologic history is divided, although it may be convenient in some connections to make references to them.

As a basis of reference, and to provide a better conception of the time element in the evolution of landforms, as well as for its general interest, a simplified form of the geological column is reproduced in Appendix E. This tabular arrangement of the periods of earth history in major outline shows also some of the principal events in the biologic sequence which geological science has interpreted from the records of the rocks.

329. THE FORCES INVOLVED IN SURFACE MOLDING. The various forces involved in the production and alteration of landforms may be grouped for convenient study in more than one way to suit different objectives. For the present purpose it will be helpful to think of them as belonging to two major groups: (a) those forces that originate *within* the earth and (b) those that originate from *without*, or beyond, the earth.

The members of the first group derive their energy mainly from changes occurring in the earth's interior, changes such as heating through radioactivity or chemical recombination, expansion or contraction, or the removal of liquid material from one place to another. This group may be called the *tectonic forces*. They are made manifest through processes called *diastrophism* and *vulcanism*, which include the breaking, bending, and warping of the earth's crust, including its elevation and depression, and the expulsion of molten rock from the interior outward. *The tendency of the tectonic forces and their processes is to cause differences in surface elevation on the earth* and, by heaving up the crust here and depressing it there or by pouring out upon it great masses of molten lava, to construct surface features of great height and areal extent.

The members of the second group derive their energy mainly from the sun. They may be called the *forces of gradation*. They operate largely through the work of agents such as wind, running water, moving snow and ice, and living organisms. *The tendency of the forces of gradation and their processes is to bring the surface of the land to a uniform low slope or grade*. This is done by tearing down all elevations, such as may be produced by the tectonic forces, and by filling up depressions. The processes of gradation are of two types. These may be called *degradation* and *aggradation*. Under degradation may be included all the processes by which lands that stand higher than the level of the final slope, or grade, are brought down to it. Conversely, under aggradation may be included all the processes that tend to fill the sea margins, tectonic basins, and other depressions with sediment and thus bring them up to grade. The process of degradation itself may be thought of as consisting of three steps: (a) the preparation of rock material for removal, (b) the picking up of the rock fragments, and (c) their transportation. The process of aggradation consists of the deposition of the fragments.

The force of gravity operates in conjunction with both the tectonic and gradational groups. It doubtless is intimately concerned with the contraction of the earth and, hence, with various diastrophic and volcanic consequences arising therefrom. It is concerned also with the work of the wind, of running water, and of moving glacial ice. Solar energy, to be sure, indirectly causes differences in atmospheric pressure and the evaporation of the moisture which descends upon the land as rain or snow. But it is gravity that causes winds to blow and streams and glaciers to flow and do gradational work.

Fig. 113.—Jointing in granite. Joint planes commonly occur in sets all the members of which trend in the same direction. The sets may be vertical, inclined, or horizontal. (*U. S. Geological Survey Photograph.*)

The two groups of forces, *tectonic* on the one hand and *gradational* on the other, are at work continuously and, therefore, are in endless conflict. The one causes features having differences in elevation; the other tends to reduce them to a low and uniform plain. The hills, valleys, and other relief features that now exist are the present, but temporary, expression of the state of this perpetual battle.

The Tectonic Processes

DIASTROPHISM

330. CRUSTAL FRACTURE. It is well known that any rock, under sufficient stress, will break. Stresses sufficient to break even the massive rocks of the earth's crust are believed to originate in several possible ways, such as (*a*) the slow movement of plastic material from one place

to another underneath the earth's crust, (*b*) the redistribution of surface load caused by the removal of material from one part of the surface and its deposition elsewhere, or (*c*) expansion or shrinkage of the earth as a whole. Stresses sufficient to cause crustal distortion have developed so many times that the solid rock is nearly everywhere traversed by cracks called *joints*. These are so numerous near the surface that the hard exterior of the earth must resemble the crackled glaze on a piece of antique china (Fig. 113). However, the joints become smaller and fewer with depth and below a dozen miles or so are believed not to exist. This cracked surface zone is called the *zone of fracture*. The joints permit the water of the ground to circulate more freely within the rocks and enable the agents of gradation to work more readily. In some places also they play a part in the details of shape in landforms.

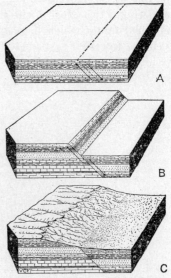

FIG. 114.—Diagram to show the development of a tensional fault in sedimentary rock. (*A*) The strata before faulting; (*B*) fault, showing direction of displacement and the fault scarp; (*C*) the reduction of the fault scarp by erosion to a dissected fault-line scarp.

Under severe stresses rocks not only break but sometimes move along the plane of fracture and are displaced. Such displacements are called *faults*. The motion that produces the dislocation often is sudden but usually is limited in amount to fractions of an inch or a few feet. The displacement is sometimes in a vertical direction, the rocks on one side of the fault being elevated as compared with those on the other. Then a cliff is produced which is called a *fault scarp*. Some faults are produced by tensional or stretching forces as in Fig. 114*A*, *B*; others by compressional or crowding forces, as in Fig. 115. In some faults the displacement is horizontal rather than vertical, resulting in the breaking and offsetting of roads and boundary lines.

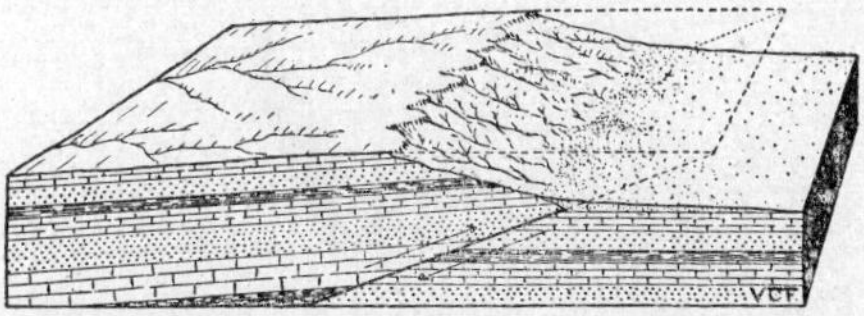

FIG. 115.—A diagram to illustrate the manner of displacement in a compressional fault. The dotted lines show the volume of rock removed by erosion during the growth of the fault-line scarp.

When many successive vertical faults occur along the same plane at intervals during thousands of years, the resulting escarpment along the line of the fault plane may attain the size of hills or even mountains (Fig. 116). Most of the Basin Ranges in Nevada are the result of tensional faults which have uptilted great masses of rock, and so is even the towering east face of the Sierra Nevada Mountains of Cali-

FIG. 116.—The latest step in the growth of a great fault-line scarp. Above is the front of the Wasatch Mountains, a fault-line scarp. Parallel to it, the low scarp of a recent fault is shown by the dark line that traverses the piedmont alluvium. (*U. S. Geological Survey Photograph.*)

fornia. The Lewis Range of Montana, in Glacier National Park, is likewise the result of faulting but of the compressional type, which caused the broken edge of the rock layers to slip up over the rocks of the adjacent plains and ride out upon them for a distance of several miles. These giant displacements required a long time for their accomplishment during which the growing escarpments were attacked by

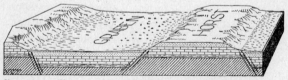

FIG. 117.—A diagram to illustrate block faulting and the formation of a graben and horst. The arrows indicate direction of relative displacement.

destructive agents, lowered, and carved up into mountain peaks (Figs. 114C, 115).

In a few places in the world parallel faults of great length have permitted the segments of earth between them to drop down. These become broad valleys, flanked on either side by fault scarps, and are known as *graben*, or rift, valleys (Fig. 117). Of this origin are such famous valleys as the Lowlands of Scotland, the upper Rhine Valley, the depression in which the Dead Sea lies, and those vast trenches in East Africa occupied in part by lakes Tanganyika and Nyasa. In other places the land between parallel faults has been elevated rather than depressed. The result is a blocklike mountain uplift called a *horst*. Some of the Basin Ranges are of that origin. To some extent faulting has a part in the making of almost all mountains.

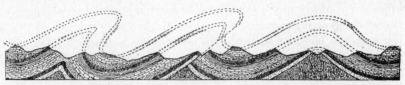

Fig. 118.—Synclinal and anticlinal mountains. The complicated folds and faults of some mountains have been studied and from the eroded remnants which make up the present mountains great structures have been projected. These probably never existed, as such, because they were eroded as they were formed. (See also Fig. 241.)

331. CRUSTAL BENDING. In certain earth deformations the stresses have been applied to rocks so slowly or under such conditions that instead of fracturing they bend or even fold. The bends and folds may be either small or of mountainous proportions and either simple or complicated. In some mountain regions sedimentary rock strata have been shortened by horizontal compression and have been pushed up into a series of wavelike folds (Fig. 118). The arch, or crest, of one of these folds is called an *anticline*, and the trough of the wave a *syncline* (Fig. 119). In the Alps and some other mountains the folding has been so intense as to cause the wavelike structures to close and tip over. In most folded mountains the arrangement

Fig. 119.—A portion of a buried anticlinal structure that has been exposed in a stream valley. (*U. S. Geological Survey Photograph.*)

of the rocks is further complicated by the fact that severe folding has been accompanied by faulting and, in many places, by intrusions of igneous materials also. The present mountains of highly folded regions seldom reproduce anticlines and synclines in corresponding ridges and valleys because time and the degradational processes have intervened, greatly altering the appearance of these structures. However, the attitudes of the remnants of the folded rocks, resistant and nonresistant, are generally reflected in features of mountain relief.

332. CRUSTAL WARPING. Similar to folding in nature, less intense, but even more important are broad deformations of the earth's crust which may be called warping. Such changes in crustal shape affect vast areas and probably are continuously in progress, but they require thousands of years to produce notable results. Through warping, broad areas of low plains land, such as formerly existed on the present site of the North Sea basin, have been lowered slowly a few feet or a few scores of feet and added to the shallow sea bottoms. By the same process great expanses of shallow sea bottom have been elevated slowly and added to the areas of the continents. Most of the state of Florida is a relatively recent addition to the area of North America. Through an understanding of this process one comes to an appreciation of the meaning of the stratified sedimentary rocks, containing the fossil remains of sea animals, that now are found far in the interiors of each of the continents. The fossil evidences in these rocks indicate that some of them were uplifted from the sea far back in geologic history; others in comparatively recent time. Similar evidence shows that some areas have been alternately elevated and depressed relative to sea level not only once but several times.

333. DIASTROPHISM AND ROCK STRUCTURES. From the foregoing it may be seen that the attitudes and arrangements of the rocks are subject to the greatest variation. Sediments, put down horizontally, do not always remain so. Likewise, igneous rocks are subject, long after their formation, to distortion and fracture. The position and arrangement of rock formations with respect to each other is called the *rock structure*, and rock strucutre is one of the very important elements in that complex of conditions out of which landforms are evolved.

334. REGIONS OF PRESENT DIASTROPHISM. Although the records of the rocks seem to indicate that all parts of the earth have been subjected to warping, folding, or faulting at one time or another, not all are now subject to equally great diastrophic changes. Instead, these processes seem to be more active in clearly recognized regions or zones. Most important of these are the borders of the Pacific Ocean. There, offshore, is a series of notable ocean deeps, while onshore are systems of mountains: the Andes, the coastal mountains of North America, Japan, and the Philippine Islands. These two, the deeps and the fringing heights, appear to be under constant stress and are subject to frequent readjustment. This is expressed in numerous faults, geologically recent, which appear to result from the elevation of the lands relative to the adjacent ocean bottoms. Other areas of recurring

change are found in the West Indian region and in a long zone extending from Polynesia and the Pacific borders through the East Indian region westward across southern Asia and southern Europe.

VULCANISM

335. VOLCANIC ACTIVITY. Vulcanism is a term applied to all those processes by means of which molten rock is transferred from deep-seated sources to or toward the surface of the earth. Although the products of vulcanism include steam and gases as well as molten rock and solid fragments, the latter are of greater environmental significance since they are the direct or indirect cause of several classes of landforms.

336. IGNEOUS EXTRUSIONS. The principal product of volcanic extrusion is lava or molten rock. Some lavas are composed of highly siliceous, acid-rock minerals which quickly become viscous and solidify as they approach the surface. Extrusions of these sometimes are accompanied by poisonous gases and steam which find difficult escape through the viscous mass and cause *explosive* eruptions. The explosions hurl bits of lava, blown to fragments, high into the air. These cool suddenly and settle close about the vent, or *crater*, in different forms called volcanic ash, cinders, pumice, or slag, intermingled with flows of viscous lava. This produces a steep-sided cone which ultimately may attain mountainous proportions.

Other volcanoes extrude lavas that are composed mainly of the basic-rock minerals. These remain liquid as they approach their solidification points rather than becoming more and more viscous as they cool down. Therefore, included gases bubble through these lavas with less tendency to explosive violence, and the eruptions are said to be *quiet*. Erupted basic lavas may flow some distance from a volcanic crater before they congeal in nearly horizontal sheets. Thus is produced a cone of relatively larger area and more gentle slopes than are those formed by acid lavas. Mauna Loa and other volcanoes in the Hawaiian Islands and indeed the Islands themselves furnish examples of the type of cone built of basic igneous rocks. They are called shield volcanoes.

Lava flows are perhaps the most extensive of the extrusive features. They issue from limited volcanic vents or pour from long crevices in the earth. In many places there are flows of solidified lava the extent of which is to be measured in square miles or scores of square miles. In a few places, and at various times in earth history, there have issued from crevices or numerous vents lavas so liquid and so copious that layer after layer, at intervals, have flooded and buried the original surface over many thousands of square miles. Such vast flows are of basic lavas, since acid lavas would hardly remain liquid so long. They give rise to great expanses of basaltic rocks which, in some regions, break down into soils of notable fertility. Among the great basaltic lava flows of the world are those of the Deccan (peninsular India), Ethiopia, southern Brazil, and the Columbia Plateau in northwestern United States (467). In the last-named region successive flows, over a long period, covered a total area of more than 100,000 square miles to an average depth of $\frac{1}{2}$ mile. In the process, valleys were filled, hills were buried, and mountains left standing like islands in a nearly level sea of lava plains.

Fig. 120.—An igneous dike which stands in relief because it is more resistant to erosion than the rocks on either side of it. (*U. S. Geological Survey Photograph.*)

337. IGNEOUS INTRUSIONS are thrust beneath the surface of the local, or "country," rock in a great variety of forms. One of them is a thin layer of igneous rock solidified in a vertical crevice. When erosion later removes the less resistant rock adjacent, such a formation, called a *dike*, may stand in bold, wall-like relief in the landscape or form a considerable range of hills (Fig. 120).

Other intrusive forms are massive and are like giant blisters under the rock skin of the earth. Such intrusions are of various forms and sizes, some of which are called *laccoliths* and *batholiths*. These great masses of igneous material are intruded deep beneath the surface where they dissolve, displace, or uplift the surrounding sedimentary or other rocks and metamorphose those that they touch through the effects of heat, pressure, or the chemical action of the hot waters and gases associated with them. In some places deposits of valuable minerals have resulted from these chemical changes in the altered rocks. Subsequent erosion in regions so intruded may strip off the uplifted rock layers, exposing the igneous rock cores beneath (Fig. 121). Each intrusion or type of intrusion may give rise to significant landforms.

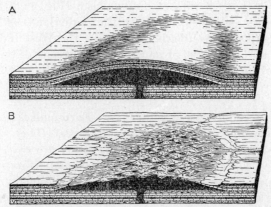

FIG. 121.—A diagram to illustrate the effects of the intrusion of a giant laccolithic mass into sedimentary rocks (*A*), and features resulting from its subsequent erosion by streams (*B*).

338. REGIONS OF VOLCANIC ACTIVITY. The distant past of geologic time includes an era of almost world-wide vulcanism, but later periods of earth history show it generally much restricted. In different periods one region or another has been affected only to have its volcanoes grow dormant and disappear under the work of the degra-

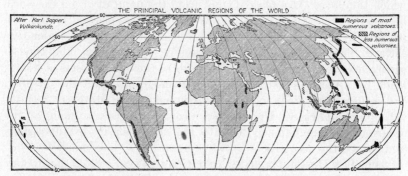

FIG. 122.—(*Denoyer's Semielliptical Projection.*)

dational processes. Usually, notable volcanic activity appears to have been closely associated with regions of principal diastrophism. It is not unreasonable that the two should be associated. Zones of crustal breaking or bending well may be the zones of weakness through which deep-seated masses of molten rock find their way to the surface most readily.

In view of this probable relationship it is not surprising to find that the world regions of greatest current volcanic activity are closely comparable to those of present diastrophism (Fig. 122). Within the zones previously described, including the borderlands of the Pacific Ocean, southern Asia, southern Europe and the West Indian region, are included not all the 300 or more active volcanoes of the world but a large proportion of them.

EARTHQUAKES

339. THE NATURE OF EARTHQUAKES.   Earthquakes are relatively small vibratory movements of the earth's crust. They are not the cause of diastrophism and vulcanism but rather are caused by those tectonic forces. The crust of the earth is in constant vibration, but the movements usually are too small to be felt. Occasionally tremors of such violence are set up that they spread wavelike over large areas and may even travel entirely around and through the earth. Earthquakes have many possible causes, but it is probable that most of the great earthquakes are vibrations set up by the fracturing, faulting, and movement of great masses of rock associated with the redistribution of balance in the earth's crust or with some phase of vulcanism.

From a point of origin near the earth's surface, earthquake waves travel rapidly in all directions. Their form and rate of motion are, however, greatly influenced by the nature of the material through which they pass. At a place distant from the point of origin there will be received one kind or set of waves which has passed through the interior of the earth and a second kind that has traveled along its surface. These differ in direction, rapidity of vibration, and time of occurrence. It is by means of the records of the different sets of waves, made by a delicate instrument (the seismograph), that the direction and approximate distance of an earthquake from stations of observation are indicated. Upon these records reports are made of the occurrence of earthquakes beneath the oceans or in distant regions from which the accounts of eyewitnesses are long in coming.

340. THE DESTRUCTIVENESS OF EARTHQUAKES.   From the amount of devastation sometimes wrought by earthquakes, the inference frequently is made that the earthquake waves must be of great size. It is, in fact, the suddenness and sharpness of the impulse delivered by the wave rather than its great motion that cause destruction. This may be illustrated by standing a piece of chalk upon a table and striking the latter a quick, sharp blow underneath. The vibration of the table

top may be too small to be seen, but the chalk may be thrown some distance upward and toppled over. Many earthquakes of major size do little damage because they happen to be most severe in areas of little or no human settlement. Great havoc is wrought when a severe wave is generated at a point beneath the earth's surface so located that it strikes, sometimes obliquely, at the structures of a great city. Recent history is too well filled with illustrated accounts of such disasters to require that they be recounted here. Chimneys, stone buildings, and other unyielding structures are demolished. Roofs cave in, walls buckle outward, and persons are killed by falling debris rather than by any violent action of the earthquake itself. Electric transmission lines are thrown down, water mains are broken, and, to complete the ruin, fire spreads unchecked by the usual means of bringing it under control.

When earthquakes of great severity occur on or near the coasts of low and flat lands, an additional hazard to life is sometimes introduced. This commonly, and erroneously, is called a *tidal wave*. It has no relation to the true tide but is merely a wave of gigantic proportions set in motion by the earthquake shock delivered upon the bottom of the sea. The water being agitated from the bottom upward, rather than upon the surface as by the wind, develops large waves. These increase in height as they enter the shallow coastal waters and sometimes reach proportions that carry them upon the adjacent shore far beyond the limits of ordinary waves. Waves of this origin, invading the densely peopled coastal flats of southeastern Asia, have, upon some occasions, destroyed thousands, even tens of thousands, of human lives.

341. REGIONS OF FREQUENT EARTHQUAKE OCCURRENCE. Inasmuch as the shocks that start earthquake waves in motion result mainly from the fracturing of rocks and secondarily from volcanic explosions, it is not surprising that the regions of most frequent earthquake occurrence are closely comparable in their distribution to those of present diastrophism and volcanic activity (Fig. 123). However, not all parts even of those famous zones are equally subject to severe earthquakes. The greater number are associated with areas of most rapid change in elevation. This is expressed in the longest and steepest slopes between mountain and plain, as in northern India, or between continental margin and ocean deeps, as in the northern Pacific Ocean near the Aleutian Islands and Japan. Small earthquakes are frequent on the Pacific Coasts of the American continents from Cape Horn to Alaska, and several of notable severity have been experienced in Chile, Mexico, California, and Alaska since the beginning of the present

century. The descent from land to sea bottom off the coasts of Oregon, Washington, and British Columbia is much less steep than that off Chile, California, or the Aleutians, and that section of the Pacific Coast has fewer earthquakes. The site of Japan, which borders one of the greatest of ocean deeps, is particularly unstable. "The number of earthquakes happening in different parts of Japan gives the average yearly frequency of some 1,500, or of about four shocks per day. In Tokyo a sensible shock occurs on the average once every three days."

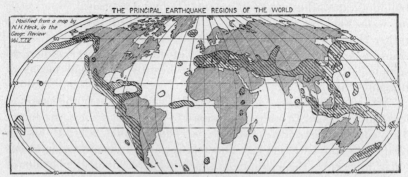

THE PRINCIPAL EARTHQUAKE REGIONS OF THE WORLD

Fig. 123.—(*Denoyer's Semielliptical Projection.*)

Most of them are of little importance, but some, such as that of Sept. 1, 1923, in densely peopled Yokohama and Tokyo, cause untold damage and suffering.

Some of the older and more stable geologic regions of the world seem free from earthquakes because none of great destructiveness has occurred there within the short span of written history. It is probable, however, that there are no regions which they may not sometime visit.

Chapter XIII. The Agents and Processes of Gradation

342. GRADATIONAL AGENTS AND PROCESSES. It has been noted previously that the tectonic forces are opposed by forces of gradation which tend to reduce to a low and uniform level all those features produced by diastrophic uplift or volcanic outpourings. Most important among the *agents* that accomplish this work are water, ice, and wind. They derive their energy mainly from two sources: the sun and the earth's gravitational attraction. The energy of the sun evaporates the waters of the oceans, which are then precipitated upon the land and returned to the sea as running water or moving ice under the compulsion of gravity. Solar energy and the force of gravity likewise are responsible for the winds, which remove some quantities of earth from the land surface and which largely condition the precipitation of moisture over the lands and the work of waves along the margins of the seas. Organic agents such as plants, animals, and man play parts in the slow gradation of the land, but their activities also are conditioned by solar energy, particularly as it is expressed in climates.

The agents of gradation work in many ways to accomplish their objective. It may help to understand them if it is observed that the processes are of two somewhat different types, although they are so intimately related that often it is difficult to determine at just what point one type of process ends and the other begins. Certain processes are completed without motion, their products remaining essentially where they were originally. These may be called the *static processes*. The completion of other processes necessarily involves motion during which material is picked up, transported, and put down. These may be called *mobile processes*. The static processes prepare rock for removal; the mobile processes bring about its removal and cause its redeposition. The latter are the processes of *degradation* and *aggradation*.

343. LANDFORMS MARK STAGES IN THE GRADATIONAL PROCESS. By whatever agent the mobile processes are accomplished, material is removed from higher elevations to lower and most of it ultimately

to the sea. During the process of removal the same material may be picked up and put down many times, each time a step being accomplished toward the ultimate destination. The intervals of deposition during the process of removal differ greatly in length. A bit of gravel carried by a stream may be lifted and put down a hundred or a thousand times in a single day only to be cast into a by-water and there to lie a hundred or a thousand years before being moved again.

Many kinds of landforms originate from steps and incidents in the gradational process. Some of them are forms carved in the solid rocks of the earth's crust by the agents of degradation. Others are formed during aggradation by the temporary (in the geological sense) deposition and peculiar arrangement of material on its way to the sea. In the development of landforms, both the degradational type and those made by aggradation, conditions of climate are of the greatest importance.

The Static Processes

344. THE BREAKING DOWN OF ROCK. Before the solid rock of the earth's crust can be removed, portions of it must be disintegrated, decomposed, or otherwise made ready for removal by the agents of gradation. The processes by means of which this is accomplished are called *weathering*. Weathering may be either chemical or mechanical in nature. Chemical weathering may be said to include all those processes of rock decomposition or decay in which some of the rock minerals undergo chemical change. Mechanical weathering includes all those processes by which solid rock is disintegrated, or reduced to fragments, but left chemically unchanged. Often one is more important than the other, but usually both are to some degree involved in the preparation of rock material for removal.

345. CHEMICAL WEATHERING results principally from the chemical union of oxygen, carbon dioxide, or water with elements in the rock minerals or from the dissolving of some of them. These chemical processes are called respectively (a) oxidation, (b) carbonation, (c) hydration, and (d) solution. They are of great importance because the chemical changes result in the formation of new minerals which have properties different from those from which they were derived in size, shape, hardness, or degree of solubility. These changes greatly affect the rate at which solid rock is prepared for removal by the mobile processes (a) by producing new minerals which are less resistant than the old to the processes of removal or (b) by the disrupting effect caused by the crowding of expanding substances. The rusting of iron is a familiar example of both oxidation and hydration, for yellow iron rust is a hydrous oxide of iron. Some igneous rock minerals contain iron,

and many sedimentary rocks include iron oxide as a cementing material. These minerals are subject to oxidation and hydration and are changed thereby. Other of the igneous-rock minerals contain combinations of elements such as potassium or calcium which, under favorable conditions, recombine with the carbonic acid in ground water. The resulting carbonate crystals are larger in size and different in shape from those of the original minerals. This change exerts a strong wedging force, tending to crowd apart the associated rock crystals and, therefore, to weaken or break up the crystalline structure of the rock (Fig. 124). Hydration tends to produce the same result, being attended, according to Merrill, by an increase in the bulk of some minerals of as much as 88 per cent. Solution works in a different way. Certain minerals, such as calcium carbonate, are changed by weathering and

FIG. 124.—Weathering granite. The disintegration of granite in place, here in a spherical manner, is accomplished by the decomposition of certain of its constituent minerals. (*Wisconsin Geological Survey Photograph.*)

become soluble in the water of the ground. Their removal in solution is called *leaching*. It leaves the rocks that contained them somewhat porous, or at least less solid and resistant than before, and the process may end in the nearly complete disappearance of such rocks as are composed largely of soluble minerals.

The chemical decomposition of rock is not local but widespread in its effects. It operates not only upon crystalline igneous rocks but upon those of sedimentary origin also (Fig. 112). Rain water in falling through the air absorbs carbon dioxide gas and becomes a dilute carbonic acid. In the ground it obtains other acids from decaying vegetation. In general, therefore, the water of the ground is really a weak acid and is capable of dissolving lime and other substances and of making chemical changes not possible in pure water.

All the processes of chemical weathering are promoted by high temperatures and abundant moisture. Chemical weathering is, therefore, most rapid and complete in the humid tropics and least rapid and complete in regions of aridity or cold. Different rocks and even different parts of the same rock weather at different rates even under the same general conditions. Therefore, after prolonged weathering some parts of a rock may be greatly changed while others are so little changed that they stand out in bold relief after the weathered material is removed. Such features are said to be the result of *differential weathering*.

346. MECHANICAL WEATHERING. Although the processes of chemical decomposition doubtless are the most important by which rock is made ready for removal by the agents of gradation, there are several processes of mechanical disintegration also. The following are some of the more effective of them: (*a*) The formation of joint planes by diastrophism is a kind of mechanical weathering. The fractures so produced often are the zones of attack for other weathering agents. (*b*) All scraping, grinding, and scouring processes, sometimes called abrasion or corrasion. (*c*) The expansive force of freezing water in rock crevices pries apart the adjacent minerals with a force that, under ideal conditions, is much greater than the pressure in a steam-engine boiler. (*d*) The growth of plant roots in rock crevices exerts a wedging force of surprising proportions. (*e*) The intense heating of rocks, as by forest fires, and their sudden cooling cause internal stresses which end in rock disruption. It may be that intense insolation and rapid cooling, as between day and night in desert climates, is sufficient, when repeated for many years, to accomplish a similar end. However, it seems unlikely that the latter process is the principal cause of rock weathering even in deserts, as was formerly believed. Mechanical weathering probably takes place in warm and humid regions, but its products are to a considerable degree obscured by the more abundant products of chemical weathering. It is in regions of cold and arid climates, where the chemical processes operate slowly, that the rock fragments produced by mechanical means attain their greatest relative importance. In these regions coarse and angular materials comprise a large part of the regolith.

The accumulated materials resulting from weathering and awaiting transportation often cover to some depth the parent rocks from which they have been derived. These accumulations make up a part of the mantle rock or regolith previously noted (325).

The Mobile Processes

347. EROSION. The weathering processes commonly are followed, but not always immediately, by *degradational* processes which remove the weathered rock fragments from the places of their origin. Specifi-

cally, these include the picking up of loose material and its transportation. These processes combined are called *erosion*. The processes of weathering and erosion together produce the general result of degradation, which is the wasting away of the land and its reduction down to the ultimate lowest possible slope, or grade, with respect to sea level. The principal agents of erosion were listed above, but they may be repeated here, since they will be used as a basis for organization in the remainder of this discussion of the agents and processes of gradation. Weathered rock is transported by the force of *gravity* which may act either directly or, on a broader scale, through the agencies of the *water in the ground, running water, moving snow and ice, waves, and wind*. To a small degree transportation is accomplished also by organic agencies, including human agency, and in other minor ways. It will be clear that *transportation* is the essential element of erosion. It may be noted also that transportation is accomplished whether the material is (*a*) carried in dissolved, and therefore invisible, form or (*b*) is lifted bodily and carried in suspension by wind, stream, wave, or ice or (*c*) merely rolls, slides, or is pushed downslope by any of these agents or by gravity itself.

The rate at which weathered material is transported by the agents of erosion obviously bears a close relation to the degree of slope of the land surface on which it rests. On steep cliffs gravity itself removes weathered rock fragments about as fast as they are loosened. This leaves the rock of the cliff bare. On flat surfaces, even in rainy regions, the products of weathering tend to accumulate to greater depths because of the slowness of the processes of transportation there. In such situations the accumulated regolith may grade downward from fine surface materials, which are completely changed by chemical and mechanical weathering, through partly changed and coarser fragments into the unweathered parent rock beneath. In the humid tropics, where chemical weathering is most active, the regolith is porous, and the surface is protected from erosion by a thick covering of vegetation. There the regolith may accumulate on some gentle slopes to a depth of 100 ft. or more. In most regions it averages considerably less than that depth.

348. DEPOSITION. Since each of the agents of erosion, under proper conditions, is capable of transporting material, it will be evident that, under other conditions, they will put it down again. This process may be called *deposition*. By it *aggradation* is accomplished, and elevations below the local grade are brought up to it by filling. Just as materials are carried in different physical conditions and by the different agents, so they may be deposited either from solu-

tion or from suspension, or they may merely come to rest after having fallen or slid some distance. They may be deposited by the wind, by running water, by moving ice, or by the waves. The various agents and conditions combine to produce classes of deposits which often are related to the development of distinctive landforms or other features of the natural equipment of areas.

From these general considerations the discussion may turn to the specific gradational agents and the various processes by which each carries on its work and aids in the development of landforms. The emphasis in this brief survey will be upon the nature of the *processes* involved. Description of the features produced, the principal concern of the student of geography, will be reserved for more detailed consideration in other connections.

Ground Water and Its Gradational Processes

349. GROUND WATER exists in the pore spaces of the regolith, in porous rocks, and in the joint cracks and other crevices of all rocks,

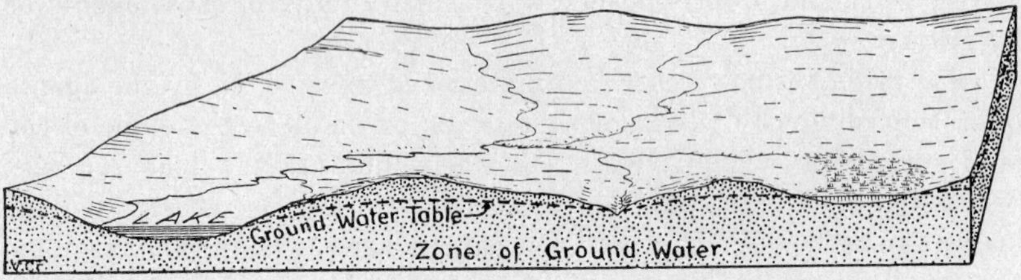

FIG. 125.—A diagram to illustrate the undulating surface of a ground-water table and its relation to the land-relief and drainage features.

in regions of humid climate, as far down as crevices and pore space extend. The greater part of the pore space, and therefore of the water, is within a few hundreds of feet of the surface, and many impervious or tightly capped rocks at great depths are essentially dry. The ground-water supply is maintained from the land surface by that part of the precipitation that seeps into the ground rather than immediately running off in streams or evaporating into the air. The surface addition of water seeps downward, as it would in a glass full of sand, until it joins with that already in the ground and fills the lower spaces first. If there is not sufficient water to fill all the pore space, the upper part of the earth may be merely damp while the lower part is saturated. The top of the saturated zone is called the *ground-water table*, or ground-water level. It is not a horizontal surface but tends to seek a common level by slow outward movement from its higher portions (Fig. 125). It is not found at a uniform depth below the surface but is usually at greater depths beneath hills and at less depths below valleys, at greater depths after protracted droughts, and at less depths after rains. In humid regions it may be near the surface, and in arid regions far below it.

350. THE GRADATIONAL WORK OF GROUND WATER mainly is chemical because, in most rocks, it moves too slowly to accomplish much mechanical erosion except in promoting landslides and soil creep by increasing the weight of the weathered material and by acting as a soil lubricant. Therefore the effects of ground water on landforms are accomplished largely through (a) solution and (b) the redepositing of dissolved minerals.

Solution is a widespread phenomenon. It has been discussed as a phase of chemical weathering, and that perhaps is its most significant aspect. It is, however, a process capable of giving rise to certain landforms. In regions of pure limestones especially, underground solution may remove rock to the extent that large caverns are formed or the rock honeycombed with small cavities, and the surface is dotted with depressions caused by solution cavities or by the collapse of cavern roofs (392). Such regions are said to have *karst* features, and in them a large part of the drainage flows in underground channels rather than in surface streams.

Under favorable conditions ground water may become overcharged with dissolved minerals and be forced to deposit some. These conditions include (a) evaporation of some of the water, (b) ,decrease in its temperature, (c) loss of some of its dissolved carbon dioxide, and changes in other conditions that tend to hold minerals in solution. The deposited minerals are chemical precipitates, comparable to those that accumulate in a teakettle. In a somewhat different way, minerals are deposited from underground water also by chemical exchange with other minerals in the rocks through which the water passes and by the work of microorganisms. The process of deposition is accomplished slowly, molecule by molecule. A well-known illustration of it is the formation of stalactites and stalagmites which grow in underground caverns through precipitation from percolating water. Of much greater importance are certain less spectacular phases of deposition. For example, ground water charged with lime may build a lime filling in the pore spaces of a bed of sand, cementing the grains of sand together into a limy sandstone. Or water charged with silica may remove the molecules of a previously deposited lime cement, replacing them with the silica, thus producing a quartzite. In the same manner silica or lime, either alone or in combination with valuable metals, such as gold, may be deposited in a rock crevice, making a *vein* (675, Fig. 126). Wood, bone, or shells are *petrified* by the removal of their substance, molecule by molecule, and its replacement by lime or silica, even the microscopic details of internal structure often being kept.

The removal and replacement of minerals by ground water are an important factor in the formation of certain earth resources, such as soil and mineral ores, as well as in the making of landforms. In humid regions the lime and other soluble substances, including plant foods, are removed from soils by solution, leaving the soils leached and often

FIG. 126.—A vein of white quartz traversing wave-worn metamorphic rock on the Maine Coast.

poor. In arid regions a lack of ground water is a cause for lack of leaching and a widespread accumulation of these same substances in the soil. In some regions of rocks bearing considerable amounts of valuable minerals the richness of the mineral ores has been increased greatly by the solution of silica and other associated substances leaving the valuable minerals in concentrated form. Other valuable ores have been enriched by the opposite kind of process, in which small quantities of mineral are selected by ground water from large masses of rock and are brought together in more concentrated form. Since these changes take place so slowly, it follows that a vast amount of time is required for their accomplishment.

Running Water and Its Gradational Processes

351. THE ORIGIN OF STREAMS. Running water has a larger part than any other of the agents of gradation in the modeling of landforms. Some of the work is done by the rain directly or by thin sheets of water moving over the ground during downpours of rain, but the larger part is done by streams, because in them the water is deeper and has more inherent force. Streams are fed (a) by the immediate runoff of water during rains; (b) by the underground water issuing through seepage and springs; and (c) by the release of water temporarily held in storage in lakes, swamps, snow, and glaciers. The turbulent force of running water over the land surface dislodges and removes weathered rock, and in the process it develops channels or valleys. It is the patterns and peculiarities of stream-cut channels and valleys that give

characteristic details of relief to most of the lands of the earth. It is evident that since the number and size of the streams of a region depend much upon its supply of precipitation, so, therefore, do many of the peculiarities and characteristics of its landforms.

DEGRADATION BY RUNNING WATER

352. THE EROSIONAL WORK OF STREAMS. The most widespread degradational activity of running water is accomplished by the hydraulic action or surface wash of the runoff, which is that part of the precipitation that does not at once soak into the ground or evaporate into the air. The runoff may start its work as a sheet of water, but ordinarily it does not progress far before it is concentrated into rivulets which eventually are enlarged and are maintained by springs and the seepage of underground water. Streams flow in valleys, and most valleys start as gullies. It is the work of running water to make them

FIG. 127.—A gully head that almost visibly is gnawing its way up a slope which directs the flow of rain water into it. (*Photograph by F. W. Lehmann, C. B. & Q. Railroad Company.*)

longer, deeper, and wider. A normal gully begins at the base of a slope and grows in length by erosion at the point where surface water pours in at its upper end. In a sense it gnaws its way headward into uneroded land (Fig. 127). New gullies branch from the sides of the first one and lengthen in the same manner (Fig. 128). In rock or regolith of uniform resistance the gullies normally have a branching, treelike, or dendritic, relation to each other (Fig. 238). Gullies of this kind may grow on unprotected slopes in such numbers as to create a great problem

FIG. 128.—As a gully grows in length by headward erosion, tributary gullies branch from its sides and grow in like manner. (*Photograph by F. W. Lehmann, C. B. & Q. Railroad Company.*)

in the control of soil erosion (633). Not all the gullies thus formed grow to great length, but in time some of them may. During that time each long gully will have acquired tributaries, each tributary will have subtributaries, and these in turn will end in a multitude of gullies which reach and drain all parts of the region. A major stream of water and all its tributary streams is called a *river system*. The elongate depression that each stream cuts for itself is called its *valley*. The higher land separating two adjacent stream valleys is called an *interfluve*. The valley of the major stream and all its tributary valleys and gullies are called a *valley system*. The entire area of land drained by a river system is called a *drainage basin*. The line along an upland separating two adjacent drainage basins is called a *divide*. On the divide surface drainage destined for the respective streams is parted, as on the ridge of a house roof, although some divides are low, and the line of water parting is therefore indistinct.

Valleys are deepened when their streams, using sand or gravel as tools, scour or abrade their own beds and transport the material thus loosened. The rate at which a stream is able to deepen its valley depends upon (a) the velocity of the running water, (b) the volume of the stream, (c) the nature and abundance of the tools available to it, and (d) the resistance of the material into which the valley is being eroded. The velocity of a stream is determined, in turn, by several conditions among which the most important is its *gradient*, or the degree of the head-to-mouth slope of its bed. Streams with steep gradients are swift and are able, given tools, to deepen their valleys more rapidly than other streams of similar volume but with lower gradients and, therefore, lower velocities. In a river system the newer tributaries and headwater streams usually have steeper gradients than the waters of the middle and lower courses where erosion has been longer in process. For that reason the tributary streams may be eroding rapidly while the main stream, in its lower course, may have a gradient so low that it is no longer able to cut downward, and more material collects in its channel than it is able to transport. The carrying capacity of a stream increases as the sixth power of the velocity, and, according to Geikie, a stream having a velocity of about $\frac{1}{6}$ mile per hour will barely move fine clay. At a velocity of $\frac{1}{4}$ mile per hour it will move fine sand; at $\frac{1}{2}$ mile, coarse sand; at $\frac{2}{3}$ mile, fine gravel; and at $1\frac{1}{2}$ miles per hour it will transport pebbles about an inch in diameter. When any part of the stream has deepened its channel to a gradient so low that it flows sluggishly and is barely able to transport the material supplied to it by its tributaries it will deposit sediment temporarily in its valley bottom. It is said then to be a *graded stream*, or a stream at grade. If time is permitted for a stream to continue, without interruption, the extremely slow process of erosion below the level of grade, it will reach ultimately the lowest gradient at which it can flow. Then it will be unable to transport any material and therefore unable to degrade its valley further. Such a stream is said to have reached its *baselevel*.

353. THE CHARACTERISTICS OF YOUNG STREAMS AND THEIR VALLEYS. Streams that have just entered upon their work of erosion and still have rather steep gradients are called young streams. They are cutting downward more vigorously than laterally but have much to do before they reach their baselevels (Fig. 129*A*). While the downward cutting is in progress the valley is widened at the top as material from its sides falls or slides into the stream or is carried in by rainwash. The transverse profile of the young valley is therefore V-*shaped* (Fig. 260). In loose material, which washes or slides easily, the V is likely to be broad and open, while in hard rocks it is likely to be narrow and gorgelike (Fig. 258). In regions of high elevation young valleys of the gorge or canyon type may be hundreds or even thousands of feet deep, while in regions of low elevation they may be only a few feet in depth, although their shapes are similar. Both are young in terms of stage of development, although there may be a vast difference in their ages measured in terms of years.

Young streams rapidly eroding often find their courses through rocks of unequal resistance, which erode at different rates. The abrupt changes in gradient, which result from the *differential erosion*, cause the courses of many young streams to be interrupted by waterfalls and rapids. In older streams, which are nearing grade, time has permitted erosion to carve away even the hardest rocks, and the falls and rapids tend to disappear (Fig. 130).

354. THE CHARACTERISTICS OF MATURE STREAMS AND THEIR VALLEYS. As a stream approaches baselevel, the limit of its downward erosion, both stream and valley take on new characteristics. The stream, its gradient decreased, becomes less swift and is readily turned aside. It begins to swing against its valley walls, cutting at their bases and pushing them apart by undercutting them. Widening becomes more rapid than deepening, and the stream ceases to be direct but swings from side to side on a

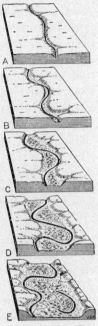

FIG. 129.—Diagrams illustrating changes in the transverse profile of a valley. (*A*) The V-shaped profile of a young valley; (*B*) the start of meandering; (*C*) retreat of valley bluffs; (*D*) meander belt and long meander; (*E*) meander cut off and floodplain widened by trimming of bluffs.

widening valley floor in broad loops or *meanders* (Fig. 129D). The valley ceases to be narrow and V-shaped and acquires width and a flat valley floor as a result of its continuous shifting of position and trimming of the valley walls.

355. STAGES OF EROSIONAL DEVELOPMENT. As stream valleys develop so do the relief features of the regions through which they flow. In areas where the streams generally are young the valleys are narrow, the tributaries are undeveloped and few, and the interfluves are broad and little dissected (Fig. 131A). It is evident in such areas that the streams have only well begun the task of reducing the whole block of land to its ultimate low baselevel. A region with a surface of that kind is said to be in a stage of *youth*.

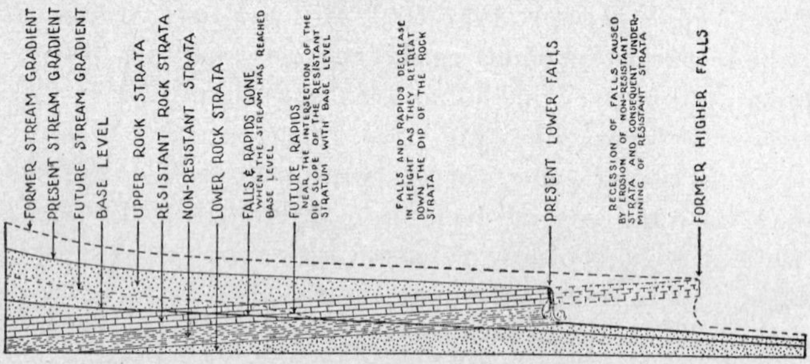

FORMER STREAM GRADIENT — PRESENT STREAM GRADIENT — FUTURE STREAM GRADIENT — BASE LEVEL — UPPER ROCK STRATA — RESISTANT ROCK STRATA — NON-RESISTANT STRATA — LOWER ROCK STRATA — FALLS & RAPIDS GONE WHEN THE STREAM HAS REACHED BASE LEVEL — FUTURE RADIUS BELOW THE INTERSECTION OF THE DIP SLOPE OF THE RESISTANT STRATUM WITH BASE LEVEL — FALLS AND RAPIDS DECREASE IN HEIGHT AS THEY RETREAT DOWN THE DIP OF THE ROCK STRATA — PRESENT LOWER FALLS — RECESSION OF FALLS CAUSED BY EROSION OF NON-RESISTANT STRATA AND CONSEQUENT UNDERMINING OF RESISTANT STRATA — FORMER HIGHER FALLS

FIG. 130.—A diagram to illustrate one common cause of waterfalls and the reason why such falls retreat upstream, leaving a gorge, and eventually disappear.

As erosion proceeds many new tributary streams and a large number of gullies are formed. These dissect the former broad interfluves. Valleys grow deeper and wider, and the divides between adjacent streams grow more steep and narrow, until finally only a maze of hills remains of the former broad upland and the whole area is characterized by sloping rather than flat land (Fig. 131B). This stage of development may be called *maturity*. In it the flat upland of youth has ceased to exist, and the new and extensive flat lowlands of old age have not yet come into existence.

Progress of erosion beyond maturity enables the streams, first the larger ones and then the tributaries, to reach their respective grades. Beyond this point there is still some degradation of the land surface as the divide areas are slowly reduced by weathering and slope wash and are removed by the streams. The region ultimately acquires broadly open and level-floored valleys separated by low, rolling divides which are but the remnants of the former youthful interfluves (Fig. 131C). This stage of development may be called *old age*.

In a few places in the world there are plains that illustrate the extreme of erosional old age. After all the streams of a region reach grade the reduction of the land level is exceedingly slow, but it proceeds as long as the streams are able to carry any material, even in solution. Thus, in the end, even the low divides of old age are reduced to broad, undulating areas with perhaps a few hills in localities of unusually resistant rock or in positions so situated as to be less attacked by tributary streams. If the slow process is not interrupted, a plain of low relief is formed with undulating surface and occasional hill rem-

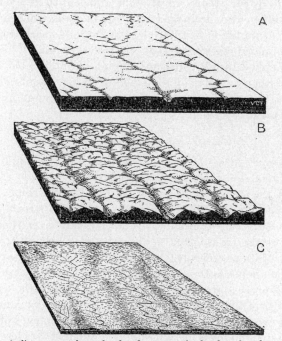

FIG. 131.—A diagram to show the development of a land surface by stream erosion from youth (*A*) through maturity (*B*) to old age (*C*). The dotted white line indicates the baselevel toward which the streams are working.

nants of the once broad uplands. *Such a plain is that uniform low slope or grade that is the objective of all gradational processes.* It is called a *peneplain* (almost a plain), and the remnant hills are called *monadnocks*.

Peneplains are not uncommon among the land surfaces of the world, but certainly, in most instances, the slow processes of their final reduction have been terminated by diastrophic changes which have elevated them somewhat with respect to the sea. Thus the streams are given new baselevels, acquire steeper gradients, and start upon the dissection of the peneplains in new cycles of erosion. For that reason no peneplain of the present is very low or very flat.

It is clear that the actual time required for a region to pass through all the erosional stages from the features of youth to those of old age will depend upon a number of factors, such as the height of the original youthful plain above its baselevel, the kinds of rock to be eroded, the quantity of rainfall, and other climatic conditions. Measured in terms of years, the time required must be, at the very least, extremely long. It is estimated, for example, that the material carried into the Gulf by the Mississippi River is sufficient to reduce the average elevation of the entire drainage basin 1 in. in about 800 years, but that the rate of degradation in the Colorado Basin is nearly twice as fast. It is not intended, therefore, that the terms "young," "mature," or "old," as applied to relief features, should be interpreted in terms of years but rather in terms of the stage of advancement or completion of the work of reducing the local land mass to the uniform low slope of the peneplain.

AGGRADATION BY RUNNING WATER

356. HOW STREAMS DEPOSIT MATERIAL. If the supply of weathered rock available for stream transportation exceeds the carrying capacity of the stream it becomes overloaded, and some of the load will be deposited. The term *alluvium* is applied to stream deposits of all grades and forms of accumulation. The action of running water tends to sort the transported material roughly according to the size and weight of its particles before putting it down. This sorting action causes stream deposits to accumulate as beds of gravel, sand, silt, and clay. In the process of deposition streams put down the coarsest and heaviest parts of their loads first, because they carry such material less easily. However, the carrying power of a stream changes often, and it is common to find beds of alluvium of different grades one above another.

Streams become overloaded in several ways, such as (a) by having much new sediment brought to them without corresponding increase in carrying power or (b) by loss of water through decrease in rainfall, through seepage, or through evaporation. However, it is likely that the most common cause for stream deposition is loss of velocity. Decrease in stream velocity may come about gradually, as a result of the decreasing gradient from the headwaters toward the mouth, or it may come about suddenly. A sudden decrease in velocity may occur at an abrupt change in land slope, as, for example, where a mountain stream flows out upon a flat plain, or it may occur as a result of the checking of the stream current where it enters a body of standing water, such as a lake or the sea.

357. WHERE STREAMS DEPOSIT. The different conditions that cause streams to deposit cause the deposited materials to accumulate in several characteristic places with reference to the stream course and in several commonly recognized forms. The places of deposition may be noted here, and the forms assumed by the different kinds of deposits may be left for later and fuller consideration.

On Valley Flats. A stream is likely to deposit some of its overload in its own channel, often on the inside of a bend where the velocity of the water is least. It is there that *sand bars* or similar deposits of mud or gravel accumulate. Their formation is a normal part of the develop-

FIG. 132.—The small stream shown here is widening its valley bottom by undercutting on the outside and depositing on the inside of a bend. (*Photograph by F. W. Lehmann, C. B. & Q. Railroad Company.*)

ment of an aging stream. The formation of many sand bars chokes the stream channel and increases its tendency to flood in times of high water. Gradually, by swinging out against the valley wall on one side and depositing on the other, the stream produces the broad valley flat of old age and at the same time covers the flat with river sediment (alluvium) (Fig. 132). Such a valley flat, covered with alluvium, is called a *floodplain* (Fig. 129).

When a sediment-laden stream rises in time of flood, overflows its channel, and spreads out upon the flood plain, much material is deposited immediately along the stream banks where the water first goes out of its proper channel and loses its velocity. There the alluvial accumulation is thickest, and it generally forms low, broad ridges bordering the stream. They are called *natural levees,*

At the Stream Mouth. Nearly all streams are able to carry some sediment down their entire courses and out at their mouths. Usually most of that sediment has been a long time on its way, having been incorporated into bars and floodplains, re-eroded, put down, and picked up thousands of times on its slow journey. Finally it is deposited where the stream velocity is checked upon entering a lake or the sea. Extensive accumulations of sediment in that kind of location are called *deltas.* Not every stream has a delta. Some carry but little sediment; others deposit their loads on sinking coasts or upon such as have deep waters or are so exposed to violent wave and current action that the sediment is spread over the adjacent sea floor and thus is prevented from making large accumulations.

Fig. 133.—The conformation of a small and fairly steep alluvial fan in Nevada. The apex of the fan lies at the mouth of the gully from which the material was eroded. (*Photograph by John C. Weaver.*)

The process of delta building is accomplished by addition to the banks of the stream during overflow and by the elongation of its channel through deposition at its end. The elongation produces a flat, fingerlike extension on the coast which lowers the stream gradient so much that presently it breaks over its banks and takes a new and shorter course to the sea, only to repeat the process. Thus the stream acquires more than one exit, and these are called its *distributaries* (Fig. 157).

At Sharp Decreases in Valley Gradient. The velocities of mountain streams are checked suddenly where their courses extend out upon adjacent plains. It is at this point that some streams choke their own courses with alluvium, turn aside and choke again, and, repeating the process, ultimately build broad fan-shaped or conical piles of alluvium which are called *alluvial fans* (Fig. 133). In humid regions many mountain streams have sufficiently large and constant volumes to be able to move their loads of debris still farther down their courses and do not form alluvial fans. Even in humid regions, however, fans of large size accumulate at the bases of very steep mountain slopes, and those of small size often are to be seen at the mouths of small gullies where there are no permanent streams but where much water runs during a rain. Along a fresh road cut, on a sidewalk, or at the mouths of little gullies fans may be seen, perfect in shape but no more than a few inches across. It is in dry regions, however, that alluvial fans reach their greatest development. There the intermittent and frequently torrential flow of mountain streams favors the development of these forms, and they may grow until they reach a radius of several miles. Along the bases of some mountain ranges every stream has its alluvial fan, large or small, and they are so crowded that adjacent fans spread and join, making a continuous *piedmont alluvial plain* (Fig. 171).

Moving Ice and Its Gradational Processes

358. MOUNTAIN GLACIERS. Glaciers, which are bodies of ice in slow motion, arise from accumulations of snow which, by the pressure of its own weight and by internal melting and refreezing, becomes consolidated into ice. The perennial snows of high mountains give rise to valley glaciers. Plunging avalanches carry snow from adjacent slopes into a valley head, where it attains great depths and gradually is transformed into loose, crystalline ice. Under its own great weight the thick mass settles, recrystallizes into solid ice, and expands, thus slowly pushing its lower portions down the valley. So long as the supply of snow is renewed from above, the glacier will continue to move.

The protruding ice tongue that creeps forward conforms to the shape of the valley in which it lies. Its rate of motion is governed by (a) the thickness of the ice, (b) the steepness of the valley gradient, (c) the temperature of the ice, and some other conditions. At most it is but a few feet per day. The advancing end of the ice tongue, extending down the valley, ultimately reaches lower elevations, where higher average temperatures prevail and the ice wastes by melting. As long as the average forward movement of the ice is greater than the amount lost by melting, the front of the ice tongue will continue to advance. When the rates of advance and melting are equal, the ice front will remain in the same position. If a series of warm years increases the rate of melting, so that it exceeds the rate of ice supply, the ice front will recede up the valley. The glacier is said then to be wasting, or to be in retreat. It is, however, only the location of the ice front that retreats, for the ice continues to move downslope or at most remains stagnant.

Some valley glaciers in high latitudes, for example in Alaska, are able to push so far down their valleys that they reach the sea. There, instead of melting away, their ends are continually broken off by the buoyance of the sea water, and the pieces float away in the form of icebergs (Fig. 263).

359. CONTINENTAL GLACIERS. Great continental ice sheets, such as now occupy most of Greenland and Antarctica, formerly covered northern North America and much of northwestern Europe. A continental glacier is in some respects like a valley glacier but in others different. It starts with the accumulation of snow fields but not necessarily in regions of high altitude. Having attained considerable depth and area the snows are slowly transformed into ice, and the mass spreads outward under its own weight and in all directions. It is fed by snowfall over its entire surface.

It is a mistake to assume that the appearance of the great North American and European ice sheets must have been preceded or accompanied by climatic conditions vastly different from those of the present. The only requirement for continental glaciation is that the snowfall be enough more, or the temperature enough lower, than at present so that the snow of one year is not quite all melted when that of the next year begins to fall. If that condition prevailed the accumulation would spread inch by inch and century by century until its margin reached a position where loss by melting equaled the rate of advance. The disappearance of a great glacier, conversely, would result from a decrease in snowfall or an increase in temperature of an amount such that the average wastage exceeded the additions from snowfall. The time required for either the growth or the disappearance of a continental glacier has probably to be measured in tens of thousands of years. The reasons for the changes of condition that brought them into existence and later destroyed them are not definitely known.

360. AREAS OF FORMER CONTINENTAL GLACIATION. The areas principally affected by the relatively recent (Pleistocene, see Appendix E) glaciation are shown in Fig. 134A, B. The European ice sheet radiated from centers located in the Scandinavian region and Scotland and extended southward into England, the Netherlands, Germany, Poland, and Russia. The centers of North American glaciation were situated adjacent to Hudson Bay. From the American centers ice spread outward but more extensively southward. It reached to a line that trends from New York City westward across southern New York State to northeastern Ohio and from there nearly along the present courses of the Ohio and Missouri Rivers toward the Rocky Mountains. Adjacent to the glacier margins the ice may have been only of moderate

depth, but it increased northward to thicknesses that may well have been a mile or more, sufficient at least to bury the mountains of New England. Within the glacial boundary the only district to escape burial

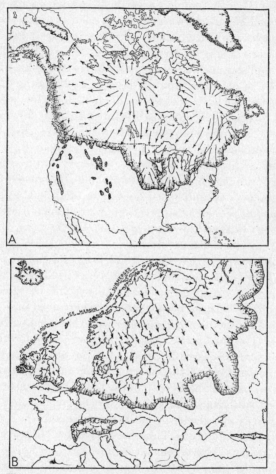

Fig. 134.—The maximum extent of the continental glaciers of North America and Europe. (*A*) The letters indicate the Keewatin, Patrician, and Labradorean centers of glacial movement. (*B*) The principal center of European glaciation was in the highlands of Scandinavia.

beneath the ice sheets was a large area located in southwestern Wisconsin and adjacent parts of Illinois, and possibly of Iowa and Minnesota. It is known as the *Driftless Area.* At the time of the great continental ice sheets there were much larger glaciers in the mountains of both North America and Europe than now exist there.

361. How GLACIERS ERODE. Clean glacial ice is able to erode rock mainly by pushing and by "plucking." Rock pinnacles or other unstable or detached rocks are readily toppled by the great weight of the advancing glacier, and loose earth is plowed up by it or frozen into the ice and carried forward. Even in solid bedrock the jointed or fractured blocks are frozen about with ice and are lifted or plucked from their seats. Using as tools the rocks thus obtained, the ice is able to accomplish another, and equally important, part of its erosion by the process of *abrasion*. Angular boulders, pebbles, and sand which are frozen fast at the bottom of the ice are held down by its great weight and pushed forward by its irresistible force. In their slow motion they gouge, groove, scratch, and polish the rock surface over which they pass. In the process the tools are themselves scoured, scraped, and reduced in size. They lose their sharp angularity and become partially rounded, or "subangular" (Fig. 183). Long-continued glacial scour has in many places accomplished notable erosion, but, in general, the resulting features are not of so great an order of magnitude as those of stream erosion. Rather, they appear to be, in the main, the reshaped features of previous stream erosion.

362. How GLACIERS DEPOSIT. The load of a glacier is comprised of rocks and earth intermingled without regard to size or weight. It is carried in part upon the ice surface or frozen into its mass, but even more largely in its bottom, because that is where most of it is obtained. The lower layers of ice in some glaciers are so crowded with clay, sand, and boulders that the earthy material is more abundant than the ice. When its bottom is so greatly overloaded the glacier readily loses its frozen grasp upon some of the material which then is left resting upon the ice-scoured bedrock below. Upon the top of this deposited layer the still-burdened ice creeps slowly forward. During the final stagnation and wasting away of a glacier its entire remaining load is let down upon that already accumulated. .Thus were formed, beneath the great continental glaciers, vast expanses of unassorted ice-deposited material, called *boulder clay*, or *till*. In regions of nonresistant bedrock and near the margins of the regions of former glaciation the till has accumulated to thicknesses of many feet or even several scores of feet. In regions of resistant bedrock and near the centers of glacial origin it is generally less abundant and is entirely lacking in some localities. In the latter regions the ice was less able to secure debris and, being less heavily burdened, was able to move most of the available material outward toward its margins. Specific glacial deposits are called *moraines*, and the till, because it was held in the bottom of the ice, is called the *ground moraine*, sometimes also the *till sheet*.

363. WHERE GLACIERS DEPOSIT. The ground moraine which was formed under the ice is only one of several forms of glacial deposit, or *glacial drift*. At places where ice advance was for a long time nearly balanced by the rate of melting, the edge of the ice remained almost stationary for years or scores of years. About these stagnant margins accumulated great ridges of drift, which, as a class, may be called *marginal moraines*. Those formed about the margin of the ice at its most advanced position are called *end moraines*, while similar ridges formed at times of pause or slight readvance during its stagnation and final wastage are called *recessional moraines*. Marginal moraines are comprised of drift that is in part shoved or plowed in front of the moving ice and in part fallen or washed out of its melting margin (Fig. 181).

There is much of the glacial load, however, which does not stop under the ice or upon the moraines about its margin. This material is carried beyond the ice margin by the streams of water that result from the melting of the ice. Like all stream-transported earth, it is sorted somewhat according to weight, the fine muds being carried farthest, and the coarser heavier materials being put down close in front of the ice. There are made by this process deposits of stream-sorted materials, such as gravel and sand, some of which extend away from the ice margin after the manner of river floodplains. The deposit of a glacial stream is classed generally as *glaciofluvial* rather than as glacial material. When these stream-sorted glaciofluvial deposits are arranged in floodplain form, they are known as a *valley train;* and when they are spread in broader fanlike deposits about the ice margin, materials of the same origin are called *outwash plain* (Fig. 189).

364. GLACIAL DISTURBANCE OF DRAINAGE. The processes of glacial erosion and deposition both disturb the normal processes of stream development. Glacial erosion, unlike stream erosion, does not produce a uniform slope or gradient. Instead, glacially eroded surfaces exhibit numerous upgrade slopes in the direction of ice motion, rock basins, and ice-scoured hills, whose patterns of arrangement result from the accidents of the direction of ice flow, its erosive capacity, and inequalities in the resistance of the rock formations. In regions of glacial deposition also there is little of local plan or order in the thickness and arrangement of the drift. Consequently, the drainage of both ice-eroded and drift-covered regions appears without pattern, wandering, aimless, falling here over a ledge of rock or collecting there as lake or swamp in a depression (Fig. 188). Such stream patterns do not grow entirely as the result of headward erosion but come into existence with the uncovering of the surface at the disappearance of the glacier.

365. NEWER AND OLDER DRIFT.   Among the glacial deposits of North America are striking contrasts as to apparent age. In the younger drift freshly scratched boulders, newly piled hills, and unfilled depressions indicate an origin in very recent geologic time. Other deposits, clearly glacial in nature, contain many weathered boulders, hills much subdued by rainwash, and depressions so generally filled that lakes and swamps are few. From these and other evidences it is known that the continent was invaded by ice sheets at least three times at intervals of many thousands of years, but all of them in relatively recent (Pleistocene) geologic time (Fig. 197, Appendix E).

The Gradational Processes of Waves and Currents

366. WHERE LAND AND SEA MEET.   The oceans, seas, and lakes of the earth cover more than 71 per cent of its surface and are important agents in the making and changing of landforms. Their work is accomplished by means of movements of the water, especially waves and currents. These are induced mainly by the wind and, to a lesser extent, by the tides and other causes. Although waves and currents are found in the open seas as well as in coastal waters they do not reach the bottoms of deep seas and so produce no change there. Their work is restricted to the shallow sea margins with waters of less than 600 ft. depth. Even in these ocean shallows the amount of wave work is small, and by far the greater part of it is performed along the coastal margins in waters of no more than a few feet or a few tens of feet in depth. The total areas subject to change by this force are, however, considerable, since the shorelines of all the lands have a combined length of many thousands of miles.

The work of waves and currents, like that of rivers and glaciers, has two phases: degradational and aggradational, or erosional and depositional.

367. HOW WAVES AND CURRENTS DEGRADE LAND.   The greater part of marine erosion is accomplished by waves. Waves, most of which are caused by the wind, are undulatory motions of the water. In small waves the motion is confined to surface waters, but in great ones there is sufficient agitation to cause some churning of the bottom at considerable depths. This action aids in the removal of material from elevations on the shallow ocean bottoms. With the help of currents the material is gradually shifted to lower or more protected places, a process that results in a general leveling of the sea floor near the shore where the agitation of the water often extends to the bottom.

There is little forward motion of the water in the waves of the open sea. A wave is the motion of a shape, not of a mass. The wave form

moves forward just as waves may be seen to run across a field of
standing grain or may be sent along a shaken rope. However, as a
wave enters shallow water a change comes over both its shape and its
motion. The wave form shortens horizontally and increases in height.
It drags on the bottom; inclines forward, eventually to topple, or
break, with a motion that throws forward a considerable amount of
water (Fig. 135). The water thrown forward by breaking waves rushes
upon the shore only to lose its velocity and run back, under the pull
of gravity, beneath other oncoming waves. The returning water is
called the *undertow*, and it has sufficient force to be an important factor in erosion.

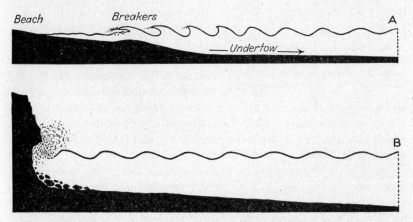

Fig. 135.—Diagrams to illustrate wave forms and action in both shallow and deep
shore waters. (*A*) Waves drag in shallow water, change form, topple, and break some
distance from shore. (*B*) In deep water they break directly on shore.

The erosive work of waves is accomplished both by the forward
motion, or slap, of the water as the waves break and by the sand and
rocks that they carry and use as tools. In either case the principal
work is done where the waves break. On exposed coasts, where deep
water lies immediately offshore, even great waves do not break until
they reach the shoreline. There the force exerted by the sheer weight
of the water in great waves is truly impressive. Blows of a ton or more
per square foot are not uncommon. This is sufficient to dislodge and
move about rock fragments of great weight. The effect of the undertow
is to move the broken fragments away from the shore into deeper water
where they are caught by oncoming waves and moved shoreward again.
By this means waves are furnished with tools that greatly increase
their erosional effectiveness. Sand, pebbles, and sometimes great
boulders are hurled upon the shore, especially at the bases of exposed

headlands. There they are thrown forward and rolled back in endless
repetition, scratching and grinding against each other and the solid
rock of the shore, accomplishing notable erosion. The general effect
of wave erosion is to cut back coastal projections, decreasing the area
of the land, straightening the coast, and developing, in the process,

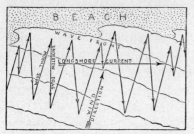

several characteristic coastal features such as wave-cut cliffs and
marine benches (523).

When the direction of the wind
is such that waves strike a shore
obliquely the combined effects of
the diagonal shoreward motion of
the breaker and the offshore motion
of the undertow is to cause both
water and the wave-transported
material to progress slowly, by
angular, in-and-out paths, along the

FIG. 136.—A map diagram to illustrate the in-and-out path of a pebble
under the combined forces of oblique
waves, undertow, and longshore current.

shore. Where the winds are prevailingly from one direction there is
set up by this means a continuous flow of water, or *longshore current*,
which has much to do with the distribution and forms of coastal sediments (Fig. 136).

368. How Waves and Currents Aggrade. The products of
wave erosion, together with sediments emptied into the sea by rivers,
are shifted about by waves and currents but ultimately are deposited
by them. Their tendency is to settle first in low places, aggrading them
and leveling the sea floor. Because wave activity does not extend to
great depths, the sediment, nearly all of which is land derived, does
not spread far from shore. The coarser is deposited first, and the finest
is carried farthest out. This process results in a general assortment of
shore deposits according to their sizes. Large boulders seldom are
moved far from the places of their origin. Pebbles of comparable size
are collected as deposits of shingle and beach gravel. Sands are more
easily moved, cover vast expanses of shoreline, and extend out into
waters of some depth. Beyond these, and also in protected shore waters,
are collected the silts and muds that remain longer in suspension and
are deposited in the quiet offshore waters of greater depth or in those
of protected bays or coastal lagoons. In areas so situated that little
mud is deposited there, lime is precipitated from solution and accumulates together with the limy and siliceous shells of small marine
organisms.

Thus are originated the sands, muds, and limes which in many
regions have been uplifted from shallow sea margins and have become

the stratified sedimentary rocks of the continents. Changes of condition during the deposition of marine sediments, such as increase or decrease in depth of water or change in the supply of sediments, result in the sequent deposition upon one part of the sea floor of sediments of different kinds. For that reason it is usual to find undisturbed sedimentary rocks including sandstones, shales, and limestones, in any order of sequence, one above another.

369. WHERE WAVES AND CURRENTS AGGRADE. During the progress of coastal aggradation under the influence of waves and currents, the deposits of sediment alongshore assume a number of distinctive forms and modify coastal outlines. These have some importance among the characteristics of coastal regions and greatly affect the manner of their human use. Although the features themselves are to be considered in other connections, it may be noted here that they are formed mainly in shallow water. The breaking of waves on shelving bottoms and the slacking of currents in the quiet waters of sheltered bays and in the lee of projecting coastal features all provide conditions under which sediments accumulate.

The Gradational Processes of the Wind

370. HOW THE WIND DEGRADES. The wind is an important transporting agent. The air is never without dust in suspension, and winds of high velocity are capable of moving sand and even pebbles for some distance. Some of the materials carried by the wind are thrown into the air by volcanic explosions, but the greater part is obtained by the wind directly from the earth. This process of surface degradation, during which dust is whipped up by the wind and is transported from one place to another, is called *deflation*.

The process of deflation is least effective in regions where soil particles are moist and adherent or are protected by a covering of vegetation. They are most effective in regions of aridity and scanty vegetation such as the deserts, exposed areas of beach sand, the recently dried muds of river flats, areas of newly deposited glacial drift, or bare plowed fields. Over large areas of desert surface all the fine material has been removed by the wind, leaving a *desert pavement* of the heavier gravels and pebbles (Fig. 208).

The process of deflation is to some extent aided by wind abrasion. The wind-transported particles scratch, polish, and reduce each other and to some extent the solid rock, producing fine particles which in their turn are removed from the region.

371. HOW WIND AGGRADES. Wind, like streams and waves, deposits its load of coarse material promptly but is able to carry fine

particles farther and distribute them more widely. Loose sands are supplied in abundance by the weathering of desert rocks or by wave deposition on shorelines. Where the sands are not anchored by vegetation or moisture they are whipped up by wind and drifted into the sheltered lee of some obstruction, where the decrease in wind velocity permits some to be deposited. Thus is begun the growth of a *sand dune* which, by its own height, provides further shelter and promotes its own growth. The growth of a dune often is accompanied or followed by a change of its location. A film of sand is stripped from the windward slope of the dune and deposited in the lee of the crest. By continuous subtraction from the windward and addition to the leeward the dune moves slowly, but seldom far, from the source of sand supply (Fig. 218).

The dust supplied by rock weathering and abrasion in dry regions is drifted by prevailing winds over wide expanses to the leeward. There probably is a considerable quantity of wind-borne dust in most soils, but in regions immediately to the leeward of arid lands, where deflation is active, it is particularly abundant and may attain great thickness. Considerable accumulations of wind-deposited dust are called *loess* (444). In northern China there are extensive deposits of loess that in places reach more than 100 ft. in thickness. In central Europe and central United States also are widespread loess deposits which may have originated in part from the muds of glacially enlarged drainage-ways during the glacial period.

Section D. Landforms

372. The foregoing discussion of earth materials and processes leads naturally to a consideration of the earth features resulting from the operations of those processes upon earth materials. This, it may be repeated, is a matter of immediate concern to the student of geography. The purpose of this section of the book is to describe and depict some of the significant and recurring surface features of the land, to sketch their patterns and locate regions in which they are found, and to indicate something of their relative degrees of human utility. The principal groups of landforms to be considered, as distinguished by their several characteristic features and degrees of relative relief, are (a) plains, (b) plateaus, (c) hill lands, and (d) mountains.

Within each of the above principal groups there are surface features of a smaller order of size. These are the hills and valleys, the broad uplands and flat lowlands, and the many other landforms with which the daily affairs of men are concerned. Analytical study of the variety of features characteristic of any one of the major landform groups shows (a) that they are capable of separation into types upon the basis of their shapes and manner of arrangement and (b) that each type results from the interaction of earth processes in a region with given conditions as to climate and as to kind and structure of rock. It is the purpose of the chapters that follow in Sec. D of this book to describe the groups of landforms and their distinctive types of features and to indicate the manner of their association. By constant reference to the brief discussions of materials and processes in Sec. C the likenesses or differences between features may be sharpened and made clearer.

REFERENCES FOR SECTION D

Atwood, Wallace W. "The Physiographic Provinces of North America." Ginn and Company, Boston, 1940.

Bonney, T. G. "Volcanoes: Their Structure and Significance." G. P. Putnam's Sons, New York, 1913.

Bowman, Isaiah. "Forest Physiography." John Wiley & Sons, Inc., New York, 1911.

Braun, Gustav. "Grundzüge der Physiogeographie." B. G. Teubner, Leipzig, 1930.

Fenneman, N. M. "Physiography of Western United States." McGraw-Hill Book Company, Inc., New York, 1931.

————. "Physiography of Eastern United States." McGraw-Hill Book Company, Inc., New York, 1938.

Gautier, E. F. "Sahara: The Great Desert." Translated by D. F. Mayhew. Columbia University Press, New York, 1935.

Geikie, James. "Earth Sculpture." John Murray, London, 1898.

————. "Mountains: Their Origin, Growth, and Decay." D. Van Nostrand Company, Inc., New York, 1914.

Gregory, J. W. "Geography; Structural, Physical, and Comparative." Blackie & Son, Ltd., London, 1908.

————. "The Nature and Origin of Fiords." John Murray, London, 1913.

Hettner, A. "Die Oberflächenformen des Festlandes." B. G. Teubner, Leipzig, 1921.

Hobbs, W. H. "Earth Features and Their Meaning." The Macmillan Company, New York, 1931.

Johnson, D. W. "Shore Processes and Shoreline Development." John Wiley & Sons, Inc., New York, 1919.

Lobeck, A. K. "Geomorphology." McGraw-Hill Book Company, Inc., New York, 1939.

Loomis, F. B. "Physiography of the United States." Doubleday, Doran and Company, Inc., New York, 1937.

Marr, J. E. "The Scientific Study of Scenery." Methuen & Co., Ltd., London, 1920.

Passarge, S. "Die Grundlagen der Landschaftskunde." L. Friederichsen & Co., Hamburg, 1920.

Peattie, Roderick. "Mountain Geography." Harvard University Press, Cambridge, Mass., 1936.

Supan, Alexander. "Grundzüge der Physischen Erdkunde." Walter de Gruyter Company, Berlin, 1930.

Tyrrell, G. W. "Volcanoes." T. Thornton Butterworth, Ltd., London, 1931.

Worcester, P. G. "A Textbook of Geomorphology." D. Van Nostrand Company, Inc., New York, 1939.

See also the list of references included under *Section C.*

Chapter XIV. Plains of Stream Degradation

General Considerations Relative to Plains

373. How Plains May Be Distinguished. It is recognized commonly that, of the four principal classes of landforms, plains have the greatest areal extent and general habitability and that most of the world's great plains are situated in their respective continents so that they slope toward bordering seas without notable interruptions to the continuity of their surfaces. However, an acceptable basis for definitely distinguishing plains from each of the other major subdivisions is not easy to arrive at because plains lands, in many places, grade almost without interruption into hill lands or plateaus. One significant difference among the four classes of features is found in their respective degrees of roughness. This may be measured in terms of *local relief*, *i.e.*, the difference between the elevation of the highest point and that of the lowest point within a limited area (376). *The term plain is here applied to all land that is relatively low with respect to sea level and has a local relief of less than about 500 ft.*

All plains lands are by no means alike in their elevations above sea level. Some broad plains reach altitudes of several hundreds of feet while others are depressed and stand, behind barrier rims, at elevations somewhat lower than sea level. There are other differences between plains also. Some are very flat while others are rolling or even rough, within the limits of their general relief. However, in spite of their great variability, plains are much the most habitable of the major landform subdivisions of the continents. Because of their low degree of local relief they have, generally, low angles of slope. They are, therefore, easily traversed by routes of transportation, and the surfaces of such as are climatically suited to crops largely are capable of tillage. In some parts of the American corn belt as much as 70 to 80 per cent of the total land area is plowed and planted to crops. That leaves but 20 to 30 per cent to be devoted to pasture, wood lots, farm buildings, roads, towns, and all other uses. This could not possibly be true of plateaus, hill regions, or mountains. Plains have, therefore, as compared with plateaus, hill lands, and mountains, large food-producing capacity, and it is not surprising that they contain the principal centers of world population.

374. GENERAL DISTRIBUTION OF THE WORLD'S PLAINS.   A study of the location and distribution of the world's great plains (Plate VII) will reveal the significant fact that much of the greater part of them are situated in their respective continents in a manner such that they are tributary, both physically and commercially, to the Atlantic Ocean. Some are directly so while others, such as the plains of northern Asia, are only indirectly tributary to the Atlantic. The Siberian plains, although they are, in large part, nearer to the Pacific Ocean, are separated from it by considerable mountain or plateau barriers. Only the smaller plains of southern and eastern Asia, Australasia, and western America face upon the Pacific Ocean. This condition is to be expected, in view of the fact that the borders of the Pacific comprise the most extended world region of young and growing mountains.

375. THE DETAILS OF PLAINS RELIEF include uplands and lowlands, ridges and valleys, hills and hollows, all within local ranges of elevation of 500 ft. or less. In some respects they are like the similar features found in plateaus, hill lands, and mountains except that they have less relief and much greater areal extent. However, there are so many essential differences between the characteristic features of plains and those of the lands of greater relief that the former are worthy of separate and extended consideration.

A survey of the plains regions of the world from the viewpoint of their smaller relief features indicates that there are extensive areas in which essentially the same combination or association of features is found throughout. One of these areas of physiographic unity is likely to be a region of uniform rock composition and tectonic history which has been acted upon by the same gradational agents to about the same degree. Because of differences in the shapes and arrangements of their features, plains regions of different origins and histories do not look alike. For that reason it becomes necessary to classify them in order that they may more adequately be described.

376. CLASSES OF GREAT PLAINS.   For the purpose of convenient description the major plains lands of the earth may be grouped in several different ways. The basis of the grouping will, of course, depend upon the purpose for which it is made. The following are possible groupings, each of which has its own merits from the standpoint of regional geography: (a) Plains may be classified in accordance with

their climatic situation. There are, for example, humid tropical plains, arid tropical plains, subarctic plains, and others. Such a grouping of the plains of the world recognizes an important element, the climatic one, concerned in the development of the landforms of plains but does not thereby give a complete background for the understanding of all the landforms commonly found in plains of each of the climatic regions. (b) Plains are sometimes classified, in accordance with their situations in their respective continents, as coastal plains and interior plains. (c) They may be classified also in accordance with their prevalent conditions of geological composition and rock structure. Upon this basis one may recognize plains of horizontal sedimentary rock; peneplains of ancient crystalline rock; plains of glacial deposition; and others. (d) Highly important, from the geographical point of view, is the comparative roughness of plains. The element of roughness is significant because it is indicative of various aspects of the human utility of plains, such as the freedom of drainage, the rapidity of soil erosion, or the ease of tillage. Moreover, it is measurable with some accuracy in terms of local difference in elevation, or local relief.

The comparative roughness or local relief of landforms may be indicated by means of the maximum difference in elevation found within any chosen area of restricted size. A study of local relief in the United States, upon which the following classes were based, employed for the purpose the area of a quadrangle of $7\frac{1}{2}'$ of latitude and longitude, including horizontal distances not exceeding 10 miles. Upon this basis one may recognize (a) *flat plains*, having a local relief of less than 50 ft.; (b) *undulating plains*, having a local relief of from 50 to 150 ft.; (c) *rolling plains*, having a local relief of from 150 to 300 ft.; and (d) *rough dissected plains*, having a local relief of from 300 to 500 ft.

Each of the above broadly descriptive classifications is based upon conditions which need to be understood before the habitat significance of a plains region and the details of landform developed upon it can be appreciated fully. A classification involving all the elements indicated above certainly would be more explicit but also more complicated and less inclusive. Under such a classification one might list, for example, a gently undulating coastal plain of unconsolidated, horizontal, marine sediments in humid subtropical type of climate; or, in contrast, a rolling, ice-scoured, interior plain of peneplaned crystalline rocks in subarctic climate. Such detail, if it were followed through its logical development, with examples cited from all parts of the world, would far exceed the limits of space imposed by a brief consideration of the general subject of plains.

As a practical approach to this subject a major subdivision of plains is made in the following pages upon the basis of the dominant agents and processes concerned in their origin. Those processes are (a) stream erosion, (b) stream deposition, (c) the work of glaciers, and (d) the work of the wind. Each class of plains is then considered in terms of its inherent characteristics. These include (i) degree of local relief; (ii) the shapes of valleys; (iii) the shapes of interstream, or divide, areas, including ridges and isolated hills; and (iv) the types and conditions of drainage. Not only does every plain include particular examples of each of these classes of features, but it is characterized by a distinctive pattern or arrangement of these features with respect to each other. It will be understood that the differences between the types of features and the patterns of their arrangement in plains are the result of the operation and interaction of the several tectonic and gradational forces previously considered. Among the conditions involved are (a) differences in climate; (b) differences in kind and structure of rock; (c) differences in the kinds of gradational agents, past or present, that have molded the surface forms; and (d) differences in the stages of completion to which the several agents have carried their respective processes of surface modification.

It is not expected that the classes of plains to be discussed are entirely mutually exclusive or that they will include every part of each of the world's great plains. There are certain omissions and some overlaps. For example, the plain of southeastern Wisconsin is fundamentally a stream-eroded plain, but it is covered by a veneer of glacial drift which in some places quite obscures and in others only partly obscures its stream-eroded features. The same region may be considered, therefore, as an illustration of both stream-eroded and glaciated plains.

Stream-eroded Plains

377. Plains in which the principal details of landform result from the erosional or solvent action of surface waters are of various rock structures, either simple or complicated. In order that erosional details of the various types may be seen in their areal associations with each other, it will be well to examine plains resulting from the erosion of different types of structure and to view them at different stages in their erosional progress. To that end may be considered first the simple features of a newly emerged coastal plain and later those of stream-eroded plains developed in rocks of greater age and various degrees of structural complexity.

378. THE FEATURES OF NEWLY EMERGED COASTAL PLAINS.   The gently sloping surfaces of many coastal plains are continued beneath the margins of adjacent seas as *continental shelves*. Although they are covered by shallow seas, the continental shelves truly are parts of the continental blocks. It would require but slight elevation or depression of the land relative to sea level to add considerably to, or subtract from, the areas of coastal plains (Fig. 137). It has been indicated previously that the continental shelves are the sorting and settling places for the sands, muds, and limes which come directly or indirectly from the land (368). Because they are continually worked over by waves and currents the sediments are so evenly distributed within their respective zones that the surfaces of the continental shelves are smooth and essentially flat. The slow emergence of a portion of a

FIG. 137.—The flat swampy surface of the Florida Everglades, part of a newly emerged plain.

continental shelf would add to a continental margin a low and almost featureless plain. It would be comprised of loosely compacted and alternating layers of sands, muds, and lime which normally would lie nearly horizontal or have a slight inclination seaward. Such a plain would be mainly of tectonic origin since weathering and erosion would have, as yet, little opportunity to change its features.

Plains of this manner of origin have been formed in various parts of the earth during its long history, but, although they may be flat following their emergence, they do not long remain featureless. As the land emerges, inch by inch, it is attacked by the agents of degradation. Streams, originating far inland, continue their courses across the new land of the coastal margin. Rainwash develops tributary gullies in it and produces erosional landforms. However, the valleys of low coastal plains cannot be deep because baselevel is close below the surface. They may, in humid climates, be numerous, each section of the plain discharging its drainage into the sea by independent channels. Even where streams are numerous their gradients are likely to be so low that their tributaries are unable to erode quickly into all parts of the inter-stream areas. The latter tend therefore to remain flat and to be poorly drained. They contain swamps, small and large, which lie in minor depressions of the ancient sea bottom or its coastal margin and do not have streams with gradients sufficiently steep to drain them.

When valleys are eroded on such low gradients as those of a newly emerged plain it is clear that if the erosion is followed by a very slight subsidence of the land relative to sea level it will be sufficient to enable the sea to creep landward in the lower portions of the valleys. Such an encroachment of the sea will turn stream mouths into bays and stream

Fig. 138.—Flat but well-drained coastal plain in Texas.

valleys, already at baselevel, into tidal marshes. Features of this kind will be discussed later in connection with the shore features of plains lands (449).

379. EXAMPLES OF NEWLY EMERGED PLAINS.   There are several plains in the world whose characteristic landforms indicate that they belong to the newly emerged class. Among them is that portion of the United States included in the coastal margins of the states of Virginia, the Carolinas, Georgia, and parts of the Gulf Coast from Florida to Texas (Fig. 138). Most of this plain is flat, the local relief being less than 50 ft., and, although the difference in their respective elevations is slight, there are large areas of both river-bottom and upland swamps. The upland swamps, locally called *pocosins*, or *bays*, are situated upon the divides or interfluves and are ex-ceedingly numerous (Fig. 139). Although they generally are of small size, a few of them are of notable extent. The largest are the Everglades of Florida; the Okefenokee Swamp, located astride the Florida-Georgia boundary; and the Dismal Swamp of North Carolina and Virginia. The swamps of the Atlantic and Gulf Coastal Plains, both upland and river bottom, are so numerous and so large that they comprise nearly two-thirds

of all the ill-drained lands of the United States. Other coastal lowlands also are characterized by the presence of large swamps. Such is the nature of the broad coastal flats of eastern Nicaragua and the eastern coast of South Africa.

On the Arctic fringe of Eurasia, both east and west of the Ural Mountains, are newly emerged plains. In them the features of poor drainage, common to plains of this class, are accentuated by permanent frost in the ground.

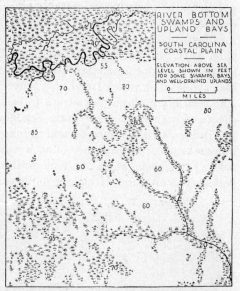

380. BELTED COASTAL PLAINS. Some coastal plains are characterized by features of erosion more than by the flat surfaces of newly emerged sea bottom. They have been above sea level long enough and have sufficient elevation so that streams have etched their surfaces into low relief (Fig. 140). Sedimentary

FIG. 139.—The interfluves in this area have not been entirely reached and drained by the stream tributaries. Compare the elevations of different swamps.

rocks of unequal resistance to erosion, conditions of climate, and

FIG. 140.—The undulating surface of the inner coastal plain in central Georgia. The low interfluve is cultivated, but the slopes and bottoms of the creek valleys are wooded.

accidents of major stream position combine to produce features the forms and patterns of which are distinctive.

Upon the inner and more elevated portion of the Atlantic and Gulf Coastal Plains of the United States stream erosion of the young sediments has produced a notable arrangement of features. Here are exposed, one after another, the landward edges of the lower and older members of the whole series of gently inclined coastal-plain strata (Fig. 141). Erosion has beveled their surfaces and has exposed them so that they appear as alternate bands or belts several miles wide and many miles long which trend, in a general way, parallel with the coast. The relation of these rock strata to each other is like that of several sheets of paper piled so that, beginning at the bottommost, each protrudes a little distance beyond the one above it. If the papers were of different colors the exposure of each would produce a band or belt of color. A region in which the rock strata are so exposed is known as a belted coastal plain. It has an undulating surface and, because it is

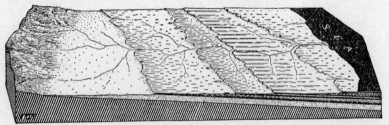

Fig. 141.—A diagram to illustrate the cuestaform ridges, intervening lowlands, and related rock structure of a belted coastal plain. The rock strata shown in solid black are indicated as having superior resistance.

somewhat higher and has slightly steeper stream gradients, it has not the great areas of swampland that are found on its newly emerged seaward margin just previously described.

Because the belts are made up of strata of lime, clay, and sand they differ in their features of soil, drainage, and relief. The sediments, although geologically young, have been somewhat consolidated by pressure and cemented by minerals deposited from solution. They are inclined toward the coast at low angles but not so low as that of the slope of the plain in the same direction. Streams have carved more readily into the less resistant of these formations, leaving the exposed edges of the more resistant, often sandstones, standing in relief. Owing to the attitudes of the rocks, long low ridges are thus produced alternating with broad lowlands. The ridges, under humid climate, have been carved into belts of hills. They have a relief of from 100 to 200 ft. above the lowlands, trend roughly parallel to the coast, are asymmetrical, and usually present steeper faces toward the inland direction and more gentle slopes to seaward. The relation of the alternating ridges and lowlands above described to each other and the manner of their erosion by streams will become apparent from a study of Fig. 141. Ridges of this kind are called *cuestas*. Their steeper inland faces are called *escarpments;* and their gentler slopes are called *dip slopes.* Figure 142 shows the conspicuous ridges of the Alabama Coastal Plain, together with the pattern of the streams now adjusted to the rock structures of the region. The valleys between the ridges are called lowlands, and the innermost valley, which is adjacent to the older land, is called the *inner lowland.* Extensive plains that include a series of cuesta ridges and intervening lowlands may be spoken of as *cuesta-*

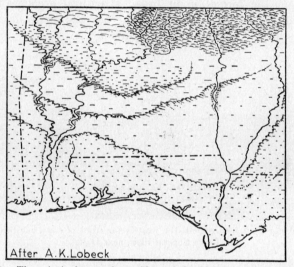

After A.K.Lobeck

FIG. 142.—The principal cuestaform ridges of the Alabama Coastal Plain. The escarpments face northward.

form plains. It happens that the broad inner lowlands on both the Alabama and Texas Coastal Plains are eroded in chalky limestones which have given rise to soils of great productivity (625). These lowlands, which are called the *Alabama Black Belt* and the *Texas Black Prairies*, have become major centers of population and agricultural wealth (Fig. 143).

381. STREAM-ERODED PLAINS IN OLDER SEDIMENTARY ROCKS. Many plains of gently inclined sedimentary rock, located well to the interiors of continents, show features somewhat like those of the belted coastal plain. These have been developed by stream erosion but are different from those of coastal plains because the ancient strata have been somewhat changed, by diastrophism and the cementing action of deposition by ground water, both as to their positions and as to

their resistance to erosion. It is probable that erosion, in these older plains, since their emergence as coastal plains, has removed scores or even hundreds of feet of rock that formerly lay above the present surfaces. During this slow process the original surface of the coastal plain, with its ill-drained depressions, has completely disappeared, and the streams have adjusted themselves to the conditions of structure and hardness in the different rocks. These older and better consolidated sediments have existed through long periods of geologic history and have, in some places, been involved in minor tectonic movements which have resulted in changes in the inclination of the strata or in the formation of broad structural arches and basins. Stream carving in the rocks of which they are made has produced several distinctive kinds of plains features.

Fig. 143.—White Rock escarpment, the west-facing front of a low cuestaform ridge on the Texas Coastal Plain near Dallas.

382. STREAM-ERODED PLAINS, YOUNG AND OLD. Although plains are lands of low relief, even they pass through the successive stages of erosional development from youth to old age. This is true of coastal and cuestaform plains no less than of others, and the features of such plains merely mark special developments due to the differential erosion of inclined sedimentary rocks. But not all stream-eroded plains have cuesta and lowland features. Some have been eroded in sediments the attitudes of which coincide so nearly with the slopes of the present surfaces that single rock strata are exposed over large areas. Others have been eroded in regions of faulted sediments, and still others in regions of crystalline rocks of great age and structural complexity, which formerly were hills or even mountains. As their erosion proceeds the landforms of these plains reflect the local peculiarities of rock structure, climatic condition, and the stage of completion to which the streams have carried their work.

In regions where stream erosion is the principal gradational process, some plains are smooth because they are young, and the erosional process has barely begun; some are smooth because they are old, and erosion has proceeded as far as it can; and a few are smooth because they have been stripped down to the smooth surface of some resistant and widespread rock formation. In general, the roughness of a plain, that is, the thoroughness and depth of its stream dissection, depends upon the elevation of the plain with respect to the local baselevel and upon the stage to which the erosional cycle has advanced. Therefore, plains of whatever rock structure may be classified also, according to the stage of their erosional development, as young, mature, or old (355). A newly emerged coastal plain is likely to be young. It may be eroded, but it cannot be very rough because its baselevel is so close beneath the original surface that even mature dissection by streams cannot produce deep valleys. Some elevated interior plains are undissected, flat, and very young, but others, where erosion is well advanced, are so rough that they reach the arbitrary limit of 500 ft. of local relief set for plains and approach hill country in appearance. Plains that have been reduced to old age by stream erosion usually have undulating surfaces.

383. *Young stream-eroded plains* are characterized by broad, smooth interfluves which are traversed at intervals by narrow, steep-walled valleys. In some young plains the major valleys have reached grade and have developed broad bottoms in which the streams meander before the tributary valleys have become so numerous as to dissect the interfluves minutely. In such plains tributary gullies may be most numerous close to the main stream, where the gradient from upland to valley flat is steep. There they dissect the valley walls, making a fringe of rough land (sometimes called "river breaks") between the graded valley flat and the smooth upland. These features are particularly characteristic of plains developed under semiarid climates, such as the High Plains of the United States (Fig. 144). In regions of young plains the broad interfluves generally are the principal sites of agricultural settlement, routes of transportation, and urban centers. Minor valleys are narrow and subject to flood. Their walls are steep and are the least usable of the plains lands. The broad bottoms of some major valleys contain usable land; some are important commercial thoroughfares, and, in dry regions, they are more easily adapted to the requirements of irrigation agriculture than are the uplands.

384. *The Streams of Young Plains and Their Valleys.* The streams of young plains have, from the beginning, relatively low gradients. This does not mean, however, that they do not have the charac-

teristics of youth (351) but merely that the features are not so persistent. In their downward cutting they encounter rocks of unequal

Fig. 144.—Sharply dissected bluffs or river breaks separate flat river bottoms from rolling interfluves in parts of the Great Plains. (1) Rolling interfluves; (2) river breaks; (3) river bottoms.

resistance and develop falls and rapids. Many of these are of low elevation, but, if they occur in the courses of large streams of uniform flow, they may have great capacity for producing water power. Because streams in plains commonly reach grade quickly, they take on the characteristics of maturity before the land through which they flow reaches erosional maturity. Therefore, by the time plains reach maturity the streams that flow through them generally have well-graded courses in which falls and rapids are infrequent or have disappeared entirely (Fig. 130). However, evidence of unequal resistance in the rocks of the valley wall sometimes persist in the form of rock benches or terraces along the valley sides. These result from differential degradation, the upper surface of a resistant rock stratum forming a terrace while its eroded edge forms the steeper slope below (Fig. 145).

Fig. 145.—Rock terraces, flat-topped, steplike benches, bordering the Platte River in southeastern Wyoming. (*U. S. Geological Survey Photograph.*)

The stream systems of young stream-eroded plains generally are dendritic, or treelike, in pattern (Fig. 238). In regions of horizontal strata or uniform rock they are likely to remain so throughout their development. In regions of inclined strata or diversified rocks other patterns are likely to develop only with the adjustments of streams to structure that come with more advanced erosional stages.

385. *Mature stream-eroded plains,* such as those of southwestern Wisconsin, southern Missouri, the Ohio Valley, or the Highland Rim of Tennessee show a variety of forms as to both relief features and use. In plains of early maturity the interfluves, although narrowed by increasing dissection, often have more flat land than do the valleys and are the areas of principal settlement. However, their development involves an increase in the proportion of land in slopes and a corresponding decrease in the area of flat land. In later maturity the interfluves are reduced to mere ridges; and the farms, roads, and villages

are more largely concentrated in the broadened valleys (Fig. 146). Examples of local variations in the patterns of relief features and cultural forms may be found in each of the regions named above and in many other maturely dissected plains.

In certain plains regions of semiarid climate and nonresistant or poorly consolidated sediments mature dissection produces landforms of peculiarly intricate pattern and sharp detail. Under these conditions rapidly eroded gullies dissect the upland minutely, but there is little softening of the contours of the features by soil creep or continuous rainwash. The result is a surface of a type known as *badlands*. Considerable areas of badlands of this kind are found in the plains of western Nebraska and the Dakotas, where they attain the relief characteristic of hills (483, Fig. 239).

Fig. 146.—Rough dissected plain in southwestern Wisconsin. The local relief in this region averages about 500 ft., but in some localities it exceeds that figure and the surface is truly hilly. (*Wisconsin Geological Survey Photograph.*)

386. *Old stream-eroded plains and peneplains* are characterized by broadly open valleys. The remnants of former interfluves exist as low rolling divides between the streams but are too low to have any notable relation to the human occupance and use of the plains (Fig. 131C). It is probable that some peneplains have developed from the long-continued gradation of plains of horizontal sedimentary rocks, which originally had youthful relief features but have passed through the stages of maturity and old age. However, it is certain that others were originally not plains at all but mountain regions of highly complicated structures. The time required for the complete leveling of high and geologically complex mountain regions is so long, and the later stages of the process are so slow, that few if any of the peneplains of crystalline rock ever were perfectly finished. Unreduced portions in the form of erosion remnants, or *monadnocks*, usually are to be found standing in bold relief above the general level of their surfaces

as reminders of the greater heights at which the regions once stood. Moreover, although many peneplains are known, none is now found that is either very low or very flat. It may be supposed that before the slow process was finished it was interrupted by diastrophic change which elevated the land sufficiently to steepen the gradients of the streams and permit them to erode the peneplains into undulating or rolling plains whose uplands lie at the general level of the ancient surface and above which the occasional monadnocks rise still higher. Some peneplains have been so greatly elevated that portions of their former flattish surfaces are now found among the heights of hill regions or mountains.

387. LOWLAND PENEPLAINS. Some ancient peneplains, although somewhat re-eroded, still are so comparatively level that they may be classed as

FIG. 147.—Spencer Mountain, a monadnock on the partially re-eroded peneplain of the Appalachian Piedmont, near Gastonia, N. C.

plains. The Appalachian Piedmont of the United States and parts of the Amazonian plain (Plates VI, VII) may be cited as examples of crystalline peneplains whose present surfaces have developed under conditions of warm and humid climate. They are characterized by rolling surfaces, occasional monadnocks, and deep accumulations of weathered and leached regolith. On the Appalachian Piedmont the remnants of the ancient peneplain still are broad, although newer valleys have been carved into its surface. The uplands are the sites of the principal cultural forms and are given over largely to farming which, in many localities, has resulted in a rapid erosion of the soil. In this region also some of the monadnocks are of more than local importance. Such are Stone Mountain, near Atlanta, Ga., King's Mountain, famed as a battle ground in the American Revolution, Spencer Mountain, North Carolina (Fig. 147), and others.

There are in some regions of arid climate areas of stream-eroded piedmont plain (pediments) the beveled surfaces of which are so closely associated with desert phenomena that comment upon them will be reserved for discussion with the features developed under arid climates (437). Also there are extensive areas of crystalline peneplain whose present details of surface have been produced by agencies other than stream erosion. Such are the glaciated peneplains of Canada, northeastern United States, Sweden, and Finland (418). These, too, will be considered in other connections.

388. CUESTAFORM PLAINS. The development of interior plains by differential stream erosion on gently inclined, older sediments is not uncommon. One special result of this process is the formation of cuestas and lowlands like those of belted coastal plains, although some are of larger size. Of that origin are the plains of much of the upper Mississippi

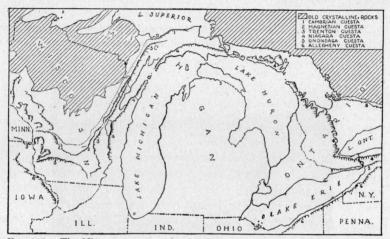

FIG. 148.—The Niagara cuesta and other less marked ridges produced by stream erosion in the older sedimentary rocks of the Great Lakes region. Parts of some of the ridges are deeply covered by glacial drift, and their approximate positions are shown by broken lines.

Basin. In them the escarpments of some of the cuestas present features of bold relief, the height and irregularity of their crests depending much upon the thickness and resistance of the rock formations to which they are due. In general, however, the ridges of cuestaform plains are not bold features but are dissected into belts of hills whose heights are not great when compared with the widths of the intervening lowlands.

389. *Examples of Cuestaform Plains.* In southeastern England the Lincoln Wolds, the Cotswold Hills, the several Downs, and other ridges are cuestas formed by the differential erosion of inclined rock strata. Mainly the ridge-making rocks are porous chalky limestones which have resisted erosion by their absorptiveness. In the Mississippi Basin various sedimentary strata incline gently away from the old land of the Lake Superior

Highland and disappear beneath the newer sediments of the Gulf Coastal Plain. The outcropping edges of the more resistant of them, mainly sandy or cherty limestones and dolomites, form a series of cuesta ridges (321, Fig. 148). One of these is the Military Ridge of southwestern Wisconsin. Another, and a most persistent one, is the Niagara cuesta, an outcrop of a hard magnesian limestone. It traverses northern Illinois, eastern Wisconsin, upper Michigan, and peninsular Ontario and finally dies out in western New York. Its projecting crest is the cause of the Door Peninsula of Wisconsin, the Manitoulin Islands, the Bruce Peninsula of Ontario, and the escarpment that gives rise to Niagara Falls. The dip slopes and intervening lowlands of these cuestaform ridges are undulating farm lands, although in central Wisconsin the inner lowland is a broad and relatively infertile sand plain resting upon an underlying sandstone. Minor features upon these plains include groups of hills which are remnants of the cuesta escarpments, detached and left isolated by differential weathering and erosion. Such hills, which lie out beyond the margin of the main body of the rock of which they are composed, are called *outliers*. They are exemplified by the Mounds of southern Wisconsin. The same processes have given some of these outlying hills bold or even fantastic and castellated forms.

390. PLAINS OF CONCENTRIC RIDGES AND LOWLANDS. In the long histories of the older sedimentary rocks have occurred minor changes of level which have resulted in widespread and gentle warping of the rocks. Some such are expressed in various of the curves of the cuesta ridges shown in Fig. 148. Others resulted in low broad structural arches or domes or equally broad structural basins. The latter include several rock strata, some of considerable resistance and others easily eroded, nested together like a pile of shallow saucers of decreasing size. The subsequent differential erosion of a structural basin produces a series of roughly concentric lowlands and cuestas with *out-facing* escarpments. The Paris Basin of France is a notable example of a plain of this class (Fig. 149). Its five or six low cuestaform ridges have been partially dissected by streams and stand as concentric but broken ridges upon a fertile plain. The shapes, heights, and arrangements of these cuesta ridges have played important parts in the appearance of the plain, its agricultural uses, the pattern of its avenues of transportation, and the military defense of Paris, which is its natural focus. The London Basin is a similar, though somewhat elongated, structure which is traversed on its major axis by the Thames River.

Structural arches or domes, when subsequently their tops are attacked and removed by weathering and erosion, also produce concentric lowlands and cuestaform ridges but with *in-facing* escarpments. In England, for example, the south flank of the London Basin forms the north flank of an arch the chalk cuestas of which are called the

North Downs and the South Downs. Their escarpments face in upon the sands and clays of a rolling plain called The Weald (Fig. 150).

391. *Important American Plains of Concentric Features.* In the United States there are several notable examples of plains formed by the erosion of structural arches. The most important are those developed by the erosion

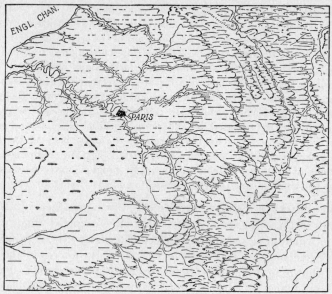

Fig. 149.—The principal cuestaform ridges and out-facing escarpments of the Paris Basin.

of a long low arch which extends from southwestern Ohio to northern Alabama. Upon it are two oval cuestaform plains. These are the Bluegrass Region of Kentucky and the Nashville Basin of Tennessee. Each is about the size of the state of Connecticut. The upper formations of the arch pri-

Fig. 150.—A north-south cross section through the outskirts of London showing the surface features and rock structures of the London Basin and the Weald. The section is 100 miles long, and its vertical scale is several times exaggerated.

marily are composed of sandstones and other siliceous rocks from which are derived soils of rather low fertility. In Tennessee this is called the Highland Rim (Fig. 151). In the basins the removal of the overlying rocks has exposed easily weathered limestones, one of them a phosphatic limestone. The degradation of these less resistant rocks is responsible for the formation of the basins, the undulating plains and silt-and-clay-loam soils of which are noted for their productivity (Fig. 152). About the margins of the basins are many outliers, isolated remnants of the rim rock that have been detached by differential erosion and left in the form of conical hills upon the basin plain. These are so thickly distributed that they form a fringe which, in Kentucky, is called the region of the Knobs.

MAP
OF
CENTRAL
TENNESSEE
INCLUDING THE
NASHVILLE
BASIN

☐ Calcareous rocks of the Central Basin.
■ Silicious rocks of the Highland Rim

A GENERALIZED CROSS SECTION
H. RIM   KNOBS   CENTRAL BASIN   KNOBS   HIGHLAND RIM

FIG. 151.—The many knobs or erosion remnants of the rim rock together with valleys deeply eroded in the Highland Rim give the Nashville Basin a fringed appearance on a geological map. Note the cross section below the map.

FIG. 152.—The undulating plain of the inner Bluegrass Region of Kentucky.

Karst Plains

392. SOLUTION FEATURES. In various parts of the world are small plains, and there are some of considerable size, the distinctive surface features of which result from the solvent work of underground water rather than from stream erosion. They may be called *karst* plains (350).

Regions of this kind are underlain by sediments which include layers
of pure limestone. In some karst plains the soluble limestones make up
the surface rock formations and are covered only by residual earth;
in others they lie beneath some thicknesses of other rocks. In either
case, however, the surface features show evidence of the removal of
material beneath the surface and mainly in solution.

In contrast with stream-eroded plains, karst plains are distinguished
by a general absence of valleys. They are not always entirely lacking,
since some large streams originating in border areas may cut entirely
across a karst plain. Small valleys, however, generally are not numerous, some districts of hundreds of square miles' extent having few if
any. Instead of stream-eroded drainage patterns, karst plains have
undulating, rolling, or sometimes rough surfaces in which numerous
depressions without visible outlets are separated by low irregular
ridges or hillocks without definite pattern of arrangement. Some of the

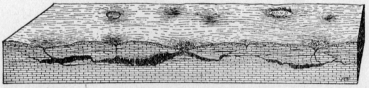

FIG. 153.—A diagram illustrating karst plain features. Sinks of various types are shown
in relation to features of limestone solution underground.

depressions are large and irregular in outline; others are small and
nearly circular. The depressions and their intervening ridges result
from the unequal solution of the underlying limestones. Some of the
basins are produced by surface solution, the water finding its outlet
through the bottom into solution caverns, along joints, or into other
underground channels. Some, on the other hand, appear to be the
result of the subsidence of the roofs of former caverns. They vary in
size from a few feet in diameter to sprawling depressions several miles
in extent. Commonly they are designated by the general term *sinks*
(Fig. 153). Some sinks are many feet deep, are steep-sided, and have
obvious openings through which the surface drainage runs underground. Others are so shallow as almost to escape notice. In some the
bottom outlets are partially or wholly stopped by clay or other
materials, and the drainage escapes so slowly that swamps, temporary
lakes, or even permanent lakes accumulate in them. Seldom, however,
do the lakes rise to the point where they overflow their basins and spill
into neighboring depressions through surface channels.

Associated with the underground drainage of karst plains is the
formation of numerous caverns, mainly small, which in some regions

thoroughly honeycomb the soluble limestones beneath. Fed by surface drainage, the waters of many solution cavities pass along joint plains or dissolved channels and sometimes join ultimately in underground streams of considerable size or issue as springs of remarkable volume (538). In a few karst areas thick limestone formations have permitted the solution of caverns of great size and extent, such as Mammoth Cave, Kentucky. The partial collapse of cavern roofs in these regions results also in the formation of natural bridges. Features of that kind are not uncommon, but mainly they are of small size.

FIG. 154.—A view in the karst plain of central Florida. The lake lies in a solution basin and it furnishes some frost protection to grapefruit groves on its southern and eastern sides.

393. NOTABLE KARST REGIONS. Areas of solution features take their name from the Karst, a rough denuded limestone plateau and hill region which lies back of the Adriatic shore of Yugoslavia. Of the same rock type is the neighboring lowland of Apulia, the rolling plain of the "heel" of Italy. Broad sinks, there called *dolines*, are interspersed among barren limestone uplands. Because the sinks are low and soil floored they are the principal tilled areas, but in the rainy season the underdrainage cannot remove the inflowing water fast enough to prevent them from being very wet or even flooded. Other karst plains are found in North America, especially on limestone platforms bordering the Gulf of Mexico. The most extensive of these are located in Florida, Cuba, and the peninsula of Yucatán. The last named is a gently undulating plain. Although its central portion reaches elevations of 500 ft., most of it is less than 100 ft. above sea level. It has an average annual rainfall of about 35 in., but the landscape appears to be dry. There are no streams. Here, according to Huntington, a rocky surface, strewn with fragments of impure limestone, drains into numerous sinks, called by their Indian name *cenotes*, most of which are steep-sided, cavernlike, and vary in depth from 25 ft. near the coast to as much as 400 ft. in the higher localities. At the bottoms of the sinks are springs and pools of water which, in former times, were the principal sources of water supply.

The principal Cuban karst area is a broad strip of undulating plain 150 miles in length south of Habana. It differs from the Yucatán plain in being covered by deep porous red earth. Sinkholes are not numerous, yet the plain is almost streamless because the surface water drains quickly through the porous soil into a cavernous limestone beneath.

The rolling upland plain of central Florida shares with the adjacent karst regions a substratum of soluble limestone. Unlike the others it is

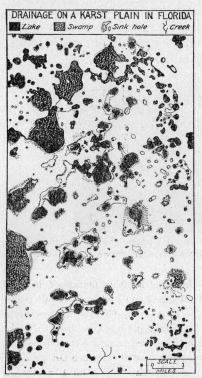

covered in large part by sands of some depth, but occasionally there are admixtures of thin strata of clay. Some parts of this plain have surface features that obviously are of karst type. Sinkholes of all sizes are separated by low sandy ridges, or hills; small caverns are numerous; and underground drainage issues in springs, one of which has the largest flow of water of any spring in the United States. The region as a whole is not without surface streams, but one of its most persistent characteristics is its lakes, ponds, and pools, of which there are thousands (Fig. 154). Some of these are known to lie in solution depressions which have their under-drainage impeded by accumulations of clay over their bottoms. It is probable that most if not all the depressions are of that origin or result from the collapse of cavern roofs. In addition to the depressions occupied by water are thousands of others, some so small and shallow as easily to escape notice, which either are ill drained or are water filled or swampy for at least a part of the year (Fig. 155).

FIG. 155.—Numerous sinks, lakes, and swamps dot this Florida karst plain, but there are almost no surface streams.

Another karst region in the United States is the undulating to rough plain in south central Kentucky which is underlain by a cavernous limestone. Considerable parts of this region are so dominated by solution features that sinks and their associated knolls and ridges are the principal relief features. Under primitive forest conditions many if not most of the sinks had free underdrainage. Since clearing, soil erosion has stripped clay from the adjacent hills and deposited it in sinks until many of them now are ill drained and contain at least temporary ponds. In the underlying limestone are many springs and caverns, often with hillside openings. Mammoth Cave, in this region, is widely known for its giant cavities and great underground extent.

Chapter XV. Plains of Stream Aggradation

394. ALLUVIAL PLAINS. Alluvium may be thought of as weathered and eroded material which has been halted in stream transit between higher lands and the sea. Attention has been directed previously to the nature of alluvial deposits and also to the manner and some of the characteristic places of their deposition (356). It may be emphasized now that, with minor exceptions, alluvium is deposited in the form of plains, and usually in flat plains, where it is spread out and awaits a future removal and the continuance of its transportation. In terms of the length of geologic time alluvial plains are temporary structures. Some, indeed, are of very recent origin; their accumulation still is in progress, and their surface forms record the manner of their upbuilding and certain of the incidents in the process. Others are vastly older; the details of the manner of their construction and incidents in the process are lost; and their surfaces are characterized rather by features that mark stages in the progress of their destruction. These are distinguished by the term *older alluvium*. The details of surface form in four principal classes of alluvial plains may be considered. These are (*a*) delta plains, (*b*) flood plains, (*c*) piedmont alluvial plains, and (*d*) plains of older alluvium.

Delta Plains

395. THE GREAT DELTA PLAINS. Delta plains are the surfaces of newly built-up accumulations of river sediment which is deposited at the mouths of streams upon their entry into bodies of quiet water. Not all great streams have deltas, but all great deltas are the deposits of large streams. Some of the most extensive delta plains may readily be discovered on the maps of a student atlas. They are the delta of the Nile, from which all such deposits take their name (its triangular central portion resembles in shape the letter Δ of the Greek alphabet), and the deltas of the Po, Rhine, Indus, Ganges, Irrawaddy, Hwang,

Orinoco, and Mississippi. There are as many more delta plains of almost equal size, but less well known, while of small deltas there are thousands (Fig. 156).

396. THE DELTA OUTLINE. The process of delta building, previously noted (357), is the cause of some peculiarities of delta shape

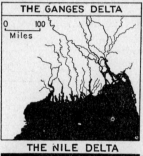

FIG. 156.—Delta outlines.

and delta surface. The normal growth of the delta through the seaward extension of the distributary channels causes it to have a tendency to present to the sea a somewhat digitate (fingerlike) outline. This feature is pronounced in the case of the Mississippi Delta (Fig. 157), but it is less noticeable in some others and is hardly apparent on the delta of the Hwang.

The manner of delta formation by addition to both the surface and the margin is responsible not only for the shape of the delta margin and its surface features but also for a great deal of the trouble and labor that are the lot of most delta inhabitants.

397. THE DELTA SURFACE. Although it is true that delta plains are very flat, since they generally have local relief of much less than 50 ft., they are not without significant differences in elevation. The seaward margin of the delta is lowest. There is the newest formed portion of the surface which continues out beneath the sea a little distance. Films of the finest mud are added to the seaward margin when the delta surface is flooded by the river, and silt and sand are thrown up there by the deposition of waves and currents. This seaward margin is built up so slowly and is so flat that, on large deltas, vast areas of the coastal fringe are little above salt water, and beyond the shoreline the coastal waters are exceedingly shallow except near the mouths of the principal distributaries. Along the delta border are marshy islands of new sediment, and it is traversed by a network of shallow and sluggish channels. The upstream portion of the delta is highest, and it grows in height as the delta increases in age and extends in area. As the distributary channels lengthen by building seaward, the stream gradient is thereby flattened, causing a decrease in stream velocity. This in turn causes the stream to drop sediment in its own channel and to overflow its banks and deposit material upon the delta surface. Flooding is repeated, and the surface is built up until a uniform gradient is maintained (Fig. 164). However, the difference in surface elevation is not great even on large deltas. The highest portions of the upper delta of the Mississippi, which lie nearly 200 miles from the river mouth, are only about 40 ft. higher than the delta margin.

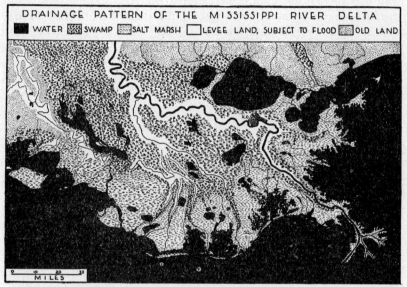

DRAINAGE PATTERN OF THE MISSISSIPPI RIVER DELTA
■ WATER ▨ SWAMP ▨ SALT MARSH ☐ LEVEE LAND, SUBJECT TO FLOOD ▨ OLD LAND

MILES

FIG. 157.—The Mississippi River Delta has fringing areas of salt-marsh grass, belts of wooded swamp, and strips of tilled levee lands. Note that the levee lands grow narrow downstream and disappear.

The features of greatest relief upon the delta surface are its *natural levees* (357). These are low and broad ridges of alluvium which border the stream channels on either side (Fig. 158). They are found along the main stream of the delta, along its distributary channels, and also along the smaller independent streams which traverse the surfaces of large deltas. They are highest near the banks of the stream that

NATURAL LEVEE RIVER ARTIFICIAL LEVEE

FIG. 158.—A diagram to show the transverse profiles of natural and artificial levees. Vertical scale considerably exaggerated.

builds them but, at least on the Mississippi Delta, rise no more than 15 or 20 ft. above the adjacent delta surface. They are both higher and broader on the older upstream portion of a delta than near its newer seaward margin. From their crests they slope away from the stream with surfaces so gently inclined that, to the eye, they appear perfectly flat. However, drainage detects the difference, and, while the higher parts of the levees along the stream banks are generally well drained, their lower portions which slope away from the stream end in fringing swamps. The width of the great upper-delta levees of the Mississippi, between river bank and swampland, commonly is from one to two miles on either side of the river. The levees of the great river near its mouth and also of the smaller delta streams may be only a few yards wide, and in the salt marshes of the seaward fringe no levees may be yet developed (Fig. 159). It is characteristic of the levees of delta streams and distributary channels that they become lower and narrower downstream until they taper to points in the coastal marshes and there disappear (Fig. 157).

Fig. 159.—Narrow natural levees parallel this small distributary bayou on the Mississippi Delta. The road, somewhat built up, occupies the crest of the levee. Another road parallels it on the other side of the bayou. The houses stand in the edge of the swamp, and each has a houseboat.

Because the levees are the highest and best drained portions of the delta surface, they are the principal sites of human settlement. Houses and towns are found upon them, and roads and railways tend to follow them and to parallel the streams. Farms occupy the gently sloping surfaces and extend away from the river toward the lower swamplands. For protection against stream overflow artificial levees are, in some places, built near the stream upon the top of the natural levees. In times of high water on the Mississippi Delta the river surface may rise nearly to the top of the artificial levees or even overflow them. At such times it stands several feet higher than the roads and farms on the natural levees behind them and many feet above the swamps beyond. A break in the artificial levees at that time permits the flooding of a large part of the delta surface, and water may completely submerge the smaller levees of the lesser streams or even the great levees themselves (Fig. 160). On some great deltas, such as that of the Ganges River, no artificial levees have been built, and both the delta swamps and the natural levees are regularly flooded in the rainy season. There the inhabitants have built compact mounds of earth on which are located their houses and village settlements barely above the reach of high water.

398. DELTA DRAINAGE.   The low flatness of the delta surface and the fact that its streams flow down the middle of broad levee ridges at

FIG. 160.—High water on the lower Mississippi floodplain. The artificial levee is the only land remaining unsubmerged. The main channel of the river is seen in the far distance. The locations of several natural levees associated with minor channels are indicated by the belts of submerged woodlands and the town. (*Official Photograph, U. S. Army Air Corps.*)

elevations slightly higher than the average surface of the plain create a difficult problem in drainage. They also give rise to some of the characteristic features of deltas, such as broad marshes and shallow lakes. Upon this peculiar surface, where the rivers are higher than the plain, surplus water from rainfall or river overflow cannot join the main river drainage because it would have to flow uphill to do so. As a consequence the water accumulates in the low flat areas between the distributary channels in the form of swamps or shallow lakes or finds its independent way to the sea through sluggish creeks which wind across the fringe of coastal marshes. It might be expected that these low areas between the levee ridges would gradually fill with sediment as a result of stream overflow through breaks in the levees. It may be, however, that the great weight of the load of sediment deposited on the levees results in a slow diastrophic depression of the whole delta surface, and that this keeps the low areas between the distributaries in a continuous state of near submergence, resulting in swamps and lakes.

Figure 157 shows the distribution of the principal lakes and marshes of the Mississippi Delta with respect to the major and minor drainage channels and their levees. The swamps of the higher delta contain fresh water and are high enough so that many of them are periodically dry. Before the day of the lumberman they were occupied mainly by a natural vegetation of water-tolerant trees, especially the gumwoods and cypress. The swamps of the lower delta and its seaward margin are of two types. Those situated on the low natural levees are wooded, like those of the upstream delta, while those in the still lower inter-distributary areas and on the coastal fringe and islands are so little above sea level that they are easily inundated by the sea and have brackish waters. They are never dried out and are covered mainly by vast expanses of tall coarse grasses, the habitat of numberless muskrats.

399. POPULOUS DELTAS. Some deltas, both large and small, have very large human populations. The delta surfaces are flat and are composed of new, unleached, and therefore fertile, soils, the silts and clays derived from the great variety of rocks found in the drainage basins of great river systems. Although in their natural state most deltas contain large areas of swampland, their food-producing capacity is large. On the populous deltas the ever-increasing need for land to yield food for so many people has led to most intensive uses of the delta surfaces. The inhabitants of parts of the Ganges Delta, for example, grow a long-stemmed variety of rice whose rapid growth keeps pace with the rising waters of the flood season. The people of some other delta regions have found it necessary to change some of the natural features of the delta or to alter the normal processes of stream overflow and deposit of sediment. Means of better adapting the features of delta surface to human use are found in the stupendous drainage projects of the Rhine Delta and in the irrigation projects of the Nile and other deltas.

400. *The Netherlands coast* includes the merged deltas of the Rhine, Meuse, and Scheldt Rivers. Originally the region had the features common to delta surfaces, and the streams, by flood, built their levees and extended the coastal marshes seaward. Through several centuries a growing need for land has encouraged the inhabitants of this region to reclaim the marsh lands and actually to crowd the sea off the delta margin. Small areas of

lower levee and interlevee swampland have been, one after another, made secure from flood by constructing artificial levees, or dikes, entirely around them. Each enclosed area, called a *polder*, is kept sufficiently drained for agriculture by a network of drainage ditches leading to a pump at the lowest corner of the polder. This lifts the water from the polder into a bordering stream or canal which lies between or in channels on top of the dikes. In time new polders were made near the old, and eventually the sea was encroached upon. Now large areas of drained lands lie between 5 and 10 ft., and some are as much as 15 ft., below sea level. The older polders, of which there are hundreds, are irregular in outline and formerly were pumped by picturesque windmills. The newer ones, designed with modern engineering skill, are larger and more regular in shape and are pumped by engines. The newest and greatest project has been designed to cut off and drain the Zuider Zee, a great and shallow coastal embayment, which was much like Lake Pontchartrain near New Orleans (Fig. 161).

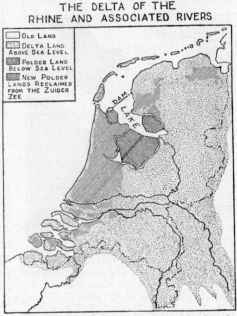

THE DELTA OF THE RHINE AND ASSOCIATED RIVERS

OLD LAND
DELTA LAND ABOVE SEA LEVEL
POLDER LAND BELOW SEA LEVEL
NEW POLDER LANDS RECLAIMED FROM THE ZUIDER ZEE

FIG. 161.—The extent of reclaimed land in the Netherlands in relation to the area of the Rhine Delta. (*After K. Jansma.*)

401. *The great delta of North China* is comprised largely of loessial silts derived from the highlands of North China and deposited by the Hwang and some other streams. So abundant are the sediments that they have filled a broad embayment of the Hwang Hai (Yellow Sea) and half surround a large, hilly island which once stood in it. This former island is now the Shantung Peninsula (Fig. 162). The Hwang flows across the northern part of its plain on a levee ridge which in places is as much as 20 ft. high. It is depositing silt so rapidly that frequently the river overflows the artificial levees built to hold it and, like the Mississippi, spreads over the adjacent delta surface. Owing to the silting of its channel the Hwang is of little use for navigation. At times of low water the inhabitants remove large quantities of silt from the stream bed partly to keep the channel open and partly because of the value of the mud as a fertilizer. The rapid aggradation of the delta surface near the stream is attended by the danger of a

sudden change in its course during time of flood. Some of the changes are minor, but the stream has several times shifted its course to the opposite side of the Shantung Peninsula. Such a change, on a densely peopled plain, is a major disaster. In 1852 the stream changed from a course on the south side of the plain to near its present course on the north side of the Peninsula and emptied into the sea more than 250 miles distant from its former mouth. In addition to the several major changes, there are unnumbered smaller ones recorded in the 4,000 years of Chinese history. Each has been accompanied by appalling loss of human life.

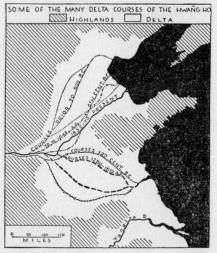

Fig. 162.—The great delta of North China, its relation to the Shantung Peninsula, and some of the many channels the river has occupied within historic times. (*After maps by G. B. Cressey and D. W. Mead.*)

402. *The Great Delta Plains of Arid Lands.* A few of the great delta plains of the world are in the coasts of deserts. They are built by large streams that are fed by the abundant precipitation of mountain regions and have sufficient volume to flow completely across the desert areas with few tributaries and to discharge their loads of sediment into the bordering seas. Such may be called exotic streams. Outstanding among them are the Nile, the Tigris-Euphrates, the Indus, and the Colorado. The delta of the first named has a density of human population comparable with that of the plain of North China. The people are supported by agriculture which depends almost wholly upon the practice of irrigation, to which the configuration of the delta surface lends itself well. In these arid-land deltas the main problem is not, as in the Netherlands, to get the water up from the delta surface into the distributary channels but to get it from the channels out upon the delta surface, which is much simpler. In times of high water it may be accomplished by gravity alone. In times of low water lifting may be resorted to, or, by damlike structures, the river level may be raised until only a small lift, if any, is required, to take water out through ditches in the levees, whence it may be distributed by gravity down the gentle back slopes of the levees which are the cultivated farm lands. The deltas and floodplains of these major exotic streams, therefore, constitute one class of desert oasis. They are the largest and most productive oases in the world.

The Nile, after receiving its last important tributary, traverses 1,000 miles of desert, where it loses volume by the removal of water for irrigation, by evaporation, and by seepage. It arrives at the upper delta much decreased in volume. On the delta so much more water is required for irrigation that only a little is discharged through the distributary mouths into the Mediterranean Sea. Several important consequences arise from this fact. (*a*) There are no disastrous floods on the Nile Delta. (*b*) So much sediment is discharged on the delta head and so little about its margins that the surface has a slope of about 60 ft. per 100 miles, three times that of the Mississippi Delta. (*c*) The steeper slope and smaller water supply make drainage easier. Nearly the whole surface is cultivated, and lakes and swamps are found only about the delta margins.

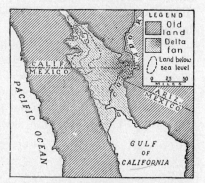

The delta of the Colorado River has been built into and across the northern portion of the long tectonic depression occupied by the Gulf of California. It was built in from the east and after extending across to the western wall of the depression it blocked off about 150 miles of the former upper end of the Gulf. Evaporation of the water there has left the plain called the Salton Basin, a part of whose floor lies nearly 275 ft. below sea level. Water from the Colorado River is distributed by

Fig. 163.—The apex of the delta fan of the Colorado River is at the east side of the long embayment into which it is built. The location and extent of Salton Sink are indicated by the broken line. Salton Sea lies in its lowest portion, its bottom 274 ft. below sea level.

ditches over the surface of the delta for the irrigation of crops. Although the river now discharges southward into the Gulf of California it has several times shifted to a northward distributary and emptied into the low basin called Salton Sink (Fig. 163). The whole delta area is known as the Imperial Valley.

Floodplains

403. FLOODPLAIN AND DELTA. Floodplains are the alluvial deposits spread by aggrading streams upon the floors of their valleys

Fig. 164.—A longitudinal profile of a delta to illustrate the merging of floodplain and delta surfaces. (1) Sea level; (2) original shoreline; (3) small delta; (4) delta elongated and stream grade raised; (5) present delta front; (6) sea; (7) present shoreline; (8) present stream grade in which delta and floodplain merge; (9) original stream grade.

during the process of valley widening and stream overflow (357). The floodplain begins to form in the lower course of the stream where it first reaches grade. This is the same point at which the delta begins to form. As the delta grows seaward the decreased stream gradient (397) causes frequent stream overflow, during which sediment is deposited not only at the delta head but also in the lower stream valley and thence progressively upstream (Fig. 164). Thus the two are blended, and it is difficult to say just where delta ends and floodplain begins. However, some streams that have no deltas have well-developed floodplains.

404. THE WIDTH OF FLOODPLAINS. Floodplains are confined within the bluffs cut by the lateral erosion of a meandering stream (354). The valley walls may not be high, and usually they are much gullied, but they mark an abrupt change from a stream-dissected upland on the one hand to a flat plain of recent alluvium on the other (Fig. 165). The width of a floodplain, *i.e.*, the distance from one

FIG. 165.—The flat surface of the Platte River floodplain in western Nebraska contrasted with its abrupt and dissected bluffs. Compare with Figs. 129*E*, 144.

valley wall to the other, depends much upon the size of the stream that builds it and upon its stage of advancement in the cycle of river development. In the valleys of small but aggrading creeks it may be only a few yards. In the valleys of large streams the plains may be of any width up to several miles. Usually they narrow in the upstream direction toward the headwaters, where the tributary streams may be so young as to have no floodplains at all. The Mississippi floodplain, where the stream flows between Iowa and Wisconsin, is from 1 to 3 miles wide; in the latitude of southern Illinois it is about 6 miles; but below Cairo it broadens rapidly and, including the plains of minor streams that join it, ranges between 25 and 75 miles in width. It is reported that the floodplain of the lower Amazon, the greatest of all rivers, generally is less than 30 miles wide.[1]

[1] Marbut, C. F., and Manifold, C. B. The Topography of the Amazon Valley. *Geog. Rev.*, Vol. 15, p. 617, 1925.

405. THE FLOODPLAIN SURFACE. The surface features and the conditions of drainage that characterize the typical floodplain are similar to those of the upstream part of a delta. It is comprised principally of a monotonously flat surface upon which areas of levee land alternate with areas of swamp. On small floodplains the levees that border the stream often are so small as to be hardly noticeable. However, bordering meander bends, they are likely to be enough higher than the remainder of the floodplain so that they interfere with the drainage of water from the bluffs toward the stream. For that

FIG. 166.—The floodplain and levees of a small stream among the hills of Japan. The stream may be located by noting the footbridges that cross it. The path follows one levee, and rice fields lie on the lower levee and floodplain surfaces.

reason swamps or marshy spots are likely to be found toward the margins of the plain between the stream and the valley walls (Fig. 166).

The distribution of levee and swamplands on broader floodplains usually is not so simple as that indicated above. The valley floor is a place of rapid change. It is widened and shaped by erosion and deposition which go on at the same time. It is the work of a meandering stream which touches first one valley wall and then the other. A meander curve becomes elongated by erosion on the lower outside of its bend and by deposition of the inside (Fig. 132). By this process also the meanders themselves tend to migrate slowly in the downstream direction, changing both their shapes and their positions. In times of high water their changes are rapid. Increased volume gives temporarily increased transporting power, and overflow causes the deposition of much sediment upon the immediate stream banks, raising the levees. The general effect of these activities is that alluvium is picked up in one locality and put down in another, distributed and redistributed over the valley floor, and that levees are broadened by overflow here and narrowed or lowered by erosion there. Eventually meanders that have grown overlong are cut off and abandoned by the stream when it shortens its course by cutting through a narrowed neck of alluvium (Fig. 129E). The ends of the abandoned meander channel presently are filled with silt, and the unfilled portion exists as a horseshoe-shaped pond, or *oxbow lake*, bordered by its levees. Lakes of this kind no sooner are formed than they begin to be filled

Fig. 167.—An air view of the small floodplain of the La Crosse River, Wisconsin, showing numerous scars of abandoned meanders, many of them now cultivated. (*Official Photograph, U. S. Army Air Corps.*)

and obliterated (a) by sediment deposited during general river floods, (b) by rain-washed sediment from the adjacent surface, and (c) by the growth and decay of aquatic vegetation. The surfaces of broad flood-plains are likely, therefore, to contain many oxbow lakes in all stages of destruction. Some, which are of recent formation, appear as curving open lakes; some contain but the dwindled remnants of abandoned channels; others remain as boggy, sedge-filled marshes; while still others may be described only as *meander scars*. The latter are marked only by bits of woodland swamp or low ground, the horseshoe-shaped outlines of which hardly would be noticed save from an airplane (Fig. 167). Associated with each of these abandoned channels are sections of abandoned levees, also in various stages of destruction (Fig. 168).

Another element in the pattern of the broad floodplain is furnished by small tributary streams. Small streams entering the plain from the bordering uplands are sometimes prevented from joining the main stream at once because of the upward slope of its natural levees. Instead they turn down valley and, after paralleling the main stream some distance, find a place of entrance. The junction of the St. Francis and Yazoo Rivers with the Mississippi (Fig. 169) illustrates this condition. To the features of the floodplain, therefore, are added the meanders, oxbow lakes, levees, and swamps created by tributary

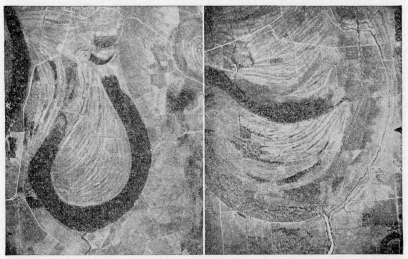

FIG. 168.—An oxbow swamp and other great meander scars on the lower Mississippi floodplain, viewed from the air. The color intensities in the photographs indicate differences in the vegetation, either natural or cultivated, which in turn indicate differences in soil and drainage. (*Official Photographs, U. S. Army Air Corps, Courtesy of U. S. Geological Survey.*)

streams. In consequence, the broad floodplain is likely to have a complicated pattern which may consist of meandering stream channels, large and small; of new levee lands; old subdued levees; oxbow lakes and their swampy remnants; together with broad floodplain marshes. The silts and clays deposited on broad floodplains make productive soils, and generally they are used for agriculture. The levee lands are naturally the best drained and are the first to be used. On the Mississippi floodplain large areas of swampland remain unreclaimed. On some Old World floodplains, however, such as those of the Nile and Yangtze, where land is scarce and life and labor cheap, even the swamps are drained and cultivated.

406. ALLUVIAL TERRACE LANDS. Many floodplains are fringed at intervals with smaller alluvial plains which stand at elevations

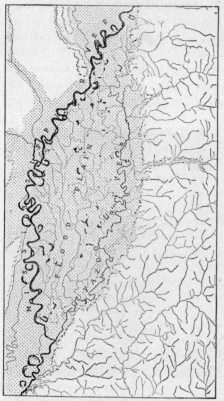

somewhat above that of the present plain. These are called *alluvial terraces*, or benches. Although they lie above the floodplain they are unlike the valley walls which flank them in that they are stream deposited. Usually they are bordered by abrupt descents of a few feet to the level of the newer plain. They are the remnants of older and higher floodplains into which the stream has subsequently eroded a new plain, owing to some cause that has decreased its load of sediment or has increased its carrying capacity. Some valleys exhibit a series of alluvial terraces at different levels which mark stages in the erosion of the old valley filling (Fig. 170). Although alluvial terraces seldom are high or continuous, they frequently contain many acres and sometimes many square miles of land. Because alluvial terrace land is sufficiently

FIG. 169.—After the upper headwaters of the Yazoo River enter the broad bottomlands the stream follows the bluffs for 175 miles before it finds entrance into the Mississippi.

above present river level to be free from floods, it generally is well

FIG. 170.—A diagram to illustrate the development of alluvial terraces by the partial re-erosion of an older and more abundant deposition of alluvium. Natural levees border the present stream course.

drained and admirably adapted to cultivation. However, because the terrace is above the present flood level its soils are no longer enriched by additions of alluvial mud and, being older, they are, in regions of abundant rainfall, likely to be somewhat leached. Sites of this kind are suitable also for river towns. The inhabitants of flood-plains commonly distinguish between the present floodplain and successive terrace levels by speaking of them as "first bottoms," "second bottoms," etc.

407. FLOODPLAINS AND RIVER FLOODS. The flatness of floodplains, the nature and direction of their levee slopes, and indeed the very manner of their formation indicate that they are subject to river overflow. In some rivers floods are of periodic occurrence, and in others they come at irregular intervals, while some streams are so controlled by nature as to be little subject to flood. The causes of river flooding are many. Some of them are natural while others are the result of human interference with natural conditions. Usually the most disastrous floods are at least partly the result of human disturbance of the balance of conditions established by nature.

Periodic floods, such as those of the Nile, the Orinoco, and other tropical streams, result from the marked seasonal character in the savanna type of precipitation over the river basin. Nile floods have been for many centuries the means of renewing the fertility of the alluvial soil of that populous valley by the addition of an annual layer of silt. They have served also to store water in the soil of the arid land to aid in the maturing of crops. The recent construction of dams reduces the inconvenience of floods and enables a more economical use of both the land and the water, but it largely prevents the distribution of the fertile mud over the floodplain by causing it to settle in the quiet waters above the dams. The alternation of protracted drought with widespread flood on the floodplain of the Orinoco has so far had the effect of retarding attempts to make effective use of that broad and flat plain.

Disastrous floods on the Mississippi and its tributaries usually occur in the early spring. They result from heavy rainfall on a frozen or saturated earth, frequently supplemented by the rapid melting of a winter's accumulation of snow. Sometimes both of these conditions come at the same time in different parts of the basin. The general deforestation of the eastern half of the Mississippi Basin during its settlement and agricultural utilization probably has increased the flood menace by removing the forest litter which formerly absorbed moisture and served to retard the runoff. As settlement on the Mississippi floodplain increased, protection from flood became as necessary as it did on the delta. Artificial levees of earth were extended from the delta to the floodplain and now total hundreds of miles in length. It was found that the height of the early levees was not sufficient to prevent overflow, and their level has been raised several times. In consequence of the building of higher levees the river has been forced to transport material that otherwise would have been spread over the floodplain. This in turn has caused silting of the channel and a raising of the river grade. As the levees have increased in height, therefore, so have the succeeding floods, and there is no more security from them now than formerly. The problem of flood control is one given much study, but the method of its solution is complicated and, as yet, by no means certain.

A break in the artificial levee in time of severe flood pours a torrent of water upon the floodplain, and the gap widens by erosion. If the break gets beyond control large areas may be completely inundated except for a few sections of higher levee. Upon these gather the refugees, both human and animal (Fig. 160). The inhabitants of isolated bits of low older-levee lands back in the swamps sometimes have no opportunity to reach the higher artificial levee or any other place of safety in time to escape the rising waters. The lower floodplain and delta courses of many streams are protected from flood by artificial levees as those of the Mississippi are. Notable examples are seen on the floodplains of the Yangtze, the Po, and other streams whose fertile lands are densely peopled.

Piedmont Alluvial Plains

408. ALLUVIAL FANS. Piedmont alluvial plains are made up of alluvial fans so closely spaced that their margins are merged in one continuous plain. Previous reference has been made to the manner and place of formation of alluvial fans and to the conditions under which they tend to merge. It was noted also that they attain their greatest development in regions of dry or subhumid climate (357).

The surface features of this class of alluvial plains may be understood better if the configuration of the simple alluvial fan is first considered. In some respects the processes and forms of fan growth are like those of the delta but in others significantly different. Streams with steep gradients furnish abundant sediment, much of it coarse in texture. The material clogs the stream channel at the point where the mountain gradient changes to that of the bordering plain. The choked stream breaks over its banks, tending to form distributary channels with natural levees, as in the delta. However, the fan distributaries do not, like those of the delta, continue so long in the same course as to build fingerlike projections at their ends. Instead, the rapid accumulation of material encourages frequent shifts of channel which have the effect of causing the building to proceed evenly upon all parts of the fan margin. This produces a nicely rounded or semi-circular outline and gives the feature its fanlike shape (Fig. 133). The deposition of material, especially the heavy or coarse material, is most abundant at the apex or head of the fan, where the stream velocity is first checked. The finer material is carried farther out and is spread upon the fan margins. As the feature grows in size, the ordinary flow of the stream that produces it may be wholly absorbed by seepage into the coarse upper-fan deposits, and all its load of sediment may be put down there. Only in time of flood may the enlarged stream have sufficient volume to flow completely across the fan and beyond. This condition results in the upper part of the fan's having the steeper slopes while those toward the margin grow progressively more gentle. However, although the slope of a fan surface is characteristically steeper than that of the delta surface, not even the upper slopes of a great fan are very steep, and its marginal areas are so gently sloping as to seem an almost flat and featureless plain. The slopes of the fan

Fig. 171.—A section of the great piedmont alluvial plain bordering the San Gabriel Mountains of southern California. The head of this fan lies at the mouth of the mountain valley. (*Photograph by Fairchild Aerial Surveys, Inc., Los Angeles. Courtesy of California Fruit Growers' Exchange.*)

are, moreover, not merely in one direction from the mountain base but extended radially from the fan head, giving the fan a slightly convex surface. This is a matter of great convenience in use of irrigation water. Because of the radial slope of the fan, irrigation water applied at its upper end may be distributed by gravity to all parts of the fan surface.

409. PIEDMONT ALLUVIAL PLAINS. The bases of mountain slopes in dry and subhumid climates commonly are fringed by alluvial plains comprised of coalesced fans, some of which are large and some small, their size depending upon the volumes and deposits of the several streams draining the mountain front. The heads of the several fans may be distinguished at the mouths of the valleys (Fig. 171). They are

composed largely of gravel and sand, and their surfaces often are strewn with boulders distributed by flood waters following torrential rains in the mountains. The porosity of these coarse soils, their inability to retain irrigation water, and their bouldery surfaces cause the higher parts of the fans to be somewhat avoided for intensive agricultural use

Fig. 172.—The coarse deposits of the upper part of a large fan in California provide a supply of commercial gravel. The nearly level surface of the fan is in striking contrast with the mountains behind it.

although they may furnish gravel and sand for constructional purposes (Fig. 172). At no great distance from the mountain front the slopes of the bordering fans flatten out, their soils become finer, their margins spread, and they merge into a continuous alluvial plain (Fig. 173).

Fig. 173.—A profile view of a series of alluvial fans merged into a small piedmont alluvial plain which borders low mountains in the San Fernando Valley, California. The steeper upper slope of one fan, seen at the left center where it heads between the mountain spurs, may be contrasted with its more gentle lower slope toward the right.

Such a plain may appear practically level, yet it is not so in fact. Not only does it slope away from the mountain base but each of its component fans has its faintly convex surface, and where they are blended together the resulting plain has a scalloped margin. Between the individual fans are broad shallow depressions.

Many piedmont alluvial plains are covered only with desert shrubs or sparse grasses, but the fine dry-land soils are high in mineral plant foods, and such as have available supplies of irrigation water are capable of great productivity. Although their surfaces are dry, natural conditions provide many alluvial fans with supplies of water for irrigation. (*a*) The water of the mountain stream that builds a fan may be impounded in its mountain valley whence it may be led out upon the fan surface. (*b*) The natural stream flow disappears, except in time of flood, into the coarse debris of the fan head. However, it collects underground in the great storage reservoir of the porous fan material and slowly seeps outward toward the fan margin. This water commonly is recovered for use in irrigation, in some regions through wells, and in others, as in parts of Asia, through tunnels driven underneath the fan surface. Just as the floodplains *above* some irrigated deltas are irrigated, as in the case of the Nile, so are some of the floodplains *below* or beyond the lower margins of alluvial fans. Provided the supply of water is sufficient, it is sometimes led by canals out beyond the irrigated areas of the fans and applied to the alluvial valley bottoms as far as the supply permits. The slopes of fans and piedmont alluvial plains may be recognized, therefore, as a second class of oasis only a little less extensive than that associated with the deltas and floodplains of exotic streams (402).

410. ALLUVIAL BASIN PLAINS. Some structural basins or valleys are nearly encircled by fans which extend inward from the flanking highlands and create alluvial plains which slope gently upward on all their margins. Beneath some such plains the accumulated fan deposits are deep, and the basins are said to be alluvium filled. The mountain drainage which seeps through the porous upper parts of the fans in a filled basin sometimes reappears as ground water about the lower edges of the concentric fans. For that reason alluvium-filled basins, even under arid climate, commonly have at their centers areas of marsh, shallow lakes, or alkali flats (438).

411. NOTED PIEDMONT ALLUVIAL PLAINS. Because piedmont alluvial plains have deep fertile soils and are admirable sites for the practice of irrigation, some of them, which have abundant and dependable water supplies, are noted for their agricultural wealth. Among them are the Sacramento and San Joaquin valleys of California, the Los Angeles-San Bernardino lowland of Southern California, the Vale of Chile, the Samarkand district of Russian Turkistan, the Tarim Basin, and many others. Conditions in the San Joaquin Valley illustrate the landforms developed by valley filling.

The San Joaquin Valley portion of the Great Valley of California is a structural trough between the Sierra Nevada Mountains and the Coast Ranges. From the latter more than 50 small wet-weather streams flow eastward into the basin, bringing alluvium which is spread in a seemingly flat and quite featureless plain along the western margin of the valley. Drainage from the abundant snows and rains on the windward, west-facing slopes of the higher Sierra Nevada Mountains is carried down to the eastern margin of the valley by eight large streams and more than a dozen smaller ones. These have contributed alluvium to the general filling of the valley and have, in addition, built large alluvial fans. The largest of the fans is that of Kings River. It spreads outward into the valley 50 miles from the mountain base, crosses the axis of the structural trough, and blocks the drainage of its dry southern end (Fig. 174). Thus Tulare and Buena Vista Lakes are created, and areas about the margins of the fans are made marshy. Large supplies of irrigation water from the snowy Sierras supplied to the gently sloping and highly tillable piedmont plain have turned each great fan into an oasis upon which there is an intensive agriculture devoted principally to fruits. This contrasts sharply with the extensive, livestock-ranch type of agriculture which prevails on the unirrigated western margin of the plain.

THE BRANCHING PATTERN OF THE DISTRIBUTARIES OF THE (1)KINGS, (2)KAWEAH, AND (3)TULE RIVERS, CALIFORNIA, ON THEIR ALLUVIAL FANS

0   10   20
MILES

FIG. 174.

412. DELTA FANS. Some streams that have fairly steep gradients and are abundantly supplied with sediment enter the sea and build deltas. As these grow, their flat surfaces serve further to check stream velocity, fans form upon the delta tops, and the two grow in association. Such features may be called delta fans, and some of them are of great size. The delta of the Colorado River is, in fact, a large delta fan. Small delta fans occupy fringing embayments of many mountainous coasts, as, for example, in Japan, where various of the small marginal plains are delta fans. Some of them are bounded on the landward side by the abrupt escarpments of recent faults. These steep slopes, composed in part of volcanic ash, older alluvium, and other easily eroded materials, furnish so large a supply of sediment that the streams, even in that rainy climate, cannot transport it fast enough to prevent the accumulation of fans. In a land so generally mountainous as Japan, these fragmentary but fertile plains are densely peopled and intensively used. Of similar construction are the productive lowlands of Valencia, Spain, and the Canterbury Plain, a gently sloping plain 40 miles wide and 175 miles long on the east coast of South Island, New Zealand. Each of them, however, is made up of the combined delta fans of several streams which drain the bordering mountains, and they might properly be called "piedmont alluvial delta-fan plains," if one wished to employ a term so awkward.

Plains of Older Alluvium

413. THE NATURE OF OLDER ALLUVIUM. Certain of the world's considerable plains are described as plains of older alluvium. The

material composing them differs from that of recent alluvial plains in being much older. In humi l climates it is generally much leached and less fertile. In some regions it has been changed into weakly cemented rock. These plains have been so long deposited that their surfaces have lost most of the distributary channels, levees, and other forms characteristic of recent alluvial plains and now have features that are more the result of erosion than of deposition. In consequence of these changes they generally are well drained. The internal structure of such plains betrays their origin, however, for they are unlike the well-stratified, marine sediments of coastal plains in that they are made up of the irregularly bedded deposits of ancient streams.

The largest plains of this type are distributed beyond the margins of great mountain systems and were no doubt, at the time of their formation, vast piedmont alluvial plains. Subsequent diastrophic or other changes of condition have caused the present streams that cross them to cut new valleys into the surfaces of the plains and to build floodplains of new alluvium across them at somewhat lower levels. Above these new floodplains, areas of the older alluvium stand as separate and sometimes isolated plains. Many of them are bluff-bordered, tabular in form, and have surfaces that are gently undulating or even so flat that they are poorly drained. Some have also in their surface layers a considerable admixture of volcanic ash and loess, the accumulation of a long period of time.

414. IMPORTANT PLAINS OF OLDER ALLUVIUM. There are many small plains of older alluvium. In Japan old delta fans, uplifted relative to sea level since their formation, are now dissected by streams and stand as islands of older alluvium in the newer plains or as terraces between the newer plains and the mountain slopes. Because of their greater age and exposure to leaching, under heavy rainfall, the small plains of older alluvium have red soils of greater maturity and lower fertility than those of the plains of new alluvium. Moreover, because of their porous ashy soils and their elevated position, they have excessive drainage, and it is difficult to get irrigation water to them for the cultivation of rice. Consequently the manner of their agricultural utilization is entirely different from that of the newer floodplains and delta fans.

Some plains of older alluvium are of vastly greater size than those of the type illustrated in Japan. In northern India the broad structural depression of the middle and upper Ganges and Indus valleys is filled to great depth with older alluvium. Into its surface the present streams that drain the Himalaya mountain front have cut new valleys as a result of an increase of elevation with respect to sea level. There they have constructed floodplains of new alluvium. The interstream areas, there called *doabs*, are tabular or mesalike remnants of an ancient alluvial plain. Some of these are of large area, but generally they are less productive agriculturally than the present floodplains. A similar situation is found south of the Alps. Deep accumulations of older alluvium are there spread out upon the northern flank of the Po Plain and, subsequent to their deposition, have been deeply trenched and terraced by the present Alpine tributaries of the Po. The higher and coarser parts of the older alluvium, called *alta pianura*, are partially iron cemented and have infertile soils. Southward they grade into the recent and more fertile alluvium of the Po and its tributaries.

The Pampa of Argentina is underlain by deep accumulations of clays, sands, and marls reaching commonly to a depth of 2,000 ft. or more.[1] These are believed to be the alluvial deposits of streams flowing from the Andes upon a gradually subsiding plain. The surface layers over much of this vast and very flat plain have also a large admixture of loess. Because of their low rainfall, low elevation, and almost imperceptible slope these plains are

Fig. 175.—The Argentine Pampa, near Rosario. A low flat plain comprised largely of older alluvium. (*Photograph by H. G. Olds.*)

neither much leached nor deeply eroded. Subhumid climate also has produced a dominant natural vegetation of grass which has added a large component of humus to a soil high in the mineral elements of plant food. The result has been the formation of a flat stoneless plain, highly tillable and of great fertility (Fig. 175).

In the United States almost the entire eastern front of the Rocky Mountains is bordered by plains of older alluvium. These were deposited as a piedmont alluvial plain by the shifting courses of former streams which flowed from the mountains. They are composed of clays, sands, and gravels so generally permeated with lime that some of the layers are cemented into moderately resistant rocks. The original surface of this vast plain, which extends from the Llano Estacado (Staked Plains) of Texas northward to Montana, probably was very flat at the time of its formation. Some areas such as the Staked Plains remain as flat as the Argentine Pampa, but that is not true of the larger part and especially the northern part. Changed conditions have

[1] Stappenbeck, R. "Geologie und Grundwasserkunde der Pampa." Erwin Nägele, Stuttgart, 1926.

led to the erosion of the plain by the same drainage that formed it. All the streams that traverse the Great Plains have cut new valleys which, by their common direction, have dissected the older alluvium into striplike inter-fluves with a west-to-east trend. In the process of eroding their present courses some of the streams have cut steep-walled valleys several scores of feet in depth and have built new floodplains from one to several miles in width. The margins of these valleys are in many areas much gullied (383), but the interfluves generally are tabular in form. Those of the southern por-tion, as was noted above, are broad and very flat; but those of the north are more rolling; and the present surfaces are not those of stream deposition but result from erosion. The soils of these upland surfaces are developed under semiarid climate, are unleached, and are highly productive where they can be irrigated. In general, however, the region is crossed by bands of irrigated crops on the new alluvial bottoms of the major streams while the interfluves of older alluvium are devoted to dry-land crops or to grazing (Fig. 165).

Chapter XVI. Glaciated Plains

415. CLASSES OF GLACIATED PLAINS. In northern North America and northwestern Europe are extensive glaciated plains (360). Their original surfaces were developed by stream erosion on both complex crystalline rocks and those of simple sedimentary structure. Although the larger relief features of these plains were produced by tectonic forces or by stream erosion, most of the details of landform that characterize their present appearance are the result of glacial action. Therefore, while these great plains already were plains before the time of glaciation, their surfaces were extensively remodeled by the work of ice.

All phases of glacial activity were involved, and their imprints are left upon the plains. In many localities there may be found in close association, and in great variety of detail, the forms produced by glacial erosion, glacial deposition, and deposition by the waters that flowed from the melting ice. It is recognized, however, that within the regions of continental glaciation some areas have predominantly the kinds of surface features that result from glacial erosion while in others the features are mainly those that result from glacial or glacio-fluviatile deposition. Plains thus distinguished may be called *ice-scoured plains* and *drift plains* respectively. It may be observed in this connection that plains of the ice-scoured type are most prevalent in regions of crystalline rocks and that they are on the inner rather than on the marginal portions of the glaciated areas (Figs. 134 and 197). There the thin regolith and the general resistance of the rocks provided relatively small amounts of local glacial drift. That which was formed was comprised in large part of rocks resistant to glacial crushing, and these remain as coarse boulders intermingled with some quantities of finer material. The plains of deep glacial drift are found more commonly in association with regions of sedimentary rocks, which generally were more deeply eroded and more easily crushed than those of the crystalline areas. It may be noted also that, in both North America and Europe, the direction of ice motion was generally away from the regions of crystalline rock toward those of sedimentary formation and that, therefore, the products of ice erosion in the crystalline areas were deposited elsewhere. That is the reason for the numerous *erratic boulders* of igneous or metamorphic rock found in drift plains which are underlain by sedimentary rock only (362).

The features of the two classes of glaciated plains may be discussed separately.

The Features of Ice-scoured Plains

416. THE ICE-SCOURED SURFACE. The stream-eroded hills and valleys that previously existed on the plains over which the great con-

FIG. 176.—The rounded hills and rock basins of an ice-scoured surface in northern Canada, where vegetation is scant. Note the different elevations of the lakes. (*Royal Canadian Air Force Photograph.*)

tinental ice sheets crept probably were not completely erased by glacial scour in most instances, unless they were very small. Almost universally, however, they were reshaped by an ice sheet thick enough to bury them deeply beneath its overpowering weight. A first ice invasion of a region doubtless was sufficient to remove the mantle of soil and weathered rock which had accumulated there under previous conditions. Angular profiles, where such had been developed by the usual processes of weathering and stream erosion in rocks of unequal hardness, were then subdued by glacial erosion.

The surface configuration of plains where ice scour was predominant is characterized by rounded rock hills and broad open valleys with comparatively low local relief. Over the valley floors a thin veneer of glacial debris may serve inadequately as the parent material of a soil. Strewn with subangular boulders (361) torn from the adjacent slopes by the ice, the drift of ice-scoured plains commonly is neither deep enough nor continuous enough to be tillable except in patches or localities. It may, however, serve as anchorage for stands of forest, especially the shallow-rooted conifers. Through the veneer of drift, which sometimes barely covers the lowlands of the ice-scoured rock surface, project the smoothed and rounded tops of rock hills still less completely covered (Fig. 176). Many of these rock hills are entirely without soil covering, except the small quantities of earth lodged in joint cracks and other pockets. Such surfaces, scoured and polished by ice erosion, often bear the grooves and striations scratched upon them by ice-pushed pebbles. In some localities groups of small ice-scoured hillocks protrude so thickly from the grass-covered drift that they appear from a distance like sheep at rest. They are called *roches moutonnées*. Some larger hills of the same origin have striking inequalities of slope (Fig. 177). A long and gradual incline marks the side up which the ice pushed its slow and grinding way, and the lee slope is left shorter and steeper as a result of the quarrying or plucking action of the ice as it pulled away jointed blocks of rock in its forward motion. The name is applied to them also.

FIG. 177.—*Roches moutonnées* in the ice-scoured region of northern Minnesota. The hills in the background also show ice-scoured form.

417. DRAINAGE FORMS IN ICE-SCOURED PLAINS. The changes in relief produced by ice scour are not of a large order of magnitude as compared with some produced by other agents, but they are sufficient to disarrange completely the preexisting drainage. It may be supposed that, during the long period of preglacial erosion, streams had become somewhat adjusted to the characters and structures of the rocks of the plains and that they had developed definite patterns as the result of that adjustment. The present drainage of the ice-scoured plains is noted particularly for its indefinite pattern and its lack of adjustment to rock structures. The universal effect of the accident of glaciation is to return the drainage of a region to a stage of youth in which it is characterized by numerous lakes, waterfalls, and rapids.

Lakes are particularly numerous in plains of severe ice scour (Fig. 178). Many of them lie in rock basins eroded by the ice with its characteristic disregard for uniform gradient. Such basins often are broad, only moderately deep, and are dotted with islands which are ice-scoured rock hills of the irregular plain. Glacial lakes of the rock-basin type are likely to be enduring as well as numerous. There are several reasons why they are less subject to quick destruction than are lakes of some other origins. (*a*) Streams that flow into rock-basin lakes flow over ice-scoured regions, mainly in rock channels, and have little sediment to spread over the lake floors or with which to build

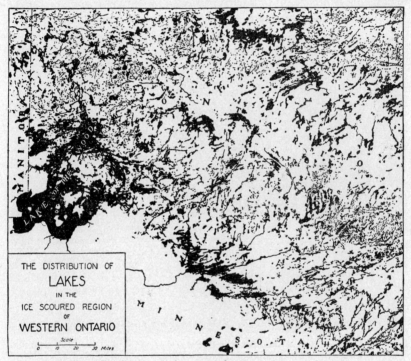

Fig. 178.—Sprawling lakes, mainly in rock basins, occupy much of the ice-scoured plain of western Ontario. They are proving a valuable resource in the development of the summer-resort industry. (*After Map 24A, Province of Ontario, Department of Surveys.*)

deltas. (*b*) The outflowing streams are clear and, therefore, unable quickly to erode notches in the hard rock rims and thus lower the lake levels. (*c*) Ice-scoured regions are in large part unsuited to agriculture and generally remain in forests, whose littered spongy floors tend to prevent rapid runoff and thus to keep the ground-water table high and lakes at uniform levels. Some small rock-basin lakes show almost no tendency to destruction even after the vast lapse of time since the disappearance of the last ice sheet. On the other hand, there are some that were shallow by origin and have been filled subsequently by the remains of marsh vegetation such as sphagnum moss. In Canada bogs of that type are called *muskeg*.

The same disregard for uniform gradient that enabled glaciers to erode rock basins caused them to leave rock ledges or other abrupt changes of slope to be discovered by the drainage of ice-scoured plains. Streams in such regions found their courses by overflow from basin to basin after the ice was gone, and the wandering patterns of their arrangement are in consequence of the slope as it was left by the ice. On such ungraded courses falls and rapids are numerous, and in

Fig. 179.—An air view of the lake-dotted, forest-clad plain of ice-scoured crystalline rocks north of Lake Superior. (*Royal Canadian Air Force Photograph.*)

regions of hard rock they are, like the lakes, enduring (Fig. 299). Moreover, the utility of the streams of ice-scoured plains for water-power development is high compared with that of streams in plains of other kinds. The streams are relatively free of silt; the falls, though seldom great, are numerous and widely distributed; and the discharge of water over them is much regulated by the presence of many natural lakes and swamps and by the floors of widespread forests in the drainage areas.

418. EXTENSIVE ICE-SCOURED PLAINS. The most extensive ice-scoured plains of the world are found close to the centers from which the great Pleistocene glaciers of Europe and North America radiated (Fig. 134*A*, *B*).

These regions are (a) the Laurentian upland plain of Canada and (b) the plains of Sweden and Finland. The fact that the preglacial surface in each of these regions was a peneplain of ancient crystalline rocks instead of less resistant sedimentary rocks probably had much to do with the cleanness of ice scour and the preservation of the ice-eroded forms. The time that has elapsed since glaciation, although it is tens of thousands of years, has not been sufficient for slow weathering under high-latitude climate to produce any great change in the ice-carved forms of the hard rocks (Figs. 197, 198).

A general view over either of the regions named shows an irregularly rolling plain, covered in large part by coniferous forest. Much of the forest, especially on the interstream ridges, is thin and poor, and knobs or patches of bare rock outcrop at frequent intervals. Better forest and patches of tillable soil in the depressions indicate some accumulation of drift. Areas of swamp, which are marked by different classes of vegetation, occupy rock and drift basins too shallow to contain lakes. Among the woodlands lie thousands of rock-rimmed lakes, most of them small, but some large and dotted with islands (Fig. 179). Connecting the lakes are streams with queer sprawling patterns, their tributaries meeting at strange angles, and their placid reaches frequently interrupted by the white water of foaming rapids. Examination of reasonably detailed maps of Finland or of the district lying north and west of Lake Superior will reveal the remarkable development of lakes in those regions and the other peculiarities of drainage in ice-scoured plains (Fig. 178). According to Blanchard and Visher, there are more than 35,000 lakes in Finland, and they occupy more than 11 per cent of the area of the country. Certain sections of the Superior Highland are more than 25 per cent lake area, but that is not true of the ice-scoured region as a whole.

The Features of Drift Plains

419. THE GENERAL RELATIONSHIPS OF DRIFT PLAINS. The drift plains of the principal regions of continental glaciation are of greater area and of much greater human significance than are the ice-scoured plains. They occupy most of the broad outer margins of the glaciated regions in both North America and Europe, and over them are spread the debris carried from the ice-scoured plains intermingled with a much larger quantity obtained locally or transported only a short distance. Their features are the products of both ice scour and the deposition of drift.

The drift is of variable thickness. In places it is deep, as in the valleys that existed before glaciation, but it may be thin or almost absent upon the tops of some adjacent ice-rounded rock hills. In some localities drift completely buries the rock surface under an unbroken mantle which may be several tens of feet or even 400 or 500 ft. in thickness. The surface features of the drift are relatively independent of those of the underlying rock. Drift commonly is deep in the bottoms of buried preglacial valleys and thinner over the tops of adjacent rock hills, although the reverse is sometimes true. In general the effects of continental glaciation upon relief were to smooth and make more level the regions in which deposition was the dominant activity. This was brought about by more severe erosion of the stream-cut rock hills of the preglacial surface than of the valley bottoms and by a greater deposition of drift in the valley bottoms than on the hilltops (Fig. 180*A*). In some localities, however, rough moraine deposited upon a smooth rock surface had the opposite effect (Fig. 180*C*).

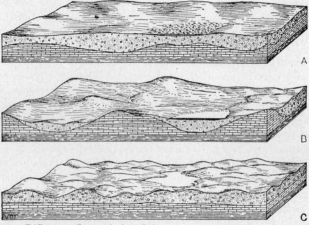

FIG. 180.—Different effects of glacial deposits upon previous rock surfaces. (*A*) A hilly rock surface made more smooth by drift; (*B*) a rock surface of considerable relief partly buried by drift; a rock-controlled drift surface; (*C*) a smooth rock surface made irregular by the deposition of rough moraine.

420. GENERAL FEATURES OF DRIFT PLAINS. It has been noted previously that glacial drift is comprised of several classes of deposits, some of which are put down underneath the body of the ice itself whereas others are associated with its margins or with the streams of melt water flowing from the ice (363). Because of this fact the typical drift plain has various classes of features arranged in diverse but recognizable patterns. The most extensive and fundamental element in this complex is the till sheet or ground moraine, an undulating surface which covers most of the area once occupied by the glacier. About the margins of the till sheet, and also upon its surface, may be found varying amounts of the other classes of deposits. Ridgelike marginal moraines (end or recessional) often are arranged in broad festoons, one behind another (Figs. 181, 189). Bordering them, either beyond the till sheet or upon its surface, are areas of stream-sorted and

deposited sand and gravels or beds of fine sand and clay which accumulated in temporary lakes.

Each major class of drift is characterized by distinctive features of surface configuration and differences in composition which have both advantages and disadvantages for human occupance and use. They may now be presented for more detailed consideration under the following headings: (a) *till plains;* (b) *marginal moraines;* (c) *glaciofluvial plains*, and (d) *glaciolacustrine plains*.

421. THE TILL PLAIN (362) is a mantle of unstratified drift deposited underneath the glacial ice. It is a widely distributed surface

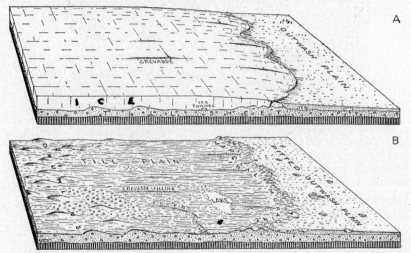

FIG. 181.—A diagram to illustrate the relationship of several classes of glacial and glaciofluvial deposits to the parts of the glacier by which they were formed. (*A*) A plain partly covered by the margin of a stagnant glacier; (*B*) the same plain after the disappearance of the ice by melting.

deposit and is the foundation upon which other forms of drift rest in many localities. In it are rock materials of all degrees of size from large boulders, such as can be carried only by glaciers, down to the finest of clay or rock flour (Fig. 182). These ingredients are thoroughly mingled and show no separation into strata of different size or weight classes such as are deposited by running water. The till generally is comprised of materials which largely are of local origin. In regions of sandstone bedrock it has commonly a large component of sand, and in shale regions a large component of clay. Usually, however, there are foreign materials present also. Some are fine materials such as sand, clay, and pulverized limestone brought from regions of different kinds of rock. Others, called *erratics*, are pebbles and boulders of harder sedimentary rocks or of igneous or metamorphic rocks which have been transported scores or even hundreds of miles from their nearest known sources. Such rocks often are conspicuous because of their large size or their hard and unweathered condition. Many of them are sub-angular in shape and show scratches and other evidence of having

FIG. 182.—An exposure of glacial till showing the unassorted clay, pebbles, and boulders of which it is composed. Note the subangular shape of the large boulder at the left. (*Wisconsin Geological Survey Photograph.*)

been reduced in size by scraping and grinding against other boulders and the bedrock during their travels (Fig. 183). In regions of resistant bedrock especially, boulders of local origin may be so numerous in the till as seriously to interfere with the cultivation of the soil. Such is the case, for example, in New England, where the till sheet is thin and

FIG. 183.—A subangular boulder showing glacial striae. (*U. S. Geological Survey Photograph.*)

the surface features are about as much the result of ice scour as of the deposition of drift. Unlike the normal weathered regolith (Fig. 112), which grades downward into the underlying bedrock from which it is derived, the till sheet is similar in composition from top to bottom, however deep it may be. Moreover, it ends abruptly and rests upon the hard and little weathered surface of the ice-scoured bedrock beneath.

422. THE SURFACE FEATURES OF THE YOUNG TILL PLAIN. The relief features of the till surface generally are of a minor order of size. The principal and widespread characteristic is a gently undulating surface which includes broad low hills, or swells, and wide shallow

FIG. 184.—The undulating surface of a till plain. (*Wisconsin Geological Survey Photograph.*)

depressions, or swales, the latter often without outlets (Fig. 184). These result from the unequal deposition of the ground moraine. The various elevations and depressions are arranged according to no recognizable pattern, and commonly the local relief is less than 100 ft. Exceptions to this condition are found in areas that had a consider-

FIG. 185.—A rock-controlled drift surface in southern Wisconsin. The principal hills are rock thinly covered with till, but the intervening lowlands have a deep drift cover. (*cf.* Fig. 180*B.*) (*Wisconsin Geological Survey Photograph.*)

able preglacial relief. There the principal hills are rock-cored and are but thinly veneered protrusions of a rock surface having a relief too great to be completely buried by the till sheet (Figs. 180*B*, 185).

In a few localities only are there hills of considerable height which are composed entirely of the glacial till. The exact manner of formation of these peculiar hills is not known, but commonly they are half-

FIG. 186.—A pair of drumlins on the till plain of central New York. Their shapes indicate that the direction of glacier movement was from right to left. (*cf.* Figs. 181, 187.) (*U. S. Geological Survey Photograph.*)

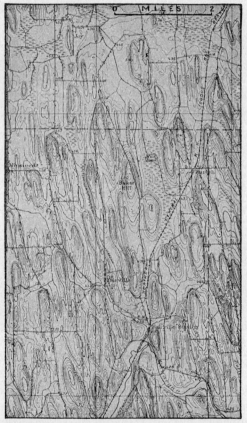

FIG. 187.—The relief pattern of part of a large drumlin region in central New York.

egg-shaped, their higher and steeper ends facing in the direction from which the ice came (the reverse of the *roches moutonnées*, 416). They are called *drumlins* (Fig. 186). Some of them reach heights of 100 ft. or more and may be a mile long, but many are smaller. Where conditions under the ice were favorable to the formation of one drumlin they apparently were equally favorable to the formation of others, for commonly they are found in groups that occupy many square miles (Fig. 187). The individual drumlins of a group are separated by the undulating surface of the till plain, from which they rise somewhat abruptly.

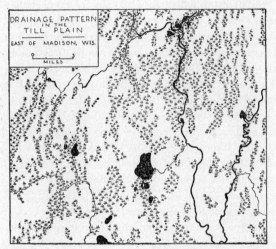

Fig. 188.—The drainage pattern associated with drumlins in a portion of a Wisconsin till plain.

423. DRAINAGE FORMS AND DRAINAGE PATTERNS IN YOUNG TILL PLAINS. The drainage condition of till plains of recent glaciation must be described as generally poor. The uneven and patternless dumping of the till is reflected in the ill-developed pattern of the streams which, in consequence of the slope of a surface of swells and swales, spilled from one depression into the next after the disappearance of the glacier (Fig. 188). These streams, like those of the ice-scoured plains, are youthful. Their courses are interrupted by swamps, lakes, falls, and rapids. In regions of deep till the falls and rapids were soon eroded out of the soft material and are not now numerous. Indeed, some small streams flowing through the unconsolidated till have quickly acquired graded courses and show well-developed meanders and other evidences of stream maturity. In many till plains, however, the downward cutting of a stream in the glacial drift has discovered here and there a buried ridge of the preglacial rock surface and has developed falls or rapids of greater permanence having economic value as water-power sites.

The numerous lakes and far more numerous swamps of the till plain lie mainly in depressions due in part to ice scour and in part to the unequal deposition of the drift. The depressions, or basins, thus formed are of two somewhat different kinds. (a) Some are due to the erosional reshaping, unequal filling, and morainic blocking of preglacial river valleys. Some of the lakes formed in such basins are large, deep, and permanent. The Great Lakes of North America lie in basins that are mainly glacial modifications of preglacial river valleys. Ice scour enlarged these valleys, and morainic dams blocked them, although a gentle crustal warping has also been involved in their formation. Owing to successive drift dams across a single preglacial valley, lakes may occur in succession forming a chain, as does the series of four near Madison, Wis. (b) Other basins are the impressions of large ice blocks which became detached from the margin of a stagnant glacier as a result of melting along crevasses. Basins of these origins may be many square miles in area, or they may be mere ponds, but, whether large or small, they are likely to be shallow. Lakes in the smaller morainic basins are maintained by direct rainfall, by springs about their borders, or by inflowing brooks from limited drainage areas.

The permanency of the numerous small lakes of the till plain is not great. Inflowing drainage is abundantly supplied with silt and tends to fill a basin quickly. Outflowing drainage is able quickly to cut a notch in the soft morainic rim, lowering the outlet and with it the lake level. Such as are maintained by rain and springs and drain wholly by seepage through the drift depend for their existence upon the position of the ground-water table. In the till plains of America, even before the agricultural occupance of the land during the past century, thousands of lake-filled basins left at the retreat of the last glacier had been filled or drained by natural processes, including the growth of vegetation, and converted into marshes. Generally the basins are partly filled with peat, the acid half-decayed remains of rank vegetative growths. Some are now covered with grasses and appear as marsh meadows. During the last century other thousands of small lakes and ponds in America have dwindled in size or have become marshes, owing to the increased rate of fill resulting from clearing and plowing on adjacent hillsides or to the lowering of the ground-water table which follows general deforestation. Likewise, thousands of acres of small marshlands have been artificially drained, and their surfaces put to agricultural or pastoral uses.

424. MARGINAL MORAINES AND THEIR ARRANGEMENT. A period of balance between the rate of glacial advance and the rate of melting permitted the position of the ice *margin* to remain stationary or to change but slightly. During such a time the moving ice continued to drag forward in its bottom, or to carry forward in its mass or on its surface, quantities of drift all of which were deposited about its relatively stationary margin as a *marginal moraine* (363, Fig. 181). Thus were created ridges or belts of drift of greater thickness than the till sheet and with notably different detail of form and pattern of arrangement.

Periods of temporary marginal halt occurred (*a*) at the place of its greatest advance, during the time of hesitation between general advance and excessive wastage; and (*b*) at intervals during the long time required for the slow and complete wastage or melting back of the glacier. Moraines put down about the margin of the ice at its most advanced position are called *end moraines. Recessional moraines* were built upon the top of the till plain at places of hesitation or temporary readvance during glacial wastage. It appears to have been a general condition of glacial disappearance that atmospheric temperature, the supply of snow, or other elements of environment caused the rate of waste to be most irregular. Advances, or slight readvances, during which marginal moraines great or small were formed, alternated with periods of waste so rapid that only small amounts of marginal deposit were put down upon the surface of the till. This is indicated by successive morainal ridges separated by areas of till plain.

The patterns of arrangement of marginal moraines greatly affect the appearance and use of regions in which they occur, and also they may be used to indicate the extent of the area covered during the period of greatest glacial advance or at any stage during its retreat. It is certain that all parts of a long ice front of from 1,000 to 2,000 miles neither advanced nor wasted away as a unit but did so unequally as a series of lobes or tongues separated by embayments. Evidence of that is found in the pattern of arrangement of the principal end moraines and other marginal moraines left by the last continental glacier of North America. They form a series of intersecting arcs or of interlacing and irregular scallops (Fig. 189).

425. THE SIZE AND COMPOSITION OF MARGINAL MORAINES. Marginal morainal ridges vary greatly as to size and form. Some are so meager as to be hardly noticeable; others are single narrow ridges a few yards in width and only a few feet high. However, some are comprised of belts rather than ridges of drift and have rough or strongly undulating surfaces which are pitted with steep-sided depressions,

These belts commonly are from 1 to 5 miles in width, many miles long, and contain hills which reach elevations of 100 to 200 ft. higher than that of the bordering till plain. Such moraines clearly were not deposited by the ice while its margin remained unmoving. They are

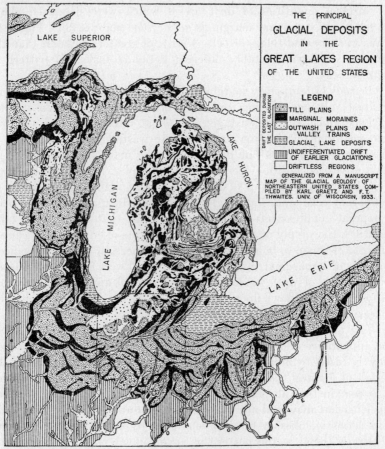

THE PRINCIPAL
GLACIAL DEPOSITS
IN THE
GREAT LAKES REGION
OF THE UNITED STATES

LEGEND
TILL PLAINS
MARGINAL MORAINES
OUTWASH PLAINS AND VALLEY TRAINS
GLACIAL LAKE DEPOSITS
UNDIFFERENTIATED DRIFT OF EARLIER GLACIATIONS
DRIFTLESS REGIONS

GENERALIZED FROM A MANUSCRIPT MAP OF THE GLACIAL GEOLOGY OF NORTHEASTERN UNITED STATES COMPILED BY KARL GRAETZ AND F. T. THWAITES. UNIV. OF WISCONSIN, 1933.

Fig. 189.—The pattern of arrangement of the glacial, glaciofluvial, and glacio-lacustrine deposits in the Great Lakes region. (*Reproduced by permission of F. T. Thwaites.*)

compound ridges resulting from deposition during a period of many minor changes of position.

The drift that makes up marginal moraines includes both unstratified and stratified forms. Much of the material, having been pushed forward into its present position by an advancing ice edge, is boulder clay, like that of the till plain. Other parts, and especially the surface materials, were deposited with the partial aid of waters flowing from the melting ice and issuing from channels on the ice or under it. The effect of stream sorting on the drift was to remove the clay and other finer materials and transport them out beyond the marginal moraine. That tended to leave the surface of the morainal ridge much more gravelly and with a higher proportion of large boulders than characterizes the till plain. Even in regions where the adjacent till has not many boulders marginal moraines may be so stony as to interfere with their cultivation.

Fig. 190.—Two views showing the rough kame-and-kettle surfaces of marginal moraines. (*Photographs by John R. Randall.*)

426. The Surface Features of Large Marginal Moraines. The rough and knobby surface peculiar to belts of marginal moraine sometimes is called *kame-and-kettle moraine* (Fig. 190). Kames are rounded or irregular hills, sometimes even ridges, of imperfectly stratified glacial gravel. It is believed that they are mainly the conelike or deltalike deposits of streams from the ice front. Being formed of gravelly drift against the ice front, many of them slumped backward upon the withdrawal of the ice, leaving mounds of rounded shape and disturbed strata dotting the morainic surface. Kettles are steep-sided hollows, often quite round, in the drift. They are particularly abundant in marginal moraines, where many of them appear to have originated, like many of the lake basins of the till plain, through the separation of large blocks of ice from the glacier edge and their existence there until the glacier was so far withdrawn that the surface depressions caused by their melting could not be filled with other deposits.

Not only is the surface of the typical marginal moraine rough and stony, but it is dotted with lakes and ponds which lie in the kettle holes. Lakes of this kind vary from small round ponds to some of considerable size (Fig. 191). Many of them have neither visible inlet nor apparent outlet. They are maintained by surface drainage and by springs in the glacial deposits and are prevented from overflowing by outward seepage through the gravels of the morainic ridge.

Pleasantly irregular surfaces, numerous lakes, and scattered woodlands, left by farmers on steep or stony surfaces, cause belts of marginal moraine to be sought as playgrounds by the inhabitants of adjacent flatter plains.

427. Glaciofluvial Plains. Drainage from a long ice front was discharged through many small, temporary, and shifting streams. Often they were overloaded, and, escaping from the confines of narrow

Fig. 191.—Small kettle ponds surrounded by boulder-strewn kames in a marginal moraine near Whitewater, Wis.

crevasses or subglacial tunnels, their velocities were checked immediately beyond the marginal moraines. There they built glaciofluvial deposits which have features somewhat like those of floodplains or alluvial fans (363). Some marginal moraines are fringed for miles with *outwash plains* of water-sorted and therefore stratified drift which was washed out from the ice front (Figs. 181A, 192). These are characterized by flat surfaces and an internal structure of rudely stratified sand, gravels, and small boulders (Fig. 193). In general, the clay component of the drift is not present in the deposits because it was carried farther on by the streams that built them. The largest boulders, on the other hand, usually were left behind on the moraines. Outwash plains are of frequent occurrence in association with end and other marginal moraines. The generally flat surfaces of some outwash plains that are underlain by till are dotted with kettle holes which appear to have resulted from the melting of stranded and perhaps buried ice blocks left during the glacial wastage (Figs. 181, 194). Plains of that kind are called *pitted outwash*. They are common among the extensive outwash plains of southern Michigan (Fig. 189). During spring thaws, when the soil still is frozen, the kettles are likely to contain small ponds, but they are not commonly occupied by permanent lakes because of the free drainage of surface waters through the underlying gravels.

Fig. 192.—The flat or gently undulating surface of an outwash plain. (*Wisconsin Geological Survey Photograph.*)

Because of the materials of which outwash plains are composed they commonly are of rather low agricultural productivity as compared with till plains. Even though their surfaces are very flat, they are in some

Fig. 193.—A cut through an outwash plain showing sand and gravel washed free of clay and rudely stratified according to size. (*Wisconsin Geological Survey Photograph.*)

places stony and in others sandy, and usually they are subject to drought because of the free underdrainage. They are, however, provided with naturally crushed and rudely sorted sands and gravels for constructional use, and the supply is abundant since some of the outwash deposits are many feet thick (Fig. 195). The large commercial gravel pits of the Great Lakes region mainly are located in outwash plains.

428. CHANNEL DEPOSITS. The abundant drainage of a glacier margin in some places was spread fanwise upon outwash plains but in others was

FIG. 194.—The undulating surface and numerous hollows of a pitted outwash plain. (*cf.* Fig. 181.) (*Wisconsin Geological Survey Photograph.*)

confined within definite channels. Some such were within the ice; others were beyond its margin. The streams leading away from the fronts of some glacial ice lobes seem to have been heavily burdened, since their channels now are floored with glaciofluvial deposits for many miles beyond the former ice margin. These aggraded glacial stream beds are called *valley trains*, and

FIG. 195.—A view showing outwash gravels and marginal moraine in association. The smooth surface of the outwash plain is shown above the gravel pit, and the position of the bordering moraine is indicated by the low hills in the right background. (*The Sheboygan Press.*)

they bear the same relationship to outwash plains that floodplains bear to piedmont alluvial plains. Valley-train gravels and sands now are found in the floodplains or alluvial terraces (406) of the Mississippi, lower Wisconsin, and other streams the channels of which led away from the front of the great North American glacier (Fig. 189).

The temporary streams that discharged from the glacier margin flowed from the ice sometimes at the bottoms of deep crevasses in the ice and sometimes in ice tunnels (Fig. 181). Being heavily loaded, they aggraded their beds and built narrow deposits of glaciofluvial drift within the confines of crevasse or tunnel. If the stagnant ice melted away without sufficient forward motion to erase so fragile a feature, it clearly would remain to mark the course of the ancient stream. Such deposits are not uncommon and are called *eskers*. They appear as sinuous ridges of gravel somewhat like an abandoned railroad grade. Some of them continue, with interruptions, for many miles (Fig. 196). They also are potential sources of gravel for use in construction.

429. THE DRIFT PLAINS OF AMERICA AND EUROPE. Those parts of glaciated North America and Europe in which the features made by glacial deposition predominate over those that result from ice scour

FIG. 196.—A narrow sinuous ridge of the esker type. It contains glaciofluvial drift and may have been deposited in an ice tunnel or in a crevasse. (*Photograph by John R. Randall.*)

are roughly indicated in Figs. 197 and 198. Not only are the drift plains extensive, but they include a large part of the most populous and highly developed sections of those continents. Also, by reason of the strong contrasts possible in the surface forms, composition, and drainage of drift, they contain localities of very different appearance and utility. There are poor areas, such as the Northwestern Pine Barrens of Wisconsin or the Lüneburg Heath of Germany. There are productive areas, such as the plains of eastern England or those of western Ohio. Each of the regions of continental glaciation has its areas of lake-dotted marginal moraine and its areas of till plain with drumlins, marshes, and undulating cultivable lands. However, in the drift plains of both continents are some contrasts which cannot be explained in terms of local variation of glacial action or of underlying rock.

430. NEW DRIFT PLAINS AND OLD. The characteristic features of drift plains, as they were described above, are mainly those of glacial deposits so recent that they have been little altered by weathering and erosion since their deposition. There are associated with them, in both North America and Europe, extensive plains which bear unmistakable evidence of being ice deposited but which clearly are much older (365). The gradational processes have been so long at work upon them that they have reduced some of the irregularities and created new ones. Morainal ridges have been subdued, kames worn down, kettles filled, and lakes drained or filled, so that the number and irregularity of these features are much less than in the newer drift. Erratic boulders

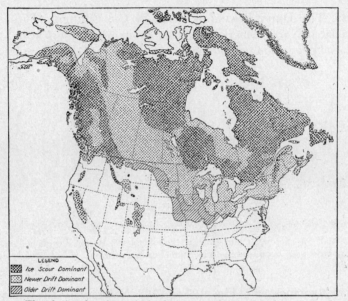

Fig. 197.—The glaciated regions of North America distinguished as to the dominance of older drift, newer drift, and ice scour.

have been weathered until many of them crumble into earth, and gravel deposits have been disintegrated or buried beneath later alluvium or deposits of loess (445). The result of these changes has been to produce more gently undulating plains, better drained and with finer and more uniform drift. On the other hand, the greater age of this drift has permitted erosional features to develop which locally increase the irregularity of the surface. The aimless pattern of the drainage characteristic of new drift has been reformed and approaches the dendritic pattern of stream-eroded plains. Stream valleys have been cut through the drift into underlying rock. In places the drift is largely removed and becomes thin or patchy, so that the surface features are not greatly different in appearance from those of the driftless plains beyond the margin of former glaciation. Even marginal moraines are so changed that the former positions of some of them may be conjectured only from remnants. The distribution and comparative

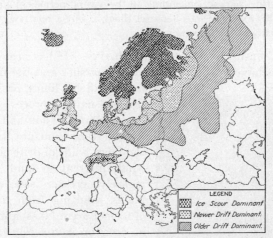

FIG. 198.—The regions of older and newer glaciation in Europe, the latter subdivided as in Fig. 197.

extent of the new and older drift sheets of America and Europe are indicated in Figs. 197 and 198.

431. THE OLDER DRIFT SUBDIVIDED. In the older drift itself students of glaciology recognize drift horizons of several distinct ages. These are

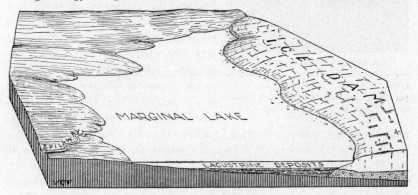

FIG. 199.—A diagram to illustrate the formation of a temporary lake between the margin of a glacier and a low divide across which the surplus drainage escapes. Glacio-lacustrine deposits are seen in the lake bottom.

separated by layers of plant remains and other evidences of great lapse of time. While the latest of them is far older than the newer drift, it may be noted that even the oldest of them is much younger than the sedimentary rocks upon which they rest. This can lead only to the conclusion that, however many thousands of years it may be since the disappearance of the last ice sheet, it is many times that number since the coming of the first one. Also, that the "ice age," including all the several periods of glacial advance and wastage with intervals between them, is but a relatively recent event in earth history (see Appendix E).

432. GLACIAL LAKES AND LAKE PLAINS.   It has been shown how glacial lakes have been converted into marshes and the marshes into farm land by filling or by draining through natural processes or human intervention. Thousands of small flats of that kind are found among the farm lands of drift plains. Somewhat different in kind, and of immensely greater size, are a few plains resulting from the existence of former great lakes now diminished in area or completely disappeared. It has been observed that the lakes of the drift plains are due to some kind of glacial obstruction of present drainage. This is in some degree true even of the Great Lakes. However, in an earlier stage in their history the drainage of the Great Lakes, and of several other large lakes which have now disappeared, was obstructed by the ice of the glacier itself. Where the ice front rested upon a surface that sloped down toward the glacier it furnished drainage that could not escape

FIG. 200.—A present exposure of finely stratified or *varved* clays which accumulated in the bottom of a temporary lake of the glacial period. (*Wisconsin Geological Survey Photograph.*)

and, therefore, was impounded in a lake that had the ice front as one margin. The lake rose until it found an outlet at the lowest point on its rim (Fig. 199). Temporary former glacial lakes of that kind are known as *marginal lakes*. The final wastage of the ice barrier back of a marginal lake removed the obstruction that caused it. The drainage sought a new and lower outlet, and the lake dwindled in size or disappeared entirely. During the periods of their existence marginal lakes modified the land surfaces that they covered and in their disappearance left behind unmistakable features which are called *lake plains* or *lacustrine plains*. Their distinguishing features are level surfaces which are comprised largely of the wave-worked ingredients of the drift; silts and clays where they were abundant; but sometimes sand also (Fig. 200). Plains of this origin have a flatness similar to that of newly emerged marine plains. There are few extensive plains more level than these (Fig. 201). They include also shore features such as beach ridges, offshore bars, and deltas that are comprised largely of glacial sands and gravels. These features are spread at intervals that mark successive stages in the lowering of the outlet and the decrease of the lake area.

Many of the areas shown in Fig. 189 to be lake plain, such as parts of the Upper Peninsula of Michigan, had surfaces too rough to be completely submerged by the temporary lakes of glacial times. They now contain areas of lake plain interspersed among rocky hills. Many of

FIG. 201.—The extremely level surface of a glacial-lake plain near Saginaw, Mich. (cf. Fig. 189.)

the latter, during the existence of the enlarged lakes, must have been islands. In places also, stream erosion since glacial time has dissected the lacustrine plains so thoroughly that only remnants of their flat surfaces now are to be seen.

433. NOTABLE LACUSTRINE PLAINS. Glacial lake plains are found in Europe, and there are in America several of great extent and unusual economic significance. Notable among these are the lake-plain margins of the present Great Lakes, the Lake Agassiz plain, the southern part of the Ontario Clay Belt, and the sand plain of central Wisconsin. During the wastage of the last ice sheet the southern portions of the Great Lakes were exposed while the great ice dam still lay across the lowest and present outlet through the St. Lawrence Valley. Drainage from the ice front during that time was forced to seek other and higher outlets. This caused the formation of lakes of larger area than

those of the present. The bottoms of those more extensive lakes, containing the unleached glacial silts and clays, are now flat and fertile plains in northern Ohio, eastern Michigan, western New York, and elsewhere (Figs. 202, 189). Even the city of Chicago stands in large part upon one of them. They are bordered by a series of beach ridges and other shore features which mark the lake levels at the stages of successive outlets. These slightly elevated ridges were much used as thoroughfares in the days of early settlement because they were well drained. Several are now the sites of important roadways established at that time. Examples of such roads are seen in U. S. Highway 31 west of Rochester, N. Y., and U. S. 20 both east and west of Cleveland, Ohio.

FIG. 202.—The principal glaciolacustrine plains and glacial spillways of North America.

In the same manner glacial drainage was impounded in a large marginal lake between the wasting ice front in central Canada and the higher land of central Minnesota. A broad and shallow lake created upon this slope found for a long time its lowest outlet through the course of the present Minnesota River into the Mississippi. The wave-worked sediments that were spread over the floor of that formerly extensive body of water, which is known as Lake Agassiz, now comprise the flat and fertile Red River Plains. Lakes Winnipeg and Winnipegosis now occupy the lowest portions of the depression, the remainder of the lake having disappeared when the ice dam was removed.

Upon the ice-scoured surface of the Laurentian Shield where morainic deposits generally are scant, coarse, and infertile is a region known as the Ontario Clay Belt. It is a district of growing agricultural value and is comprised in part of sediments laid down in a marginal lake. So also is the plain of central Wisconsin, but in this instance both the drift from which the sediments were derived and the lake bed upon which they were deposited were composed largely of sandstones. The lake plain of central Wisconsin is therefore flat but not fertile.

434. IMPORTANT GLACIAL SPILLWAYS. Summer melting along an extended ice margin must have produced large volumes of drainage water. It would be strange if streams of sufficient size to carry so much water had not left their marks upon the landscape. The principal marks are ancient spillways. These are broad valleys eroded in the drift or in rock beds where ice-front or marginal-lake drainage cut across low divides into established rivers leading to the sea (Fig. 203). Many such spillways are known, both in

America and in Europe. Several of them are now occupied by streams that seem ridiculously small in valleys that appear to have been eroded by streams of the size of the Mississippi. Figure 202 shows the location and drainage relationships of the principal American spillways. It will be recognized at once that some of them are of unusual significance as routes of present-day transportation. The Chicago outlet provided a naturally graded

FIG. 203.—The flat-bottomed channel of a former glacial spillway, not now occupied by any stream. (*Wisconsin Geological Survey Photograph.*)

site which made possible the economical construction of the Illinois and Michigan Canal and later the Chicago Sanitary and Ship Canal. It is traversed also by railway lines and an important highway. The Mohawk Valley outlet toward the Hudson River furnishes the lowest and best graded route across the Appalachian Highland. It became a busy thoroughfare after the construction of the Erie Canal through it and now carries a high

PRESENT RIVERS AND ANCIENT GLACIAL SPILLWAYS IN N. EUROPE

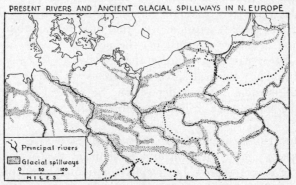

Principal rivers
Glacial spillways
0   50   100
MILES

FIG. 204.—The glacial spillways that drained the long European ice front toward the west at various of its stages of disappearance. (*After Paul Woldstedt, Das Eiszeitalter.*)

concentration of rail and highway traffic. Figure 204 shows the network of spillways which carried drainage from the wasting ice fronts of Europe. The channels made by that drainage cut across the present trend of the river valleys of the North European Plain and provide natural access from one of them to another. The German system of canals utilizes these graded courses to link together the natural waterways of the country.

Chapter XVII. Plains in Dry Climates

Desert Plains

435. It may be assumed that the features of arid desert plains result from the operation of the same tectonic and gradational processes that have been considered in connection with the features of other plains. However, the features of arid plains do not look like those of plains in humid regions, because the work of the gradational agents under arid climate is sufficiently different so that many distinctive features are produced. The outstanding differences between the features of arid-land relief and those of humid regions may be attributed largely to the following: (*a*) the much slower rate of weathering in arid regions than is found under humid conditions; (*b*) the meagerness of the vegetative cover of desert surfaces, with resultant lack of protection against erosion; (*c*) the intermittent but typically rapid runoff of desert streams; (*d*) the peculiar and highly selective nature of desert-stream erosion; (*e*) the prevalence of basins of interior drainage; and (*f*) the widespread occurrence of features that result from wind erosion or wind deposition. So general is the distribution of the latter that arid plains might almost be called aeolian plains.

436. FEATURES RESULTING FROM THE SLOWNESS OF DESERT WEATHERING. Both chemical and mechanical weathering act upon the rocks of desert regions, but owing to infrequent precipitation and low atmospheric humidity they act slowly. The rate of erosion is rapid by comparison, since both wind and flood waters are active eroding agents. The slowness of weathering and the comparative activity of erosion result in the exposure of unweathered rock features in bold outlines and sharp details which, in humid climates, would be softened in contour by rock decomposition or by burial underneath an accumulation of weathered debris. For that reason, and because there is so little vegetation to conceal them, fault scarps, the eroded edges of

374

sedimentary strata, or stream-eroded bluffs commonly stand out prominently upon the desert plain. Even small features fail to lose, in spite of long exposure, that angularity of profile and freshness of detail that make them appear to be of recent origin (Fig. 205).

437. FEATURES RESULTING FROM THE PECULIARITIES OF DESERT-STREAM EROSION. In humid plains the streams that result from well-distributed rainfall and the addition of ground water through springs and seepage flow steadily and cut valleys the forms and patterns

FIG. 205.—The steep undercut banks of a desert stream channel in Arizona. The stream, here easily forded, sometimes is a flood that occupies the entire channel. The small embankments beyond the car mark the heights of lesser floods. (*Photograph by DeCou, from Ewing Galloway.*)

of which have become familiar. In arid regions most streams are intermittent, but occasionally they flow in great volume as a result of the fall of torrential rain upon the bare surface of earth, which is parched and incapable of absorbing moisture rapidly. Under these conditions, according to Johnson,[1] the intermittent streams have a tendency to acquire a load quickly by downward erosion at their headwaters in the bordering highlands while in their middle courses on the plains they tend to choke their own channels, build sand bars, and subdivide

[1] Johnson, Douglas. Rock Planes of Arid Regions. *Geog. Rev.*, Vol. 22, pp. 656–665, 1932.

into many shallow, braided channels in which occasional torrents of water spread and shift from side to side. Instead of cutting greatly downward in their middle courses desert streams tend therefore to swing laterally, undercut the edges of bordering elevations, and plane them off, leaving the eroded surfaces covered only by a veneer of alluvium. It is a kind of erosion that is not widely developed in humid regions.

One result of the desert type of stream erosion is the formation of smooth rock floors, usually covered by veneers of gravel. Such plains often are found about the bases of desert mountains, from which they incline outward at low angles, bordered on the one hand by the steeper slopes of mountains and on the other by the gentler slopes of alluvial deposits. They have been called *pediments*. Although the

FIG. 206.—The long eroded slope of this pediment, which borders one of the Basin Ranges of Nevada, has a veneer of desert alluvium. (*Photograph by John C. Weaver.*)

construction of a pediment appears to begin in the graded middle course of the stream valleys, the process creeps headward as the valleys get older. Lateral erosion gnaws at the foothills and ultimately extends into the shrinking mountain mass itself. Finally the highland may be eroded entirely away during the progress of the cycle of erosion.[1] The pediment is, therefore, a type of rocky plain peculiar to the desert, and examples of it are known in most arid plains. They are abundantly developed about the mountain ranges of the North American desert (Fig. 206). In the Sahara are broad expanses of rocky desert plain, some of which are from 100 to 200 or more miles across. Some of them are believed to be parts of ancient peneplains which perhaps are the remnants of still more ancient highlands baseleveled by desert erosion. If this is true, then they are fully developed pediments which have been slightly elevated in more recent geological time, stripped of their alluvial veneers by the work of wind and water, and gashed by steep-

[1] Blackwelder, Eliot. Desert Plains. *Jour. Geol.*, Vol. 39, pp. 133–140, 1931.

sided stream channels, now dry.[1] Having little soil, these rocky plains have little even of desert vegetation, and they are the most completely desert of all arid plains. In northern Africa they are called *hamada*, and the term may well be applied to similar rock plains in other deserts.

The effect of sidewise erosion of the dry-land type in regions of horizontal sedimentary strata is seen also in flattish surfaces that are not necessarily baseleveled. By lateral cutting, less resistant formations are stripped away down to the surface of a more resistant stratum the surface of which then practically coincides with the surface of the plain. Such plains are called *stripped plains*. The effect of lateral cutting also is manifest in the transverse profiles of stream valleys in arid plains. Where valleys of considerable size have been cut in desert plains they commonly are steep-sided and flat-bottomed and clearly are being widened by undercutting of the valley walls (Fig. 205). The result is the dissection of the upland into flat-topped, or tabular, blocks which are separated by flat-bottomed valleys. The slopes between upland and lowland are steep, and lateral erosion, coupled with a slow rate of weathering, tends to keep them so.

Many desert plains have dry valleys of the flat-bottomed, steep-sided form.[2] Some of them are utilized as routes of travel because they furnish well-graded paths across otherwise dissected uplands. Upon their bottoms seepage water and soil water stored from the latest rains suffice to support more forage for beasts than may be found upon adjacent uplands. In the dry stream channels natural water holes or the digging of shallow wells may provide drinking water at usable intervals. In some desert valleys there is a sufficient supply of spring or well water in favored spots to provide for a limited irrigation of crops. Such spots are the sites of another kind of oasis (402, 409).

438. ALLUVIAL BASINS OF INTERIOR DRAINAGE. In many arid plains are structural (tectonic) basins into which are discharged the drainage waters of the plain and with them great quantities of alluvial filling. In humid lands streams that flow into structural basins fill them with water, creating lakes which overflow the lowest point upon the rim, and the drainage ultimately reaches the oceans. Few streams in arid plains have sufficient volume or permanence to flow to the ocean. Intermittently they flow and sometimes with great volume, only to be swallowed up in the desert floor or to spread in shallow lakes over

---

[1] Gautier, E. F. The Ahaggar: Heart of the Sahara. *Geog. Rev.*, Vol. 16, pp. 378–394, 1926.

[2] In America the Spanish name *arroyo* is the term most commonly applied to small stream channels in the dry lands. The Arabic term "oued," or *wadi*, is used for similar features in the Saharan region.

the lowest parts of their basins, where exposure to sun and dry winds soon evaporates them. Flood water, therefore, moves toward the center of the basin, but none flows out. For that reason the desert plain may be said to be typically a region of *interior drainage*. Only a few streams, those of greatest volume and permanence, and especially those exotic streams that derive most of their waters from highlands beyond the desert, are able to flow across it and reach the sea. Only for the great streams is baselevel determined by sea level. For the others it is determined by the levels of the alluvium-filled basins or temporary lakes into which they flow.

THE DRAINAGE OF DESERT BASINS.   The basins of desert plains generally are broad and shallow features. Within them lie accumulations of alluvium which aggrade and flatten the basin floors. Upon the flanks of

FIG. 207.—A playa basin in Nevada. Its deep alluvial filling has a glistening white crust of salt, and wind-blown salt clings to the rocky island included within it. (*Photograph by John C. Weaver.*)

some, especially the smaller and deeper, the filling is collected in the form of encircling alluvial fans. Basins of that type have been called *bolsons*.[1] In many of the shallower basins the alluvium is spread uniformly over the gently sloping plain. The lowest portion of the typical basin of interior drainage shows evidence of concentration of drainage there in the form of marshes or lakes. If the general rate of inward drainage is balanced by the average rate of loss through evaporation, a lake is likely to exist. It will be a salt-water lake, because water is continually removed from it by evaporation while the salts contained in the inflowing water, especially the common salt, remain behind in solution and eventually reach concentrations that make some salt lakes more salty than the oceans. If the rate of evaporation generally is in excess of the rate of inflow, temporary, or *playa*, lakes will result from occasional torrential inflows of water. These are followed by periods of excessive evaporation. The marshy beds of these ephemeral lakes

[1] The term *bolson*, a Spanish word meaning a large pocket, was applied originally to mountain-rimmed basins of interior drainage. Its meaning is here extended to all basins of interior drainage in dry lands.

commonly are mud covered and are strongly charged with salt or soluble soil alkalies.[1] When thoroughly dried they commonly are incrusted with salts and sometimes are glistening white in color (Fig. 207). In this class of deposits are not only those of common salt and other compounds of sodium and calcium, which are called *alkali*, but also some of economic value. Among the latter are the borax deposits of southwestern United States and the famous sodium nitrate deposits of northern Chile (703).

The great salt lakes of the world lie, as may be expected, in basins of internal drainage, some of which are plains of great size. Noted salt lakes are the Aral and Caspian Seas, which are surrounded by the plains of Russian Turkistan; and Lake Eyre in southern Australia. The latter usually is a dry salt plain and its level is, like that of the Caspian, lower than sea level. Great Salt Lake and several other permanent salt lakes also are situated in basins of interior drainage but at such elevations above sea level that they may be considered in connection with plateaus.

439. FEATURES RESULTING FROM WIND EROSION. The sparsity of vegetation in arid plains regions gives unusual scope to the erosional activities of the wind (206). Some of the minor landforms show abundant evidence of the abrasive effect of wind-blown sand. Wind abrasion aids differential weathering in the production of curiously etched, rounded, or polished details of rock surface, some of them in fantastic shapes. Of much more widespread importance than this minor activity is the general process of *deflation* (370). Dust and sand are removed from all parts of the desert surface but perhaps most abundantly from the lower portions of interior drainage basins, where the material is generally finer. This process has the effect of deepening the basins which otherwise tend to be filled by alluvium. It is the only means by which earth may be removed from the desert basin.

440. DEFLATION and the deposition of the products of deflation result in the formation of a number of significant dry-land features. Upon the margins of desert basins it is less effective in the removal of material because the material there usually is more coarse and rocky. The surfaces of pediments yield little that wind may transport, and the upper margins of fans are made up of the coarser stream-transported materials. Such fine material as exists or is provided by local weathering is quickly removed, leaving behind the fragments that are too heavy for wind removal. These remain until they cover the surface, forming what is called a *desert pavement* (Fig. 208). In some regions the pebbles and fragments of the desert pavement are covered by a thin coating of iron oxide and other chemicals which is polished by dust abrasion to a glossy surface called *desert varnish*. They color the plain with glistening yellow, brown, red, or even black. In those parts of a

[1] In America these features are called *alkali flats*. Similar features in other deserts are known by various names, such as shotts, vloers, vlei, and salt pans.

desert plain that are deeply covered with alluvium deflation removes the finer surface material leaving a gravelly desert pavement, underneath which is alluvial soil. Because of their deeper soils such areas hold more moisture than the rocky hamada and are likely to have a little more vegetation. Great expanses of flat, pebbly or gravelly, alluvial, desert plains of the kind just described are, in the Sahara Desert, called *reg*.

In the central portions of large desert basins of alluvial filling the deposits are less coarse and more subject to deflation. Dried and crumbled playa muds are unprotected by vegetation and are easily removed. Under intense insolation dancing whirlwinds lift dust high into the air and not only transport it but may even remove much of it entirely from the basin to regions well beyond its borders. It is probable that the total thickness of surface material thus removed from the floor of the desert basin is great enough to be an important factor in maintaining the basin shape.

Fig. 208.—The pebbles and rock fragments of a desert pavement, in western Nevada. (*Photograph by John C. Weaver.*)

441. Aeolian Sand Plains. From the foregoing it is clear that the popular conception of the arid plain as a sea of wind-blown sand is not well founded. Not many large desert areas are so much as one-fourth sand covered. However, there are many regions of sandy desert. The abundant rock grains in them are derived (*a*) from the disintegration of sandstone and other bedrock in the locality where the sand deposits are found or (*b*) from local accumulations of transported fragments separated by wind sorting from both the finer and the coarser products of rock weathering elsewhere. The finer weathered particles, removed as dust, are whirled high into the atmosphere, carried entirely away, and deposited as loess far beyond the limits of the region. The coarser fragments remain behind as components of the desert pavement. The sand, however, is carried in the lower atmosphere, transported to considerable distances, and lodged in quantity, often in the form of sand ridges or sand dunes, on sites so sheltered as to have reduced wind velocities or in some other way to favor the accumulation of sand.

442. *The Features of Sand-ridge and Sand-dune Areas.* Sand plains are of some extent in most deserts (Fig. 313). They cover great areas in Sahara and in parts of central and western Australia.[1] In the latter region, under an average of about 10 in. of annual rainfall, the sand hills, according to Madigan,[2] assume a striking form and pattern of arrangement and support a sparse dry-land vegetation.

The peculiarity of the Australian sand hills is that they are arranged in parallel ridges which trend with the direction of the locally prevailing trade winds, generally southeast to northwest. The ridges average about 40 ft. high and are separated by long, stony, gravelly, or sandy flats from a few rods to several miles wide. These gigantic "washboard" corrugations are remarkably continuous, single ridges extending almost unbroken for scores or even hundreds of miles. They appear to be wind formed but are not now actively moving. Such movement as is now going on in them is lengthwise, sand slowly drifting from their windward ends toward the leeward. In central Nebraska also there is a large sand plain, but it has developed under subhumid climate and prairie vegetation, and its surface is characterized by areas of stagnant grass-covered dunes (Fig. 310).

In the Sahara and other deserts of extreme aridity sand-hill or dune regions of great size and barrenness are encountered (371). They are comprised of dunes of fresh sand which are separated by pockets or hollows, some of which are of considerable size. The dunes, both large and small, usually present gentle slopes to the prevailing winds but fall off steeply to the leeward (Fig. 209; see also Fig. 224). High winds drift sand up their gentle windward slopes and over their crests, where the grains drop in the shelter of the leeward slopes. By this process the dune form is created and maintained, and the whole feature is caused to migrate slowly with the prevailing wind, yet the general migration must be very slow. Some Saharan dunes have been accurately observed for many years without any significant change in their position being noted. In other regions observations have shown that some dunes move at rates up to 50 or 100 ft. per year. In any case the continuous abrasion of drifting sand, together with the great aridity, is sufficient to prevent vegetation's making any active growth upon the dune surface. From the top of a conspicuous dune, which may be as much

---

[1] Talbot, H. and Clarke, E. A Geological Reconnaissance of the Country between Laverton and the South Australian Border. *Geol. Surv. W. Australia, Bull.* 75, 1917.

[2] Madigan, C. T. The Australian Sand-ridge Deserts. *Geog. Rev.*, Vol. XXVI, No. 2, pp. 205–227, 1936.

as 200 or 300 ft. high, those of smaller size present a view like that of a billowing sea. A large expanse of bare sand dunes and sand flats hundreds of square miles in area in the Sahara is called the *erg* by the desert inhabitants.

443. WATER SUPPLIES IN DUNE REGIONS.   Some large regions of desert sand dunes are difficult to traverse and have sparse human populations, if any, because of their rough surfaces, scant vegetation, and deficient water supplies. The great Libyan *erg* of eastern Sahara is reputed to be peculiarly devoid of both water and vegetation. Yet that is not true of all of them.

FIG. 209.—The billowing, wind-rippled forms of sand dunes in the American desert. Note the mud floor and some vegetation in the depressions or pockets where water has stood. The distant hills in this view are low mountains, not sand dunes. (*Photograph by Ewing Galloway.*)

Even light rains sink readily into the porous sand hills, where the water is stored and yielded in favorable sites to springs or wells. In western Sahara some of the notable oases lie in the midst of great dune areas. Some of them are located in series on favored sites along old desert stream channels which have been overrun and largely buried by migrating dunes. In the buried channel sufficient water concentrates by seepage to supply irrigation to restricted basins among the dunes. In these still another class of oasis may be recognized, highly important locally but generally of small size and much less significant than the principal classes previously noted (402, 409, 437). Even where there is not sufficient water for irrigation, not all dune areas are devoid of vegetation. Within the pockets and basins among the dunes seepage of rainwater is sometimes able to provide the basin floors with

sufficient moisture for the growth of pasture. Sand-dune grazing areas of
that kind are found in the desert regions of all the continents, including
those of the United States.

Loess Plains

444. THE FEATURES OF LOESS PLAINS. Some of the considerable
plains of the world are loess mantled (371). Not all loess deposits are
plains, because aeolian dust comes to rest upon hill and valley alike
and is found in regions of great relief as well as upon lowlands. The
thick loess mantle that covers the rough surface of northwestern
China has been much eroded also and in places is of extreme irregularity. Elsewhere are loess deposits that, if not so deep as those of
China, are of equal or greater area. Some of these are found upon
extensive plains, but they are not in themselves the cause of the plains.
They merely cover and perhaps increase the levelness of plains due
to other physiographic causes.

445. THE NATURE AND DISTRIBUTION OF LOESS. The dust of
which loess is composed is fine, but it is chemically undecomposed.
Its character indicates accumulation by wind transportation over
distances great enough so that coarse material is not included with it.
Its unleached condition indicates also that the material is derived from
sources in which mechanical rather than chemical weathering is
predominant. Such sources are found in, and the loess deposits are
believed to have been derived from the deflation of, (a) arid lands and
(b) the bare drift deposits and abundant stream muds which were
associated with the retreat of the former continental ice sheets.

Loess deposits are deepest and most widely distributed in regions
of steppe environment because, generally, those regions border the
deserts, and because there the soil is sufficiently moist to support a
grass cover so that the loess, once deposited, is not easily removed
again by the wind. In central United States and central Europe the
principal loess deposits are believed to have been derived, at least in
large part, from the muds of the fresh drift and the drainage ways
associated with the wastage of the former continental glaciers. Loess
of that origin is found well beyond the borders of the steppe regions
and even to some extent in regions of humid climate and forest vegetation. The internal structure of loess is unstratified, highly porous, and
characterized by fine vertical tubes which probably are related to the
existence of former plant roots. Owing to its structure it has the
property of standing in vertical faces when cut through by streams
or roadways, even though the material is so soft as to crumble to dust
when pressed between the fingers (Fig. 210). Unweathered minerals,

porous structure, fine texture, and high water-holding capacity help to explain the reputation for high fertility held by loessial soils.

446. THE GREAT LOESS PLAINS.   Because loess plains underlie some of the most productive agricultural regions of the world, attention may here be directed to the situations and characteristics of several of them.

North China.   The large loessial component in the material of the delta plain of North China has been noted (401). Although this plain is composed largely of river sediment much of it is of loessial origin. Either it is loess derived by stream erosion from the hill country to the west, or it was deposited by the wind on the delta surface and subsequently reworked by the shifting delta streams. Although such materials are not loess in the usual meaning of the word, true loess is believed to be a large component in the soils of all North China and as far beyond as the plains of Manchuria.

FIG. 210.—A recent road-cut through a loess hill in the prairie region of eastern Nebraska.

North America.   Loess is likewise an important surface component over a large area in interior United States. It is particularly abundant in association with parts of the older drift, especially the western margin of the area of older glaciation and the drainage ways leading from it (430). There the raw glacial deposits appear to have been subject to deflation for thousands of years under semiarid climatic conditions. In a few places only are the deposits so deep, so unchanged by weathering or stream work, so continuous, or so extensive as to constitute what properly may be called loess plains. The deepest accumulations are found in the plain that includes southern and eastern Nebraska and about the western one-fifth of Iowa (Fig. 211). There the loess in many places reaches a thickness of from 60 to 100 ft. Since the Missouri River valley traverses this region there are numerous exposures of eroded vertical loess walls along its bluffs, as, for example, at Council Bluffs, Iowa. The border zone, which has been dissected by small streams tributary to the Missouri, also has valleys of a peculiarly abrupt and steep-walled type. The loess-mantled uplands are of undulating surface.

Other deep and extensive accumulations of loesslike earth cover much of eastern Iowa, adjacent parts of Wisconsin, central Illinois, and extend down the eastern bluffs of the Mississippi River. These generally are less deep than those of the Missouri River region, but locally they attain great thickness

FIG. 211.

(Fig. 212). Still another notable deposit of loess occupies a part of the rolling plateau of eastern Washington and Oregon, where it buries the lava surface.

Dust storms are not unfamiliar phenomena even now in the High Plains and Mississippi Basin. The great dust storms of recent years have been made worse by periods of drought, and the material carried by them has accumu-

FIG. 212.—An old road-cut through the wooded loess bluffs of the Mississippi River near Natchez, Miss.

lated locally in large quantities. Some dust is carried to great distances, however. Observation of some storms has shown that they distribute dust in appreciable quantity as far eastward as New England. In one storm the quantity deposited at Madison, Wis., was estimated at about 25 tons per square mile.[1] It is probable that there is at least a small admixture of loessial

[1] Winchell, A. N., and Miller, E. R. The Great Dustfall of March 19, 1920. *Am. Journ. Sci.*, Vol. 3, pp. 349–364, 1922.

material in the surface regolith of most of eastern North America, southern Europe, and other parts of the world.

Europe. Associated with the region of older glaciation in central Europe also are considerable deposits of loess or loams of high loess content. They occur over a long belt which extends from central Germany eastward through southern Poland into Russia, where loess is a significant element in the fertile "chernozem" soil, as it is in Nebraska and Argentina (626, Fig. 213).

Argentina. The Pampa of Argentina also is characterized by large areas of loess. In part they are aeolian loess, and in part they have been

THE PRINCIPAL LOESS DEPOSITS OF CENTRAL EUROPE

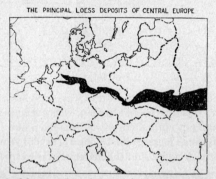

Fig. 213.—The principal loess region of Europe is closely associated with the margin of the older glacial drift. (*cf.* Fig. 198.) (*After Paul Woldstedt, Das Eiszeitalter.*)

disturbed by streams, are interbedded between stream-deposited sands and clays of older alluvium, and are, therefore, like some of the deposits of North China, not true loess (401). In western Buenos Aires province the loess and loessial alluvium reach a total thickness of 50 to 100 ft. and in a few places as much as 500 ft.[1] These deposits are believed to have been removed by deflation from the arid belt near the Andes where extensive accumulations of rubble, gravel, and sand remain. The region of greatest loess accumulation has, like that of Nebraska, a subhumid climate.

[1] Stappenbeck, R. *Op. cit.*, pp. 382–409.

Chapter XVIII. The Shore Features of Plains

447. The Significance of Shore Features. The line at which the sea meets the land is a line of transformation. On its two sides are different scenes, different uses, and different means of communication. At that line the flow of trade from land to land by way of the sea must be handled for its ocean voyage. That process is in some places much aided, and in others distinctly handicapped, by the shape of the shore outline, the nature of the land features and depths of water associated with it. The habor and freight-handling problems of a regular, or smooth, shore outline are different from those of one that has deep embayments or other features of a complex irregularity. The problems and profiles of shores which are flanked by mountainous highlands are different from those which open upon gently sloping plains. Because of the differences noted it will be found convenient to consider here, and at comparative length, the essential characteristics of the shores of lowland regions. Thus there will be reserved for later and briefer comment such modifications of the general features of coastal outline and profile as are found in association with plateaus, hill lands, and mountains.

448. Conditions Affecting Shore Outlines. The positions and shapes of shorelines are not unchangeable. On the contrary, several agents and processes work separately or together to bring about their constant reshaping and development. Among the more important of the conditions involved are the following: (a) changes in the relative elevation of land and sea, (b) changes resulting from wave erosion, (c) changes resulting from wave deposition, (d) changes resulting from land deposits, and (e) changes brought about through the work of corals and other organic agencies. Shoreline changes of the greatest extent would obviously result from any displacement of the land surface with respect to sea level. For example, if the land on a gently sloping plain, extending seaward as a broad continental shelf, were elevated only a few feet by diastrophic change or if there were a

387

correspondingly slight lowering of the sea level by the withdrawal of water from the sea and its retention in great continental ice sheets, a large area of the shallow sea bottom would be exposed. The shoreline, under these circumstances, would migrate slowly seaward and occupy a new position on the flat sea bottom. Such a shoreline would be characterized by regularity and lack of minor indentations. Landward from this shoreline there would be a plain of low relief having only such features as were made by wave erosion and deposition during the emergence and by the land-derived drainage that had to cross it (367). Seaward one would expect to find very shallow water resting upon a gently inclined sea bottom. Such a simple initial shoreline of emergence probably would not remain long unchanged. Waves and currents, by their gradational work, presently would add features that would complicate its outline, and it may be doubted whether there are in existence any extensive examples of the simple shoreline of emergence.

449. SHORELINES OF SUBMERGENCE AND THEIR FEATURES. Broad diastrophic changes resulting in the depression of a coastal plain would permit a landward encroachment of the sea and would establish a new shoreline upon what was previously the land surface. Such changes are known to have occurred, and they produce shore features whose outlines are not readily erased by the gradational work of waves or streams. The same result clearly would follow a general rise in the level of the oceans, and it may be that such a rise did occur at the close of the glacial period as a result of the return to the oceans of vast quantities of water which had long been held on the lands in the great masses of glacial ice. Changes of the kind indicated would result in a submergence of the coastal slopes of the land. Under those conditions the horizontal surface of the sea must intersect with the eroded surface of the land, and the shoreline would assume a position which is that of a contour line upon the former land surface (Fig. 11). The measure of its irregularity would be determined by the slope of the land surface and the degree of its previous erosional dissection.

The slow inundation of low coasts results first in the formation of shorelines of great irregularity. The relief features of an eroded plain, such as a coastal plain, usually are low but broad. Wide, shallow valleys are separated by broad, low interfluves (Fig. 140). Valleys of that kind have such low gradients that even a slight inundation permits the sea to enter them for some distance, causing bays. The interstream areas, at the same time, remain only partly submerged and appear as irregular peninsulas or as islands. Some such bays are highly irregular in outline. If the valleys were eroded in horizontal sedimentary or in massive rocks they normally are dendritic in pattern, and the bays that occupy them

assume the branching forms of the valleys. Others are of simple outline, especially such as occupy glacially scoured troughs or depressions
caused by faults transverse to the shoreline. Embayments resulting
from submergence are called "drowned valleys" or *estuaries*, and
shorelines characterized by them are called *ria shorelines* (Fig. 214*A*).

450. RIA SHORELINES. Examples of ria shorelines and estuarine
rivers upon coastal lowlands are numerous. Most of the eastern shore
of North America is characterized by embayments of that class. Some

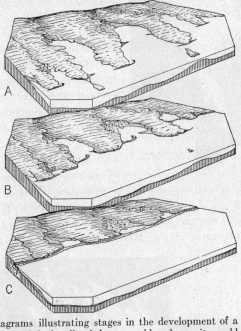

FIG. 214.—Diagrams illustrating stages in the development of a shoreline of submergence; (*A*) erosion of the headlands begun and beaches, spits, and hooks are forming;
(*B*) depositional features extensive, shoreline retreating; (*C*) shoreline worn well back
and all features approaching old-age stage.

of the individual estuaries, Chesapeake Bay, for example, are of the
dendritic type (Fig. 215). Others, like Delaware Bay and the lower
Hudson and St. Lawrence Rivers, are simple in outline.

The shorelines of northern New England and eastern Canada are
of great irregularity, owing to the submergence of plains of ancient
crystalline and sedimentary rocks of complicated structures and
varying degrees of resistance to erosion. Some of the narrow bays are
in part the result of faulting in the rocks of the coastal zone. However,
the present shorelines are not merely those of stream erosion and submergence but have also many details of outline and profile given them

by ice scour during the period of their complete coverage by the continental glaciers. Although the features of submergence have been somewhat modified by wave and current action, some sections retain the high degree of irregularity of their youthful state. Such a shoreline is well illustrated by Casco Bay, Maine, which, according to W. D. Johnson, is a ria shoreline only slightly modified by glacial scour (Figs. 216, 217).

FIG. 215.

451. THE UTILITY OF RIA SHORELINES. In its youthful stage of development the ria shoreline has numerous estuaries together with certain deposited features, and it is one of great irregularity, with an abundance of sheltered water. Provided its bays are sufficiently deep, and many of them are, this kind of shoreline is one of numerous harbors and of great commercial possibilities. This is shown by the great use made of the Chesapeake, Delaware, New York, and other estuarine bays of eastern North America. The same is true of western Europe. The estuaries of the Rivers Mersey, Thames, Elbe, Weser,

FIG. 216.—The ria shoreline of Casco Bay has many islands, rocky peninsulas, and narrow inlets.

Seine, and Gironde have been capable of such great commercial use because submergence has deepened their waters, making possible the establishment of ocean ports at considerable distances from their mouths. The larger estuaries in the coastal plains of other continents serve in like manner, including that of the Rio de la Plata, which is the approach to Montevideo and Buenos Aires.

452. SHORELINE FEATURES RESULTING FROM MARINE EROSION. A newly established shoreline is subject to attack and modification by wave and current erosion. The attack is most effective upon those parts of the shoreline that are most exposed to the great waves of the open sea, especially the ends of projecting headlands. It is least effective in narrow or well-enclosed bays where waves of great size and force cannot reach. The effect of erosion upon the projections of exposed shorelines is to cut them back slowly and eventually to remove them, thus straightening the shoreline (Fig. 214*A*, *B*, *C*). On exposed coasts of easily eroded rock the rate of cutting is sufficiently rapid so that whole shorelines are known to be retreating landward at measurable rates. The shoreline of one part of England, for example, is known to

FIG. 217.—A view to seaward from the landward end of one of the long arms of Casco Bay, Maine, at low tide.

have been cut back as much as 2 miles since the time of the Roman conquest. Shorelines of resistant rock retreat much more slowly.

During the erosional process certain characteristic shore features appear. Wave erosion is most effective near average sea level and cuts a notch in the shore profile there. This it enlarges by undercutting and, on strongly eroding shores, produces steep cliffs and bold headlands. The erosion of cliffs in unconsolidated material or weak rock is likely to proceed with comparative evenness, but, in resistant rocks, inequalities in rock hardness or the presence of joints and other lines of weakness sometimes cause it to proceed unequally. Some of the results of differential erosion are the formation of eroded coves, detached chimneylike pinnacles of rock, and half-submerged projections upon the sea floor (Fig. 218).

As the sea cliff retreats landward under erosion, it leaves behind an eroded base which inclines gently seaward a little below sea level. It is called a *wave-cut terrace*. Some shorelines are bordered by marine terraces of that origin many hundreds or even several thousands of feet wide (Fig. 219). The shallowness of the water, especially on the newer landward margins of these features, and the presence of submerged rock projections cause them to be a menace to navigation.

453. SHORELINE FEATURES RESULTING FROM MARINE DEPOSITION. *Onshore Features.* The rock debris provided by wave and current

FIG. 218.—The features of a wave-cut cliff on the exposed coast of Cornwall, England. (*Photograph by Burton Holmes, from Ewing Galloway.*)

erosion, together with that derived from streams, is distributed in several characteristic forms along shorelines, and, being added to the land, it greatly affects the shape and utility of the shore outline. On the more steeply sloping shores bordering sea cliffs, large quantities are moved offshore and are deposited beyond the margin of the wave-cut terrace in a form which may be called wave-built terrace. Material so deposited is of interest in its relation to the formation of sedimentary

FIG. 219.—A profile to show the association of features on an eroding shoreline.

rocks, but it is deeply submerged and affects the shore outline but little. Of much greater present importance are the deposits that accumulate in the shallow shore waters and assume shapes and positions that greatly affect the appearance and use of the shoreline.

In the early stages of the erosional development of the shoreline of a coastal plain sediment is carried by waves and currents into the protected waters of coves and bays, where it accumulates as *beaches* of sand or pebbles. Locally these fill irregular bay heads, but their fronts are smoothly curved by wave and current action, and the deposits assume shapes that give rise to the name *crescent beaches*. As the headlands are cut back, the abundant debris accumulates in the shore waters and forms beaches even in front of the eroding shores. This material is subject to continuous removal and redeposition. With the aid of shore currents and undertow it is shifted along-shore until it comes to an angle in the shoreline or to the deeper water of a bay, where it is built up on the bottom in ridge form. These submerged ridges are added to until they grow above the water surface and project seaward or into the bays as points of sand or gravel which are called *spits*. In the mouth of a broad bay the shoreward movement of waves and currents past the projecting point of a spit may cause it to grow with a shoreward curve, when it is called a *recurved spit* or "hook." Such features are exemplified in the shapes of Sandy Hook, at the entrance of New York Bay, and the curved tip of Cape Cod. In a narrow or shallow bay such a deposit may grow entirely across the entrance, forming a *bay bar*. By deposits of similar nature adjacent islands may be connected with the shore (Fig. 214*A*).

Offshore Features. Shores having low relief and very shallow waters are characterized by wave-deposited features of another type. Along such shorelines the erosional work of the waves is weak because great waves begin to drag on the shallow bottom, change form, topple, and break at distances of hundreds or even thousands of feet out from the shoreline (369). In doing so they wash forward loose bottom material, only to drop it just landward of the line of breakers and build there a submarine ridge nearly parallel to the shoreline. As this feature grows in height it appears first above sea level as a series of narrow islands (Fig. 220*A*). Further deposition by waves and the drift of longshore currents fills gaps between some of the islands and connects them. This forms a long low bar that is called an *offshore bar* (Fig. 220*B*). Between offshore bars and their mainland shorelines are long shallow lagoons. Drainage from the land discharges into the lagoon and seeks an outlet through the bar, and in the lagoon the water level rises and falls periodically with the tide, which flows in and out through gaps, or *tidal inlets*, between sections of the bar. This tends to keep some of the gaps scoured open.

An offshore bar does not extend indefinitely parallel to the mainland shore with complete separation from it by a lagoon. Rather it touches the mainland at intervals, especially at projecting points, thus interrupting the continuity of the lagoon. For that reason the

formation of a bar, broken by inlets, and of segmented lagoons tends
to complicate a previously simple shoreline and greatly to lengthen it.
It might appear that the many inlets, bays, and islands thus formed
would afford protection to shipping and greatly increase the commercial
utility of such a shoreline. To some extent they do so, especially for
small craft. Canals dredged through the lagoons, connecting one with

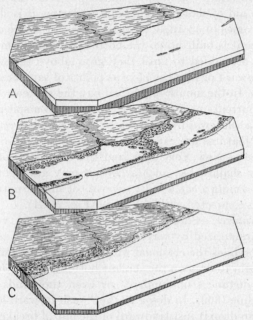

Fig. 220.—Diagrams illustrating stages in the development of an offshore bar on a
shore of low relief and shallow water. (*A*) The beginning of a submarine ridge by wave
deposition near the line of breakers; (*B*) the growth of an offshore bar flanked by lagoons;
(*C*) under wave pounding the bar migrates shoreward and the lagoons narrow, fill, or
disappear.

another, afford long protected routes for light coastwise traffic. It is
to be noted, however, that, owing to the nature of the shore, storms
are likely to produce very rough water outside the bar, and the approaches to the inlets are shallow, as are the lagoons and channels
behind them. Many ships are grounded and lost on shores of this
kind, and they are hardly less dangerous than rocky shores or marine
erosion.

The formation of an offshore bar is followed by its slow migration
landward and its eventual disappearance. Waves erode material from
the bottom in front of the bar, thus deepening the water there, permitting them to attack and cut the front of the bar itself. This material

is thrown up on the bar shore and is shaped into sand dunes or is wind-drifted back toward the lagoon, widening the bar at the rear as it is cut away in front. This process narrows the lagoon, and river sediment does its part also by aggrading that shallow body of water. After partial filling by sand and silt the lagoon acquires a fringing salt-water vegetation and, at low tide, may be only an expanse of featureless marshland. Eventually the shoreward migration of the bar carries it to the mainland, the lagoon disappears, and the bar becomes merely a beach upon a shore of simple outline (Fig. 220C). The time required for a transformation of the type described is long, but the shallow coastal waters of the world show numerous examples of offshore bars and lagoons in various stages of progress from youth to old age and extinction.

454. EXAMPLES OF LOW COASTS AND THEIR SHORELINE FEATURES. Among the numerous examples of low coasts with shallow water offshore the Gulf and South Atlantic Coasts of the United States are outstanding. Except where the Mississippi River Delta intervenes, they show generally the estuarine features resulting from submergence and numerous offshore bars which indicate shallow coastal waters. Padre and Matagorda Islands, on the Texas Coast, are offshore bars, and behind them are extensive lagoons and broad shallow estuarine bays. Indian River, on the east coast of Florida, is a long narrow lagoon. Be-

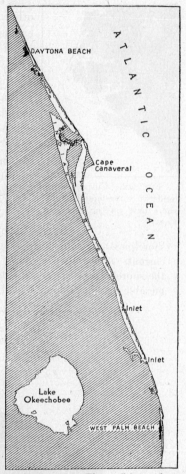

FIG. 221.—The offshore bars and lagoons of the eastern coast of Florida.

yond it lies an offshore bar which extends coastwise for more than 100 miles, interrupted only by narrow tidal inlets. This association of bar and lagoon broadens northward into the complicated, current-built, dune-covered projection of Cape Canaveral (Fig. 221). The Carolina shoreline shows similar features (Fig. 222). The long bars developed there are made up of segments that meet at sharp angles. These appear to result from the influence of various shore currents. They enclose not only lagoons but such broad bodies of water as Pamlico, Albemarle, and Carrituck Sounds, which are in part estuarine.

FIG. 222.—Cuspate fore-lands or wave-modified off-shore bars on the Carolina Coast.

The bars on the New Jersey shore, on the other hand, are nearly straight, and they enclose only narrow lagoons. Similar features are found on many other lowland coasts. The North Sea Coast from Netherlands to Denmark is fringed by the long chain of the Frisian Islands, which are separated from the mainland by narrow lagoons. The large lakes on the coast of eastern Germany are cut off from the Baltic by long curving bars that appear to be intermediate in nature and manner of formation between bay bars and offshore bars (Fig. 223).

455. SHORELINE FEATURES RESULTING FROM LAND DEPOSITS. Portions of certain shorelines are characterized not so much by the deposits of waves and currents as by those of rivers, glaciers, and the wind. Among these are the shorelines of the great deltas and delta fans of the world and of innumerable smaller ones. Usually these features present broadly convex

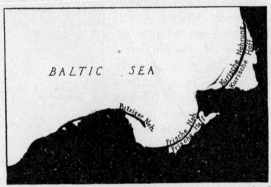

FIG. 223.—The Haffs or lagoons and their enclosing Nehrungs on the Baltic Coast of Germany.

fronts to the sea, and their simple outlines are sometimes interrupted by the fingerlike projections of distributary levees.

Glacial deposits likewise modify the details of shorelines in some localities. For example, the great embayment which includes New York harbor is estuarine, but the shoreline features of the Long Island Sound portion of it result from the submergence of the irregular deposits of a till plain, while the more regular south shore of Long Island is the submerged margin of a great glacial outwash plain. The projecting base of Cape Cod is a partially submerged marginal moraine, while the complicated shoreline of Boston Bay is a submerged till plain in which isolated drumlins create several of the adjacent islands. In Antarctica and parts of Greenland and Alaska portions of the shorelines are created by glacial ice itself.

Wind-blown sand is in many places an accompaniment of shoreline development, although it does not often modify the shore outline notably. As soon as beach sands begin to be thrown up by the waves they are readily dried and are then slowly moved by the wind and collect in the form of *dunes*. On low shores with abundant sand and onshore winds, the dunes may be closely spaced and of considerable size. In profile they are like those of the

FIG. 224.—A shore dune in North Carolina encroaching upon woodland. Its steep leeward slope is clearly shown. (*U. S. Geological Survey Photograph.*)

desert (442), and they move in similar manner. They may migrate some thousands of feet or even a very few miles; but generally they move inland, and in humid climates they tend to become stagnant and overgrown with vegetation before they have traveled far (Fig. 224). Considerable areas of dune sand are found along the shores of Cape Cod, parts of New Jersey, Virginia, and other sections of the east-facing coast of the United States. In general, these are not so large in area and do not move so far inland as the dunes of the low west-facing coasts of southwestern France, Belgium, Netherlands, and Denmark. There it has been necessary to go to great expense in attempting to plant vegetation upon drifting sand or in other ways to prevent dune encroachment upon highly valuable land or other property. In the United States there are other dune areas, as at various places on the shores of the Pacific Ocean and on the eastern shore of Lake Michigan.

456. CORAL-REEF SHORELINES. The shallow waters of many tropical coasts are characterized by reefs of limestone comprised of the crumbled skeletal structures of minute marine animals called corals. Under certain

conditions corals grow abundantly in shallow waters some distance from a shore, and their deposits form a *barrier reef* which is separated from the mainland by a broad lagoon. Of this nature is the great reef which for 1,000 miles parallels the northeast coast of Australia. Other coral reefs form about islands. Some small reef-encircled islands, perhaps volcanic, seem to have undergone slow submergence while the coral fringe about them has continued to grow. Such encircling reefs now appear at the surface as low, and more or less complete, coral rings, called *atolls*, which enclose circular lagoons (Fig. 225). Fringing reefs grow with such rapidity in some clear, shallow, warm waters as to push a shoreline seaward in spite of wave and current erosion.

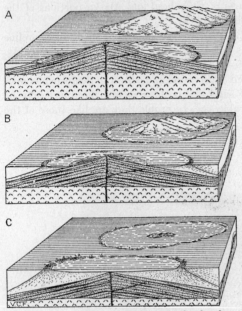

Fig. 225.—Diagrams to illustrate the development of atolls. (*A*) Fringing coral reefs about islands; (*B*) growing coral deposits keep pace with submerging islands; (*C*) atolls fringed with growing corals replace the mountainous islands.

The shoreline of parts of Cuba is an interesting illustration of the effects of coral growth combined with submergence. Old fringing reefs of hard coral upon a shore of softer limestones were elevated and stream eroded. The streams cut fairly wide valleys in the soft rocks back from the shore but only notches through the hard coral rim.[1]

A later partial submergence has drowned the river valleys, creating many commodious bays each having a narrow entrance. Cuba has many of these "bottle-neck" harbors (Fig. 226).

Shorelines and Ocean Tides

457. TIDES AFFECT THE FEATURES AND USES OF SHORELINES. The commercial utility of shorelines is much affected by the depth of their waters as well as by their outlines. The shallow waters and regular shorelines of emerged plains coasts do not favor commercial development, while the estuaries and bays of submerging coasts offer unusual facilities for that use. However, the appearance and use of shorelines

[1] Vaughan, T. W., and Spencer, A. C. The Geography of Cuba. *Bull. Amer. Geog. Soc.*, Vol. 34, p. 116, 1902.

of either class are somewhat modified by the occurrence of tides. By their periodic rise and fall, tides alternately deepen and shallow the shore waters, thereby causing difficulties in harbor construction and the movement of commerce. Tidal currents scour channels and keep open some that otherwise might quickly be choked with sediment, but they also create problems of navigation for those who use the channels.

458. THE NATURE OF TIDES. The tides are broad but very low bulges of the sea which result from the gravitional relation of the earth to the

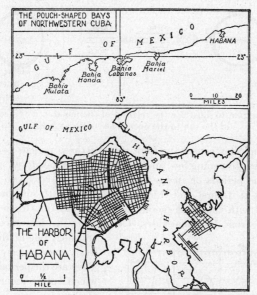

THE POUCH-SHAPED BAYS OF NORTHWESTERN CUBA

THE HARBOR OF HABANA

FIG. 226.—A series of pouch-shaped or "bottle-neck" bays in Cuba, and, below, details of outline for that one upon the shores of which the city of Habana is situated.

moon and the sun. Without the involved explanation of the cause of tides being attempted, the following facts regarding them may be accepted: If there were no continents, and if deep oceans covered the entire earth, the moon and the sun each would cause two tidal bulges. The two caused by the moon always would be exactly on opposite sides of the earth from each other (Fig. 227). Their positions would be unchanging with respect to a line extending from the moon through the center of the earth, but they would advance westward across the oceans, because the earth rotates eastward. A given place on the earth would thus, during the time of one daily rotation, pass through each of the two lunar tidal bulges and each of the intervening lows. It should, therefore, have two periods of high tide and two of low tide during each 24 hr. However, the moon advances in its 28-day orbit about the earth at a rate that would delay the tidal recurrence somewhat, and the true period between successive high tides would, therefore, be approximately 12 hr., 25 min., rather than 12 hr.

The two tides caused by the sun also would be on opposite sides of the earth from each other and would have a relation to the sun like that of the lunar tides to the moon, but they are less than one-half as high as those caused by the moon. At times of new moon and of full moon the earth, moon, and sun are nearly in line, the lunar tides and the solar tides occur in the same places, and the height of the solar tides is added to that of those caused

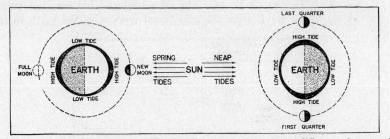

Fig. 227.—A diagram to illustrate the relation of the moon in its different phases and of the sun to the occurrence of ocean tides.

by the moon. This causes the high tides of those periods to be unusually high and the intervening low tides of the same periods to be unusually low. They are the periods of *spring tide*, which recur every two weeks. When the moon is at its first and third quarters the earth-sun line is nearly at right angles with the earth-moon line. The solar tides then fall between, and detract from, the lunar tides. That causes the difference between low and high tide at that time to be less pronounced than usual. They are the periods of *neap tide*, which also recur every two weeks.

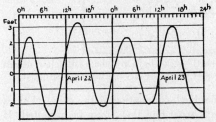

Fig. 228.—The intervals and amounts of tidal rise and fall at New York during a 48-hr. period in 1920. (*After H. A. Marmer.*)

459. The Occurrence of Tides. Although, under ideal conditions, equal high tides should succeed each other at intervals of 12 hr., 25 min., that is not the actual condition in many places. Owing to the trends and outlines of different coasts, the depth of coastal waters, the shapes and sizes of the several oceans, and other causes, there is a considerable variation in the height of successive tides at any given station and in the intervals between them. In general, the tides of the Atlantic Ocean conform most nearly to the ideal type. This may be illustrated by a curve showing the actual rise and fall of the tide at New York (Fig. 228). On some shores, notably parts of southern Asia and the Caribbean and Gulf shores of America, there is but one high tide per day.[1] The shores of the Pacific Ocean generally are characterized by what may be called mixed tides. In them each alternate high tide is much lower than the preceding one. This condition may be illustrated by a curve showing the actual tidal rise and fall at Honolulu (Fig. 229).

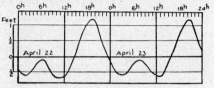

FIG. 229.—The intervals and amounts of rise and fall of a tide of mixed type at Honolulu. The period is the same as that in Fig. 228. (*After H. A. Marmer.*)

460. TIDAL RANGE. Not only do the tides of various places differ considerably as to time of their rise and fall, but they differ even more greatly as to amount of rise and fall. The average difference in water level between low and high tide at any place is called its *tidal range*. In the open ocean it is so slight as not to be noticeable. As the tidal bulges, or waves, approach coasts, however, they tend, like other waves, to increase in height. The amount of the increase is determined by a number of factors. The tides of nearly enclosed bodies of water, such as the Mediterranean and Baltic Seas, are so slight as to be negligible. In sheltered waters, such as the Gulf of Mexico and the Caribbean Sea, the range is small, usually less than 2 ft. Common tidal ranges on exposed coasts are between 5 and 10 ft., though in some places less and in others more. In a few localities, some of them the sites of important commercial ports, the tidal range is so great that it is a distinct handicap to the use of the shore. Some harbors, notably Liverpool, England, have required expensive improvements to offset the disadvantages of the continuous rise and fall of the water level while ships are loading and unloading cargo at the wharves. Places of great tidal range mainly are situated upon funnel-shaped bays or estuaries, where the tide wave tends to pile up as it moves landward. Cherbourg, France, has an average tidal range of 17 ft., and Liverpool has a range of 29 ft. The head of the Bay of Fundy, N. S., has 42 ft. and, at time of spring tide, sometimes as much as 50 ft. of extreme tidal range. Even in the rivers and harbors tributary to the Bay of Fundy ships are temporarily stranded at low tide only to be afloat again a few hours later when the tide sets landward.

[1] Bauer, H. A. A World Map of the Tides. *Geog. Rev.*, Vol. 23, pp. 259–270, 1933.

Chapter XIX. Plateaus

461. The Distinguishing Features of Plateaus. Plateaus may not always be distinguished easily from the other major physiographic subdivisions of the land. In general, they are characterized by broad uplands of considerable elevation above sea level. Some parts of plateau surfaces are likely to be traversed by deeply cut and relatively narrow stream valleys which give them, as a class, a high degree of relief. But the deep narrow valleys characteristically are so widely spaced that only a small part of the entire plateau surface is dissected into steep slopes. The ideal plateau is, therefore, high and deeply trenched by narrow valleys, and its interstream areas are broad and flat topped. It is the perfect example of the youthful stage in the cycle of erosion.

However, few plateaus are ideal in form. High and much dissected plateaus, on the one hand, grade into hill lands and mountains, while low and little dissected plateaus, on the other, grade into plains. The only features by which plateaus may conveniently be distinguished from plains are their relative degree of local relief and their abrupt termination. *Tabular uplands having a relief of more than 500 ft. may be arbitrarily defined as plateaus.* In addition, some plateaus are situated so that they terminate in escarpments which make them appear high from at least one side. Most of the great plateaus of the earth have an average elevation of at least 2,000 ft. above sea level. That, however, is not particularly distinctive, since some plains are higher. The High Plains of the United States reach an altitude of more than 5,000 ft. but usually are thought of as plains, because, except in their southern portion, they join the interior plain of the continent without the interruption of any high escarpment.

462. Plateaus Classed According to Their Physiographic Relationships. The great plateaus of the earth, shown in Plate VII, are of three major types, when classed according to their physiographic relationships: (*a*) intermontane plateaus, (*b*) piedmont plateaus, and (*c*) continental plateaus, or tablelands.

463. *Intermontane plateaus* are segments of the earth's crust uplifted in association with mountains and more or less nearly surrounded by them. The highest and some of the most extensive plateaus are intermontane in situation. The plateau of Tibet is an eastward-sloping highland much of the surface of which lies at elevations between 10,000 and 15,000 ft. above sea level. On the south of it rise the great heights of The Himalayas, and on the north are those of the Kunlun. Eastward and westward are mountain borders also, and surplus drainage escapes from the high-rimmed plateau only through deeply cut valleys and gorges which notch the mountain margins. The Altiplane, or high plateau of the Andes, lies between eastern and western ranges of the mountains, also at elevations between 10,000 and 15,000 ft. These are the highest of the great intermontane plateaus, but others of similar situation are found at lower elevations. Among them are the dry plateaus of Mongolia and the Tarim Basin, in Asia; the plateau of Mexico; and, in the United States, a large part of the Great Basin and the Columbia Plateau.

464. *Piedmont plateaus* lie between mountains and bordering plains or the seas. Of small piedmont plateaus there are many, but large ones are few. One illustration is found in the plateau of Patagonia. Andean streams have cut it into roughly parallel blocks somewhat like those of the High Plains of the United States. However, instead of grading into plains the Patagonian Plateau terminates near the Atlantic in an escarpment 300 to 600 ft. high. The Colorado Plateaus of the United States are, in a sense, piedmont also. They are bordered on the north and east by the high ranges of the Wasatch, Uinta, Rocky, and San Juan Mountains. On the west and south they stand above the adjacent basins in escarpments which are from a few hundreds to as much as 5,000 ft. in height.

465. *Continental plateaus*, or *tablelands*, rise with some abruptness from bordering lowlands or from the sea on most or all of their margins and, in general, do not have conspicuous mountain rims. Some tablelands are small and flat, being merely sections or detached portions of larger plateau surfaces. Others, however, are of great area and have highly complex surface features. Much of Africa, Arabia, and Spain, parts of Australia and peninsular India, and ice-covered Greenland and Antarctica are great tablelands. So much of Africa is tableland that it is sometimes called a continental plateau. The tableland is notably higher in the southern and eastern parts of the continent than in the central and northern sections. The surface of the southern plateau averages nearly 3,000 ft. in elevation above sea level, and in places it exceeds 5,000 ft. The Congo Basin and the Saharan tablelands average

only about 1,000 ft. in elevation, but, in several places at least, that general elevation is maintained to within short distances of the coast, and the coastal slope is comparatively steep.

Tablelands in general are areas of relatively recent crustal elevation, and such as have shorelines commonly show regular outlines. In proportion to its great area, Africa has a short shoreline because of its simplicity of outline. For the same reason, it is a coast poorly provided with natural harbors for commercial ports, except in a few places.

466. *The Continental Plateau of Africa.* The tableland character of Africa is clearly shown by the gradients of its major streams. Arising in interior uplands, each of the great African rivers, the Nile, Zambezi, Limpopo, Orange, Congo, and Niger, has a middle course of relatively gentle gradient after which it plunges over the plateau escarpment in falls or rapids which make it unnavigable. The fall of the Nile is distributed among its six famous cataracts which are separated from each other by distances of from 150 to 200 miles. The Congo, near its mouth, descends nearly 1,000 ft. from the plateau surface over a stretch of wild rapids. The Zambezi River leaves the plateau by means of Victoria Falls, which are half as wide and twice as high as Niagara. It then descends through a 40-mile gorge and over a series of rapids before it reaches the level of the coastal plain. Even the smaller Orange River has a 300-ft. waterfall in its lower course. The impossibility of reaching the interior of Africa by uninterrupted stream navigation is one of the reasons why that continent was the last to be penetrated by Europeans, although it was bordered on the north by the Mediterranean centers of civilization.

The full height of the African plateau is not in all places reached directly from its bordering plains but by a series of plateau steps. This is notably true in the Union of South Africa, where the first step up from the narrow coastal plain is the Little Karroo, a low plateau having an average elevation of about 1,800 ft. This is succeeded by the Great Karroo at about 2,500 ft. elevation; and that, in turn, by the High Veld at about 4,000 ft. Each step is rimmed by low mountains or hills. The approaches to the lower tablelands of northern Africa are much simpler and less impressive.

467. PLATEAU CLASSES RELATED TO ROCK STRUCTURES. Plateaus, like plains, are underlain by rocks of different origins and attitudes, and their conditions of structure are reflected in some of the relief features of the plateau surfaces. Among the major plateaus of the world one or more examples may be found of each of the following classes: (*a*) plateaus underlain principally by horizontal strata, (*b*) plateaus of basaltic lavas, and (*c*) plateaus whose surfaces are uplifted baselevel plains in ancient crystalline rocks (*cf.* Plates VI, VII).

The Colorado Plateaus illustrate the class first named. In this vast region, which is equal in area to the combined areas of Ohio,

Indiana, and Illinois, sedimentary strata which total several thousands of feet in thickness lie in nearly horizontal position upon a foundation of crystalline rocks (Fig. 230). In some places the sediments are faulted, slightly arched, or covered with recent volcanic products, but the principal surface features result from the erosion of nearly horizontal strata. The many segments that comprise the plateau region mainly are flattish, tablelike or steplike plateaus, though some are much dissected. Most of them have been developed on sedimentary strata by dry-land erosion, and they lie at various levels, separated by bold escarpments or by canyons. The surface of the immense plateau of

Fig. 230.—The Grand Canyon of the Colorado River. The narrow inner gorge, cut in crystalline rock, is in striking contrast with the intricately carved steps eroded in the sedimentary rocks above. Note the flatness of the distant plateau surface.

South Africa likewise is dominated by the widespread distribution of a persistent system of sedimentary rocks.

The Columbia Plateau in Washington, Oregon, and Idaho is an outstanding example of the lava plateau. Over an area as large as that of the combined states of New York, New Jersey, and Pennsylvania the surface is underlain by black basaltic lavas. They occur in nearly horizontal flows of variable thickness one upon another and bury an uneven surface of former erosion (336, Fig. 231). The structures of the northwestern part of the Deccan Plateau of India and part of the plateau of eastern Africa are of similar nature.

The plateau of Western Australia may be taken as an example of the third of the above classes. It is predominantly a crystalline peneplain uplifted. Similar structures are found in parts of the plateaus of eastern Brazil, where faulted crystalline rocks are covered only in part by later sediments, and also in parts of central Africa and peninsular India (*cf.* Plates VI, VII).

468. PLATEAU FEATURES RELATED TO CLIMATIC CONDITIONS. The greater elevation of plateaus makes them even more subject than plains to the development of surface features that reflect the conditions of climate under which their degradation was accomplished. In fact, it is safe to say that the primary classes of plateau landforms are those which depend upon climatic environment and that those growing out

FIG. 231.—An exposure of the Columbia Plateau basalts in a canyon wall, showing beds that result from successive lava flows. The base of the wall is flanked by talus slopes. (*U. S. Geological Survey Photograph.*)

of the rock structures are of secondary importance. It is for that reason that plateaus are divided, for the purpose of the following discussion of their features, in accordance with their climatic situations.

Plateau Features Developed in Dry Climates

469. MANY PLATEAUS ARE DRY. The greater number of the world's plateaus have arid or semiarid climates. There are several reasons for that condition. (*a*) It happens that some of the most notable of broad tectonic uplifts are situated near the margins of the tropics, and their areas fall within the range of trade-wind influence. (*b*) Intermontane plateaus, whatever their general climatic associations, are in the lee of mountain barriers on all sides. (*c*) Certain tablelands present their higher sides to the prevailing winds and decline gently to the leeward. This has the effect of increasing precipitation on the plateau front and of diminishing it on the plateau surface.

(*d*) Because plateaus are high the air above them contains less water vapor and is not likely to afford abundant rainfall. (*e*) Plateau uplifts in regions supplied with abundant precipitation do not long retain their plateau features. Unless they are geologically recent or are composed of highly resistant rocks they shortly are much dissected. Some present hill regions or mountain masses are, in fact, plateau uplifts which have been dissected by streams until their surfaces are no longer plateaulike.

470. DRY-PLATEAU VALLEYS. The valleys of arid plateaus generally have the features characteristic of erosional youth. Some streams have only shallow valleys, since they are held up to temporary baselevels by resistant strata or by lack of water. However, the exotic and other principal streams are likely to have intrenched themselves deeply into the plateaus and to flow in canyons. The same is true of some tributary streams, even of some that flow only intermittently. The development of canyons, large and small, is the normal result of several conditions. (*a*) Orographic precipitation in bordering mountains furnishes water for streams able to cross the dry-plateau surface and descend to the sea beyond. (*b*) The plateau surface is high above its baselevel. Thus the exotic streams are characterized by high gradients and are able to erode deeply. (*c*) Most high plateaus are comprised of solid rocks able to stand in steep slopes when dissected by stream erosion. (*d*) The slow rate of weathering and small amount of slope wash normal to dry climates tend to preserve the steepness of the valley walls. Notable plateau canyons of great length and depth are those of the Colorado and Snake Rivers in the United States, that of the middle course of the Zambezi in South Africa, and the Tibetan courses of the Brahmaputra and other streams that leave the great Asiatic plateau region. Of lesser canyons in most dry plateaus there are thousands, most of them without permanent streams.

The typical dry-plateau canyon is not a natural thoroughfare. Its narrow bottom offers little place for a roadway, and its stream, if any, seldom is navigable. Its course is likely to be steep, boulder strewn, and interrupted by rapids and falls. Moreover, it is subject to sudden and large changes in stream level. Its bottom is reached from the plateau upland only by a steep climb down a precipitous valley wall or by the difficult route of a tributary canyon. It is too deep and too steep to be crossed easily and yet too wide to bridge economically. The deep dry-plateau canyon is more effective as a barrier to communication than as a route of transportation, and the accessibility of the plateau upland is, therefore, in inverse proportion to the degree of its dissection.

471. THE GRAND CANYON of the Colorado River in Arizona is the most magnificent of its kind. It is the work of a silt-laden, mountain-fed stream of high gradient. The stream crosses high arid plateaus from which it receives but few permanent tributaries. In one part of its valley it has cut through more than 4,000 ft. of nearly horizontal sedimentary strata and more than 1,000 ft. into crystalline rocks beneath. The erosion of the latter has produced a narrow inner gorge, above which the walls rise in a series of giant steps which are etched by undercutting in the unequally resistant sediments. The exposed edges of the more resistant sedimentary strata form the sheer rises and some of the benches. Those of the less resistant strata form the intervening slopes (Fig. 230). The intricate forms of the walls, which hold most of the scenic grandeur, result from arid-land weathering and erosion on a large scale along both joint and bedding planes.

472. DRY-PLATEAU ESCARPMENTS. Among the conspicuous features of dry plateaus are cliffs and escarpments (Fig. 232). They

FIG. 232.—The angular face of a long plateau escarpment in New Mexico.

result primarily from stream erosion and faulting, the same processes that produce humid-land escarpments. They differ from the latter in the hard sharpness of their outlines. Slow weathering tends to preserve their sharp outlines, and occasional torrential rains cause the intermittent streams to flood and to erode laterally, undercutting and steepening the valley walls and cliffs. Even though the escarpments of dry plateaus are well preserved, it does not follow that they are regular in outline. Generally their faces are scarred by many dry ravines, their upland rims are etched into sharp promontories, and often these in turn are notched by gullies. Weathering attacks through joint planes and branches laterally from them into other joint planes, thus working behind and detaching portions of the rock mass. This gives to many escarpments fringed or crenate outlines of great intricacy of detail which are very little obscured by regolith or vegetation. In some kinds of rock the weathered features stand as colonnades or pyramids of complicated form (Fig. 233). Piles of *talus* (earth and rocks dislodged from above by the processes of weathering, which the forces of erosion are unable to remove as fast as they accumulate) lie in abundance against the bases of dry-land escarpments except in places so situated that they are swept at rather frequent intervals by the lateral erosion of intermittent streams (Figs. 231, 234).

Not only do many dry-plateau cliffs have an angular and minute detail of form, but also they have a variety and brilliance of color unknown in humid regions. Dry air and frequent wind abrasion do not favor the abundant growth of the lichens and other small plants which cover the rock cliffs of humid regions with a monotony of grayish

FIG. 233.—Fantastic details resulting from the differential weathering and erosion of a dry-land escarpment in Bryce Canyon, Utah. The steep sides and flat top of the mesa in the middle distance are well shown. (*National Park Service, U. S. Department of the Interior.*)

green. The rocks of dry-land cliffs, therefore, exhibit the full value of their colors, which range from the pure white of gypsum beds through the grays, buffs, and reds of various sedimentary rocks to the dull greens, browns, and black of igneous formations. These strong colors often are set against a foreground of desert floor painted in the soft yellowish gray of alkali soils or the glossy browns of desert varnish.

473. DRY-PLATEAU UPLANDS. The interstream areas of dry plateaus characteristically are flat or rolling uplands. Some are of vast extent and are not sharply distinguished from plains. Others, like the Colorado Plateaus, are separated by escarpments into several

upland levels at different elevations. Some bear upon their surfaces irregularities caused by volcanic activity or faulting. Such features are lava flows, volcanic cones, or short and broken ranges of hills and mountains uplifted along fault lines. The latter find examples in the short Basin Ranges which characterize the Great Basin section of the intermontane plateaus of western United States (330).

In American dry lands, a plateau upland of small to moderate size and tabular form (flat top and steep sides) is called a *mesa* (Figs. 233, 234). Usually mesas are portions of larger plateaus from which they have been detached by the formation and widening of arroyos, or canyons. In fact the normal progress of erosional development in dry plateaus, through canyon formation and lateral cutting, tends to separate and ultimately to isolate such features. As the valleys

Fig. 234.—A sandstone mesa (left) and a low butte (right) that have been separated by dry-land erosion from the larger upland or mesa in the background. Note the talus slopes. (*U. S. Geological Survey Photograph.*)

are widened the marginal plateau blocks are reduced in area through erosional attack on all sides, but they retain their flat tops. Features of the same origin but of smaller size often are called *buttes* (Fig. 234). In some dry plateaus of poorly consolidated sediments erosion has almost completely destroyed the flat upland. Only small mesas, buttes, and pinnacled divides remain separated by fantastically carved arroyos. Surfaces of that kind merge without distinction into low mountains, on the one hand, or, on the other, into hill country of the badland type (483).

474. PLATEAU BOLSON LANDS. Some dry plateaus, like some dry plains, are comprised of *bolsons* or regions of interior drainage (438). Because the streams of plateau bolsons drain toward their lowest interior points and not into the oceans, each bolson has its own local baselevel of erosion and cannot be deeply dissected. Thus their surfaces have many of the same general features as those of basins

in dry plains, from which they may be distinguished mainly by their greater actual elevations above sea level and by the fact that some of them are intermontane in situation. In them are to be found the same rocky pediments, the same alluvial fans, the same desert pavements, and similar collections of drifting sand. At their lowest points, likewise, are features that give evidence of collecting drainage. Some of them contain notable salt lakes. Such are Sevier Lake and Great Salt Lake, Utah; Mono Lake, California; Tengri Nor, Koko Nor, and others, in the plateaus of Central Asia; the lakes of Persia; and Lake Poopó, Bolivia. Not all lakes of dry-plateau basins are salt. Some of those at higher elevations overflow into lower basins and are kept fresh thereby. That is true of Lake Titicaca, Bolivia, which overflows into Lake Poopó, and of Utah Lake, which overflows into Great Salt Lake. Many plateau basins have not enough water to maintain permanent lakes but contain salt marshes. Examples are seen in the "pans" of South Africa, the Tsaidam Swamp of Central Asia, the Salar de Uyuni of Bolivia, and the Humboldt Salt Marsh of Nevada.

Plateau Features Developed in Humid Climates

475. GENERAL FEATURES. Plateaus that are situated in regions of humid climate tend to be more minutely dissected by stream erosion than are those in regions of dry climate. Some, indeed, are so dissected that they have lost most of their plateau characteristics. The degree of dissection differs, however, not only with the amount and distribution of precipitation but also with the altitude of the plateau, the gradient of its streams, and the kind and structure of its rocks. The Eastern Highland of Australia, the eastern front of the Brazilian Plateau, and the western front of the Deccan Plateau of India receive heavy rainfalls, are near the sea, and have gradients so steep that they have been dissected into hill regions, locally called mountains. In Brazil and India the precipitation on the broad plateau uplands, though fairly abundant, is less than on the fronts. The drainage from them takes longer routes to sea level and erodes less deeply. Also, in some cases at least, dissection is further retarded by the establishment of temporary baselevels upon the surfaces of resistant rock formations, as, for example, in the rainy Congo Basin of Africa. Although the dissection of that plateau is in progress the basin still is in the youthful stage of erosion, and its surface is relatively flat.

476. THE MINOR FEATURES OF HUMID-LAND PLATEAUS differ from those of arid plateaus largely because of vigorous downward stream erosion and the greater rapidity of the weathering processes. Some of the stream valleys

are canyonlike, but generally they have walls that are less steep and less continuous than are those of the dry plateaus, since they are more frequently notched by the valleys of the more abundant tributary streams. Broad divides with rounded and irregular upland surfaces are common. In plateaus of slight dissection the upland features do not differ greatly from those of plains under similar climatic conditions. In those of deep dissection the uplands take on tabular form but usually with more rounded features than those of arid lands. This is particularly true in areas of igneous and metamorphic rocks. Resistant sedimentary formations sometimes retain angular escarpments, but usually the rapidity of weathering is sufficient to mantle their lower slopes with piles of talus. In the humid plateaus of the tropics remarkably deep accumulations of regolith blanket both upland levels and lower slopes, and cliffs of bare rock are exposed mainly on upper slopes, where they have been bared by soil creep. Indeed, it is probable that the rounded forms common to uplands in the humid tropics are due more to the slow creep and flow of the deeply weathered regolith than to its removal by surface erosion. Plateau landforms of the dissected type here indicated are illustrated by the broad uplands and deep gorges of limited areas in the Allegheny-Cumberland highland, the highlands of southwestern China, and the Ardennes highland of western Europe. Parts of these uplands are so greatly dissected that they approach hill regions in appearance and merge with them in features. Similar features are common also in the plateaus of eastern Brazil, Central America, and equatorial Africa.

The Great Ice Plateaus

477. SURFACE FEATURES.   Vast sheets of ice cover most of Greenland and the Antarctic continent. Presumably they are so nearly like the great ice sheets which once covered large parts of North America and Europe that they may be considered examples for the study of the conformation and behavior of the former continental glaciers (359). Both of the existing glaciers may be regarded as great desert plateaus. The Greenland plateau is to a degree intermontane, since its ice is largely held within fringing mountain walls. That of Antarctica for the most part rises sheer for several scores of feet and then slopes rapidly up to a flattish interior which has an average elevation of about 7,000 ft. and a maximum of more than 9,000 ft. in the region of the south geographical pole. Its vast expanse includes an area about one and two-thirds times the size of the United States, almost entirely ice covered.

The surfaces of the great ice plateaus are notably different in features from those of other plateaus. In general they are flat. On their surfaces are parallel ridges a few feet in height, called *zastrugi*, which result principally from the work of the wind and drifting snow. But, owing to the cold, there are no streams, and consequently there are no features comparable with the mesas and canyons of the arid plateaus or with the rounded blocks of those in humid climates. If features of such great size could be formed, the slow movement of the plastic ice would presently close the valleys, engulf the eminences, and reduce the surface to its present monotony of uniformity.

478. MARGINAL FEATURES. Only upon their margins do the great ice plateaus exhibit any variety in surface features. In this respect the plateaus

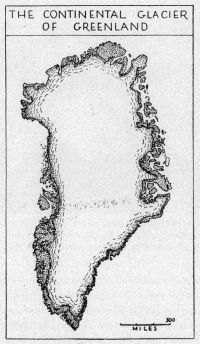

THE CONTINENTAL GLACIER OF GREENLAND

FIG. 235.

of Antarctica and Greenland differ considerably. The ice surface of Antarctica descends from the high interior, and the marginal ice thins and is traversed by deep cracks. Except in a few localities, where it is held back by fringing mountains, the ice everywhere overruns the land margin so that the exact position of the shoreline of the continent is not known. The ice edge, whether it is at the land margin or well out into the adjacent sea, is marked by sheer cliffs. From these walls great icebergs are split off by the buoyant effect of the sea water. Some of them are of large area, tabular in form, and almost mesalike in their relation to the parent mass. The icebergs, large and small, disintegrate by melting and disperse as masses of floe or drift ice which fringe the continent for many miles and combine with the ice wall to make it relatively unapproachable.

The highland or mountainous rim of Greenland, and the higher summer temperatures prevailing there, produce somewhat different features upon the margin of that ice plateau. Not everywhere does it descend to the sea (Fig. 235). Since it is held back by the highlands, much of its southern and western front wastes by melting some distance inland. Where it does discharge into the sea it does so by means of tongues of ice, some narrow, some wide, which protrude through gaps in the bordering highland. Between parts of the ice tongues and surrounded by them are islands of rock, called

Fig. 236.—Tongues from the Greenland ice plateau protrude coastward through the fringing mountains and create nunataks by the isolation of peaks. (*Photograph by Rasmussen. Courtesy of the Geographical Review, published by the American Geographical Society of New York.*)

nunataks, which are the peaks of ice-enveloped hills or mountains. These become more numerous near the plateau margin where the hills are higher and the ice thinner (Fig. 236). There are nunataks in Antarctica also, but they are considerably less numerous. From the tongues of Greenland ice which discharge directly into the sea are derived irregular icebergs which, although they are not so large as some seen in Antarctica, are of ample size to create a hazard to navigation when they drift southward into the foggy North Atlantic steamship lanes in the spring (Fig. 263).

Chapter XX. Hill Lands

479. HILL LANDS DISTINGUISHED. The word hill has the misfortune to be applied in common use to elevations as greatly different as mounds and mountains. However, it is desirable that hills be set apart for consideration because there are some ways in which both their appearance as elements of landscape and their degrees of human utility differ from those of plains, plateaus, and mountains.

Hill lands are different from plains, even rough plains, in that they have, by definition, considerably greater relief. They differ from plateaus in that they are more minutely dissected and have smaller upland areas. They resemble mountain regions in that they include land of which a large part is in steep slopes. Some very rough hills are mountainlike in comparison with adjacent plains and locally are called mountains. However, in most hill regions the features are less massive than those of mountains, their parts are less complicated, and their detailed features are of a smaller order of size. Although the lines of distinction must be drawn arbitrarily, it will be useful to think of hill lands as being those parts of the earth's surface which, (*a*) are so dissected that much of the land is in considerable degrees of slope, (*b*) have uplands of small summit area, and (*c*) have local relief of more than 500 but less than about 2,000 ft.

The principal world regions of hills, shown in Plate VII, differ considerably, both between regions and between parts of the same region. They differ in their relations to other classes of physical features, in their climatic situations, in their geologic structures, and in their details of relief. It will be observed from Plate VII that some of them border plateaus, of which they are the dissected margins. Others fringe mountain masses; and still others stand alone in the midst of plains. Few, if any, hill regions derive their features directly from faulting, folding, or volcanic activity. Instead, they acquire them as a result of climatically controlled weathering and erosion in highlands of various origins and structures. Consequently, there are some hill

415

regions that have developed under similar climates but in different kinds of rock; others that have developed in similar rock structures but under great differences of climate. Given similar conditions of structure and climate, there arise also differences in relief features which are due to local inequalities in the stage of maturity to which the erosional cycle has progressed. There are, for example, hill regions that have evolved through the submature dissection of plateaus. These may retain considerable parts of the old plateau surface in the form of broadly rounded hills which are separated by narrow and steep-sided valleys. However, hill lands of ideally mature dissection are reduced almost entirely to a succession of hills, narrow ridges, and V-shaped valleys in which level land may occupy less than 5 per cent of the total area. Some hill regions have been so long subjected to erosion that they are past the extreme irregularity of maturity. Such a region may retain only remnants of its former highland in the form of subdued hills of small summit area, among which open rolling valleys and basins are interspersed.

It is obvious that the advantages of hill lands for human settlement and use are intermediate between those of plains and mountains. Maturely dissected hills, having many steep slopes, are badly adapted to tillage. Although those in early maturity of erosion may include some fairly level, plateaulike uplands, these are likely to be separated from each other and from outside regions by steep-sided valleys. Hill regions in a more advanced erosional stage, however, have broadly open valleys and reduced slopes and offer greater advantages for agriculture. Resources of other types are not lacking in hill regions. Because their slopes are in part steep and untillable, some have retained their forests, and they give rise to streams having steep gradients capable of development for water-power production. Rough lands, forests, and swift streams tend also to give them scenic attractiveness and to encourage their development as resort centers. Some also, by the nature of their geologic origin, contain mineral resources of value and have attracted mining industries and settlements.

In the following paragraphs a few of the more common kinds of hill lands may be considered with respect to some of their characteristic features and patterns of arrangement.

Stream-eroded Hill Regions

480. HILLS IN REGIONS OF HORIZONTAL STRATA. Some of the roughest hill lands of the world have resulted from mature stream dissection of nearly horizontal sedimentary strata of unequal resistance. In regions of arid climate elevated highlands of that type would

remain long undissected, maintain a youthful stage of erosion, and have plateau features. In humid regions, the progress of the erosional cycle being more rapid, mature dissection by streams and their numerous perennial tributaries destroys the upland surface and reduces

Fig. 237.—An aerial view of the Allegheny hill region of West Virginia shows it to be a stream-dissected upland with a dendritic valley pattern. (cf. Fig. 131B.) (*Photograph by John L. Rich. Courtesy of the Geographical Review, published by the American Geographical Society of New York.*)

the whole to a maze of hills and valleys. An understanding of the features of such regions and their patterns of arrangement can be reached most readily by studying the development of the dendritic drainage pattern (352). The valleys control the pattern of relief, and the hills are but the remnants of the former upland. An excellent illustration of this class of hill land is found in that part of the Appalachians called the Allegheny-Cumberland hill region, which extends from northern Pennsylvania to northeastern Alabama. Its features are so distinctive that some of their details may be considered (Fig. 237).

481. *The Allegheny-Cumberland hill region,* under humid climate, is deeply and maturely dissected and has local relief which, in general, is between 500 and 2,000 ft. In some localities it exceeds 2,000 or even 3,000 ft. of relief and there assumes the characteristics of low mountains. By the inhabitants most of the region is called mountains; by geologists it is referred to as a plateau, because it was once an undissected upland of which limited portions still are flattish; but geographically it is a hill region.

The stream pattern of a large part of the Allegheny-Cumberland hill region is dendritic (Fig. 238). The major streams, having larger volumes, have been able more nearly to grade their courses. They have broadened their valleys and developed narrow floodplains. The secondary streams occupy V-shaped valleys which, however, may be followed by roads and railroads and form the least difficult routes of penetration into the interior of the region. The minor tributary valleys are of great number. They push into the flanks of every section of the upland and by dissection have reduced most of the divides to ridges or to series of isolated hills which are separated by notches or saddles (Fig. 131*B*). The arrangement of the hills appears patternless, but close observation shows that they follow the trend of the divides of which they are the dissected remnants.

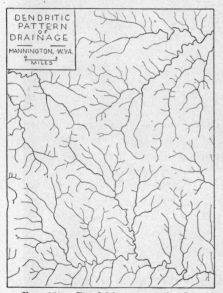

Fig. 238.—Dendritic pattern is characteristic of stream development in the maturely dissected Allegheny-Cumberland hill region. (*cf.* Fig. 237.)

The larger hills of any given locality in this region have nearly uniform height—the height of the former upland. The smaller hills are lower, because they have been reduced by the close approach of adjacent valleys. Many of them are so separated by erosion that they have the appearance of cones or pyramids. Their general angles of slope are not steep, except where they are sharply undercut by a major valley. Along some of the principal streams the notched and serrate valley walls rise steeply 1,000 to 1,500 ft. Owing to the alternation of resistant and nonresistant sedimentary rocks some of the hillsides consist of sheer rises of a few feet separated by benches or gentle slopes. However, because of the more rapid progress of weathering under humid climate, the benches and rises are much less pronounced in appearance and less sharp in outline than those of arid lands.

Although a large part of the Allegheny-Cumberland hill region has reached the stage of mature dissection, some parts of it have passed maturity, and others have not yet reached that stage. On its western margin, especially near the Ohio River, where the original elevation was not great, the streams have more quickly reached grade. In consequence, the valleys are wider and more open, the hills are lower, their slopes less steep, and their tops more broadly rounded than in the heart of the region. On parts of the higher eastern margin of the region, for example, in West Virginia near the bold east-facing escarpment known as the Allegheny Front, erosion has hardly progressed beyond the youthful stage. There the surface is nearly plateaulike (476). A broad upland is carved by minor streams into low but rugged hills separated by rolling plains. Through it a major stream, the New River, has cut a gorge more than 1,000 ft. deep.

In the more subdued relief of the western part of this region, especially near the Ohio River, good roads and well-developed farms occupy the spacious valleys while the rounded hills are pastured and only the steeper slopes remain in woodland. In the maturely dissected districts crop land is limited in extent, since both bottomlands and flat uplands are nearly lacking. Most of the slopes are wooded, but some of surprising steepness are cultivated. Roads, railroads, and settlements are in the narrow valleys. Many of the settlements, largely coal-mining camps, are strung along the valleys in linear pattern (Fig. 332). In some of the localities of submature dissection, roads, farms, and villages are found on the uplands, although the gorgelike valleys serve as the principal avenues of through railway transportation.

482. OTHER HILL REGIONS OF HORIZONTAL STRATA. The Allegheny-Cumberland hill region is undoubtedly the largest region in the world of the class of landform above described, but there are many others of some size and importance. Among them are the Ozark hill lands and the Boston "Mountains" of Missouri and Arkansas, the hills bordering the Drakensberg Mountains in southeastern Africa, some of the hill districts of peninsular India, and parts of southern Germany.

483. BADLANDS. It has been noted previously that mature dissection of plains of poorly consolidated sediments produces very rough surfaces (385). Some of that nature have a high degree of local relief and, under subhumid climate, have been eroded into astonishingly complicated hill forms and patterns. These are not essentially different in stage of development from the Allegheny region but differ considerably from it in steepness and in fineness of erosional detail and in having lower relief. It was the bewildering maze of sharp hills and

dry ravines that led the French fur traders to call those of the High
Plains, near the Black Hills, *mauvaises terres pour traverser*. They are
eroded in thick beds of clay and in large part are but deeply and
minutely dissected plains (Fig. 239). Still other badlands are found in
certain easily eroded rock formations in the dry southwestern plateaus
and mountain borders. However, extremely rapid dissection in almost
any uniform material will produce similar features. Badland forms
eroded in crystalline metamorphic rock of uniform texture are known
in the treeless highlands of dry northern China.

Fig. 239.—The features of badlands in western North Dakota. (*U. S. Geological Survey
Photograph.*)

484. Hills in Regions of Folded Sedimentary Strata. Certain hill regions are characterized by ridges and valleys of linear and
roughly parallel patterns of arrangement. These contrast sharply with
hills having the dendritic valley pattern discussed above. The linear
pattern results from the erosion of elongated folds or crustal wrinkles
made by lateral compression in sedimentary rocks of unequal resistance
to erosion. Among the notable areas of that kind of surface configuration are the Appalachian ridge-and-valley region which extends from
northeastern Pennsylvania southward to Alabama, the Ouachita
Mountains of Arkansas, and the Jura Mountains on the French-Swiss
border.

485. *The Jura Mountains* illustrate the parallel arrangement of hills
in their least complicated form of development. In them ridges, most of
which are not more than 500 to 2,000 ft. in height above the adjacent

Fig. 240.—A view across the parallel ridges and valleys of one section of the folded Appalachians. Water gaps cut two of the ridges at the extreme right. In many parts of the ridge-and-valley region the valleys are much wider than those shown here and contain large areas of farm land (see Fig. 242). (*Photograph by Fairchild Aerial Surveys, Inc.*)

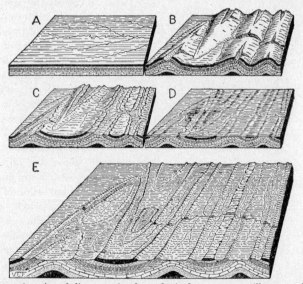

Fig. 241.—A series of diagrams in chronological sequence to illustrate the development of linear ridges, parallel valleys, and enclosed valleys. (*A*) horizontal strata; (*B*) anticlinal and synclinal folding, with pitching anticlines; (*C*) erosional mountains cut in the folded structures; (*D*) the region baseleveled; (*E*) the peneplain slightly elevated and re-eroded. Linear ridges, broad valleys, enclosed or canoe-shaped valleys, and water gaps are shown. They are of the types seen in the folded Appalachians.

valleys, trend for many miles in a northeast-southwest direction, roughly parallel with one another. They are high cuestaform ridges, the eroded bases of resistant members of anticlinal and synclinal folds. The intervening valleys, eroded in the less resistant sediments, are fairly broad. Although they are not excellent land, they contain most of the farms, roads, and villages of the region. Access from one valley to another is through notchlike gorges, locally called cluses, which have been cut across the linear hills by the major streams as they eroded downward in developing the present relief.

486. *The Appalachian ridge-and-valley region* is the most notable example in the world of parallel ridges and valleys (Fig. 240). It differs from the Jura region in that it is in a second cycle of erosion. During its first cycle rugged mountains, the product of intense folding and faulting, were reduced to a peneplain. The region has since been somewhat reelevated, the streams have cut into the plain along the courses in which they previously flowed, and their tributaries have adjusted themselves to the structural conditions by etching out new valleys in the less resistant strata. There are several important results of the progress of this second cycle of erosion. (*a*) Broad, rough-floored valleys have been carved in the less resistant rocks, mainly limestones and shales. (*b*) The upturned edges of the resistant members of the folds, usually sandstones and conglomerates, are left standing in relief in the form of long, even-crested ridges the summits of which represent the surface level of the old peneplain (Fig. 241). The major ridges range in height from 500 to 1,500 ft. above the adjacent valleys. They seldom are more than 3 miles wide, but some of them extend almost unbroken, and of remarkably uniform height, to lengths of 25 to 100 miles or more. (*c*) Narrow notches, called *water gaps*, have been cut through the ridges where the major streams run across their trend. Other

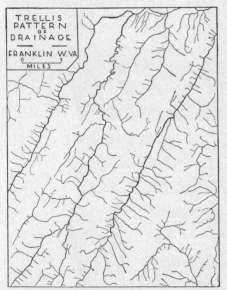

FIG. 242.—The type of drainage pattern developed in association with relief features and rock structures like those shown in Fig. 240.

notches, begun by streams that changed their courses and abandoned the notch, are called wind gaps. These gaps are the gateways between adjacent valleys. (*d*) The streams in accomplishing this erosion have adjusted their courses to the trend of the rock structure with the result that a somewhat rectangular pattern of drainage, called *trellis drainage*, has evolved (Fig. 242).

Some of the valleys of this region are noted for their great continuity, and a few for their agricultural productivity. The most famed is the "Great Valley," which, under several local names, extends from New York to Alabama. The ridges, because of their steep slopes and thin infertile soils, remain principally in woodlands. A general view "across the grain" of the region includes wooded ridge beyond wooded ridge, with intervening valleys

FIG. 243.—Looking from the air along the crest of a ridge in the folded Appalachians. The river cuts the ridge at right angles and has made a water gap. The fields of the cultivated valleys are snow covered while the wooded ridge shows dark. (*Photograph by Fairchild Aerial Surveys, Inc.*)

upon whose undulating to rolling bottoms are the fields and patchy woodlands of farms, together with highways and villages (Fig. 243).

Enclosed Valleys. Not all the ridges of the Appalachian ridge-and-valley region are parallel. The anticlines and synclines of which they are the eroded stumps sometimes terminate abruptly, pitch gently beneath the valley level, or merge with one another. Such structures are the causes of great variation in the shapes, sizes, and continuity of the valleys and, consequently, in the patterns of settlement and the routes of transportation that follow them. Figure 241 shows two enclosed, canoe-shaped valleys which result from the erosion of anticlinal structures. Such a valley may be underlain by limestone and contain productive agricultural land, but it is isolated, since the narrow water gap of the stream that eroded it is the only low-level gateway to it.

487. HILLS IN REGIONS OF COMPLICATED ROCK STRUCTURES. Among the hill regions of the earth it is probable that the greater number are comprised of intermingled rocks of many different origins and highly complicated structures. Some of the regions are, in fact, the eroded remnants of ancient mountain highlands the rocks of which have been repeatedly faulted, folded, and subjected to igneous intrusion. Not only are the rock structures that are concerned with the formation of hills of this class of great variety, but also the features differ as a result of development under unlike conditions of climate. In most hill regions of complicated structure, differential weathering and erosion in unlike rocks are the cause of the principal features of relief. In some it is the structural features, such as extensive faults, which dominate the scene. In hill regions situated in the rainy low latitudes climatic conditions tend to unify surface features by minimizing the effects of rock character and structure, just as arid environment tends to emphasize those factors.

The unifying effects of rainy tropical climate are brought about mainly as a result of active weathering. Chemical decomposition of rock is so rapid that features which, in colder or more arid climates, would erode into angular summits here weather into rounded uplands. Owing also to active weathering and the leaching influence of ground water, the typical soils of the humid tropics are highly porous (618). Much of the abundant rainfall soaks into the ground, and the rain-soaked regolith tends to creep or slide. This process sometimes bares the rock upon the steepest upper slopes, but at the same time it tends to soften the transition from upland to lowland with deep accumulations of weathered material. This is notably true of hills eroded in massive granite rocks. In them the rounded form of the uplands is to be seen even in middle latitudes, as, for example, in the hills and low mountains of the southern crystalline Appalachians (Fig. 244).

Elsewhere, to a greater degree than in the rainy tropics, hill features and hill patterns are influenced by complicated rock structures. Basaltic lava flows may protect weaker rocks beneath and erode into tabular, mesalike hills, even in humid climates. Alternating masses of resistant and nonresistant crystalline rocks give rise to areas of interspersed hills and basins. Extensive fault scarps themselves produce ridges which are dissected by streams into hills, or their fault zones develop linear areas of weakness which streams find and degrade into valleys.

Because of the extreme variety of physical conditions involved in the making of their features, hill regions of complicated rock structure are highly individual and may not readily be grouped into classes according to type. However, attention may be directed to certain hill regions the features of which will serve to illustrate some kinds of hill relief which are distinctive but which are of much more complex origins than the kinds previously described.

488. *The Youthful Plateau-hill Region of Eastern Australia.* The highland of eastern Australia is a dissected plateau. Its composition of ancient granites, old sediments, and younger volcanic rocks gives it great local diversity. In one respect it has some degree of unity. From uplands of 2,000 ft. or more elevation many streams, fed by abundant rainfall, descend

FIG. 244.—Rounded forms resulting from weathering and erosion in massive granites. A valley in the crystalline Appalachians of North Carolina. (*U. S. Geological Survey Photograph.*)

steeply coastward through deep gorges. Their tributaries have carved the seaward margin of the highland into a hill region of steep slopes and rounded uplands. About the stream headwaters considerable blocks of undissected upland persist, but nearer the coast the hills are more subdued, and the valleys broaden into basins in the rolling surfaces of which there are remnants of the former uplands, still round-topped and steep-sided but reduced to narrow spurs or isolated hills.

489. *The Crystalline Appalachian Highland of the South*, popularly known as the Blue Ridge Mountains, is comprised of igneous and metamorphic rocks of great age and structural complexity. Formerly it was a peneplain, a remnant of ancient mountains. Following reelevation, it has again been much eroded. In part of its broader and higher portion the region has a local relief of more than 2,000 ft., and its surface has the characteristics of low mountains. Most of its area, however, is a hill region of great irregularity, its various rocks having been weathered and eroded in different ways. Especially toward the western margin of the region, some rocks of great resistance

stand out as ranges of mountains and have steep bare slopes. A much larger part is eroded into hills of rounded summits and subdued relief, the flowing contours of which are well mantled with regolith and clothed with timber (Fig. 245).

490. *The California Hill Region of Linear Faulting.* The California Coast Ranges, especially those south of San Francisco, are comprised of sediments of several kinds and degrees of resistance, together with some igneous and metamorphic rocks. They have been severely folded and are arranged in a parallel ridge-and-valley pattern in some ways like that of the Appalachian ridge-and-valley region. However, the California hills have been subject to much more recent faulting and less folding than the Appalachians, and many faults, more or less parallel, traverse the region. Some of the faults are very long, one of them more than 500 miles, and they bear

FIG. 245.—*The subdued relief and eroded basins of the crystalline Appalachians in western North Carolina. (Photograph by Cline.)*

a close relation to the positions and arrangement of the linear valleys. The intervening ridges are developed on the more resistant sedimentary rocks.

491. SUBDUED VOLCANIC-HILL REGIONS. In many parts of the world specific hill regions owe their elevation wholly or in part to the superior resistance of some form of intrusive or extrusive igneous rock. In the rainy tropical climate of the Guiana Highlands, where rounded uplands are usual, there are mesalike hills of sedimentary rocks protected by capping layers of igneous rocks, the result of former lava flows.[1] In the High Plains of the United States, the Black Hills are carved from a dome-shaped uplift caused by a batholithic intrusion. The igneous rock is exposed in the central area of the hills, which have a local relief of about 2,000 ft. The Palisades of the Hudson River and the Watchung Ridges, near New York City, owe their existence to the differential erosion of ancient basaltic intrusions.

[1] Liddle, R. A. "A Geology of Venezuela and Trinidad." p. 7, J. P. MacGowan, Fort Worth, 1928.

In the Central Highland of France and the Eifel of western Germany are hill regions of a type found in modified form in other parts of the world also. Upon a platform of older rocks are the remains of lava flows and volcanic cones. Erosion has long since modified these surfaces but has not entirely removed the volcanic features. Subdued volcanic cones remain, and also domelike hills which are the weathered stumps of the lava cores or plugs that led to the former volcanic outlets (Fig. 246).

492. THE GREAT HILL REGION OF EASTERN ASIA. Of all the hill regions of the world, that of eastern Asia is most extensive and least well known. It includes not only the large mainland areas in Siberia, Manchuria, and Central and South China, but also most of Chosen and Japan. Within its scope are rocks and structures of such diversity that it includes hill regions of many kinds of features and patterns of arrangement. In the large area of South China are strata of various ages, much faulted, in places folded, and interspersed with ancient, metamorphic crystalline rocks. The large human population of that region is distributed through the limited valley and basin areas among the hills.

FIG. 246.—Domelike hills in central France that are the remnants of ancient volcanic cones. (*After a photograph by Tempest Anderson.*)

Ice-scoured Hill Regions

493. THE CHARACTERISTICS OF ICE-SCOURED HILLS. In a previous consideration of ice-scoured plains (Chap. XVI) the features resulting from ice erosion were described. Within the areas of continental glaciation there were hill regions also in which the original features, caused by an earlier stream erosion, were of a greater order of magnitude than those of the plains. High as they were, however, these hills did not greatly exceed the thickness of the continental ice sheets. Except for occasional rock masses, which may have projected in the form of nunataks through the glaciers, they were engulfed and overridden. The effect of ice scour upon the hill features is pronounced, whether the original features were stream-eroded portions of ancient crystalline highlands or of maturely dissected sedimentary uplands. The intricate patterns caused by gullying were erased, and there were substituted rounded features generally devoid of pinnacled promontories or sharp contours (Fig. 247). Mantles of regolith were swept away, and their place taken by thin stony soils or bare rock. Some of the ice-shaped hills show the steepened lee slopes of *roches moutonnées* on a scale that produces landscapes of scenic grandeur in spite of relatively small

actual relief. Associated with the scoured and rounded hills are broad open valleys, usually thin-soiled and boulder strewn. Agricultural land is scant and poor, save in areas of more than usual morainic accumulation. Some ice-scoured hills have no agricultural use but are given over wholly to timber. In others, meadows and pastures occupy the greater part of the area, and the slopes and uplands bear only poor timber or shrubby heath.

The drainage of ice-scoured hills, like that of ice-scoured plains, shows abundant evidence of glacial disturbance. Waterfalls and

Fig. 247.—The flowing contours of an ice-scoured hill region in Vermont. The hill features are subdued, and the valleys are drift mantled. (*Photograph by Underwood and Underwood.*)

rapids, small and great, interrupt the courses of streams the valleys of which, remade by ice, trend across the grain of rocks of unequal resistance to erosion. Lakes and swamps also abound, even amid the highlands. Some are small morainic ponds or marshes of temporary nature. Others occupy ice-eroded rock basins and are beautifully set amid forested hills.

494. NOTED REGIONS OF ICE-SCOURED HILLS. It happens that the more noted of the ice-scoured hill regions are situated in areas of ancient crystalline rocks (Fig. 248). These include the more rugged portions of the Canadian Shield, the Adirondack Mountains, parts of New England, the Highlands of Scotland, and parts of the ancient highland of Scandinavia. They have many features in common. Except for some heath-covered hills

such as those of Scotland, they mainly are clothed with coniferous forest, are deeply snow covered in winter, and have little agricultural development. Their industries principally concern the utilization of pasture and forest resources; the employment of the water powers in the manufacture of wood products and paper; and the capitalization of their resources of hills, lakes, and woodlands in the attraction of the summer vacationist.

Fig. 248.—Thin soils and smooth rock surfaces on the ice-scoured slopes of the Adirondacks.

In the Pennine Hills of northern England, the Green Mountains of Vermont, and the hills of southern New York, glacial features are different from those described above to the extent that they reflect ice scour in highlands of less resistant rock. Having large inclusions of sedimentary rock, they provided more abundant glacial drift, and, although the hills resulting from ice scour are equally rounded, they generally are less bare than are

Fig. 249.—A valley in the glaciated hill region near the Finger Lakes of western New York. The hills are ice scoured, but the flat valley floor is deeply underlain by drift.

those in the ancient crystalline highlands. The valleys have more abundant drift, and, although the drift is stony, they offer better agricultural possibilities than those in which crystalline rocks predominate. In the horizontal sedimentary strata of the New York portion of the Allegheny hill region that is particularly true. Before glaciation those hills presumably were similar in features and pattern to the hills of Pennsylvania. They have been much subdued by the work of the ice. Hilltops were rounded, and valleys were partially filled with morainal and glaciofluvial deposits which flattened their bottoms and made them much more suited to agriculture (Fig. 249). In some of the valleys morainal dams have obstructed the southward flow of preglacial streams and thus have created the valley lakes which are called the Finger Lakes (Fig. 250).

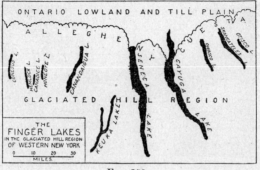

FIG. 250.

495. THE SHORE FEATURES OF HILL LANDS. The shorelines of hill lands are different in many significant ways from those that characterize the meeting of plains with the sea. The steep and often serrate shores of hill lands commonly are bordered by sea bottom

FIG. 251.

which slopes less gently than the continental shelf that borders plains. Shore features developing after the emergence of such coasts are likely to be characterized by great regularity, as are those of the coasts of emerging plains. However, the deeper waters offshore are less likely to provide conditions suitable to the formation of offshore bars and lagoons. Features resulting from the submergence of narrow and steeply sloping coastal valleys are likely to be of greater number and finer detail than are those of the coasts of submerged plains. Indeed, it is from the many parallel bays (called *rias*) on the hill-land coast of northwestern Spain that the term "ria shoreline" is derived (Fig. 251). The shorelines of hill lands have, in fact, much in common with those of mountain lands, and further discussion of them is reserved for that connection (524).

Chapter XXI. Mountains

496. The Distinguishing Features of Mountains. Moun-- tains, like hills, are distinguished from plains and plateaus by the smallness of their summit areas and the large proportion of their surfaces in steep slopes. Yet mountains are more than enlarged hills. In general they have greater relief and are more massive than hills; they have more rugged contours; and their surface features are more complicated in pattern. However, mountains are of wide variety in size and form. Great mountains are easily recognizable as such, but it is not easy, neither is it usually essential, to distinguish between low mountains and hills. Summit elevation above sea level is not significant, since even the bases of both hills and mountains in the far interiors of continents often are many hundreds of feet in elevation. A better basis of distinction is the criterion of local relief, previously used. A region does not have truly mountainous features unless the local relief exceeds 2,000 ft. That arbitrary limitation excludes from the list of mountain regions many areas of rough surface which locally are called mountains.

Above the lower limit of 2,000 ft. of local relief, here established as distinctive of mountains, are several possible classes of mountains. Four are suggested which may be delimited, as was done for plains, in terms of the maximum difference in elevation to be found within a horizontal distance of about 10 miles. The classes follow: (*a*) *low mountains*, having local relief of 2,000 to 3,000 ft.; (*b*) *rough mountains*, having local relief of 3,000 to 4,500 ft.; (*c*) *rugged mountains*, having local relief of 4,500 to 6,000 ft.; and (*d*) *sierran mountains*, having local relief of more than 6,000 ft.

Although steep slopes are among the distinguishing features of mountains, few of them are in fact so steep as popular belief would make them. The average slope of most great mountains probably does not exceed an angle of 20 or 25° from horizontal. A few exceed 35°, especially near their summits, where erosion proceeds rapidly along

431

joint planes. The fact that mountain slopes commonly are made up, stairlike, of gentle inclines separated by abrupt rises or sheer cliffs has led to a popular exaggeration of the extent of the latter. Seldom is the sheer or overhanging mountain precipice more than a few score feet in height. The great and seemingly vertical walls hundreds of feet high found in some mountains are not vertical. In fact, they seldom exceed angles of 70° and are capable of ascent, at least by the animals whose habitat they are.

Several of the distinguishing features of mountains conspire to make them the least habitable of the four major groups of landforms (372). Narrow valleys and the large proportion of land in slope limit the area of tillable land to a small part of the total. Steep slopes mainly are stripped of their regolith, and where soil is present it is in constant danger of destructive erosion if disturbed by the plow. Forests and grass serve to utilize the soil on slopes and to aid in its retention. They are, therefore, among the most important of potential mountain resources. The conditions of mountain origin that give rise to complexity of rock structure commonly give rise also to mineral ores, and these may be added to the last of mountain resources of potential value for human use. So also may the potential water powers created by abundant precipitation and high stream gradients. Moreover, mountains adjacent to great centers of population on plains have large actual or potential use as playgrounds. One reason for this is their great height and the modification of climate that arises therefrom. Another is the variety and beauty of their erosional and drainage forms. A considerable part of the population of the Alps and some other mountains subsists upon income derived from those who come to view mountain scenery or to enjoy mountain climate or mountain sports.

497. THE DISTRIBUTION OF GREAT MOUNTAINS. Attention has been called previously to the probable relation between the tectonic activity of the regions of the Pacific Ocean border and other localities and the formation of mountains (334). The major regions of mountain distribution, shown in Plate VII, emphasize that relationship. The great mountains of the world, the Andes, those of western North America, eastern Asia, The Himalayas, Caucasus, and Alps all lie within or upon the margins of areas of known crustal instability. It may well be that they are the crumpled margins of segments of the earth's crust which have, as units, recently undergone, or are now undergoing, adjustments of elevation.

498. CLASSES OF MOUNTAIN FEATURES. A combination of diastrophic and volcanic forces, applied along the extensive and somewhat indefinite margins of crustal segments of the earth, has

produced mountain uplifts of great variety in shapes, sizes, and arrangements. These are attacked by the agents of gradation, even as they grow, and are carved into equally varied features. The features are known, according to their respective sizes and arrangements, by such names as cordillera, system, chain, group, range, ridge, and peak.

A mountain *peak* is ordinarily a feature of a minor order upon a range, but in some instances, such as the great isolated volcanic cones, one of them stands alone and comprises the whole mountain mass. A mountain *range* is an arrangement, usually somewhat linear, of many peaks, ridges, and their included valleys (Fig. 252). Ordinarily the term range is applied to mountains that have a general unity of form, structure, and geologic age. The term *group* is sometimes used to describe peaks and ridges of rangelike size but not typically rangelike in shape. Such are the nearly circular, nodal, or massive patterns

Fig. 252.—The crest line of a linear mountain range in Colorado, showing some of its peaks and lateral ridges or spurs. The crest is a part of the continental divide.

of peaks and ridges resulting from the erosion of laccolithic igneous intrusions.

Several associated ranges are referred to as a *mountain system* if they have some unity of position, form, or structure but are separated by trenches or basins. The Rocky Mountain system is an example. The term *cordillera*, although it originally meant an extended range or chain, has come to be applied to a large regional grouping of mountain systems.

499. CORDILLERAN REGIONS. Most of the great mountains of the earth are found in four cordilleran regions. They are (*a*) the North American cordillera, which includes the Rocky Mountain and Sierra Madre systems, the Basin Ranges, the Alaska - British Columbia Coast Mountains, the Cascade - Sierra Nevada systems, and the Coast Ranges; (*b*) the cordillera of the Andes; (*c*) the cordillera of southern Europe, which includes the Carpathians, the Alps, the Pyrenees, and the mountains of Spain and northern Africa; (*d*) the Asian cordillera, which is comprised of the Himalaya, Kunlun, Tien Shan, and Hindu

Kush mountains, which converge upon the nodal group of The Pamirs, together with the Caucasus Mountains and intermediate ranges.

The arrangement of the members of the great cordilleran groups with respect to each other, to the shapes of the continents in which they lie, and to the plains and plateaus adjacent to them should be studied with the aid of an atlas. The included mountains show by the frequent occurrence of faulting and earthquakes or volcanic activity that many if not most of them are young and even now in the process of growth. In other parts of the same continents certain ancient mountains, now reduced by erosion, indicate the existence of other cordilleran groups in earlier periods of earth history.

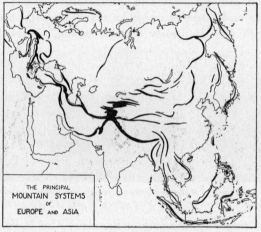

THE PRINCIPAL
MOUNTAIN SYSTEMS
OF
EUROPE AND ASIA

FIG. 253.

500. MOUNTAIN SYSTEMS are significant in the realm of human affairs, directly because of the barriers that they interpose upon the movements of people and indirectly through relation to the distribution of climatic and other natural phenomena. The effectiveness of mountain barriers largely depends upon the height, continuity, number, and arrangement of the mountain forms. These conditions in turn depend upon (a) the character of the rocks involved in the mountain uplift, (b) the nature of the processes that brought about the uplift, and (c) the climatic environment under which erosion has progressed and the stage of completion to which it has been carried.

The patterns of arrangement of the great mountain systems profoundly affect the elements of landscape, both natural and cultural. Inspection of them, as they appear in an atlas, will show how generally they are deployed upon the earth's surface in broad arcs. This pattern is exemplified by The Himalayas and is common in the systems of Asia

(Fig. 253). Other examples are not hard to find. The Carpathians, the northern Andes, the ranges of Alaska, and others show it clearly. Comparison will indicate that not a few political and other cultural boundaries conform to these curved lines.

501. MOUNTAIN RANGES. The ranges that comprise the world's major systems, chains, and groups of mountains differ widely in their patterns of arrangement. Several recognized patterns result from the erosion of as many different classes of tectonic structure. Four of the major patterns may be noted, as follows: (a) roughly parallel ranges resulting from the differential erosion of strata that have been arched, wrinkled, or folded, and faulted by the forces of lateral compression. In such mountains some of the major longitudinal valleys may be of structural origin, the bottoms of synclinal folds. More commonly they result from differential erosion, certain of the more resistant rocks standing in relief as the mountain ranges. (b) Isolated or widely spaced ranges that are simply faulted as the result of lateral tension. Some of these are of great size; others are small. Some are tilted by a succession of faults along a single plane. Others are tilted horst blocks (Fig. 117). Upon any of them erosion is certain to have wrought great change of shape before they attain mountainous proportions. (c) Massive mountains with radial or featherlike range patterns resulting from the erosion of domed structures which were caused by laccoliths or other giant intrusions of igneous rock. The overlying sedimentary rocks upon such an intrusion may be almost entirely removed by erosion, and the ranges and valleys of radial pattern eroded in the massive rocks beneath. However, the eroded edges of the sedimentary formations sometimes lie as encircling ranges of cuestaform foothills about the flanks of the principal mountain mass (Fig. 121). (d) Conical mountains, or ranges comprised largely of such mountains. These are cones produced by volcanic extrusion.

502. RANGE PATTERNS IN VARIOUS MOUNTAINS. The erosion of young mountains the uplift of which was brought about by folding with associated faulting produces systems with more or less parallel ranges, the intervening valleys resulting from differential erosion. In some places the erosion has been so great that the resistant rocks of anticlinal folds have been removed, and the valleys are cut in the less resistant formations beneath. Between the valleys are mountains in which the attitudes of the rocks show them to be the remnants of former synclines (Fig. 118). Other of their valleys are structural rather than erosional, some of them due to downwarping and others to faulting, although even those features usually are modified to some degree by gradational processes.

Examples of mountains of somewhat parallel arrangement are numerous. Detailed maps show that the Carpathians, Atlas, Himalayas, Andes, and other mountains contain ranges the major axes of which trend in the same general direction. Some of the ranges of the Rocky Mountains show a significant alignment also. Where they cross the Canada-United States boundary they are comprised of nearly parallel ranges which are separated by two linear "trenches" of remarkable length. Farther south, the ranges of Colorado are more widely spaced and are separated in part by broad basins, locally called "parks." The Alps are the eroded bases of faulted and folded strata in the formation of which the compression was so great that many of the folds were crumpled and overturned. Their structure is, therefore, highly complicated, but certain of their longitudinal valleys which are of tectonic origin are to be seen on any good map of those mountains (Fig. 6).

Some great mountain ranges, and many smaller ones, appear to have been formed principally by faulting. The 400-mile-long range of the Sierra Nevada Mountains of California is carved by streams and glaciers in the edge and upland of a faulted block the escarpment of which, in places more than 2 miles high, faces eastward and the upland of which inclines less steeply westward (Fig. 114C). The bold west-facing front of the Wasatch Mountains in Utah is likewise the result of displacement along a fault zone, the gentler slopes being generally toward the east (Fig. 116). Some of the many adjacent Basin Ranges also are eroded fault blocks. They show a general north-south alignment and are separated by broad bolsons (Fig. 206). Faulted block mountains of similar type and linear arrangement are found in a large region which includes Palestine, Arabia, and part of eastern Africa. Some of them are so freshly faulted that the latest additions to their growth remain almost unmarred by erosion. In all of them, however, the crests are deeply scarred, even in the arid climate of the Great Basin.

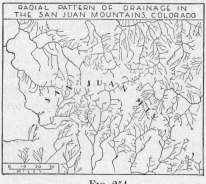

RADIAL PATTERN OF DRAINAGE IN THE SAN JUAN MOUNTAINS, COLORADO

FIG. 254.

Not all linear mountain ranges, however, are to be ascribed to diastrophic causes. In some, faulting and folding do appear to have been the principal causes; but in others the cause seems to have been vulcanism. Certain mountain ranges are largely composed of volcanic materials, erupted along lines of weakness in the earth's crust. The cones thus formed assume somewhat linear arrangement, and the ranges may be considered volcanic even though they rest upon platforms of older rocks. The islands of Java and Sumatra and others of the East Indies are of that origin. Several of the principal peaks and many of the lesser ones in the Cascade Mountains of the United States also are volcanoes in roughly linear arrangement.

Mountain groups that are of volcanic or laccolithic origin commonly have massive or compact rather than linear forms, and a few are roughly circular in outline. The eroded ridges and valleys of some of them have intersecting, featherlike, or radial patterns or some modification of the radial relation. The Henry Mountains of Utah, and other smaller groups in the region, are examples of laccolithic mountains (Fig. 121). The sediments, updomed by igneous intrusion, now are eroded away from the uplands and appear only as encircling cuestaform ridges. The San Juan Mountains of Colorado are the eroded remnants of a high plateau composed of lavas and volcanic ash. Streams and glaciers have carved it into a mountain mass of great ruggedness and nearly radial pattern of drainage (Fig. 254).

503. VOLCANIC CONES. In addition to the mountain masses caused by volcanic intrusion or extrusion, there are many notable examples of single volcanic mountains or volcanic cones, some of which are active and occasionally in violent eruption. Their general distribution has been noted previously (Fig. 122). Some of the great volcanoes are surrounded by lesser cones and also by mountain peaks carved by erosion in the massive uplifts of which the volcanoes are a part. Others stand alone. Some volcanoes of the type first noted have great summit elevation, but they do not all have great local relief, since they stand upon foundations of great altitude. A number of those that stand alone upon lowlands are famous for their beauty of form. Although not many of them reach high altitudes, some have great local relief because they rise practically from sea level. The peak of Fuji (not now an active volcano), in Japan, is not quite 12,400 ft. above the sea, but the mountain is a tall and striking landscape feature because it stands alone and reaches its full height within about 15 miles of the sea (Fig. 255). Some other cones of great fame or beauty of form are Mount

FIG. 255.—The symmetrical cone of Fuji Mountain rises more than 12,000 ft. above Suruga Bay and its bordering alluvial plains. (*Photograph by H. Suito.*)

Egmont (not active), in New Zealand; Mount Mayon, in southern Luzon; Etna, in Sicily; and Vesuvius, near Naples. Such famous American volcanic cones as Mounts Rainier, Hood, Shasta, Popocatepetl, and Chimborazo (20,700 ft.) are much higher but are not more inspiring sights. Even the higher Hawaiian cones (10,000 to nearly 14,000 ft.), although they are tall, are of less striking aspect than the cones first mentioned because of their flattish or domed profiles the slopes of which lie at angles which generally are between 4 and 10° (336).

504. THE FEATURES OF VOLCANIC CONES.   Reference has been made to the steep slopes characteristic of volcanic cones that erupt acid rocks (336). Most of the world's volcanoes are of that type, but their cones, while they are steeper than those of the Hawaiian type, are by no means uniform as to slope or contour. Some cones that are made up largely of viscous acidic lavas are broadly rounded in form. Those that are composed of fine ashy material, which drifts readily in the wind, also are broad and low. Accumulations of rough, angular, scoriaceous lavas, on the other hand, will lie at angles as high as 35 or 40° without slumping and make the steepest cones.

Most of the world's great volcanic cones are of structures that may be called *composite*. They are made up of layers of viscous lava interbedded among layers of ash, scoria, and other forms of volcanic products erupted at different times. The layers are penetrated by dikes of lava which arise from the central duct. Through some of the lateral crevices thus opened, materials reach the surface and form secondary, or *parasitic*, cones upon the sides of the principal one. Thus, simple volcanoes, of the type of Mount Mayon, are nearly perfect cones, but others that develop parasitic cones have less regular form. Because of the collection of the heavier and coarser ejected fragments near the volcanic vent, the upper slopes of most composite cones are steeper than the lower slopes. The latter are made more gentle by the widespread distribution of ash and alluvium, and some are productive agricultural land. Upon the lower slopes and in the valleys adjacent to volcanoes that have been recently active, however, are likely to be found solidified streams or flows of fresh and unweathered lava. The breaking up of hardened external crusts by flowage while the lava beneath still is plastic causes the surface of many lava flows, when finally they are cooled, to be a porous and jumbled mass of blocks of sharp scoriaceous rock of no potential value and difficult even to cross (Fig. 256).

Like other highlands, volcanic cones are attacked by the agents of erosion and have features caused by them. Their flanks, especially of such volcanoes as those in the Cascade Mountains, that have been a long time inactive, are scored by stream gullies, often radial in pattern. Differential erosion etches into relief resistant dikes and lava flows or removes the finer ash and spreads it as alluvium upon the adjacent lowlands. Rain-saturated ash beds sometimes slump or flow as volcanic mud also, and their paths are marked by destruction. In middle latitudes, many dormant volcanoes have had their surfaces shaped in part by glacial erosion.

505. *Volcanic craters*, the vents through which the volcanic products are erupted, are of great variety in form. Some are small and funnel shaped, especially such as are the vents of high, active, and perfect cones. Some, which are the craters of dormant and partially destroyed cones, are of great diameter and are believed to result from the explosive destruction of the upper portion of the former cone or by its subsidence through the withdrawal

of lava from underneath. Such enlarged craters are known as *caldera*. Crater Lake, in the Cascade Mountains of Oregon, occupies a basin formed by the subsidence of an ancient cone. It is about 4 by 5 miles in diameter and has a newer but very small cone within it. Other crater lakes of smaller size are not uncommon. Some of relatively recent origin are found in New Zealand, and others of greater age are located among the ancient volcanic hills of central France and the German Eifel. On the coasts of Italy and New Zealand are similar crater basins, their rims breached by wave erosion in a way that turns them into natural harbors.

506. *Volcanic eruptions,* even of the quiet type, are awe-inspiring phenomena. Molten rock seethes within the crater; steam and other gases are emitted; and upwelling lava spills over the crater rim. If the supply is

FIG. 256.—Scoriaceous lava in a Rocky Mountain valley. (*Denver and Rio Grande Railroad.*)

copious, the lava flood may creep for miles, filling valleys, engulfing settlements, and leaving, after cooling, a rough and barren surface. However, most of the world's active volcanoes have occasional eruptions of the explosive type. Especially are they likely to be explosive in volcanoes that have been for some time inactive.

Extremely violent eruptions have been the cause of several appalling catastrophes. Examples often cited are the eruptions of Vesuvius in A. D. 79; of Krakatao, near Java, in 1883; and of Mount Pelée, in the West Indies, in 1902. Many other eruptions of great violence have passed with brief historical record, either because the regions in which they occurred were unpeopled or because no witness wrote an account. The destructiveness of explosive eruptions arises from the suddenness of their occurrence and the nature of the volcanic products. In some instances rumbling sounds and local earthquakes have given warning of a coming eruption, but of others there has been no warning. In a typical explosive eruption great volumes of superheated steam and other suffocating or poisonous gases are thrown into the air.

Mingled with the gases are large quantities of fragmented rock, shattered or blown to dust while still in the molten state by the expansive force of included gases. A giant black cloud of steam and dust billows skyward and hangs above the mountain, but eventually it drifts with the wind and is dispersed over large areas (Fig. 257). A hail of rock fragments, cinders, lapilli, and ash falls about the crater or even upon the outskirts of the cone. A blanket of dust settles over the leeward slope. Condensing steam and condensation in ascending air currents provide torrents of rain which are accompanied by lightning and thunder. Saturated with dust and ash, the runoff may turn into flows of volcanic mud which reach and bury portions of the bordering lowland. To the accompaniment of earthquake shocks, fissures sometimes open in the side of a cone, and upon them parasitic cones may begin their growth, or from them may issue floods of glowing lava.

FIG. 257.—A giant eruptive cloud hanging above Colima volcano, Mexico. (*Photograph by José María Arreola.*)

The explosive phenomenon over, and the pent-up pressure released, the eruption is likely to continue more quietly. Although not all eruptions involve the extrusion of lava, it is commonly the case that lava and the quiet emission of steam bring the period of eruption to a close, and there ensues a period of quiescence which lasts for months, years, or, in some volcanoes, hundreds of years.

Stream-eroded Details of Mountain Surface

507. It has been indicated above that the distinctive features of mountains, whatever their manner of origin, include great height and local relief, as compared with the other major groups of landforms, and small summit area. In addition to these and other common features every mountain range has an abundant detail of minor relief features which give it individuality. These include the depth and shapes of the valleys, the patterns of the minor ridges and spurs, the prevalent slope angles, the heights and forms of the summits, the presence or absence of perennial snows, and the nature and distribution of vegetation. While the height of mountain masses and other of their major features result in part from the operation of tectonic forces, the minor relief features to a large degree are of erosional origin, and they are of different forms because of differences in rock structure, climatic condition, and stage of erosional development, the same conditions

referred to so often in other connections. Some of the more important of the erosional forms may be considered at greater length.

508. VALLEY FORMS. Mountain streams usually have the high gradients of youth. A few have not. The latter are the occasional major streams that have reached grade or those minor streams the erosional progress of which is held up by a temporary baselevel. Such streams meander in flat-bottomed alluvial valleys. In others, rapid downward cutting discovers rocks of unequal hardness and develops falls and rapids. Vigorous downward erosion develops also the V-shaped transverse profile of youth (Fig. 258). Under recent cutting in resistant rock the V is narrow, and the valley a gorge or canyon, but more commonly it is broadly open. The Royal Gorge and several other canyons which cut into the Front Range of the Rocky Mountains are examples of stream-eroded valleys of the narrow and steep-sided type. Some streams in cutting through rocks of unequal resistance erode valleys that at their headwaters are broad and then narrow to gorges, subsequently opening out again downstream. Such a narrows, or gorge, is sometimes

FIG. 258.—Rapids at the bottom of this Rocky Mountain gorge emphasize the youth of its profile. (*Photograph by DeCou, from Ewing Galloway.*)

utilized as a site for the economical construction of a dam to impound water in a great reservoir which will lie in the more open upper part of the valley.

Some streams flow parallel with, rather than across the trend of, the rock structure and tend to shift their valleys sidewise down inclined strata by undercutting. This produces a cuestaform ridge and a valley with one wall steeply and the other gently inclined. The different degrees of slope of the two walls commonly are reflected in contrasting manners of human use of the land on opposite sides of such a valley.

The relatively rapid erosion of mountain slopes tends to expose rocks of unequal resistance and to produce angular and sharply defined contours. The tendency is less evident in low than in high mountains and in warm humid climates than in those that are prevailingly cold or dry. However, in most mountain valleys the slope, as viewed from a distance, is interrupted by steep declivities at the outcrops of resistant formations and by more gently inclined benches, or *terraces*, where the rocks weather more readily. Benches of that origin make possible the agricultural use of some valley sides the average slopes of which would render the tillage of the soil impossible.

Mechanical weathering is rapid on the exposed upper slopes of deep mountain valleys. Blocks of rock, dislodged by frost, fall below. There they accumulate as *talus slopes*, the upper parts of which commonly include coarse newly fallen blocks piled more steeply than the older and more weathered rock beneath (Fig. 266). At the mouths of steep ravines on the valley walls the talus piles are particularly large and tend there to be cone shaped. Such piles are called alluvial cones or *gravity cones*, and they are like the upper ends of steep alluvial fans, into which they merge without sharp distinction.

509. MOUNTAIN UPLAND FORMS. *Divides.* Between mountain valleys are uplands, persisting remnants of the original elevation. Rainfall on these uplands separates according to the surface slopes and descends by countless rivulets into adjacent valleys, modeling the upland as it goes. The uplands are, therefore, properly called "water partings," or *divides*. The minor spurs, or extensions, of the upland serve merely as divides between small tributaries of the same stream. Uplands in more strategic locations may part the waters of great river systems, and some separate the drainage destined for opposite sides of a continent. The latter are called *continental divides* (Fig. 252).

On some mountain uplands the divide is a conspicuous feature. Rock structure and the process of erosion combine to produce a bold and narrow ridge upon which the water parting is a sinuous line almost as sharply defined as the ridge of a house roof. On others the divide is not so well defined, since the uplands are in fact elongated plateaus, so frequently and so deeply cut by valleys that they appear mountainous but are not characterized by a definite crest.

510. *Mountain Foothills and Spurs.* The lowest and least massive features of mountain uplands are the foothills and spurs that fringe the principal highlands. Foothills are of many kinds, and their forms generally reflect conditions of climate and of rock structure. About some mountains, beds of unconsolidated sediments have been elevated.

and then maturely eroded into foothills of the badland type. At the bases of other mountains are linear foothills which are the outcrops of bordering sedimentary strata. Along the eastern front of the Rocky Mountains in Colorado, for example, sedimentary rocks, bent upward by the mountain-building process, have since been eroded into sharp cuestaform ridges and valleys which parallel the mountain front. Their

Fig. 259.—Foothills of the hogback ridge type parallel the Rocky Mountain front, near Boulder, Colo. The mountains are still farther to the left. (*Photograph by H. A. Hoffmeister.*)

escarpment slopes face steeply toward the mountains, and their dip slopes incline toward the bordering plains (Fig. 259). Linear foothills of that type are called *hogback ridges*.

Mountain spurs are the fringing projections of a mountain mass into the flanks of which tributary valleys are etched. In a youthful stage of erosion the spurs are likely to be abrupt, and, as they approach

Fig. 260.—Overlapping spurs in the youthful Rimac Valley in the Andes of Peru. The steepened lower slopes indicate a renewed vigor of stream erosion. (*Courtesy of Economic Geography and Preston E. James.*)

the irregular course of the main stream from opposing uplands, they may even overlap, obscuring the view up or down the valley and complicating the problems of transportation (Fig. 260). Mountain spurs with their alternating valley heads create complicated patterns of relief, and some are so difficult of access that they are areas of extreme isolation.

511. *Mountain peaks* are the distinguishing features of mountain uplands. Their varied forms hold much of the attractiveness of mountain scenery. Some mountain peaks are the result of faulting, and many are volcanic cones superimposed upon volcanic or preexisting uplands. By far the greater number of the countless mountain peaks of the earth, however, are the result of differential erosion in the uplands of which they are a part. Owing to superior resistance, to condition of structure, to accident of position, or to other causes they have

FIG. 261.—Brown Pass, in Glacier National Park, viewed from a higher one. The saddle shape of this notch is distinct. The white arrow point touches the crest of the pass, which also is a part of the continental divide. (*National Park Service, U. S. Department of the Interior.*)

been protected from erosion while adjacent rocks have been reduced to lower levels. Of a whole tectonic uplift the serrate sky line of a rugged mountain range, therefore, may mark only a narrow remnant, into which deep notches already have been cut. Indeed, it is the notches that distinguish the peaks. Each notch marks the erosional progress of a valley or gulch which, through headward erosion, is gnawing at the flank of the range. Some deep notches result from the headward approach of two valleys, one on either side of the range, toward the same part of its crest.

512. *Mountain passes* are the more accessible, and usually the lowest, notches across a mountain barrier (Fig. 261). They are lower

than the general level of other notches because of more vigorous erosion by opposing headwater streams or because of the erosion of glaciers. They are more accessible because larger valleys lead toward them.

513. *Features of Mountain Passes.* Because passes are approached from either side by steep valley gradients and are flanked, right and left, by mountain peaks, they are distinctly saddle shaped. Milner Pass, over the Continental Divide in Colorado, lies at an elevation of 10,758 ft. above sea level. On either side peaks rise more than 1,000 ft. higher, and the divergent valleys fall away sharply between. So narrow is the crest of this high pass that the head of the tributary to the east-flowing Cache la Poudre and that of the west-flowing Colorado are less than a mile apart. Many passes are narrow, but their water partings do not always slope equally on either hand. Peaks of 9,000 ft. elevation face each other across the St. Gotthard Pass, Switzerland (elevation 6,930 ft.), in which a tributary from the south-flowing Ticino River and one from the north-flowing Reuss approach within a few yards of each other. However, owing to conditions of rock structure and erosion, this saddle has very unequal slopes. The road from Ariolo, on the south, ascends, by many curves, more than 3,000 ft. in a little over 3 miles, but the road continues northward more than 8 miles before it has descended 3,000 ft. A railroad that follows these valleys across the range is unable to climb the final steep approaches of the pass and makes its way by tunnel underneath.

Not all passes have such steep approaches as those indicated above. Yellowhead Pass lies at an altitude of only 3,728 ft. in the midst of some of the highest peaks of the Canadian Rockies. It is a part of the Continental Divide, and it parts the headwaters of two great streams, the Pacific-bound Fraser and the Arctic-bound Athabaska, by less than a mile. Yet, a railway traverses that pass over a grade so gentle that it is hardly noticeable. There are many important passes of that kind.

Mountain Glaciers and Glacially Eroded Mountain Features

514. THE IMPORTANCE OF GLACIAL SCULPTURE. Stream erosion is, without doubt, the major process involved in the primary carving of mountain masses. The great valleys, ranges, and peaks of most mountains were begun, and many were brought to their present forms, by the work of running water. Countless others, however, have been changed by the unmistakable sculpture of mountain glaciers. In large part, these features are now abandoned by glaciers and are left to the further work of running water but so recently abandoned that they are as yet little changed.

High mountains, even in the tropics, project above the line of perennial snow. Others, not so high, were snowcapped during the most recent glacial period. So common are the forms of mountain glaciation that they have greatly influenced the popular ideas concerning the features of mountains in general and of the grandeur of mountain scenery. The snowcapped peak, the ice-filled valley, and the carvings and fillings of former glaciers attract and inspire the mountain visitor as other kinds of mountain features cannot.

515. MOUNTAIN SNOW FIELDS. Snows are common to all high mountains. In middle and high latitudes the winter mantle of white settles even over the lower slopes, save where exposed flanks are cleared by the sweep of the wind. The seasonal alternation from winter white to the variety of warm-season colors produced by rock and vegetation works a profound change in the landscape. The snows of many mountains are, however, permanent. They owe their preservation to the decrease of temperature with altitude. Consequently, the lower limit of permanent snow is high in the tropics, but in the subpolar regions it approaches sea level. In regions of similar temperature the snow line is lower where snowfall is abundant and higher where it is not abundant. In the same locality it is higher on mountain sides exposed to strong insolation and lower on the shaded sides. If these many variations are allowed for, it may be said that the lower limit of permanent snow in the tropics is from 14,000 to 20,000 ft. above sea level. In middle latitudes it is at elevations of from 5,000 to 10,000 ft.; and on the margins of the polar regions it varies from 2,000 ft. down to sea level.

516. MOUNTAIN GLACIERS are themselves important relief features, apart from the mountain forms caused by their erosion. Fed by frequent snowfall, a highland snow field becomes heavy. Portions of it slip and plunge by avalanche into the nearest valley head (Fig. 262). There the deepening mass undergoes a change and recrystallizes from the uncompacted form. First it becomes granular, but finally it is welded by its own melting and refreezing into solid ice. Some small bodies of it collect temporarily upon rock ledges only to spill over the edge by their own growth and expansion and to reform below. Such are called cliff glaciers.

Ultimately, however, the main accumulation in a valley head grows to such proportions that, under its own weight, it moves. In the form of an ice tongue it pushes down its valley, and then it is a *valley glacier*. It progresses in its own peculiar way, only to vanish by melting at a lower elevation (358). In its course the surface of the ice undergoes notable transformation. Irregularities of the valley floor bend and twist the solid ice causing it to open deep transverse cracks called *crevasses*. These may be expanded by melting until the surface is deeply corrugated. The tops of crevasses sometimes are overdrifted by freshly fallen snow, setting traps for the unwary adventurer upon the glacier's surface.

Upon the sides of the ice tongue there accumulate ridges of earth and rocks obtained from the valley walls. Others, derived from tributary glaciers or from projecting spurs, sometimes streak the center of an ice tongue. These, which are called lateral moraines and medial moraines respectively, are conspicuous surface features of many valley glaciers (Figs. 262, 236).

Fig. 262.—A mountain glacier and its snow fields. Crevasses are visible in the nearer ice. Ridges of lateral moraine flank the ice tongue, and medial moraine streaks its surface. (*Photograph by Ewing Galloway.*)

At the lower end of the glacier wastage by melting is rapid, and the load of earth and rock debris increases in proportion as the ice mass shrinks and may bury it entirely. Upon accumulation it forms end moraines, crescentic in ground plan and confined within the valley width. In other respects they are similar to the end moraines of continental glaciers. Morainic ridges deposited at the successive recessional positions of former valley glaciers during their wastage are found in many mountain valleys.

Some valley glaciers, especially those of coastal mountains in high latitudes and in regions of marine west-coast type of climate, are so abundantly provided with snow that the ice tongues extend to the sea.

That is notably true at present of a part of the coast of Alaska, and
it has been true of more extended coasts in the past. Glaciers that
reach the sea do not waste in the usual manner. Like those that descend
from the ice plateaus of Greenland and Antarctica, they are broken off
in sheer ice cliffs by the buoyant force of sea water upon the ice margin
(478). They also give rise to icebergs, although few of the latter are so
large as those that drift away from Greenland (Fig. 263).

517. THE FEATURES OF ICE-SCOURED MOUNTAIN VALLEYS.   Ice
erosion in a mountain valley proceeds so differently from stream erosion

FIG. 263,—In the foreground is floe ice. It has toppled off the front of this Alaskan
glacier, which descends to sea level. The separation leaves the ice front sheer.
(*U. S. Geological Survey Photograph.*)

that the surface features that it creates are unmistakable long after
the glacier has vanished. The typical ice-scoured valley is deepened;
its sides are oversteepened; and its bottom is widened and rounded.
Its transverse profile, as compared with that of the stream-eroded
valley, is U-shaped rather than V-shaped. Ice scour also tends to
remove the tips of overlapping spurs in a valley and to straighten it
into a trough (Fig. 264).

Although the broadened valley bottom is made more usable as a
result of glaciation, especially if it is left with a mantle of drift, its
slopes are rendered less so. The steepening of the lower slopes in some
ice-scoured valleys is carried to a high angle. Even for some distance
above the level formerly occupied by the glacial ice the valley wall is
made steep and rugged by the undermining of its base. Above these
precipitous slopes commonly there are gentler inclines, ice scoured and

smoothed sometimes but not oversteep. Generally they are above timber line and are covered by grasses and forage plants which serve as summer pastures. Such are the high pastures, or "alps," of Switzerland; the "field beite" of Norway with their "saeter" or summer dairies; and some of the mountain pastures of western United States. Above them rise the peaks of the higher mountains (Figs. 265, 272).

Fig. 264.—An air view of the glaciated Torngat Mountains of Labrador. A long ice-scoured valley curves into the distance, where it is flanked by cirques. Other cirques are to be seen at the right center and the background. Note the alluvial delta fan and the lake in the foreground. (*Photograph by Ewing Galloway.*)

518. The longitudinal valley profile produced by ice erosion does not always slope continuously downward from the valley head. The valley ice is able, because of its depth, to ride up and over minor obstructions of hard rock in its bed. Moreover, morainic dams interrupt the present valley gradient. Most glaciated valleys have one or more basins, and some have a succession of them, in which impounded drainage creates lakes, ponds, or marshes. In valleys of flat gradient, especially near the margins of mountain regions, glacial deepening and morainic dams are capable of providing basins of large size. The basins of the beautiful Lakes Maggiore, Como, and Garda, at the southern

base of the Alps, are of that origin (Fig. 6). So are those of the several long lakes in Glacier National Park, Lake Louise in the Canadian Rockies, and many lakes in the Andes of southern Argentina.

519. TRIBUTARY VALLEYS entering an ice-scoured mountain valley commonly exhibit a relation to it unlike that of the tributaries to a stream-eroded valley, which normally join at a common level. During the occupance of a valley by ice, the drainage of its tributary valleys,

FIG. 265.—A glaciated Alpine valley. Below is a graded valley floor of drift and alluvium. It is flanked by a wall oversteepened by glacial scour. Above that are alpine meadows (*alps*) and hanging valleys. Streams from the latter discharge in falls such as that visible at the right. The height of the wall may be judged by the houses and hotel on the level valley floor. (*Photograph by Ewing Galloway.*)

whether it is water or ice, tends to flow out upon the top of the ice and not into the bottom of the main valley. While the main valley is being deeply eroded by the glacier the erosion in the tributary valleys is generally much retarded, and it may be stopped entirely. After the withdrawal of the ice from the region, the level of a main valley floor may lie tens or even hundreds of feet below the ends of its tributary valleys. The latter appear as notches upon the side of the wall of the oversteepened main valley and are called *hanging valleys* (Figs. 265, 266). The streams issuing from them must plunge in rapids or sheer falls to reach the main valley floor. Falls of that kind are of great scenic

attraction and are exemplified by the falls of Yosemite Valley, California, and many others in the Rocky Mountains, Switzerland, Norway, and other regions of mountain glaciation. They also are most
convenient places for the development of water power. Even a small
stream, with so great a fall as some hanging valleys provide, can
develop an astonishing quantity of power.

520. THE VALLEY HEAD, in a region of mountain glaciation, is the
collecting ground for the snow which crystallizes into a glacier. At this

FIG. 266.—Scenery of glacial origin in the Canadian Rockies. At the right is a
cirque lake. Its drainage falls to the level of the second lake, and from that it must fall
far below to the level of Lake Louise, a little of which may be seen at the left in the
main valley. (*Photograph by DeCou, from Ewing Galloway.*)

point a plucking erosion beneath the forming ice broadens and sharply
steepens the valley head until it assumes the appearance of a giant
stone quarry driven into the mountain flank. Such a valley head is very
different in appearance from the pointed ravine end caused by the
headward erosion of running water. The head of the typical ice-scoured
valley is rounded, steep sided, and amphitheater shaped. It is called a
cirque (Figs. 262, 264, 266). Commonly the bottom of a cirque is more
deeply eroded than the valley just beyond it, causing a rock basin. The
existence of a small lake there adds beauty to the grandeur of the sheer
rock walls. Iceberg Lake in Glacier National Park lies in a cirque the
walls of which rise 2,500 to 3,000 ft. That cirque is only one of hun-

dreds, large and small, in the heavily glaciated mountains of North America. They are abundant also in the glaciated peaks of Europe, Asia, South America, and New Zealand.

FIG. 267.—The cirque wall and part of the comb ridge at the head of Grinell Glacier, Glacier National Park. This is part of the "Garden Wall," and the Continental Divide lies along it. On the crest line at the extreme left is the notch of another cirque, seen from the rear side.

521. GLACIATED MOUNTAIN-UPLAND FEATURES. In contrast with stream-eroded mountains, those whose features result from glacial scour exhibit great sharpness of detail. Some ranges are flanked on

FIG. 268.—The Matterhorn, a roughly quadrangular peak resulting from the headward encroachment of four glaciers. (*Photograph by Ewing Galloway.*)

either side by cirques. Erosion of the plucking, or quarrying, type at the bases of the cirque walls has reduced the width not only of the spurs between adjacent cirques but also of the mountain range, until there remains little more than a "knife-edge" divide. So close is the approach of some opposing cirques that in places the thin divide between them crumbles through, leaving the crest merely a row of alternating pinnacles and notches. These are called "comb ridges." The "Garden Wall" in Glacier National Park is such a ridge, and it happens also to be the Continental Divide (Fig. 267). Some of the broader and more accessible of the notches so made are used as passes. Gunsight, Piegan, and other passes in Glacier Park and many elsewhere are of that origin.

High mountain peaks, their bases whittled by quarrying ice erosion in flanking cirques, are reduced to sharpened remnants. They commonly assume steep and angular contours. In the Alps such peaks are called "horns," of which the roughly quadrangular Matterhorn is a notable example (Fig. 268).

The Shore Features of Hill and Mountain Regions

522. DISTINCTIVE FEATURES. The bold and striking features of all hilly and mountainous coasts give them a certain unity of landscape quality. They are not all alike, either in their approachability or in the features that affect their various degrees of human utility. However, they have at least one thing in common. A highland barrier separates the shore, whatever its origin and outline, from any hinterland that may be reached through it. From the standpoint of cultural geography, such a coast is different from the coast of a plains region, even though its shore outlines may be much the same.

The major shoreline features of mountain coasts, like those of plains, are determined largely by their recent diastrophic and gradational history. Shorelines of submergence contrast sharply with those of emergence, and some show the complicated features added by wave and current deposition. Attention is here directed to some of the principal shore and coastal features of the highlands and to the ways in which they differ from those of the lowlands.

523. THE SHORELINES AND FEATURES OF UPLIFTED HIGHLAND COASTS. Shorelines of recently uplifted mountain coasts are simple and regular in outline. The 6,000 miles of shore bordering the growing mountains and coastal hills between Oregon and the 40th parallel in Chile is remarkable for its regularity. In that entire distance there are only a few coastal indentations sufficiently large or well protected to be good commercial harbors. The tectonic disturbances which are responsible for the elevation of the coastal highlands have involved also the formation of ocean deeps offshore. On most parts of this coast the continental shelf is narrow or lacking, and even the greatest waves

break directly upon the shore. Because of this the irregular curves produced by the emergence of a faulted coast are rounded into sweeping
curves by the erosion of headlands and the filling of indentations. Bold
rocky capes and wave-eroded cliffs predominate. Some of them have
rockstrewn bases and are bordered by the shallow waters of wave-cut
terraces. Others have fringes of beach. Although some of the cliffs
are of great length and steepness, they generally are broken at intervals
by the curving beaches of small aggrading lowlands or by the spits and
bay bars that obstruct the mouths of unfilled coves.

The onshore features of this rising mountain coast exhibit, in
much of its great extent, clear evidence of its elevation by stages and

Fig. 269.—Marine terraces on the coast of California, near Los Angeles. The steplike profiles of cliffs and terraces may be seen in the distance, the surface of one of the
terraces in the foreground.

presumably by faulting. The most obvious marks of elevation are seen
in distinct wave-cut cliffs and marine terraces, now far above sea level.
Some of the stages between successive elevations were sufficiently
separated in time so that during each a new wave-cut cliff, with its
bordering terrace, was eroded. In many places, from California to
Chile, the coastal profile rises in series of giant steps, of which one
section of the California coast has 10 or more. Some of the highest are
more than 1,500 ft. above present sea level. Most of the individual
terraces are not highly continuous, since they are interrupted at
frequent intervals by local changes of level during their formation
and by stream gullying since the time of their uplift. However,
their gently sloping platforms provide many acres of tillable land on
coastal slopes that would otherwise be too steep for cultivation
(Fig. 269).

524. The Shorelines and Features of Submerging Highland Coasts. Mountains and hills of stream erosion, when partially submerged, have shorelines of great irregularity. As on a submerging plain, the sea creeps into every coastal valley and makes a bay. Owing to the steepness of stream gradients in highland regions, the same number of feet of submergence would produce a larger bay on a lowland than on a highland coast. However, highland coasts are more likely to have large changes of level than are those of lowlands. Between the bays, each ridge and mountain spur forms a hilly peninsula, rocky promontory, or island. This is the highland type of *ria* shoreline. Its features and outlines are of many varieties, but whatever their details, they are sheltered coasts. Commodious bays, abundant shelter, and good anchorage are to be had at many places. Bayhead sites upon stream-eroded slopes or small delta plains furnish excellent locations for commercial ports, but the inferior productivity and low penetrability of rough hinterlands do not favor port development.

525. *Highlands with ria shores* have many examples. They are particularly extensive and varied as to detail in western Europe and the Mediterranean borders. They include the shore of northwestern Spain, the Gulf of Corinth and other deep indentations upon the shores of Greece, and the highly irregular shores of the Aegean and Adriatic Seas (Fig. 251). Other examples of highlands with ria shorelines are found on the coast of Japan and the long hilly coast of South China.

526. The shorelines and coastal features of glaciated mountains have much the same relation to those of mountainous ria coasts that glacial mountain features have to stream-eroded mountain features. Both shorelines and coastal profiles show the effects of ice scour. Long, steep, peninsular headlands alternate with narrow, deep, and sheer-walled bays, some of the latter having unusual length. Indeed, the number and configuration of the bays are what particularly distinguish the ice-scoured coast. They are of great variety in shape, and doubtless some are merely rias, their shapes slightly modified by ice scour. Many, however, are submerged, glaciated, U-shaped mountain valleys. To these long narrow arms of the sea the Norwegian name *fiord* is applied. Fiorded coasts provide some of the finest scenery in the world. High mountain uplands are there, their summits seldom visible from the narrow fiord below. High and rocky walls, mist shrouded, rise on either hand, and occasional cascades plunge from the mouths of hanging valleys. Sharp bends and rocky islands obstruct the view, and a narrow horizon seems to shut out the world and create complete isolation. Yet the quiet waters of the fiord are easily acces-

sible, since they are so deep that they may be navigated in safety, even by ocean-going ships (Fig. 270).

The principal regions of fiorded mountain coast are in the higher middle latitudes where, during the glacial period, many valley glaciers descended to sea level. The fiords are best developed in highlands that are characterized by the marine west-coast type of climate, where abundant orographic snowfall fed the many individual glaciers that occupied, deepened, and reshaped as many preglacial stream valleys. The great fiords also are found within the flanks of the higher

Fig. 270.—A view from the head of a fiord in Norway. The village occupies a small delta but the rocky island, the steep walls, and the presence of the ship indicate deep water. (*Photograph by Ewing Galloway.*)

coastal highlands. Coasts having deep fiords and intricate pattern are (*a*) the west coast of Norway, (*b*) the west coast of North America from Puget Sound to Alaska, (*c*) the coast of southern Chile, and (*d*) the west coast of South Island, New Zealand (Fig. 271). Others of low altitude and less grandeur are parts of the coasts of Scotland, Iceland, Greenland, Labrador, and the Arctic islands.

527. The Origin and Shapes of Fiords. It is probable that many fiords are ice-scoured mountain valleys which have been submerged by diastrophic changes of level since the time of their formation. In some the great depth of the water can hardly be explained otherwise. It is probable also that mountain-valley glaciers discharging into the sea are able, by reason of the

great depth or thickness of the ice tongues, to erode their valley floors well
below sea level. After the disappearance of the ice the valley floor is occupied
by sea water, sometimes deeply and far inland. Some fiords are continued
inland by U-shaped valleys and end in cirque valley heads, a few of which
still contain glaciers (Fig. 272).

Like other glaciated mountain valleys, fiords are comparatively regular in
outline and have less of branching channels than rias. The latter also,

Fig. 271.

because of their river origin, usually become progressively more shallow
inland. Many fiords, on the other hand, because of the greater vigor of ice
erosion near the glacier head, are deeper near their landward than toward
their seaward ends. Moreover, submerged morainic deposits near the outer
ends of the fiords tend further to shallow the water there. In any case, most
fiords have ample depth for navigation, and, as harbors, their deficiencies
are not so much in the lack of adequate depth of channel as in bottoms
sufficiently shallow so that the anchor chains of ships can reach them.
Portland Canal, a fiord that forms part of the boundary between Alaska
and British Columbia, is 90 miles long, from $\frac{1}{2}$ mile to 2 miles wide, and, in
mid-channel, has water ranging from 90 to 1,250 ft. in depth. The Sogne

Fiord, the longest in Norway, has a length of 112 miles, an average width of 4 miles, and its water reaches a maximum depth of 4,000 ft.

Although most fiords are deep, many of them are not long. Submerged valleys at right angles to the coast join with cross valleys in bewildering complexity. In some places their arrangement has a crudely parallel or even rectangular pattern which suggests a relation to joint planes or other structural features in the rock. Especially near the seaward margins of some fiorded areas, the ice-scoured channels are so numerous and so varied in direction that the rocky coast is dissected into thousands of island blocks, some large and mountainous, others mere rocky points of great

Fig. 272.—A view down the U-shaped Vidde Valley, Norway. Note the hanging valley and the fact that the mountain spurs have been truncated or trimmed off (cf. Fig. 260). The white line of a cascading brook may be seen just left of the building. In the foreground is a mountain dairy farm or *saeter*. (*Underwood and Underwood.*)

menace to navigation. The island fringe of Norway is called the *Skjaergaard*, or *skerry guard* (Fig. 273). Many of the cross fiords are so arranged that, together, they make a channel that parallels the coast and is sheltered on the seaward side by an almost unbroken succession of mountainous islands and rocky skerries. By this angular passageway most of the 1,000-mile route from Stavanger to North Cape, Norway, may be made with protection from the waves of the open Atlantic. A similar "inside passage," in places extremely narrow and tortuous, extends over the equally long route from Seattle, Wash., to Skagway, Alaska. Still another affords nearly 500 miles of protected route between the Straits of Magellan and the Gulf of Peñas, on the coast of Chile.

On the coasts of glaciated hill regions submerged valleys are not so long, so deep, or so straight sided as the fiords of mountain coasts. This is particularly true of hill regions that were overridden by glaciers of the continental type rather than by valley glaciers. Under those conditions the hilltops as well as the valley bottoms are ice scoured, and there is not the great over-deepening of the valleys characteristic of fiords. To distinguish the somewhat

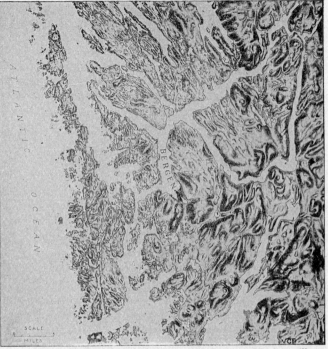

Fig. 273.—The ice-scoured coast of Norway, near Bergen. The map illustrates the pattern of the fiords on that part of the coast and the distribution of islands in the skerry guard. (*Redrawn from Topografisk kart over kongeriget Norge.*)

broad, irregular, hill-bordered bays that have been somewhat modified in shape by glacial scour the term *fiard* has been employed. Some of the bays of eastern Canada and Newfoundland and those of the hilly lowland coasts of Sweden and Finland are of that type. Between fiords, fiards, and ice-scoured rias, of the type seen on the coast of Maine, there are intermediate features of endless variety in size and shape.

Section E. Earth Resources

528. HUMAN DEPENDENCE UPON EARTH RESOURCES. Each part of the earth is equipped by nature in certain ways that set wide or narrow limits upon its potential human use. It is the number, kind, and association of these items of natural endowment that help to establish the individuality of regions. The list includes conditions of climate and the physical features of the land surface. These already have been discussed at length. However, there are other elements of regional equipment that are materials of the earth's composition or of its natural vegetable or animal life. These are not grown or manufactured by human enterprise but exist as parts of the natural earth. Unlike climate and landforms, they actually are used by man, and, because they either are obtained from the natural earth or exist in or upon it, they are called natural resources, or *earth resources*.

Since the beginning of human existence man has directed his activities with reference to such earth resources as he knew how to use for his own benefit. Among the most primitive men the list was not long. Water, roots, seeds, fruits, fish, and game supplied food and clothing. Wood and carefully chosen stones yielded shelter, weapons, and implements. A little earth and some native metals were used in making other utensils and articles of personal adornment. The advance of material civilization has increased the number of earth substances required and both the degree and the variety of human dependence upon these natural goods.

Modern society requires water, as did the old, but in such quantities as never before. The natural supplies of plants and animals long since have proved inadequate, and cultivated or domesticated species have supplemented or replaced them. Yet those provided by nature still are in demand. New woods and new metals have created new uses;

460

their application to modern industry has increased the requirement for them a thousandfold and has woven them into combinations whose patterns are constantly changing. The dependence of present civilization upon certain earth resources has grown so rapidly in recent decades that few people realize how different the present is, in that respect, from even the recent past. It is estimated, for example, "that in a hundred years the output of pig iron, copper, and mineral fuels has increased a hundredfold; that more mineral resources have been mined and consumed since the opening of the [present] century than in all preceding history."[1] Because of their vital importance in modern affairs, an understanding of the occurrence and distribution of the natural, or earth-given, resources is as fundamental to an appreciation of the broader problems of geography as is a knowledge of climate or landforms.

529. CLASSES OF EARTH RESOURCES. The natural resources available for the use of man are of two principal classes: inorganic and organic. In the former class are found those gaseous, liquid, or solid earth components that have value for direct human use or as a basis for the production of other necessary goods. Such are water, the mineral fuels, the metalliferous ores, building stones, and the valuable chemical raw materials of earth or air. Organic resources are such as are derived from the natural plant and animal life of various parts of the earth. Among them are wood, natural pasture, wild game, and fish. The soil, a resource of fundamental importance, is made up of both inorganic and organic components. With the inorganic rock fragments, which are the basis of soils, are mingled variable quantities of plant and animal remains and a world of microscopic organisms. Some organic forms in the natural environment of man can hardly be called resources. Worthless or poisonous plants and certain forms of insect or of microscopic life are parts of the natural equipment of areas, but they constitute hazards to life and the ability to make a living just as, for example, certain aspects of climate do. However, comment upon that phase of the subject of earth resources falls beyond the scope of this textbook. The resources to be considered in the following chapters of this section of the book are (a) water, (b) the biotic resources, (c) soil, (d) the mineral fuels, and (e) ores and other economic minerals.

There are some natural resources, both organic and inorganic, of which man may use as much as he desires without fear that the supply ever will be exhausted. Such may be called the *inexhaustible resources*, and air, sand, or common clay are examples of the class. Others,

[1] Leith, C. K. "World Minerals and World Politics." p. 3, McGraw-Hill Book Company, Inc., New York, 1931.

although the supply may be limited in quantity, tend to replenish themselves when they are used. These may be called the *renewable resources*, and water, wood, and natural pasture illustrate the class. Still others, such as coal, iron, or chemical salts, have required the operation of natural processes through the geologic ages for their accumulation. When once they are used they are gone forever. Such may be called *nonrenewable resources*.

530. THE CONSERVATION OF EARTH RESOURCES. The dependence of modern society upon a variety of critically important earth resources is well known. There is nothing to indicate that future generations will not need most of these resources and perhaps others that are not now thought valuable. Consequently, it is clear that present generations are charged with a responsibility toward the future, particularly with respect to the nonrenewable resources which now are being produced or wasted in large quantities. *It is, in fact, the responsibility of the present generation to secure to society, both now and in the future, the maximum benefit from the use of those materials provided by nature.* The discharge of that responsibility calls for much knowledge and a careful balancing of the earth conditions with the human factors involved. Information is needed upon the following matters: (*a*) What kinds and how much of the various resources are available? (*b*) To what extent may the more abundant and the renewable resources be substituted for the less abundant and the nonrenewable? (*c*) How may resources be used with the least waste, and how may new methods of production and use reduce waste? (*d*) In how far is it wise to sacrifice human energy and risk human life to save resources? (*e*) How may the rights of present generations be properly balanced against those of the future? Efforts to gather information and solve problems concerning any phase of this complicated matter may be considered a part of the field of *the conservation of natural resources*.

REFERENCES FOR SECTION E

GENERAL

"Report of the Mississippi Valley Committee of the Public Works Administration." Government Printing Office, Washington, D. C., 1934.

"Report of the National Resources Board." Government Printing Office, Washington, D. C., 1934. Excellent material on United States resources.

Zimmerman, E. W. "World Resources and Industries." Harper & Brothers, New York, 1933.

WATER RESOURCES

Carrier, E. H. "The Thirsty Earth: A Study in Irrigation." Christophers, London, 1928.

Dixey, Frank. "A Practical Handbook of Water Supply." Thomas Murby and Co., London, 1931.

Newell, F. H. "Water Resources: Present and Future Uses." Yale University Press, New Haven, 1920.

Voskuil, W. H. "Economics of Water Power Development." McGraw-Hill Book Company, Inc., New York, 1928.

BIOTIC RESOURCES

"Atlas of American Agriculture." Sec. E, Natural Vegetation. Government Printing Office, Washington D. C., 1924.

Graebner, Paul. "Lehrbuch der allgemeinen Pflanzengeographie." Quelle & Meyer, Leipzig, 1929.

Hardy, M. E. "The Geography of Plants." University Press, Oxford, 1920.

Haviland, Maud D. "Forest, Steppe, and Tundra." University Press, Cambridge, England, 1926.

Hayek, August. "Allgemeine Pflanzengeographie." Verlagsbuchhandlung Gebrüder Borntraeger, Berlin, 1926. Contains a world vegetation map.

Martonne, Emmanuel de. "A Shorter Physical Geography." Alfred A. Knopf, New York, 1927.

————. "Traite de géographie physique." Vol. 3, Biogéographie, Librairie Armand Colin, Paris, 1927.

Newbigin, Marion I. "Plant and Animal Geography." Methuen & Co., Ltd., London, 1936.

Rubner, K. Das naturliche Waldbild Europas. *Z. Weltforstwirtschaft*, Vol. 2, pp. 68–155, 1934. With map.

Schimper, A. F. W. "Plant Geography upon a Physiological Basis." English translation. University Press, Oxford, 1903.

———— and von Faber, F. C. "Pflanzengeographie auf physiologischer Grundlage," 3d ed., 2 vols. Gustav Fischer, Jena, 1935. Contains world vegetation map in color.

Supan, Alexander. "Grundzüge der physichen Erdkunde." 7th ed. Vol. 2, Part 2, Pflanzen und Tiergeographie. Walter de Gruyter & Company, Berlin, 1930. Contains world vegetation map in color.

Warming, E. The Oecology of Plants. English translation. University Press, Oxford, 1909.

Zon, Raphael, and Sparhawk, William N. "Forest Resources of the World." 2 vols., McGraw-Hill Book Company, Inc., New York, 1923.

SOIL RESOURCES

Bennett, Hugh H. "Soil Conservation." McGraw-Hill Book Company, Inc., New York, 1939.

Blanck, E. "Handbuch der Bodenlehre." Vol. 3, Verlag Julius Springer, Berlin, 1930.

Glinka, K. D. "The Great Soils Groups of the World and Their Development." Translated by C. F. Marbut. Edwards Bros., Inc., Ann Arbor, Mich., 1927.

Joffe, Jacob S. "Pedology." Rutgers University Press, Brunswick, N. J., 1936.

Kellogg, C. E. Climate and Soil, in "Climate and Man," 1941 Yearbook of Agriculture, United States Department of Agriculture, Washington, D. C.

————. "The Soils That Support Us." The Macmillan Company, New York, 1941.

Krische, Paul. "Bodenkarten." Paul Parey, Berlin, 1928.

Marbut, C. F. Soils of the United States. "Atlas of American Agriculture." Part 3. Government Printing Office, Washington, D. C., 1935.

Robinson, Gilbert W. "Soils: Their Origin, Constitution, and Classification." Thomas Murby and Co., London.

Sigmond, Alexius A. J. de. "The Principles of Soil Science." Translated from the Hungarian by A. B. Yolland. Thomas Murby and Co., London, 1938.

"Soils and Men." Yearbook of United States Department of Agriculture, 1938. Washington, D. C.

Whitney, Milton. "Soil and Civilization." D. Van Nostrand Company, Inc., New York, 1925.

Wolfanger, L. A. "The Major Soil Divisions of the United States." John Wiley & Sons, Inc., New York, 1930.

MINERAL RESOURCES

Bayley, W. S. "A Guide to the Study of Non-metallic Mineral Products." Henry Holt and Company, Inc., New York, 1930.

Eckel, Edwin C. "Iron Ores." McGraw-Hill Book Company, Inc., New York, 1914.

Emmons, W. H. "Geology of Petroleum." McGraw-Hill Book Company, Inc., New York, 1931.

Fox, Cyril S. "Bauxite and Aluminous Laterite." Crosby, Lockwood & Sons, London, 1932.

Jeffrey, Edward C. "Coal and Civilization." The Macmillan Company, New York, 1925.

Leith, C. K., et al. Elements of a National Mineral Policy. The Mineral Inquiry, Am. Inst. of Min. and Met. Eng., New York, 1933.

————. "The Economic Aspects of Geology." Henry Holt and Company, Inc., New York, 1921.

————. "World Minerals and World Politics." McGraw-Hill Book Company, Inc., New York, 1931.

Moore, Elwood S. "Coal." 2d ed., John Wiley & Sons, Inc., New York, 1940.

Read, Thomas T. "Our Mineral Civilization." The Williams & Wilkins Company, Baltimore, 1932.

Ries, H. "Economic Geology." John Wiley & Sons, Inc., New York, 1930. A standard general work on mineral resources of all classes.

Tarr, W. A. "Introductory Economic Geology." McGraw-Hill Book Company, Inc., New York, 1930.

Tryon, F. G., and Eckel, E. C. (Editor). "Mineral Economics." McGraw-Hill Book Company, Inc., New York, 1932.

Ver Wiebe, W. A. "Oil Fields in the United States." McGraw-Hill Book Company, Inc., New York, 1930.

Voskuil, W. H. "Minerals in Modern Industry." John Wiley & Sons, Inc., New York, 1930.

Chapter XXII. Water Resources
of the Land

531. THE VARIETY OF USES OF WATER. Water exceeds any other earth resource except air in the urgency of its need and in the quantity used. So many and so vital are the purposes for which it is required and so varied are its qualities and conditions of supply that several fields of technical science are concerned with its abundant, continuous, and safe provision. The waters of the land are derived, either directly or indirectly, from atmospheric precipitation. For that reason, regions of abundant precipitation usually, but not always, have abundant supplies of water, and their inhabitants are able to use it lavishly. In arid regions water is the element of first importance in restricting the settlement and use of land, and the supply of it is used with utmost economy.

Water supplies and water bodies are useful to man in many different ways, some of the most important of which are (a) in domestic supply, (b) for industrial processes, (c) for the irrigation of crops, (d) for the production of mechanical power, (e) as routes of inland transportation, and (f) in the added attractiveness that they give to scenic or recreational areas. The use of water for drinking and household supply ranges from a small daily ration among the nomadic people of arid lands to the daily per capita allowance of 15 or 20 gal. which is provided in modern cities. That use certainly is the most important to mankind, but it seldom requires so great a quantity of water as some others. Modern manufacturing establishments, such as steel mills, textile dyeing-and-finishing plants, and paper mills are large users of water. A choice of site for such an establishment often is made because of the availability there of an abundant supply of water having the requisite chemical properties or degree of pureness. For these uses great manufacturing cities must supply several times as much water per capita of their population as actually is used in the homes. The average total consumption of water for all kinds of uses, in 90 cities of more than 100,000 population in the United States, is the equivalent of about 125 gal. per day per inhabitant. The municipal system of Chicago supplies each day to its homes and factories an amount of water equivalent to 270 gal. for each of its residents.[1] That city has the highest per capita rate of consumption of any in the United States, and doubtless much of it is wasted because of the abundant supply close at hand in Lake Michigan.

532. SOURCES OF WATER SUPPLY. The large quantities of water required by modern urban and industrial centers are obtained from wells, springs, large lakes, and large rivers but even more generally from small streams the drainage of which is stored behind dams to create municipal reservoirs. Only about one out of four of the principal American cities obtains its water supply from wells. The remainder, and especially the largest cities, use surface waters. However, about two-thirds of the total population of the country live in small cities, in villages, and on farms where ground water, obtained from wells and springs, is the principal source of supply. For the irrigation of crops, surface waters are much more important than ground water, since the latter source supplies only about one-fourth of the land irrigated in the United States. Although the conditions found in the United States with respect to water supply are not representative of those to be found in all parts of the world, they give an indication of the required volume of this essential resource and some measure of the relative importance of the sources from which it is obtained.

The Ground-water Supply

533. THE AVAILABILITY OF GROUND WATER. It has been noted previously that a part of the precipitation is captured and prevented from flowing immediately into streams and the seas when it percolates downward into the pore spaces and crevices of the regolith and the underlying rocks. It has been noted too that, under ordinary conditions, the lower levels of these pore spaces are filled with water and that the top of the saturated zone is called the *ground-water table* (349). The water stored below the ground-water table is the source of supply for springs and wells (Fig. 125).

The availability of ground water is not everywhere the same. In regions of abundant and well-distributed precipitation the pore space in the earth is likely to be well filled, but in arid regions the rapid evaporation of moisture and the infrequent rains do not permit of a deep penetration of ground water. The supplies in arid regions are, therefore, mainly such as move slowly, deep underground, from more humid regions. Frequently they are limited in quantity and are

[1] *Nat. Resources Board, Rept.*, p. 332, Washington, 1934.

to be had only in a few localities, and those places take on critical importance in the migration and settlement of people. Even in humid regions ground water is not everywhere abundant. A copious supply depends not only upon abundant precipitation but also upon (a) earth materials of sufficient porosity to absorb and store a large quantity of water and (b) the existence of pore space, bedding planes, fracture planes, or other avenues sufficient to permit a relatively free underground movement of water from a large storage area to the well or spring from which it is being removed. Beds of gravel, sand, loosely compacted sediments, porous sandstones, and thinly bedded or cavernous limestones provide these conditions. Compact clays and shales, massive and little-fractured igneous rocks, and some other formations provide but little storage capacity for water and but little facility for its underground flow. Springs in such rocks seldom are abundant, and wells are difficult to construct and limited in flow.

534. Pore Space for Ground Water. In sandstones the pore space capable of being filled by water commonly exceeds 25 per cent and sometimes reaches 40 per cent of the volume of the rock. In unconsolidated earth or glacial gravels the figure is much greater. In massive limestones there often is 10 per cent of pore space; and in cavernous limestones there is much more than that amount. In dense igneous and metamorphic rocks the pore space is much less. In solid granites it seldom is more than 1 per cent; and in some metamorphic rocks it is said to be less than one-half of 1 per cent. In such rocks the pores are so small that they do not readily yield the little water that they contain. Numerous joint cracks or structural planes in dense rocks greatly increase both their water-holding and water-yielding capacities. However, some large regions are underlain by massive and little-fractured igneous and other crystalline rocks from which the recovery of ground water is expensive and seldom adequate.

535. The Qualities of Ground Water. No ground water is free from dissolved mineral, but the nature and quantity of the chemical salts carried in solution differ widely from region to region. A few dissolved minerals, such as sulphur or iron, impart to water a disagreeable taste or render it unfit for certain industrial processes. Some minerals give tonic, laxative, or other desirable medicinal qualities. Among the most abundant of the soluble salts found in ground water are compounds of calcium (lime), sodium, and magnesium. In desert regions seepage waters commonly are charged with compounds of these and other salts to a degree that renders them almost, if not quite, unfit for human use. In the United States these are known as *alkali waters*. In humid regions most of the readily soluble sodium compounds have been removed from the ground long since. However, limestones,

lime-cemented sediments, and dolomites (321) furnish supplies of calcium and magnesium which, although they do not much affect the taste of water, give it the quality called *hardness* which does affect its domestic and industrial utility.

Ground water ordinarily has been filtered through the earth, sometimes for many years, before it is used. It is, therefore, relatively free from mud and other suspended materials.

536. *The Hardness of Water.*   The amount or degree of hardness in water usually is expressed in terms of parts of dissolved mineral per million parts of water. Regions underlain mainly by ancient crystalline rocks or by highly siliceous sands or sandstones usually have not much available lime, and their waters may contain as little as 5 or 10 parts of hardness per million. These are the naturally "soft" waters. Water containing as much as 60 parts still is considered soft, but if it contains more than 120 to 180 parts per million it is considered "hard" water. In regions of lime-containing

FIG. 274.—(*After U. S. National Resources Board.*)

sedimentary rocks, well waters in common use contain 300 to 500 parts and, in a few places, as much as 700 to 800 parts per million (Fig. 274). Many wells in arid regions, and some even in humid regions, tap supplies of ground water so hard as to be unfit for use. Hard waters require "softening" when they are used with soap and present serious problems in certain industrial processes or in the supply of steam boilers. This is because of their chemical reactions and the undesirable precipitates that they form.

537. SPRINGS.   A spring is a concentrated natural outflow of water from underground. It may flow either continuously or intermittently, and its water may be either cold or warm, hard or soft. Springs result from a variety of conditions involving the position of the ground-water table, the configuration of the land surface, and the nature and structure of the rocks. Figure 275A illustrates the occurrence of a spring on the side of a valley which has been eroded below the level of the local ground-water table. Springs of that type are common in glacial drift and often are the main sources of supply of small brooks at the headwaters of rivers. After a period of protracted drought the level of the ground water that supplies such a spring may be lowered, and it will cease to flow until the water level is raised by

the downward seepage of further rains. Figure 275B illustrates the site of a spring caused by the movement of water downward through porous formations and then horizontally along the top of an impervious rock layer. Sands, sandstones, or porous limestones, underlain by compact clays or shales, supply conditions of that kind and often produce many springs, all at about the same level. Figure 275C illustrates the manner in which water from a wide area of rocks, even those of low water-holding capacity, may be converged upon a spring by means of joint and fault planes. In some regions water thus collected is conveyed deep underground where it comes under the influence of hot igneous rocks and finally issues as hot, or "thermal," springs or even as geysers. The latter add to the scenic attractiveness of several regions

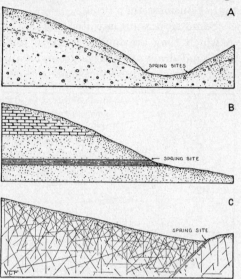

Fig. 275.—Diagrams to illustrate some of the many possible conditions of surface, material, and structure that are related to the occurrence of springs.

Fig. 276.—Old Faithful geyser in eruption. Yellowstone National Park. This famous geyser attracts many tourists, and their accommodation requires a hotel and other facilities.

in which they occur, such as Yellowstone National Park; Iceland; and North Island, New Zealand (Fig. 276). In those regions, geysers, the name of which is derived from that of one of the intermittent hot springs of Iceland, are resources of considerable value, because of the tourist business they bring.

Some springs drain water from far beyond the immediate localities in which they are found. Because they are outlets for considerable areas and draw upon large ground-water supplies some of them have large volumes and are perennial in flow.

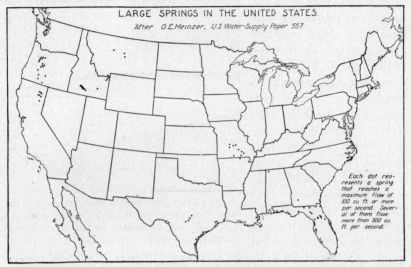

LARGE SPRINGS IN THE UNITED STATES.
After O.E.Meinzer, U.S Water-Supply Paper 557

Each dot represents a spring that reaches a maximum flow of 100 cu. ft. or more per second. Several of them flow more than 500 cu. ft. per second.

FIG. 277.—Most of the large springs of the United States occur in a few regional groups. Those in Florida, Missouri, and Texas mainly are associated with areas of cavernous limestones, while those of Idaho, Oregon, and California occur more largely in porous-lava formations.

538. *Large Springs.*   Under certain conditions of underground drainage, springs attain the proportions of considerable rivers. That is notably true in regions of cavernous limestones or of porous lavas. In such rocks, ground water descends from the surface through numerous openings and ultimately converges upon an underground channel in some volume. There are in the United States about 60 springs with sufficient flow so that each would supply all the water required by a city of $\frac{1}{2}$ million inhabitants. There are at least a half dozen that flow with sufficient volume so that any one of them would supply a city of 2 million inhabitants or any city in the country except New York or Chicago.[1] Most of the large springs of the country are included in four regions. They are the limestone areas of (*a*) northern Florida and (*b*) the Ozark region of southern Missouri; and the permeable-lava regions of (*c*) the Snake River Valley of Idaho and (*d*) western Oregon

[1] Meinzer, O. E. Large Springs in the United States. *U. S. Geol. Survey, Water Supply Paper* 557, Washington, D. C., 1927.

and northern California (Figs. 277, 278). Other regions of large springs are indicated in Fig. 277.

539. THE USE OF SPRING WATERS. In the United States are thousands of farmhouses and not a few villages that are located upon sites originally chosen because spring water was found there by a pioneer settler. Large numbers of those springs, most of them on valley slopes, still are flowing and still supply water for farm families. Others have been abandoned or have ceased to flow continuously. The drilling of many wells has drawn heavily upon the ground-water supply. The substitution of tilled crops for forest and grassland has tended to increase the rate of runoff and to decrease correspondingly the proportion of the precipitation that enters the ground. Both these changes have diminished the ground-water supply and have resulted in the lowering of the water table in many localities. This has had the effect of rendering the supply of spring water less dependable, while at

FIG. 278.—Part of the "Thousand Springs" which issue from beds of broken or porous lava in the Snake River Canyon, southern Idaho. (*U. S. Geological Survey Photograph.*)

the same time the growth of population has tended to make it less adequate and more subject to pollution. Still there are many relatively small springs which have acquired local or even wider fame for the purity or reputed medical properties of their waters. In some localities the bottling and shipment of these are a considerable industry. Moreover, a few thermal and medicinal springs of special properties or great renown serve in various parts of the world as a reason for population concentration. About them have grown, in both Europe and America, several widely known health resorts and cities of considerable size.

540. WELLS penetrate the zone of saturated earth below the water table in order that ground water may be collected in sufficient quantity and lifted to the surface. Formerly wells were made only by digging a hole to the ground-water level, and they could not be many feet deep because of the difficulty of excavating them. Millions of dug wells still are in daily use in nearly all parts of the world, although their shallow and open construction makes them particularly subject to pollution (Fig. 279). Many dug wells have only temporary supplies

of water, while others are permanent. Figure 279 shows also the relation of three wells to a fluctuating ground-water table and indicates the reason for their varying degrees of permanence of water supply; the well numbered 1 is a modern drilled well which reaches below the lowest position of the water table and has never run dry; that numbered 2 is a dug well which reaches below the ordinary water table and has water at all times, except after periods of protracted drought; that numbered 3 is dry, except for a short time after a long period of rains.

Modern deep wells, like that numbered 1 below, are made by drilling a small hole scores or hundreds of feet, through surface formations and the upper part of the ground-water zone, into the deeper waters of some known water-bearing formation, such as a porous sandstone. From a drilled well water must be lifted by a long pump rod through a pipe which is carefully encased to prevent the surface

FIG. 279.—Well No. 2 is higher than No. 1 and appears to be a safer water supply but, in fact, it is not so because of the rock structures concerned. The stippled horizons indicate porous, water-bearing formations. The dashed lines show positions of the ground-water table; 1, in wet seasons; 2, ordinary level; 3, in dry seasons.

waters from seeping into the drill hole and thus contaminating the deep-water supply. Figure 279 indicates that, while well 2 is situated higher up the slope than No. 1 and appears to be in a safer position with respect to pollution, it is in fact not so. The porous rock formation below the surface carries seepage from barns and cesspool directly toward the house well rather than away from it, as the surface slope would indicate. Many wells are located badly because of ignorance of the nature of ground-water movement and of the structure or porosity of the rocks that govern ground-water movement in the locality in which they are constructed.

The quantity of water from deep wells, as well as the quality, depends upon the nature of the underlying rock and its structure. If the well hole terminates in a thick porous sandstone of great area! extent and broad outcrop, it may yield an abundant and continuous supply of water. If the only rock beneath a locality is of the massive crystalline type the water yield may be continuous but not abundant. The rock has so little pore and crevice space that its water content is small. The rate of flow into a well in dense rock is sometimes increased by using explosives at the bottom of the hole to shatter the surrounding rock and make numerous crevices through which the water of a larger area may flow in. However, some hard crystalline rocks are so low in water content that no device can bring about a sufficient flow to justify the very high cost of drilling deep wells in them. Shale rocks, although not hard, also commonly are compact and "dry," but usually they are closely associated with other sediments which are porous. Wells in regions of cavernous limestones sometimes tap underground *streams* of water. Such wells may yield abundant supplies, but since the water has entered the underground channel directly from the surface drainage, some of it through sinkholes, it has

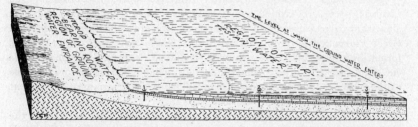

FIG. 280.—A diagram to illustrate one type of artesian structure. Well No. 1 (left) reaches the water-bearing formation, but its top is as high as the level of ground-water entrance, and it would require pumping. The others should provide flowing water.

had little natural filtering and is subject to pollution. It is likely to be little safer than the river waters of the same region, since the latter have at least been exposed to the bacteria-destroying power of sunlight.

541. ARTESIAN WELLS. Common use applies the term *artesian* to any deep drilled well from which water flows or in which the water level rises so near to the surface as to require little pumping. Originally the term was restricted to such wells as flow freely without pumping. Artesian wells are possible under any one of several sets of conditions of underground structure, one of which is illustrated in Fig. 280. The favorable situation must include the following conditions: (*a*) a water-bearing formation of sandstone or some other porous material; (*b*) the porous formation must outcrop or be exposed at the surface in a region of sufficient precipitation to fill it with water; (*c*) the formation must disappear at a low angle of inclination beneath a capping layer of some impervious rock, such as shale; (*d*) it must lead toward a region where the land surface is lower than it is at the exposed end of the porous formation; and (*e*) there must be no free exit from the porous

rock at an elevation lower than the region of the wells. A well drilled through the impervious layer and into the water-bearing formation taps a supply that is under pressure owing to the weight of the water that is backed up in the higher end of the porous formation. Water will rise in the well bore or flow from the opening as long as the rate of addition in the outcropping area exceeds the rate of loss through wells and seepage. In a few regions saucerlike structural basins of concentric relief contain water-bearing formations which outcrop about the edges of the basin and incline from all sides, underneath other rocks, toward its center, where artesian water may be had in abundance. A structure of that kind is found in the Paris Basin (391). (The term artesian, applied to wells of this class, is derived from Artois, the name of a district in northern France.)

542. *Notable Artesian Structures.* Artesian water is obtained from favorable structures, which occur locally in a great many places, and from a few that cover areas of truly great extent. One of the latter is the northern Great Plains region of the United States. There a series of water-bearing formations, especially the Dakota sandstone, outcrop at considerable elevation near the Rocky Mountains and incline eastward, under suitable capping layers, toward the lower plains. They yield artesian waters far out in the eastern part of the Dakotas.

Another vast artesian basin is found in the plains that lie west of the East Australian Highlands in Queensland and New South Wales (Fig. 281).

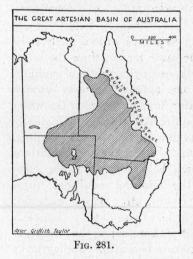

THE GREAT ARTESIAN BASIN OF AUSTRALIA

After Griffith Taylor

FIG. 281.

The abundant rain of the Highlands provides ground water which moves down the water-bearing formations underlying all the southwestern part of Queensland and the borders of the adjacent states. It is tapped by hundreds of wells, many of which flow freely. The supply of water is not generally sufficient for land irrigation, but it is most important in providing water for livestock and the pastoral occupants of these dry plains. Artesian structure is found also over large areas in central Argentina. There are many limited artesian structures and spring sites in American dry lands and those of other countries that furnish water for the irrigation of a few acres of crops in addition to that required for other uses. In these scattered bits of irrigated land may be recognized an additional class of oasis of much less individual importance than those previously noted (402, 409, 437, 443).

Unfortunately, the flow of water in an artesian basin cannot be maintained at a higher amount than that absorbed in the catchment area, where the water-bearing rock outcrops. It is, therefore, capable of depletion. Thousands of flowing wells in the Dakotas and hundreds in Australia, and careless waste of water through them, have decreased the pressures in both regions until many wells now require pumping, and the flow of others is much reduced.

The Surface-water Supply

543. THE USES AND PROBLEMS OF SURFACE WATERS. The economic utility of surface waters is so varied and the problems connected with them are so numerous that only a few of them may be touched upon. Surface drainage through streams and lakes is related to matters of economic concern such as soil erosion, flood control, power production, irrigation, municipal water supply, inland navigation, and the business of recreation. Out of these varied uses grow conflicts of human interest which lie beyond the scope of the elements of geography. However, the natural-resource qualities of surface waters may be examined briefly in their relation to some of these uses.

544. SURFACE WATERS FOR MUNICIPAL SUPPLY. Of the 300 principal cities of the United States, three-fourths are supplied with surface waters obtained from great lakes, large rivers, or, more commonly, relatively small streams.[1] Generally, the surface waters are less hard than the ground waters of the same region, because they are derived in part from the immediate runoff of rain water (Fig. 282). In periods of drought the surface

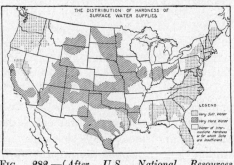

FIG. 282.—(*After U.S. National Resources Board.*)

supply fails, and the streams, fed mainly by springs, have increased hardness, to the great disadvantage of certain industries the manufactural processes of which require relatively soft water. However, surface waters are likely to contain larger quantities of sediment and organic matter, including bacteria, than ground water. For that reason many cities find it necessary to treat their water supplies (*a*) for the destruction of bacteria, (*b*) for the coagulation of very fine sediment, and (*c*), by filtration, to remove sediment. The quality of surface water varies greatly from region to region.

[1] *Nat. Resources Board, Rept. op. cit., p. 330.*

545. WATERS USED FOR IRRIGATION. The soils of arid lands generally are abundantly supplied with the mineral elements of soil fertility and require only water to make them productive. Adequate supplies of water are not easy to obtain, for the actual water requirement of crops is large (601), and inevitably much is lost by seepage and evaporation in the course of getting it to the crops. In American irrigation practice, although the amount of water required varies with the region and the crop, it is customary to provide annually the equivalent of a layer from 18 to 70 in. deep over the entire area to be irrigated. To secure so much water every type of source is drawn upon, but, the world over, surface runoff supplies most of it. Except in the rice-growing monsoon countries of southeastern Asia, irrigation is most

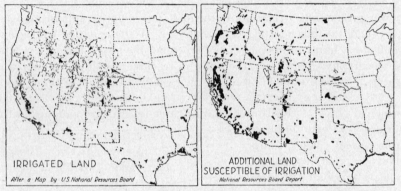

IRRIGATED LAND

After a Map by U.S National Resources Board

ADDITIONAL LAND SUSCEPTIBLE OF IRRIGATION

National Resources Board Report

FIG. 283.—The irrigated land and that susceptible of irrigation combined do not comprise a very large part of the total area of the semiarid and arid West.

practiced in lands that have less than 20 in. of average annual precipitation. Since the water requirement is generally much more than that quantity, and since always there are losses in the processes of capture, storage, and transportation, it follows that the rainfall of a large area is required to provide water to irrigate a small area. From that fact it is necessary to conclude that only a small part of the dry lands of the earth ever can be irrigated (Fig. 283).

546. THE QUALITY OF IRRIGATION WATERS is not everywhere the same. Some, particularly that obtained from underground sources, is heavily charged with dissolved salts. Such water when applied to the land sometimes leaves more soluble material in the soil, as a result of surface evaporation, than is removed through the drainage channels. This tends to increase the alkali content of irrigated lands and gradually to render them unfit for crops. Waters derived directly from mountain precipitation and the melting of mountain snows are particularly free from this defect and are much employed in the irrigation of alluvial fans upon the mountain borders.

Some part of the irrigation water applied to the land, supplemented by a part of the natural rainfall, soaks into the ground, joins the ground-water supply, and then commonly is recovered by pumping. It is then reused for irrigation unless, or until, the quantity of salts dissolved during its stay underground renders it unfit for the watering of crops.

547. PHYSICAL CONDITIONS FAVORABLE TO WATER-POWER PRODUCTION. Water has no inherent ability to develop energy in the same sense that it is able to quench thirst, supply plants, or cleanse fabrics. Its capacity to do work is attained by virtue of the solar energy which evaporates it and causes the wind to transport it onto the land, whence it is returned to the sea under the force of gravity. The essential conditions required to produce water power are *water* and *fall*, and within limits one of them may substitute for the other. A small volume of water falling a great distance may have the same capacity to do work as a great volume of water falling a short distance. Moreover, the former usually is capable of being more economically harnessed than is the great stream on a low gradient. Water power is, therefore, obtained at less cost from small mountain streams than from the great rivers of plains regions.

Several conditions of physical environment combine to furnish large water power and to make it economical to use. An ideal physical situation for water-power production might well include the following conditions: (*a*) *a large stream*, and (*b*) *a precipitous fall* in the lower course of the stream where the entire weight of the falling water may be harnessed at low cost. It is desirable that the stream be the drainage of a region (i) of large size and (ii) of abundant precipitation. It is also desirable (iii) that the precipitation be uniformly distributed throughout the year and (iv) that the runoff of the stream be further regularized by the natural storage of rain water in great areas of spongy forest floor, numerous swamps, or lakes.

548. STREAM FLOW AND POTENTIAL POWER DEVELOPMENT. A regular stream flow is desirable for water-power development because fluctuation in flow produces irregular power capacity. Ordinarily, it is not economical to build a power plant capable of utilizing the maximum flow of an erratic stream. Many power plants have capacity to use only the minimum flow, since otherwise a large financial investment in power plant would be unproductive of returns during much of the year. The construction of dams and other works for the storage of water tends to unify stream flow by capturing flood waters and holding them for use in the season of low water. This makes feasible the installation of larger power plants and the production of more power. In estimating the power-producing capacity of a site, a stream or a region it is customary for engineers to state more than one figure. These

indicate the quantity of power that could be produced without storage, with complete storage, or on any other practical basis.

549. LAND RELIEF AND POTENTIAL WATER-POWER SITES.   Formerly, usable water-power sites were limited to those available in regions where power was wanted. It had to be used at the place of its production. The development of hydroelectric power transmission has, to a degree, made the place of power production independent of the place of its use but not entirely. It is not yet economically feasible, in most regions, to send power by wire more than 300 or 400 miles. Moreover, it is not always feasible to use all the possible power of a great stream, even near a power market, because the cost of control and storage works on large streams is high. Therefore, certain power sites of great possibility go unused while others, which are physically less desirable, are developed. Most power sites are chosen because of the benefit of some natural advantage. Such are found in plains regions where a stream crosses an outcrop of resistant rock which increases the stream gradient or causes a narrows, which makes an economical site for a dam.

The disturbed drainageways of glaciated plains, both ice-scoured and ice-deposited, furnish more numerous power sites than are provided on the drainageways of stream-eroded plains. The steep gradients and diversity of rocks found in mountain valleys furnish more frequent and valuable power sites than are common to plains regions. That is particularly true of recently glaciated mountains. In them snow-fed streams descend through narrow lake-filled valleys of highly irregular gradient or plunge over the steep walls that terminate hanging valleys (Figs. 265, 266). Although potential water-power sites are numerous in glaciated mountain regions many of them are far from any feasible market for power and cannot now be economically utilized.

550. THE WORLD DISTRIBUTION OF POTENTIAL WATER POWERS.   Because of the conditions indicated above, the potential water power of the world shows very uneven distribution. In North America the western mountain cordillera has the greatest power possibilities, because of its heavy precipitation, great relief, ice-eroded mountain features, and forested slopes. That region is followed by the Laurentian Shield, which combines with its ice-scoured surface a moderate elevation, vast area, a fairly abundant precipitation, and natural water storage in myriad lakes and extensive forests (417, Fig. 179). In Europe the glaciated highland regions of Scandinavia and the Alpine countries hold the largest water-power possibilities. In Asia the conditions are most fully met on the rainy southern front of The Himalayas. In South America there are three significant districts, which are eastern Brazil, the eastern slopes of the northern and central Andes, and

southern Chile. Australia, being generally low and dry, has but little to offer in potential water power. However, Africa exceeds any other continent in this respect. Although much of its area is desert, several great rivers originate in the rainy tropical region, and each of them descends in falls over escarpments from the uplands of this plateau continent, on its way to the sea (466, Fig. 284).

551. THE VALUE OF STREAMS FOR INLAND NAVIGATION. In nearly all parts of the world, except deserts and mountains, streams are used as avenues of interior transportation. Prior to the development of railways they were so used much more than they are now. Even yet, there are large areas of several continents, including North America, where streams and lakes are the principal highways. Waterways attained early importance as routes of travel because of several advantages that they afforded over primitive land routes. Although they seldom are more direct than land routes, they are, by their nature, reduced to fairly uniform grade and eliminate most of the vertical irregularity common to land routes. Even primitive water craft carry easily burdens too heavy for man or pack animals. On routes from continental interiors outward, heavy loads may be moved on well-graded streams with little expenditure of energy, when aided by the river current.

Certain great rivers offer such advantages for transport, in regions of delayed economic development, that they still carry the major part of the traffic. The Yangtze is the principal means of moving goods to and from the far interior of China. The Congo provides extensive means of carriage in equatorial Africa, although falls cause several interruptions to navigation and prevent direct connection by boat with the coast. The Amazon drains a large area of heavy rainfall over a gradient so low and so free from obstruction as to provide ample depth and width even for any modern craft that are likely to enter there.

However, in the world as a whole, and especially in those countries better provided with railways, river navigation is of decreasing importance. That river transportation has not been able to compete more effectively with that by rail is due to important defects in the natural qualities of rivers as water thoroughfares. Some of these defects are indicated in the following statements: (a) The depth of most rivers fluctuates greatly with the seasons of maximum and minimum rainfall. This is notably true in arid and semiarid lands where watercourses so seldom are navigable that they never have had significance in that connection, except under special conditions, such as are found in the Nile. Even great rivers, like the Missouri, in regions of seasonal and

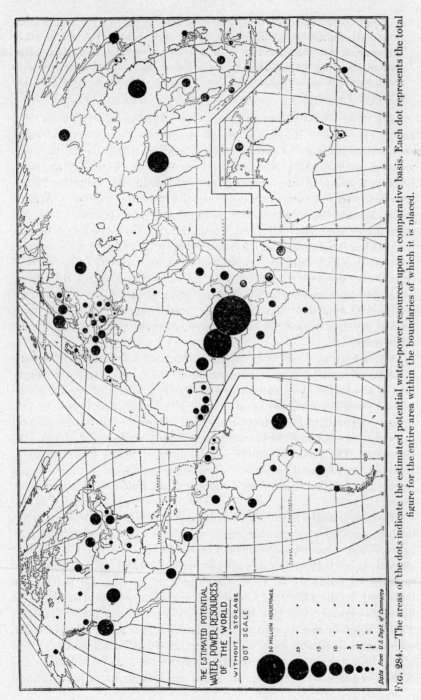

FIG. 284.—The areas of the dots indicate the estimated potential water-power resources upon a comparative basis. Each dot represents the total figure for the entire area within the boundaries of which it is placed.

highly variable rainfall, often are so shallow as to become incapable of use. (*b*) Young streams, which have fairly direct courses, commonly are interrupted by falls and rapids, while old streams of low and uniform gradients usually meander and provide long and indirect routes of transport. (*c*) Old streams constantly shift their channels and deposit sand bars which are a menace to navigation. (*d*) In some climates rivers are closed to navigation several months each year by ice. (*e*) It is difficult to provide upon the banks of a river having a variable depth and shifting channel adequate facilities for the transfer of heavy cargo between bank and boat. (*f*) Many places from which goods must be moved are not reached by navigable streams and must provide other kinds of transport facilities. (*g*) The movement of river craft is comparatively slow and especially so against the stream current.

552. The Value of Lakes for Inland Navigation. The use of the large lakes or inland seas of the world for navigation presents less difficult problems than does the use of rivers. Some are closed by ice part of the time, but not many are troubled by variable depths or obstructed channels. Owing to their fortunate position between the principal iron-ore and coal regions of the continent, the Great Lakes of North America have been provided with special craft and organized into one of the most effective routes of transportation in the world. They have played a large part in the historical and industrial development of the region in which they lie. Although there is not the same opportunity for special service in other regions, some of the lakes of other continents serve the transportational needs of their regions well. Among the most used of them are the three great lakes Victoria, Tanganyika, and Nyasa in eastern Africa; the Caspian Sea and Lake Baikal in Asia; and others of smaller size.

553. The Value of Lakes and Streams as Centers of Recreation. To most persons a visit to a lake or stream affords a pleasant diversion from the daily routine. The exhilarating sports found in swimming, fishing, and various forms of boating serve as an attraction so strong that large numbers of people make at least a brief annual trip to some body of inland water for purposes of recreation. In recent years the building of good roads and the mobility afforded by the automobile have permitted a widespread gratification of this desire, with the result that large amounts of money are spent by vacationists, and the lakes and streams that attract them have become physical assets of great value to the regions in which they lie.

The greatest number of attractive lakes is found in regions of glaciation. Some of them are the morainic lakes of regions of glacial deposition, but the larger number is found in regions of ice scour or of ice scour with associated morainic damming (417, 423). It often happens also that the conditions of ice scour which are responsible for the lakes have conspired with climate to render the surrounding land of low agricultural value. This in turn has tended to keep the region in a forested or wild condition which increases the attractiveness of the lakes and their recreational value. Lake-dotted areas are found in mountain, hill, and plain lands alike. The glacial lakes of the Alpine countries, Rocky Mountain region, high Sierras, or southern Andes add mountain scenery to their attractiveness (Fig. 266). The more accessible lakes of the hill lands of New England, the Adirondacks, or the English Lake District and Scotland and the numberless lakes in the plains of the Great Lakes region, eastern Canada, Scandinavia, Finland, or the borders of the Alps draw ever larger numbers of people to their shores. They constitute a resource worthy of studied conservation and development.

Chapter XXIII. The Biotic Resource: Original Vegetation Cover and Associated Animal Life

554. PLANTS REFLECT PHYSICAL ENVIRONMENT. Native vegetation is an expression of the composite physical environment. It is the integration of all physical factors, past as well as present, and as a consequence often provides a better basis for classifying and judging the potentialities of environments than any other one single factor or set of factors. The suitability of virgin soil for certain types of land use and crops is often clearly indicated by the vegetation cover. In their broader aspects, the great plant communities which together comprise the earth's mosaic vegetation mantle reflect chiefly *present climatic characteristics*, there being relatively close coincidence between the principal climatic and vegetation types. Modifications within the larger plant communities are usually due to soil, relief, and drainage differences, past changes in environment, fire, or tampering by human beings.

The classification and brief description of the original vegetation cover here presented is plant geography in its broadest aspects—an attempt to describe the principal plant associations, show their relationships to the environmental complex, and indicate their world distribution (Plate VIII). Over considerable parts of the earth, man, through his use of the land, has so greatly modified the original vegetation that at present it bears little resemblance to what it was in its native state.

555. *Animals*. It is impossible to classify animals in terms of environment as one classifies plants. Since the latter are immobile, they must adapt themselves to their environment by their forms and structures. Animals, on the other hand, being mobile, can, within certain limits, change or circumvent their environment, by migrating or burrowing. The plant is a captive of its environment and is compelled to wear the evidences of its captivity in the form of structural adaptations where everyone may see them. Animals, on the other hand, adjust themselves to their physical surroundings by what they *do*, rather than through their structures and forms. As a consequence no attempt

is here made to classify animals into great associations, as is done for plants. Since, however, the type of animal is sometimes closely related to vegetation characteristics, brief comments occasionally are added concerning the representative animal life associated with certain vegetation groups.

Physical Conditions Affecting Plant Life

556. PLANT ASSOCIATIONS. One does not have to be either a botanist or widely traveled to be aware of the effects of physical environment upon the characteristics and distribution of plants. Even the layman quickly observes that poorly drained locations such as swamps or the periodically inundated margins of rivers and lakes have a distinctive association of plants, which differs markedly from the vegetation cover of higher and drier sites. Certain plants, such as mosses and ferns, are found characteristically in shady, damp locations, while others such as juniper thrive best in sunlight. The above illustrations, to be sure, apply to relatively restricted areas, but in a more general way vegetation cover may have a considerable degree of similarity even over very extensive areas of scores of thousands of square miles, provided the physical environment remains relatively uniform. Moreover, similar environments in widely separated parts of the earth are likely to have plant covers that are much alike in general aspect, even though they are not composed of identical species. Thus the tropical rainforests of the Amazon Basin and the Congo, separated by wide expanses of ocean, are, nevertheless, relatively similar in general appearance and type of plants. So also are the prairie lands of Argentina, the United States, and Hungary.

Based upon common physical needs, therefore, certain plants, although unrelated to one another, are repeatedly found growing side by side in similar environments. It is with these *plant associations* over relatively *extensive areas*, occupying as they do characteristic physical environments, that the geographer is chiefly concerned. These extensive associations comprise the variegated pattern of the earth's vegetation cover. In order to appreciate the significance of the great plant associations and their distribution, some explanation is necessary of the ways in which various elements of the physical environment influence vegetation.

557. TEMPERATURE AND LIGHT. Unlike many animals, plants do not generate heat. As a consequence their very existence as well as their characteristics are greatly influenced by the temperatures of air and soil. For every species of plant there appear to be three critical temperatures: (*a*) lower, and (*b*) upper limits beyond which it cannot exist, and (*c*) an optimum temperature in which it grows most vigorously. The lower limit is sometimes called its *specific zero*. This minimum temperature is not necessarily associated with 32°, for many tropical plants perish before the freezing point is reached, while certain forms of Arctic vegetation thrive in subfreezing temperatures.

Different species resist cold in different ways. Some make the adjustment by retarding growth and arresting certain functions, such as assimilation and respiration, during the period of low temperatures. This may result in a marked external change such as takes place with leaf fall in middle-latitude deciduous trees. Certain other plants, such as coniferous trees or the evergreen shrubs of Mediterranean climates, relapse into a dormant period without any apparent outward change. In some species the plant completes its entire life cycle during the warm period, so that the vegetative portions disappear entirely throughout the season of cold and it is only by means of a seed, which is capable of greater and more prolonged resistance to low temperatures, that the plant is perpetuated. These are the *annuals*, of which, for instance, rice and corn are representative. They stand in contrast to *perennials*, the vegetative parts of which live on year after year.

The length of the vegetative period is not alike for the same plant in contrasting climates. In regions of short summers, such as Siberia, the growth period is reduced to 3 or 4 months, but at the same time the rapidity of growth during the shortened summer is great. For example, the beech, which completes its seasonal growth in 3 months in the latitude of Yakutsk, Siberia, requires 6 months in central Germany.

Not only heat but also light affects the characteristic development of plants. Reproductive functions, for instance, are favored by light. This is shown by the fact that flowers can be prevented from opening by being grown in semidarkness. Those plants that grow in shade usually are characterized by greater development of their vegetative parts, such as stems and leaves, at the expense of flowers which contain the reproductive organs. On the other hand, light tends to produce large, brightly colored flowers but thicker and shorter leaves and stems.

558. WATER. (Hygrophytes, Xerophytes, and Tropophytes.) No plants can live entirely without water. Taken in at the roots it is the principal ingredient of sap, in which mineral matter in solution is carried to all parts of the plant. Transpiration of water takes place through the leaves, the process being associated with chemical changes by which the sap is prepared for assimilation by tissues.

Plants that exist in water or in very damp and humid regions are designated as *hygrophytes*. In these the stems are usually long and relatively fragile, containing a minimum of woody fiber, while leaves are large and usually thin. Roots are likely to be shallow. The banana tree, characteristic of the wet tropics, is an example of hygrophytes. At the opposite extreme are the *xerophytes*, which are adapted to drought conditions. In these, roots are long or widespread in order to increase the depth or area from which water is obtained, while stems are likely to be shorter and stronger. Leaves are smaller and thicker, their stomata (openings for transpiration) fewer, and a hairy undercover is common. A thick corky bark or a coating of wax may further protect against rapid transpiration. Leaves even may be replaced by thorns. Certain desert species adapt themselves in a different way, namely, by accumulating supplies of water within their vegetative structures. Such a one is the fleshy-stemmed cactus.

In climates that have a wet and a dry period, or in those in which there is a distinct period of cold, many plants are hygrophytic in one season and xerophytic in the other. These are called *tropophytes*. In savanna climates, for instance, most trees drop their leaves during the period of drought and temporarily become xerophytes, for the woody stems and branches and the shiny wax-covered buds are highly conservative of water. With the coming of the rains again the buds open, and hygrophytic leaves and reproductive organs are formed. In middle latitudes the season of cold has a similar effect to that of the season of drought in the tropics, for the rise of sap is checked by low temperature as well as by low rainfall. Thus winter is a period of physiological drought during which deciduous plants lose their leaves and become xerophytic in character.

559. Soil. Although temperature and water are the two principal physical elements determining the general character of the earth's natural vegetation, modifications within the great climatically induced groups are due principally to soil contrasts (the *edaphic* factor). Thus within the northeastern pine forests of the upper Great Lakes states, the composition of the original stand depended largely on the character of the soil. On the poorest sandy soils jack pine was almost the exclusive tree. On the somewhat better sandy soils Norway pine was intermingled with jack pine; while in regions of higher fertility Norway pine occurred in mixtures with white pine and northern hardwoods. Throughout the hardwood forests of New York white pine occupied the sandy plains. In its modifying effects upon plant life the soil environment makes itself felt in a number of ways, especially through its temperature, chemical composition, and water retentiveness. Sandy or stony soils, which are very porous, may induce a xerophytic vegetation even in regions of moderate rainfall. Thin soils are likewise inclined to be droughty. Where a high percentage of salt is present, as in parts of deserts or along seacoasts, most plants will not grow. Vegetation in such areas of salt concentration has distinctive characteristics, being xerophytic in many respects. A proportion of over 3 per cent of lime in soil is likewise injurious to most vegetation. In cool, damp, subarctic regions, the barren soils of which are covered with raw and highly acid humus, such xerophytic plants as heather and furze are characteristic.

The Great Plant Associations

560. Three Principal Classes of Vegetation. Plant geographers recognize three principal classes of natural vegetation: (a) forests, (b) grasslands, and (c) desert shrub, including tundra. Each of these occupies contrasting types of environment, rainfall probably being the single most critical element leading to the threefold differentiation. As listed above, the three vegetation groups are arranged in order of diminishing rainfall, forest occupying the regions of wettest

climate and desert shrub the driest, while grasses are intermediate in their requirements.

561. WOODLAND OR FOREST ASSOCIATIONS. Within this group the tree is the essential element. Other woody plants such as bushes and shrubs, together with grasses and parasitic forms, may be present as well, but these are usually only accessory parts of the forest. The tree is not only the most powerful, but also the most exacting creature of the vegetable kingdom. When trees grow in a closed formation and are so close together that their crowns touch, the result is a genuine *forest*. If shrubs are so numerous that they prevent the tree crowns from touching, *bushwood* is the common name, while a predominance of shrubs leads to the designation *shrubwood*. Woodland associations dispute the possession of the land with grassland associations, forests in general occupying the more rainy parts of the world and becoming increasingly luxuriant with increasing temperatures.

562. *Forest Climate.* It is not unusual that forests should be more water-demanding than the other great vegetation types. (a) In general the tree has a larger transpiring surface, compared with the area of ground covered, than have other plants; (b) its transpiring surface is farther away from the water supply in the soil; and (c) by reason of its height it is more exposed to wind and evaporation. On the other hand, because of its deep and extensive root system the tree is able to tap deep-lying supplies of water and is capable of withstanding drought during the vegetative or warm season (which grass cannot), provided there is a continuous supply of water at the roots. In other words the *season of rainfall* is of little significance to trees. Low temperatures limit forest growth in the high latitudes and the high altitudes, there being little forest poleward of the isotherm of 50° for the warmest month. Wind is a critical item of environment since it is very directly related to the amount of transpiration from the plant. Strong, dry winds during the cold season, when the earth's moisture is locked up through freezing, are particularly bad, and it is this combination, in part, that determines the poleward limit of tree growth. In summary: A good forest climate is one with a warm vegetative season, a continuously moist subsoil, and low wind velocity, especially in winter. Hostile to trees in high latitudes is a climate with windy, dry, cold winters, since at that season the trees are unable to replace moisture lost through transpiration.

563. GRASSLAND ASSOCIATIONS. The vegetation cover here consists principally of perennial grasses, although other herbaceous plants may be present in considerable numbers. In the low latitudes grasslands often are called *savannas;* in the middle latitudes they go by the names of *prairies* and *steppes*, and the latter term, steppe, is gradually coming to be applied to all of the drier short-grass grasslands, tropical as well as middle latitude. Grasslands in wet and poorly drained areas are designated as *meadows*.

564. *Grass Climate.*[1] Although meadow thrives in cool moist locations, most natural grasslands are either subhumid or semiarid. Since most grasses are relatively shallow rooted, they suffer from prolonged drought *if it coincides with the warm period or growing season.* Regions with winter rains and summer drought have, therefore, the antithesis of a good grassland climate. Moisture in the deep subsoil is of little value; it is the surficial layers that are critical. Since this top moisture is quickly lost by evaporation, frequent, even if weak, precipitation is essential during the growing season. During the resting period (winter in middle latitudes) grasses can endure great drought without injury. Winds are of little significance, since grass does not grow tall enough to be greatly affected by any but the slower-moving ground currents. Most hostile to grass is drought during the growing season. It is a common sight in middle latitudes during dry summers to see pastures and lawns brown and sear, while the trees and bushes are as verdant as usual. Grass, then, is typical of subhumid and semiarid regions which have a marked concentration of the year's rainfall during the warm season.

565. DESERT SHRUB. As far as plant life is concerned, deserts are of two types: (*a*) those which are *physically* dry, with little water present in any form, and (*b*) those which are *physiologically* dry. In the latter, although water may be abundant, it exists in inaccessible forms, usually snow or ice. Sahara is representative of the first type, and the polar regions of the second. In both, however, lowly, widely spaced, xerophytic plants predominate. Neither trees nor grasses thrive, and stunted forms of either woody or herbaceous plants capable of enduring the adverse climate prevail.

Rarely are there sharp boundaries separating woodland, grassland, and desert, but almost always gradual transitions from one to the other. As a consequence there are wide transitional belts between grasslands and forests known as wooded steppe, or park savanna,

---

[1] Some have expressed the idea that grasslands, at least those in the tropics and subtropics, are not the result of climatic conditions. Rather, they would attribute them to the work of man, believing that grasses become established as a result of burnings and clearings of the forest in carrying on agricultural operations. Their notion would be that a distinctive grassland climate does not exist, since they maintain that woody vegetation can invade any region where rainfall is sufficient for grasses. See Cook, O. F. Milpa Agriculture, a Primitive Tropical System. *Smithsonian Inst. Ann. Rept.*, 1919, pp. 307-326.

where trees and grass intermingle. Similarly, transition belts occur between forest and desert and between grassland and desert.

Types of Forests and Their Distribution[1]

LOW-LATITUDE FORESTS

566. TROPICAL RAINFOREST. This type of woodland characteristically occupies warm tropical lowlands where rainfall is heavy and

FIG. 285.—Aerial view of tropical rainforest, with clearing, in the Amazon Basin. (*Hamilton Rice Expedition of 1924–1925.*)

well distributed throughout the year, there being no marked dry season. The Amazon Basin, in northern South America, and West Central Africa are the two largest areas of tropical rainforest, although it is found along many rainy coasts and islands in the tropics as well (Plate VIII).

567. *External Aspect.* Luxuriant, complex, exuberant—such is the character of tropical rainforest (Fig. 285). In external aspect it

---

[1] Trees are classified as either (*a*) hardwood or (*b*) softwood; (*a*) broadleaf or (*b*) needle leaf: (*a*) deciduous or (*b*) evergreen. Hardwood and broadleaf are practically synonymous, while the needle trees, such as pines, are called softwoods. Evergreens are those that retain some foliage throughout the year, while deciduous trees periodically lose their leaves and are therefore bare for a portion of the year. Hardwoods are both evergreen and deciduous, although the conifers are rarely deciduous.

presents a richly varied mosaic of many shades, gray, olive, brown, and yellow tints being more common than the fresh green of middle-latitude woodlands. The skyline, too, is different, the crown of the tropical forest being irregular and jagged with many crests and furrows. This comes from the great variety of trees of varying heights which comprise it. No other forest equals it in richness of species,

Fig. 286.—Side view of tropical rainforest in Brazil. Note the abundance of lianas, and the dense, almost impenetrable forest crown. Undergrowth is not unusually conspicuous. (*Field Museum of Natural History.*)

and these are intricately intermingled so that a few kinds of trees do not strongly predominate, as is usually the case in forests of middle latitudes. Pure stands of a species are practically unknown. Tropical rainforest is evergreen broadleaf in character, there being no general dormant period, each tree shedding its foliage imperceptibly as the new leaves grow (Fig. 286). Just as the climate is without seasonal rhythm, the vegetation is likewise. As a result of the continuousness of the addition and fall of leaves the forest is never bare and without foliage. Needle trees are largely absent, leaves characteristically being broad and thin.

568. *Internal Aspect.* An internal view shows the tropical rainforest to be composed of tall trees (often 150 ft. high) with large diameters, growing close together. It is not a single-storied forest, an understory of smaller trees being characteristic. The result is a dense canopy of shade with very subdued light underneath (Fig. 286). In the Congo forest Shantz found that the time required for a photograph was twenty thousand times the normal exposure in the open. The trees have few lower branches, their trunks characteristically being smooth, resembling a conifer more than an oak. Lianas, climbing plants, epiphytes, and parasites are relatively abundant.[1] This mass of vines and creepers appears almost to suffocate the trees that are its supports. Within the forest the tall, branchless trunks resemble gigantic dark columns supporting an almost impenetrable canopy, composed of the interlocking crowns of the trees and the vines and creepers that cover them. In the virgin forest, because of deep shade, undergrowth is not unusually dense although often sufficient to obstruct distant views. In regions of deepest shade only a thick mat of herbs or ferns covers the floor, so that one can proceed in all directions without following paths or even chopping new ones. Typical *jungle* conditions, with a thick and impenetrable undergrowth, chiefly are characteristic of sections where light reaches the forest floor, for example, along rivers and coasts, on precipitous wet slopes, and in abandoned agricultural clearings (Fig. 287). Reflecting the abundant moisture in the surface soil, tropical rainforest trees are shallow rooted, their great trunks commonly being supported by giant buttress roots.

Of the Amazon forest, Haviland writes:

"If the approach is by boat up one of the great rivers, which are still the only highways through the greater part of the forest region, the sight is one of unforgettable grandeur. On either side the banks are veiled by a wall of green foliage between 100 and 200 ft. high, towering above its own inverted image in the water. . . . This profusion of flowering climbers, which in some places hides the outlines of the trees themselves, is characteristic of the South American forest. The creepers cover the whole roof of the forest as with a canopy and fall to its foot at the water side like a curtain. . . . This mass of creepers is not altogether the suffocating burden or host of parasites that it

---

[1] *Lianas* are ropelike plants which entwine themselves round trunks and branches. *Epiphytes,* of which orchids are a common example, characteristically grow on the branches of tropical trees and spread their roots among the cracks in the bark. They frequently have hanging roots. *Parasites* are plants that feed from the sap of the tree on which they grow.

appears to be. In exchange for support, it affords shade which is essential to the well-being of the forest; and it has been shown that when the veil has been torn aside so that the sun can beat down on the roots, the giant trees perish. For this reason an artificial clearing is usually fringed with dead trees.

"Here and there dark caverns yawn in the wall of foliage at the water side. These are the mouths of creeks and streams shut in by overarching branches from which long aerial roots hang down like stalactites. To enter these caves by boat is like passing from the open air into a vast dim hall, supported by immense columns. The trunks of the trees rise up for 70 or 80 ft. without a branch, and the undergrowth is thin and straggling. The ground is strewn with

Fig. 287.—Interior view of the tropical rainforest in the Belgian Congo. Time required for this photograph was 20,000 times the normal exposure in the open. Undergrowth appears to be more dense than in Fig. 298. (*American Geographical Society.*)

dead leaves, though it may be remarked that the accumulation of leaf mold is not very great, owing to the rapidity of bacterial action."[1]

569. *Animal life* of the tropical rainforest is not so conspicuous as is the vegetation, although it varies in kind and abundance from one region to another. In the crown of the forest, where there is an abundance of food, a great variety of birds and some climbing animals such as monkeys and apes exist. On the darkened floor below large animals usually are not numerous, although in Africa the hippopotamus inhabits the river margins, and elephants, giraffe, and the big catlike animals may penetrate the forest for some distance. Reptiles and amphibians are relatively abundant. It is chiefly in insect life, however,

[1] Haviland, Maud D. "Forest, Steppe and Tundra." pp. 42–43, University Press, Cambridge, England, 1926.

that the tropical forest abounds. Although not conspicuous, and very elusive, the hum and sing of insect life are ever present. Ants are among the most numerous forms, and termites, a kind of destructive woodworm, are likewise abundant. Not only in the tropical forest, although there some of the most ideal conditions exist, but throughout most poorly drained areas in the low latitudes are to be found parasitic disease-carrying insects, some of them dangerous alike to man and animals. Yellow fever, sleeping sickness, and malaria, veritable scourges of the tropics, are all of them propagated through the bites of insects.

570. *Rainforest Subtypes.* Several subtypes of the general tropical rainforest are recognized. Thus along tropical salt-water coasts are the *mangrove swamp forests* which find ideal conditions in waterlogged brackish marine mud. They are most extensive in the vicinity of river mouths. Standing upon prop roots which lift the main trunk of the tree above high tide, the mangrove forest at low water presents an impenetrable tangle of roots and knees covered with algae. Occupying river floodplains and other low periodically flooded places are the *intermittently inundated forests.* Probably owing to the frequent floodings, climbing plants and lianas are less abundant than in the drier forests, while the tree types, too, are somewhat different. The *higher-lying forest* appears to have a denser undergrowth, but it probably varies considerably from place to place in penetrability. The tree trunks, as well as the crowns, are usually burdened with a host of climbing vines, woody lianas, or "monkey cables," and parasitic plants. Many tropical forests do not represent truly virgin growth, but various stages of natural reforestation following burnings and clearings by the native inhabitants.

571. Lighter Tropical Forest (Semideciduous). This forest has temperature requirements similar to those of the tropical rainforest, but in contrast to it occupies either regions of less rainfall or, more typically, those where there is a distinct, but short, dry period which imposes a partial seasonal rhythm (Plate VIII). Relatively large areas of this type of forest exist in monsoonal southeastern Asia (Fig. 288). There it often is designated as *monsoon forest*. A somewhat similar type, the *savanna forest*, occupies transitional belts between tropical rainforest and the drier true savannas (Fig. 289). But these latter areas are not always sufficiently distinct, or their situations well enough known, to permit of localizing them on a generalized vegetation map of the world. Characteristically the lighter tropical forest is broadleaf deciduous in character, although not all the trees are leafless during the dry season (Fig. 288). It is during the period of drought, nevertheless, that contrast with the rainforest is most marked. Further features of differentiation are the

wider spacing of the trees, their somewhat smaller size, and the denser undergrowth which occupies the less-shaded forest floor. Tall bamboo thickets are common in the monsoon forests, while high coarse grasses

Fig. 288.—Teak forest in the Central Provinces of India during the dry season. In this region the teak trees are not so straight or so large as they are in Burma. (*Photograph by C. V. Sweet.*)

prevail in some other regions (Fig. 289). Climbing vines and epiphytes may be numerous.

Fig. 289.—Lighter tropical forest (semideciduous) in the Belgian Congo. Large trees are sufficiently far apart that they do not cast a dense shade. Grass mantles the forest floor. (*American Geographical Society.*)

572. SCRUB AND THORN FOREST varies in density from an open parklike growth of low stunted trees and thorny plants to dense thickets of the same (Fig. 290). Where grasses mantle the forest floor

they are not dense but consist of tall forms comprising a rather open cover. The trees composing the dry scrub forest are small in diameter, rarely exceeding one foot. Normally they are deciduous in character, bearing their foliage and flowers only during the period of rains. Scrub forest commonly occurs in scattered small areas throughout savanna lands where soil conditions are unfavorable for growth of grasses. It is likewise adapted to areas of relatively low rainfall where the precipitation is irregular and undependable and interrupted by dry periods. No other tropical forest type equals it in tolerance of physical conditions.

Fig. 290.—Scrub forest in Senegal, West Africa. Such a forest has little or no value. (*Field Museum of Natural History.*)

Utilization of Tropical Forests. Although tropical forests occupy nearly 50 per cent of the earth's total forest area, at the present time they supply only the limited needs of local populations and furnish to world commerce small quantities of special-quality woods, such as dyewoods and cabinet woods. Nevertheless these low-latitude forests, especially the tropical rainforest, represent one of the world's great potential timber supplies. The problems involved in their utilization are serious—labor supply, sanitation, requirement of new logging technologies, how to utilize the great variety of species composing the tropical forest—but none of them appears to be insurmountable.

Middle-latitude Forests

573. Mediterranean Broadleaf Evergreen Scrub Forest. Mediterranean forests are a relatively rare type, for seldom are trees broadleaf evergreen and at the same time adapted to regions with long, hot periods of summer drought. In those parts of the humid tropics where pronounced dry seasons are characteristic, trees protect themselves by shedding their leaves and thereby becoming xerophytic during the dry season, although they are hygrophytic during the

periods of rains. In Mediterranean woodlands, on the other hand, adjustment is made in other ways, protective devices against rapid transpiration permitting the trees to retain their foliage, and consequently their evergreen characteristics, during the period of aridity. But although evergreen in character, there is more of a seasonal rhythm in vegetative and reproductive processes than is true of the tropical rainforest. This unique Mediterranean woodland is found in subtropical regions with mild, rainy winters and long, dry, hot summers. The climate as well as the vegetation is unusual, for the times of maximum temperature and maximum rainfall do not coincide. The largest representative area is the Mediterranean Sea borderlands, with smaller areas in California, middle Chile, southern Australia, and the Cape Town region of Africa.

Fig. 291.—Mediterranean sclerophyll woodland in California. An open stand of dwarf oak merging with California grassland. (*U. S. Forest Service.*)

Mediterranean woodland is predominantly a mixed forest of low, or even stunted, trees and woody shrubs (Fig. 291). Tall trees are rare. Where climatic and soil conditions are most favorable the virgin forest is composed of low, widely spaced trees with massive trunks and gnarled branches. Between the trees the ground is completely or partially covered by a pale, dusty, bush vegetation, which very much resembles the soil in color. From a distance, therefore, it may appear as though the ground were almost bare of small plants. In all of them woody parts are more prominent than foliage. As a protection against evaporation the tree trunks are encased in a thick, deeply fissured bark, this feature being perfectly exemplified by the cork oak. Leaves, too, which are small, stiff, thick, and leathery, with hard, shiny surfaces, are designed to prevent rapid losses of water.[1] The olive tree

[1] It is this leaf characteristic which has given the Mediterranean woodland the name *sclerophyll*.

with its massive trunk, gnarled branches, thick fissured bark, and small, stiff, leathery leaves is very representative of Mediterranean sclerophyll woodland in regions of hot (*Csa*) summers.

Fig. 292.—Mediterranean chaparral or maqui in Cape Province, South Africa. (*American Geographical Society.*)

Fig. 293.—Chaparral grading into forest on the slopes of the California mountains. (*U. S. Forest Service.*)

Even more common than the woodland composed of low trees and shrubs described above is a vegetation mantle consisting principally of shrubs and bushes in which there may be some stunted trees (Fig. 292).

This bush thicket is known as *chaparral* in California and *maqui* in lands bordering the Mediterranean Basin. In places the woody shrubs form a thick and relatively tall cover; in others it is short and sparse (Fig. 293). Chaparral in some regions may represent the original vegetation cover. In other sections it is the underwood remaining

FIG. 294.—Mixed hardwood-conifer forest (birch-beech-maple-hemlock) in Michigan. Much of this type of forest occupied lands not well suited to agriculture, so that its removal has resulted in extensive areas of relatively barren, desolate, cutover land. (*U. S. Forest Service.*)

after the low trees of the original woodland have been destroyed. The chief economic importance of chaparral usually lies in its watershed protection.

574. BROADLEAF, OR HARDWOOD, FORESTS. Within the more humid parts of the middle latitudes are found two great forest groups: (*a*) the broadleaf trees, or hardwoods, and (*b*) the needle-leaf coni-

fers, or softwoods. Over large areas they exist as mixed conifer-broad-leaf forests. As a general rule, but with important exceptions, the coniferous forests occupy the colder continental locations and so are usually on the poleward side of the hardwoods. In regions of poor, sandy soils, such as the Atlantic and Gulf Coastal Plain of the United States, or on steep mountain slopes where soils are thin or rocky and temperatures lower, conifers may supplant hardwoods even in the

FIG. 295.—A mixed hardwood forest (oak-hickory) in northern Indiana. Much of this type of forest occupied good agricultural land and as a consequence was destroyed in the process of settlement. (*U. S. Department of Agriculture.*)

lower middle latitudes. The latter condition is illustrated in the case of the southern Appalachians, which carry a long tongue of coniferous and mixed forest southward into the hardwood belt.

Temperate hardwood forests vary widely in composition, the dominant tree species differing from one region to another. In parts, especially along their poleward margins, there are numerous conifers among them, so many, in fact, that some plant geographers designate such forests as *mixed* rather than *hardwood* (Fig. 294). In eastern United States two general hardwood-forest areas are distinguished:

(*a*) a northeastern one (northern Wisconsin and Michigan, New York, and southern New England) in which birch, beech, and maple predominate but with a large infusion of hemlock and other conifers (Fig. 294); and (*b*) a central and southern one lying south of the first and terminating at the northern and western boundary of the sandy Coastal Plain (Figs. 295, 296). In this latter forest, which was originally the finest and most extensive area of hardwoods anywhere in the

FIG. 296.—Mixed hardwood forest (chestnut-chestnut oak-yellow poplar) in North Carolina. (*U. S. Forest Service.*)

world, oak, chestnut, hickory, and poplar predominate but with pines prominent toward the Coastal Plain margins (Fig. 297). The greater part of the original American hardwood-forest belt, lying as it does in an environment eminently suited for agriculture, has now been cleared and turned into farmland. Poorer cutover lands often have a brush cover. Of the 280,000,000 acres comprising the original central hardwood forest only 14,000,000 acres of virgin forest remain and the timber cut exceeds the timber growth by a considerable margin. The remaining stands are chiefly in the rougher Appalachian country and in Tennessee, Kentucky, Missouri, and Arkansas. Outside the United States, other relatively large areas of temperate hardwoods or mixed forest are to be found in Japan, Chosen, southeastern China, central Russia, Rumania, southwestern Siberia, western Europe, southern Chile, southeastern Australia, and New Zealand (Plate VIII).

575. *Deciduous Hardwoods.* By far the greater part of the temperate hardwood forest is *deciduous* in character, the trees dropping their leaves during the winter season (Fig. 295). Except in the dormant season this forest is rather uniformly bright green in color, and its profile is regular. The amount of underwood varies with density of tree stand, being much greater where an appreciable amount of light reaches the ground (Figs. 295, 296, 297). Trunks of the deciduous trees are xerophytic in character, having a relatively thick bark which protects against transpiration during winter. On the other hand, the leaves are thin and delicate, requiring no protective devices, since they remain on the tree only during the warmer part of the year. As a result of seasonal leaf fall, for the year as a whole, considerable sunlight reaches the soil under deciduous forests.

Fig. 297.—Mixed forest of oak and pine in Arkansas. This is a transition type between the oak forest father north and the pine forest of the Coastal Plain to the south and east. (*U. S. Forest Service.*)

576. *Evergreen Hardwoods.* Only along the humid subtropical margins of the middle latitudes are there important *evergreen* broadleaf, or hardwood, forests, but these are not nearly so extensive as the deciduous variety. Their principal regions are in southern Japan, New Zealand, and southeastern Australia. In many respects these subtropical forests are akin to those of the wet tropics. Lack of seasonal leaf fall, density of undergrowth, and prevalence of lianas and other climbing plants, all are suggestive of the resemblance. The number of

Fig. 298.—Air view of the swamp taiga of western Siberia. This region did not suffer glaciation. (*Photograph by Luftschiffbau Zeppelin, courtesy of the American Geographical Society of New York.*)

Fig. 299.—Taiga in the ice-scoured region of Canada. The meager soil cover permits only a thin stand of trees. Compare with Fig. 298. (*Royal Canadian Air Force Photograph.*)

species composing the forest is likewise numerous. Oaks of various kinds are among the commonest trees. Eucalyptus and acacia are important elements of the Southern Hemisphere forests.

577. CONIFEROUS, OR SOFTWOOD, FORESTS. Coniferous trees are almost exclusively *evergreen*, the addition and fall of the needles being a continuous process and not confined to any particular period or season. Unlike broad leaves, however, the needles of conifers are xerophytic in character so that shedding is not necessary to protect against a cold or drought season. On the whole, the crown of a coniferous forest does not intercept so much sunlight as does that of the broad-leaf woodland, but (*a*) since the former lie predominantly in higher latitudes where there are longer periods of low sun, and (*b*) since they are never without foliage, less sun reaches the earth. As a result there is usually less surficial vegetation, a minimum of bacterial activity, and smaller accumulations of humus in the soil.

FIG. 300.—Side view of the taiga in Yukon, Canada. Note the relative smallness of the trees. (*U. S. Forest Service.*)

578. *Subarctic Conifers.* Conifers reach their maximum development, as far as areal extent is concerned, in the severe subarctic regions of North America and Eurasia, where they form wide and continuous east-west forest belts stretching from coast to coast (Figs. 298, 299). To the subarctic coniferous forests have been given the name *taiga*. On their northern frontiers they make contact with the treeless tundra, a region thoroughly hostile to trees. The Eurasian taiga forms the single largest continuous forest area on the earth. Conifers (larch, spruce, fir, pine) predominate, although deciduous trees (alder, willow, aspen, birch, mountain ash) are scattered throughout, individually as well as in thickets or clusters. The latter are characteristic of low swampy areas

and of regions bearing a second growth. Species are few in number. Xerophytic character is conspicuous, for taiga soils are physiologically dry much of the year, water being freely accessible at the roots only during the short warm season of 3 to 5 months. Even in summer absorption of water is retarded by the coolness of the soil and the acidity of the humus which accumulates in the deep, cool shade. In these regions of long, cold, dry winters and short cool summers, trees are relatively small in size, usually not over $1\frac{1}{4}$ ft. in diameter, and growth is slow (Fig. 300). Wet swampy areas covered with sphagnum moss, and containing such trees as spruce and balsam, are numerous, these spots being designated as *muskeg* in North America. On the shaded forest floor vegetation is meager, mosses and lichens being the

Fig. 301.—Relatively dense stands of fir on the Cascade Mountains in Washington. (*U. S. Forest Service.*)

most common plant forms, and sometimes even these are stifled by the thick blanket of slowly decomposing needles. Little humus is made available to the soil, for needle leaves are a poor source of humus to begin with, while the low temperatures and deep shade act to retard decomposition and discourage the activity of soil fauna. Animal life is not so abundant as in the middle-lattitude forests farther south, although trapping is an important occupation, and the taiga is one of the principal sources of furs. The long-continued cold tends to make for heavy pelts. Wolf, bear, fox, otter, mink, ermine, squirrel, lynx, and sable are representative animals.

579. *Conifers in Lower Middle Latitudes.* South of the great belts of subarctic conifers are other areas of needle trees which, although less extensive, are nevertheless more valuable forest regions. This comes about as a result of their being composed of larger trees

and superior timber species and at the same time being more easily accessible. In western North America broken belts of conifers extend southward from the taiga following the rainier highland chains (Pacific Coast Mountains and Rocky Mountains) to beyond the Mexican

FIG. 302.—Interior view of the Pacific Douglas fir forest. This is one of the world's finest softwood forests. Trees are of large size and the stand is dense. (*U. S. Forest Service.*)

border (Figs. 301, 302). The forests of the American Pacific Coast states, western Canada, and Alaska constitute the most extensive area of fine coniferous forest anywhere in the world. Large trees, dense stand, good-quality timber, all contribute to this high rank. Most valuable of its trees is the Douglas fir, which reaches a diameter of

6 ft. or more and a height of more than 250 ft. East of the Rockies they extend southward from the taiga into southeastern Canada and the northern portions of the northeastern tier of American states—Minnesota, Wisconsin, Michigan, the Adirondacks in New York, and much of

FIG. 303.—A mixed stand of Norway and jack pines in northern Minnesota. Representative of the northeastern pine forest of jack, red, and white pines. (*U. S. Department of Agriculture.*)

FIG. 304.—Mature spruce forest in the Adirondack Mountains, New York. Representative of the spruce-fir forest of southeastern Canada and the extreme northern parts of eastern United States. (*U. S. Forest Service.*)

Maine (Figs. 303, 304). The most valuable timber trees from this eastern forest have been removed, leaving behind extensive areas of waste and cutover land of little value. South of the taiga in Eurasia valuable coniferous forests occupy the slopes of the Alps, Carpathians, and other highland regions as well as certain sandy areas of coastal plains.

Separated from this northern belt of conifers, in the United States, by extensive broadleaf forests is the *southern pine forest*, which occupies the Atlantic and Gulf Coastal Plain (Plate VIII). It is composed of 10 different species of pine of which the longleaf pine is most abundant (Fig. 305). Climatically this needle-tree forest seems somewhat out of place, for rainfall is abundant, and the growing season long. However, the poor sandy soil and high evaporation are offsetting factors, creating an environment that is generally hostile to broadleaf varieties. Open parklike character, with the ground covered by a mantle of coarse grasses or low shrubs, is typical. This southern pine forest has,

FIG. 305.—The southern pine forest (longleaf-loblolly-slash pines) of the United States, typical of the Atlantic and Gulf Coastal Plain. (*U. S. Forest Service.*)

during the last few decades, been one of the principal sources for American lumber, although the peak of its production has been passed. Extensive areas of nearly worthless cutover land are now one of the most conspicuous features of the southern-pine region. On the poorly drained floodplains of the Atlantic and Gulf Coastal Plain pines give way to a contrasting forest type composed of such trees as tupelo, red gum, and cypress (Fig. 306).

The principal regions of forest utilization in the middle latitudes are the United States and Canada in the Western Hemisphere, and northern Europe in the Old World. In the United States it is the forests of the Pacific Coast states and those of the Atlantic and Gulf Coastal Plain that provide nearly three-quarters of the American lumber supply (Fig. 307). In Europe

Fig. 306.—River-bottom forest in southern United States; principally cypress, tupelo, and red gum. (*U. S. Forest Service.*)

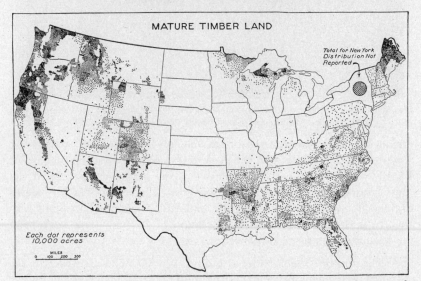

Fig. 307.—The distribution of land with timber of such size as to be currently merchantable with respect to the major product of the area. It does not include second growth cut primarily for chemical distillation, firewood, mine props, posts, and ties. (*Courtesy of U. S. Forest Service.*)

northern Russia, Finland, Sweden, and Poland are the large lumber producers. In all the regions named by far the largest cut is from conifers. Compared with the temperate forests of the Northern Hemisphere, those of the Southern Hemisphere are unimportant, although, to be sure, they are of some significance in providing local supplies of timber.

Types of Grasslands and Their Distribution

As stated in an earlier article, grass is the typical vegetation cover in subhumid or semiarid regions, particularly where winters are cold

Fig. 308.—Tall coarse grasses of the African savanna north of the equator. Their height is about 8 ft., so that they reach well into the lower branches of the small trees. The latter normally are much less prominent. (*American Geographical Society*.)

and windy and where the rain is concentrated in the vegetative season. Regions of abundant all-year precipitation are more likely to be in forest (see footnote, p. 488).

580. TROPICAL GRASSLANDS; SAVANNA AND STEPPE. Savannas dominantly are composed of tall and unusually coarse grasses growing in tufts, the latter separated by intervals of bare soil. They spring up rapidly at the beginning of the rainy season and may within a few months reach heights of 4 to 12 ft. (Figs. 308, 309). Seldom do savannas have the verdant, refreshing tints of humid meadows but instead are dull green in color with yellowish and brownish tints.

Blades are stiff and harsh, especially when dry. In the drought season the grasses become sear and brown so that they burn readily. Among the natives it is a common practice to burn off the old grasses in order to make way for new growth at the beginning of the rains. Shrubs and low trees usually are present, the latter becoming more numerous toward the humid margins, until finally grassland passes over into the savanna forests. Clumps of trees dot the savannas and give them a parklike appearance. With decreasing rainfall grasses usually diminish

Fig. 309.—Tall-grass savanna in Kenya Colony, Africa. Flat-topped acacia trees dot the grassland. (*American Geographical Society.*)

in height and become more widely spaced, while trees become fewer, until finally under semiarid conditions nearly treeless steppe, composed of shorter grasses, prevails. Throughout the tropical grasslands dense *galeria*[1] forests usually coincide with the floodplains of streams. Low-latitude savannas and steppes characteristically occupy intermediate locations between desert on the one side and forest on the other. Tropical grasslands were originally inhabited by a great variety of grazing animals such as antelope, gazelle, and giraffe, together with many of the larger carnivores. All of these have suffered greatly, however, at the hands of hunters.

[1] From the Italian word *galeria*, meaning "tunnel" and referring to the arch of trees over the river.

H. L. Shantz writes as follows concerning savanna in Africa:

"The high grass-low tree savanna is composed of a coarse, rank growth of grasses from 5 to 12 ft. high. The grasses do not form a turf, each plant usually being distinct at the base and somewhat resembling broadcast seeding of the coarser cereals. Growth is rapid, but during the drought period following maturity the grasses dry out and are burned to the ground. . . . At the beginning of the rainy season the fresh young blades shoot up again, forming a dense fresh green cover. Scattered through this grassland are a large number of trees of which the lower branches are in, or barely above, the full-grown grass cover. . . . Except where paths are made, it is difficult to walk through the grass region. . . . For a short time following the burning of the grass the whole country presents a blackened surface, with the trees standing out distinctly with scorched trunks and dead leaves. But this appearance is changed as soon as the grasses start growth and the trees again come into leaf. The paths then lead between walls of tall grass, which are difficult to penetrate. During the dry season the region resembles a dry yellow grainfield."[1]

581. MIDDLE-LATITUDE GRASSLANDS: PRAIRIE AND STEPPE. Middle-latitude grasslands are composed of finer and usually shorter grasses than those of tropical savannas. Two principal subdivisions are recognized: (a) the tall-grass prairies and (b) the short-grass and bunch-grass steppes.

582. *The prairie* is dominated by tall, luxuriant, and relatively deep-rooted grasses (Fig. 310). Usually there is a large variety of showy, flowering plants intermingled with the grasses, so that in the spring and early summer the original American prairies had the appearance of a colorful flower garden. Over most prairie regions the rainfall varies between 20 and 40 in., the principal supply coming during the summer season. Where rainfall is less than about 20 in., so that the depth of moist soil is under 2 ft., short grasses of the steppe type replace the prairie. Where the depth of moist soil is greater than about 30 in. the tall grasses flourish. Over the more humid parts of some of the world's prairie regions, including that of the United States, rainfall appears to be sufficient to support tree growth. The reason why grasses have been able to extend into these humid lands is not entirely clear. It may be the occasional dry year which prevents trees from gaining a foothold. It has also been suggested that the grass fires, started by lightning or by the inhabitants, which swept the prairies destroyed the young trees as rapidly as they were produced. The earth's principal regions of original tall grasses are (a) parts of central United States and the Prairie Provinces of Canada; (b) the Argentine

[1] Shantz, H. L., and Marburt, C. F. The Vegetation and Soils of Africa. Research Ser. 13, *Amer. Geog. Soc., N. Y.,* 1923, p. 50.

Pampa, Uruguay, and southeastern Brazil; (c) parts of southern Russia; (d) the plains of the Danube in Hungary and Rumania; and (e) possibly parts of Manchuria (Plate VIII). In most of the prairie regions the original vegetation has been destroyed through bringing the land under cultivation.

583. *The steppe*, composed of shorter, shallow-rooted grasses, is typical of semiarid regions where, as indicated above, the depth of moist soil is usually less than 2 ft. In dry years the steppe has the uniform appearance of an endless carpet. In wetter years there is

Fig. 310.—Tall-grass prairie in the region of the Nebraska sand hills. (*U. S. Forest Service.*)

greater variation due to the growth of taller plants on the short-grass sod. Within the United States two subdivisions of steppe are recognized: (a) short grass and (b) bunch grass. Short grass is characteristic of the Great Plains which lie east of the Rocky Mountains and, for the most part, west of the 100th meridian. There the meager rainfall is concentrated in late spring and early summer or just preceding and during the growing season (Fig. 311). Bunch grass occupies regions with about the same amount of precipitation as does the short grass but where it is not so much confined to the warm season (Fig. 312). It is characteristic of regions west of the Rocky Mountains, particularly in California, Washington, Oregon, Idaho, and western Montana. Because bunch grass is not continuous over extensive regions but exists rather in the form of small isolated areas or bands, it has been impossible accurately to show its distribution on the generalized vegetation map. Large parts of the middle latitude's short-grass and bunch-grass regions, although unplowed, have been overgrazed to the extent that weedy plants have taken the place

FIG. 311.—Short-grass steppe, Colorado. (*U. S. Department of Agriculture.*)

FIG. 312.—Bunch grass, Oregon. (*U. S. Department of Agriculture.*)

of the original vegetation. Great herds of bison and other herbivores once inhabited the American grasslands, but ruthless slaughter has almost exterminated them.

Desert Shrub (Including Tundra)

584. "DRY" DESERTS. Some few deserts or parts of deserts are extensive areas of rocky plain or sand and almost wholly without plant life (Fig. 313). This is the exception rather than the rule, how-

ever, for most arid regions of both low and middle latitudes have some vegetation even though it is sparse. It may be low bunch grass, widely spaced with bushes, or in places fleshy water-storing plants such as cacti; but much more commonly it is perennial xerophytic shrub. In the United States this latter type of vegetation predominates over a large part of the area west of the Rockies, interrupted here and there by bunch grass, or by forests at higher elevations. Rainfall over much of this region is under 12 in.

The perennial shrubs of desert areas grow far apart, with much bare soil showing between (Figs. 314, 315). This wide spacing is a response to low rainfall. Growth is very slow. Desert shrubs, exempli-

Fig. 313.—True desert; practically devoid of plants.

fied by such American types as sagebrush and creosote bush, are physiologically equipped through special forms of roots, stems, and leaves to withstand drought (565). Some are deciduous, others evergreen in character. Another class of desert plants, in contrast to the shrubs, depends entirely upon the erratic rainfall, germinating with a rain, ripening seeds when the moisture is gone, and dying forthwith. Such annuals do not appear xerophytic, their adaption to drought being through a very rapid development and short duration of life. Their stems and leaves are delicate, roots are thin and relatively shallow, and flowers are of considerable size. In contrast to the scanty, low, pale-green vegetation of the desert proper is the verdant color of luxuriant vegetation around oases where water is abundant. Almost knife-edge boundaries frequently separate the two. In wet or sub-irrigated land containing a high percentage of alkali, green, fleshy-leaved, salt-tolerant, plants are characteristic.

585. TUNDRA OR COLD DESERTS. Genuine tundra is composed largely of such lowly forms as mosses, lichens, and sedges, the whole incompletely covering the ground (Fig. 316). In places there is much bare, stony soil with only the most meager plant life. On the southern margins of the tundra, where it merges into the taiga or coniferous forest, vegetation cover is more complete, and stunted and creeping forms of trees and bushes are conspicuous. Grasslands exist on the

FIG. 314.—Desert shrub, chiefly sagebrush, in Nevada; of little value as grazing land. (*Photograph by John C. Weaver.*)

marine margins of the tundra. Owing to the coldness and acid character of the soil which retards water absorption, as well as to the long winter period of physiological drought when the soil moisture is locked up in solid form, most tundra plants appear xerophytic, having stiff, hard, leathery leaves, with thick cuticle. As a result of the short period between frosts the vegetative period in the tundra is reduced to two months or less. For this reason plants are compelled to hurry through their vegetative cycle, and even then many of them are frozen while still in flower or fruit. "An Arctic landscape at the approach of winter most resembles a southern country that has been ravaged by a severe night frost before winter was expected. Many plants are put to rest while still in full development. Whilst the plants were in full activity they were paralyzed by the benumbing cold." (Schimper.) Schimper cites an example of plants in the tundra of northeastern Siberia which pass through their complete vegetative cycle in three weeks.

Dry tundra is composed principally of lichens interspersed with coarse grasslike sedges. The predominance of lichens results in a

FIG. 315.—Desert shrub with scattered tufts of desert grass. Cape Province, South Africa. (*American Geographical Society.*)

FIG. 316.—Moss tundra in summer along the lower Yenisei River in western Siberia. (*Photograph by H. U. Hall, courtesy of the Geographical Review, published by the American Geographical Society of New York.*)

dull, gray landscape tone. Wetter flooded areas along streams, or shallow basins on higher ground, are often moss swamps. The southward-facing drier slopes or declivities are the flower oases, where in summer a great variety of brilliant colors are characteristic.

586. *Animals.* To animals as well as to plants tundra is inhospitable. Bird life is largely migratory, inhabiting these regions

principally in summer and wintering farther south. Large, predatory carnivores such as bears, wolves, and foxes fare badly in winter, being usually in the extremity of famine and reaching spring in an emaciated condition. Reindeer or caribou and musk ox are the two largest and most valuable of the herbivorous tundra animals (Fig. 316). Siberian tribes never feed their reindeer but compel them to forage for their food even in winter. Mosquitoes and stinging flies are thick in summer, these being among the principal torments of man and animals, forcing them to seek higher and drier sites. Most mammals of the tundra do not hibernate, all the smaller forms such as hares, foxes, wolves, and lemmings making their winter quarters underneath the snow, where temperatures are not so severe. Seal, walrus, and polar bears inhabit the coastal margins or the drift ice, where they feed chiefly on marine life.

Biotic Resources of the Sea

587. PLANT LIFE. Plant life in the seas is largely confined to those parts where light is relatively abundant, viz., (a) to the shallow coastal waters and (b) to the surface waters in general. Fixed or rooted plants are practically restricted to shallow waters close to land. Microscopic plant life, on the other hand, makes up a considerable part of the mass of floating organic substance called *plankton*. These microscopic plants at the surface of the ocean are the principal basis of sea life, for upon them myriads of small sea animals, such as Crustacea, feed, and they in turn are the most important sources of food for fish. Thus the plankton mass, composed of tiny plant and animal forms, is the principal reservoir of fish food. On the whole it is most abundant in coastal waters.

588. EDIBLE FISH. The greatest resource of the oceans is edible fish, and yet the world's annual catch, amounting roughly to $700,000,000, ordinarily does not equal the value of the American corn, cotton, hay, or wheat crop. Although seas cover approximately three-quarters of the earth's surface, the areas frequented by edible fish in large numbers, and in which they are most easily caught, are very much restricted. The type regions of fishing concentration are (a) the shallow coastal waters covering continental shelves and (b) the broad submarine elevations, called banks, in close proximity to the coasts. Most of the world's fishing is done along the margins of continents in waters whose depths are less than 200 fathoms (1,200 ft.). This concentration of fish in shallow coastal waters reflects the relative abundance of their food supply in that location. This exists in the form of (a) floating plankton, (b) waste received from the adjacent land, and (c) rooted algae in the shoal waters near shore.

589. *World's Important Fisheries in Nontropical Waters.* The commercial fishing grounds of world importance are, in general, outside the tropics and in the Northern Hemisphere. It is often stated that tropical waters contain fewer edible fish than those farther north, and a common explanation given is that there is a greater concentration of plankton in

cooler waters. This notion that both plankton and fish are less abundant in tropical and Southern Hemisphere seas is open to question. Certain it is that in the low-latitude seas the number of fish species is greater than it is in middle and higher latitudes. On the other hand, it is probably true that there are no such regional concentrations of a few valuable and better known species as there are farther north. Tropical fish suffer the further handicap of being softer and inclined to spoil more readily so that they are commercially less valuable. Locally, however, the fish resource of tropical coastal waters may be of highest importance to the native inhabitants. The outstanding significance of Northern Hemisphere fisheries, in all probability, is associated with the presence there of large areas of shallow water along the margins of the continents.

590. *Fishing Regions of World Importance.* Organized commercial fishing on a large scale is concentrated in four regions: (a) the coastal waters of Japan, Sakhalin, and eastern Siberia, (b) those of New England, Maritime Canada, and Newfoundland, (c) the coasts of northwestern Europe, and (d) the Pacific coasts of northwestern United States, Canada, and Alaska. Not only is the continental shelf around Japan and off eastern Siberia one of the world's most important fishing grounds, but Japan is also the world's most important fishing nation, her catch making up approximately one-quarter of the world's total. The annual catch of Japan is three to four times that of the United States or Great Britain, which are her closest rivals. Cool and warm currents are both present, herring being the principal food fish of the former, and sardines, bonito, tunny, and mackerel, of the latter. More than in most countries fish is a staple article of diet in Japan; in fact it is the main source of animal foodstuffs. Large quantities of fish are also used as fertilizer in this land of ultraintensive agriculture.

The life of New England, Newfoundland, and Maritime Canada is closely associated with the development of the fish resource. Fishing here is carried on both in the shallow inshore coastal waters, and in the region of the banks, the latter being more important. The North Atlantic Banks, extending as broad submarine elevations from Nantucket to the eastern coast of Newfoundland, are the world's greatest cod fisheries. Herring, mackerel, haddock, and halibut are a few of the other commercially valuable species of this western North Atlantic region. Fish such as herring and mackerel, which live relatively near the surface, are caught mainly by drift nets and lines. Other fish, represented by cod, halibut, and haddock, travel and feed in deeper waters (200 ft. or more below the surface) and are more difficult to catch. These are taken (a) by hand lines operated from the decks of fishing boats, (b) by long trawl lines buoyed up at both ends, to which are attached several hundred shorter perpendicular lines, and (c) by trawl nets. The latter are in the form of huge cone-shaped bags, and, because of their size and weight and the depth at which they are operated, they must be hauled by steam-powered vessels called trawlers. Shell fish, especially oysters, obtained from the coastal waters of the Middle Atlantic States, are another important element of the western North Atlantic fisheries. Chesapeake Bay is the principal focus of this development.

Along the Pacific Coast of North America salmon is by far the most important fish, and from that region comes practically all the world's canned salmon. The habits of this fish make it particularly easy to catch, and this fact greatly increases the danger of salmon extermination. Each spring and summer millions of adult salmon, driven by the urge to spawn, leave the ocean and ascend the streams emptying into the Pacific from northern California to the Bering Sea. Before winter sets in each salmon reaches the river or lake of its birth and there in the sand or gravel deposits its eggs. This fact that, when life is about spent, the adult salmon returns to the spot of its birth, makes it particularly easy to catch these fish in nets as they ascend the coastal rivers. The result has been a rapid rise of the salmon industry on a particular river and then a serious decline. By 1920 the salmon industry of North America was threatened with depletion. As a result of conservation measures established since that date salmon runs have increased again in some of the streams.

More than 200,000 men, drawn chiefly from Great Britain, Norway, Holland, and France, annually engage in fishing in the stormy waters of the eastern North Atlantic. In this region weather is characteristically bad and the seas rough so that the loss of life among fishermen is high. Fishing goes on throughout the year, although spring, when plankton is most abundant along the coasts, is the season of greatest activity. Herring, cod, and mackerel are the principal fish. Northwest Europe is the greatest fish-exporting region of the world, the annual shipments often exceeding 1,000,000 tons.

591. SEA MAMMALS. In addition to edible fish, there are other sea animals, such as seal, walrus, and whale, which are valuable for their skins, oil, bone, ivory, or flesh. Without exception, each of these animals has been the object of such ruthless slaughter that it has led to serious depletion of its numbers, and in some instances near extermination has been the result. The fur seal is an inhabitant of the waters and coasts of the North Pacific, more especially the Bering Sea, and those bordering the Antarctic continent. Desire for profits led to such reckless killing of these valuable animals that the industry has been practically ruined. To prevent complete extinction fur seals are now protected by international agreement. Arctic seals, valuable principally for their oil and skins, are caught off the northeast coast of North America as they drift southward on the ice floes in early spring. Their numbers, too, have been greatly reduced. A native of shallow coastal Arctic waters and sought for its ivory and tough hide, the walrus has suffered the same fate as the seal. Formerly all these animals furnished one of the principal sources of food for the natives who occupied the Arctic coasts. Whales inhabit both Arctic (North Atlantic Arctic and North Pacific Arctic) and Antarctic seas. Their particular value is for oil. In the Arctic seas whales have been so greatly reduced in numbers that the whaling industry has all but disappeared. It is now at high tide in Antarctic waters, but unless international regulatory measures are taken to conserve the whales of those regions the history of the Arctic industry will be repeated. In 1937–1938 the number of whales killed reached the record figure of over 51,000.

Chapter XXIV. Soils: Their Nature and Classification

592. The Soil Resource. Soil and water are the two most necessary earth resources. Prior to any requirement of building material, fuel, or power and therefore prior to the requirement of coal, metal, or stone is the need for these two fundamentals of existence, the sources of the most primitive forms of food and drink. Which of the two is more essential cannot be said. For food production each is useless without the other. Some regions are richly endowed with both soil and water and are capable of supporting large populations. Some have abundant soil but no water, whereas others have abundant water but little if any soil. A few, such as desert hamada, practically are devoid of either (437). Unlike the air, therefore, the soil may not be taken for granted as one of the omnipresent items of regional equipment. It differs greatly from area to area, not only in quantity but in quality and inherent capacity for serving the needs of man.

593. The Soil and Its Parent Material. A soil is a complex of mineral and organic substances. It was not created in the beginning exactly as it is now but rather is the product of development, or evolution. It is evolved from a parent material, which is the mantle rock, or regolith. It is developed by slow processes, which include ordinary physical and chemical weathering and, in addition, some that go on only under the influence of living organisms. The organisms concerned include higher animals, earthworms, abundant forms of microscopic life, and especially the kinds of natural vegetation the remains of which have been deposited upon and within the surface soils for thousands of years. For this reason the soil is considered to extend downward only so far as abundant organic life penetrates, generally not more than 5 to 8 ft. Below the soil, whatever its thickness, is the parent material of the soil, and below that is solid rock (Fig. 112).

Since, therefore, the regolith is derived by processes of weathering from the solid rock, and soil is evolved from the regolith, it is necessary to distinguish between the processes that accumulate the parent material and those that make the soil. The former have been discussed under the head of the gradational processes (344). Attention will be directed here to the processes that make the soil and to some of the different properties that they impart to it. Before entering upon that discussion it is necessary to inquire briefly into the general nature of the chemical constituents and physical properties of soils.

Fundamentals of Soil Chemistry

594. EARTH MINERALS AND SOIL COMPONENTS. The essential ingredients of soils are mineral substances, organic compounds, living organisms, water, and air. The bulk of most soils is made up of earth minerals. They are the same minerals as those discussed under the head of earth materials (315), and they are comprised of the chemical elements there indicated (314). In the case of any given soil it may be supposed that its mineral components originally were the same as those of its parent material, the regolith which lies underneath it. From its mineral components the soil derives not only a considerable part of its mass but also some of its elements of fertility and some of its peculiarities of physical constitution.

595. SOIL ELEMENTS. It was noted previously that of the many chemical elements found in the earth's crust, only a few are abundant. The same is true with respect to soil constituents. The most abundant soil components are the elements oxygen, silicon, aluminum, and iron, and they are combined in the common minerals, or their weathered derivatives, which give bulk to the soil. However, they are not necessarily the most important elements from the standpoint of the things that grow in the soil. Plants are known to require for their proper development about 15 different elements, and scientists are discovering that still others play some essential part in plant growth. Of this number some are supplied as gases directly from the air or as gases dissolved in the water of the soil. Others, including nitrogen and the necessary mineral elements, such as calcium, potash, and phosphorus, are taken in solution from the soil itself. Some of the mineral elements either are required in such small quantities or usually are present in the soil in such large quantities that their supply is not a matter of much concern in agriculture.

596. SUPPLY AND REMOVAL OF THE MINERAL ELEMENTS. The mineral elements in the regolith can be absorbed by plants only when they are included in the soil solutions. They are reduced to this state by complicated weathering processes which disintegrate and decompose them into smaller and smaller particles. These pass through the stage of fineness called clay and ultimately they reach a submicroscopic

size and undergo chemical change. In this state they combine with water and become gluelike and are known as *colloids*. It is believed that much of the nature of a soil, its fertility and agricultural character resides in its colloidal portion. The body of the soil will normally contain, therefore, particles of fresh and unweathered mineral, partially decomposed particles, and others grading down into the colloidal state. The larger particles furnish a reserve of mineral elements which are slowly made available for plant use by a continuation of the weathering processes.

Since plants absorb part of their sustenance in the form of dissolved minerals, it follows that, upon their death and oxidation, these soluble mineral substances also are returned to the soil in the form of ash. Some part of that supply is used again by other plants, but some is removed in solution by percolating ground water and, in humid regions, is carried away in the drainage waters. In arid regions, where there is little downward movement of ground water, the rate of removal of soluble salts is low, and there may be appreciable—in spots even a harmful—accumulation, of soluble minerals in the soil. In humid regions, however, the loss by leaching is heavy, and soils eventually would be entirely depleted were it not for reserve supplies present, but in unavailable form, in the unweathered rock minerals of the soil.

The slowness with which the new supply is made available often leaves humid-land soils that are continuously cropped deficient in one or more of the critical elements. The deficiency may, of course, be made up by the application of mineral fertilizers (702) but at great expense. Alternative means are commonly employed. One of the methods is called *fallowing*. That is the practice of allowing land to lie idle during one or more years in order that mineral decomposition may make available a sufficient amount of the critical elements to grow a crop. Other means include processes of conservative agriculture in which a part of the minerals removed from the land in the form of crops is returned to it in the form of animal manures mingled with straw and other plant refuse.

597. ORGANIC MATTER IN THE SOIL. Although it is true that the bulk of most soil is made up of minerals, it is the presence of organisms and of organic matter, the source of soil nitrogen, that makes soil essentially different from regolith. The organic matter is derived from plant and animal substances which, in addition to their small amounts of mineral ash, are made up largely of carbon, nitrogen, and water. Nitrogen is essential to plant growth. There is an inexhaustible supply of it in the air, but that is not available to plants, which must take it from the soil in solution. It is made available in the soil in the soluble

form of nitrates largely through the work of microorganisms, some of which are able to take nitrogen gas from the soil air and transform it. The leguminous and some other plants play an important role in this connection since their roots act as hosts to these nitrogen-transforming bacteria. Other soil organisms make nitrogen available through their ability to decompose the complicated organic remains of plants and animals which are then incorporated in the soil. Under conditions of low temperature the decomposition is slow, but under warm and moist conditions it is rapid, and both the end products of the decomposition and their relation to the characteristics of soils are different from those formed under low temperatures. In the early stages of the decomposition of plant remains one may recognize in the soil some fragments of plant tissue, but later these are reduced to a state of division so fine that they assume a jellylike consistency and are of highly complex physical and chemical properties. Finally this material also reaches the colloidal state and is taken into solution. The abundant organic matter of some soils includes the accumulations of many years. Some of it is recent and only slightly decomposed, while the larger part is so far decomposed that it exists in the jellylike or waxy colloidal form. This substance is usually referred to as *humus*.

The dissolved organic matter of the soil is constantly drawn upon by plants to furnish the nitrogen required by them, but if a proper amount of raw organic matter is added to the soil each year it gradually decomposes, and the humus supply is maintained. Some soils have by nature very small amounts of humus, but others are richly supplied with it. Some, like peat soils, are made up largely of raw or little-decomposed organic matter which has not yet reached the condition of humus.

The part played by the organic material of the soil in maintaining soil fertility is exceedingly complicated, but it includes the following: (a) The organic material, when finally it is taken into solution, furnishes food to plants, not only nitrogen but also such quantities of phosphorus, potassium, and calcium as remain from the plant and animal tissues from which it is derived. (b) The processes of decomposition yield organic acids which aid in the solution of soil materials. (c) Organic material is necessary to the existence of the microorganisms of the soil, those which break down the organic compounds, and also others which are beneficial to plants. (d) The jellylike nature of the humus causes it to have a high capacity for the absorption of water and of substances dissolved in water. This tends not only to maintain a supply of soil water for plants but also to retard the removal, or leaching, of dissolved minerals until plants can use them. (e)

The presence of humus promotes an arrangement, or structure, of the soil particles which is favorable to cultivation and plant growth (602).

598. ACID SOILS AND ALKALINE SOILS. Soil water, through the solution of carbon dioxide from the air and the addition of the acid products of organic and mineral decomposition, tends to become a weak acid. Many soil constituents, such as lime, sodium, and others which may be called the alkaline earths, have basic reactions. In the processes of chemical weathering the acid-soil waters attack the alkaline minerals, neutralize or dissolve them, and are themselves neutralized. In localities where ground water and the organic acids are abundant they tend to neutralize and remove all the readily available alkaline substances, and thereafter the soil solutions have generally acid reactions. The soil, under such conditions, is said to be acid, or sour. Strongly acid soils generally are unfavorable to the existence of earthworms and various soil bacteria, especially those that transform atmospheric nitrogen. Acid soils are likely, therefore, to be poor in available nitrogen although they may contain large amounts of undecomposed organic remains.

In dry regions the weathering of rocks furnishes alkaline earths, but supplies of both soil water and organic acids are limited. Consequently the soluble alkaline substances are not all leached out but tend to accumulate in the soil and give it an alkaline reaction or to become strongly charged with saline matter, including common salt. In some regions the supply of soil acids is just sufficient to balance, or neutralize, the alkaline substances as they are supplied from the soil minerals. The soils of such regions give neutral reactions and are well suited to the growth of most agricultural plants. Many crops will grow in soils which are either slightly acid or slightly alkaline. Some show a marked tolerance of acid soils; others of alkaline soils. However, there are some localities that have soils which are so highly acid, and others in which the soils are so strongly alkaline, that the common crops will not grow in them. They produce only weeds or shrubs of little value or nothing at all. The problem is not entirely simple, since there are various kinds and conditions of soil acidity and alkalinity. In general, however, the acidity of a soil may be reduced or corrected by the addition of an alkaline substance, especially pulverized limestone. The excess of alkaline or saline substance, which is found in the soils of some arid lands, usually is capable of removal by the application of abundant irrigation water and the provision of good drainage. This practice tends to dissolve the excess and to carry it away in the drainage waters.

From the above it is apparent that the factor which more than any other determines the acidity or alkalinity of the soil is the degree of leaching. This in turn depends largely upon the rainfall but also on temperature, vegetation, and other factors. Humid regions have in general acid soils, whereas those of dry regions tend to be alkaline or saline.

Fundamentals of Soil Physics

599. IMPORTANT PHYSICAL PROPERTIES OF SOILS. The agricultural utility of soils is not determined by their chemical properties alone or by the mere presence or absence of the critical elements of soil fertility. Certain physical characteristics have quite as much to do with their ability to produce crops abundantly. The more important among the various physical properties are (a) the size of the soil particles (soil texture); (b) the quantity of water included in the soil and the manner of its retention; (c) the manner of arrangement of the soil particles with respect to each other and the volume of the pore space included between them (soil structure); and (d) the soil color.

600. SOIL TEXTURE. The mineral particles of which soils are largely composed vary greatly in size from one locality to another and often from the surface downward also. In some soils coarse particles are predominant; in others exceedingly fine ones; whereas in many there is an intimate intermingling of particles of various sizes. The quality imparted to a soil by the predominance of one size of particle, or by a mixture of sizes, is called its *texture*. Some of the commonly recognized textural classes are coarse sand, fine sand, silt, and clay. The particles thus described may vary in size from diameters of about one millimeter in coarse sands to diameters of less than one-five-hundredth of a millimeter in clays. The clays include the finest particles capable of being seen, even with a microscope. However, other still smaller particles exist—the inorganic colloids, or colloidal clays. Soils may, therefore, include in their composition visible particles of mineral matter, visible particles of organic matter, colloidal clays, organic colloids, and material in solution. The colloidal substance appears to exist in part independently of the soil particles but mainly as a gelatinous coating upon them. Finely divided soils have larger surface areas than do soils of coarse texture. It is from the surface areas of soil particles and from the films of soil solution and colloids upon them that plant roots draw much of their nourishment. Therefore, fine soils, having large surface areas, provide large feeding areas for plant roots.

601. WATER AND AIR IN THE SOIL. Plants absorb their food from the soil solutions, but only a few crop plants are able to thrive

in soils in which the pore space between the soil particles is completely filled with water all the time. Most of them require soils containing both air and water. However, the yearly water requirement of plants is large. It has been shown by experiments to be, for various crops, as much as three hundred to one thousand times the dry weight of the mature plant. Water exists in the soil in various relationships.

The water of the soil is supplied from the atmosphere. Even in regions that are nearly rainless, the soil may not be absolutely dry, for it is capable of taking from the air that penetrates it a minute quantity of water vapor. This is held as a microscopic film of water molecules upon the outsides of the individual soil particles and especially by the soil colloids. It is known as *hygroscopic water*. It is more abundant in humid regions than in dry ones, in fine soils of large surface area than in those of coarse texture, and in soils of high colloidal content than in those low in colloids. Hygroscopic water adheres firmly to the soil particles, does not move from one part of the soil to another, and is very resistant to evaporation.

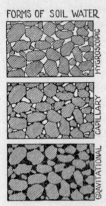

FORMS OF SOIL WATER

Fig. 317.—The ruled areas indicate soil grains, the blackened margins water, and the white areas air spaces.

Soils that are moistened frequently have thicker films of water about their particles. This is called *capillary water*. It is held upon the soil particles by its own surface tension and is absorbed by the soil colloids in great quantity, causing them to swell and giving them their jellylike consistency. The capillary film upon ordinary soil particles does not fill the pore spaces between them but exists together with soil air (Fig. 317). It is, however, with its dissolved materials, readily available to plants. When the supply of capillary water is abundant it moves slowly downward under the pull of gravity. When the supply is diminished by plant use or surface evaporation it may move horizontally, or even creep upward, under the pull of its own surface tension. In fine-textured soil water may be drawn upward in this manner from depths of a few inches or several feet, although in periods of extreme drought it may not rise fast enough to furnish plants a sufficient supply. In soils of coarse texture, both the amount and the movement of capillary water are limited. Fine soils of high organic content are capable of holding great quantities of water on their large surface areas and in their organic colloids and colloidal clays. It is this property which makes them plastic, sticky, and retentive of water when coarser but equally moistened soils are crumbly and quickly dried out. It also causes them to swell when they are wet and to shrink and crack open when they are dry. Some soils of high colloidal content, especially in regions of savanna climate, crack open so widely during the season of prolonged drought that much of the surface material crumbles and falls or is blown into the cracks. This causes a sort of natural overturn or circulation of the upper soil, which is sometimes said to "plow itself."

Immediately following protracted rains the pore spaces of soils may be completely filled with water, displacing the air. In this condition there is water in excess of that which can attach itself to the soil particles, and the surplus will move downward into the zone of ground water. This may be called *gravitional water.* In low sites, where the ground-water table coincides with the land surface, or in localities where water is prevented from downward movement by an impervious layer in the subsoil, there may be a permanent supply of gravitional water at the surface. That will create a waterlogged or swampy soil in which most cultivated plants will not grow. Where good under-drainage exists, the gravitional water moves downward, quickly in soils of coarse texture or open structure and slowly in those which are fine and compact.

It will be seen, therefore, that in all except coarse soils water moves both downward and upward. In humid regions the supply of surface moisture is sufficient to keep the downward movement con-siderably in excess of that in the upward direction. In arid regions, however, the supply of precipitation is insufficient to provide enough water to cause a gravitational movement down to the level of a deep ground-water table. Surplus gravitational water may distribute itself downward for a few feet, but later it creeps upward as capillary water bringing with it salts dissolved below. It is by this means that lime and other salts accumulate in the upper horizons of dry-land soils, while in humid-land soils they are leached out and carried away in the underdrainage.

602. SOIL STRUCTURE. Not all the important physical conditions of the soil may be explained in terms of soil texture. If that were true, fine-grained soils would always be compact and impervious to water, but such is not the case. Instead, it is found that many clays and silty soils have an arrangement of particles that is permeable to water, admits abundant soil air, and prevents the soil from being heavy, tough, or cold. This property of a soil is called its *structure.* A good soil structure is attained by the association of soil particles into groups or granules, which then behave as individuals. These groups, which are sometimes called *floccules,* may themselves be arranged into larger

compound groups and thus build up a structure in which there are
pore spaces between the particles in the floccules and larger spaces
between the floccules or larger groups (Fig. 318). Structures of this kind
are not present in all soils. They may be produced in certain soils by
proper management, and they may be destroyed by improper treatment. They commonly are found in soils of fine texture and good
colloidal content, but sandy soils
are essentially without structure,
each sand particle acting as an
individual.

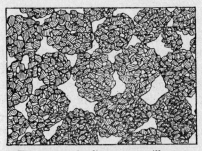

FIG. 318.—A diagram to illustrate
structure and pore space in a flocculated
soil.

603. *Pore Space in Soils.* Soils
of fine texture, in which the particles
are well flocculated, build up internal
structures in which the pore space
available for air, water, and root penetration is much greater than in most
structureless soils. In the latter the
actual amount of pore space is believed
to be sometimes less than 20 per cent of the soil volume. In highly flocculated
clays it may exceed 60 per cent. A flocculated clay is, therefore, permeable
and open in structure; but if its good structure is lost, a clay becomes very
compact, tough, and highly impermeable, because of the smallness of its
pore spaces and their partial filling by colloids which prevent the ready
circulation of water and air. Most agricultural soils include amounts of
pore space ranging between 35 and 50 per cent of the soil volume. However,
the porosity of the upper and lower portions of the same soil may differ
considerably, and time may change the porosity of a soil through changes in
chemical composition or soil management.

A good structural arrangement of soil particles, with ample pore space,
is promoted by the presence of lime and by the growth and decay of plant
roots or the addition of organic fertilizers. These form films of colloidal and
limy material which coagulate into waxy cements that attach the soil
particles together, without filling the pore spaces, and thus keep the floccules
from falling apart. The desirable structure may be destroyed by permitting
the exhaustion of lime and organic matter from the soil. With the depletion
of those materials the colloids lose their waxy coagulated form and become
dispersed and are removed from the soil by underdrainage. The weakened
cements permit the soil granules to fall apart, and their disintegration is
aided by rains beating upon the bare earth or by cultivation when the soil
is very wet. A badly deflocculated clay, when dried out, is difficult to till
and breaks up into coarse lumps which do not make a good seedbed. In a
soil of good structure the floccules maintain their identity under cultivation
but separate into groups of various sizes and shapes which are sometimes
described by appropriate terms, such as mealy, platy, granular, buckshot,
or lumpy structures.

604. SOIL COLOR.   In many regions the color of the soil is a conspicuous feature of the landscape. Important as that is to the geographer, it is not its only significance. Soils range in color through a wide variation of shades or tints from white to black. Among the commonest colors are dull shades of red, rust brown, or yellow. These are due to different forms, degrees of hydration, and intensities of the oxides of iron which exist as thin coatings or stains upon the soil grains. In some humid regions a whitish color commonly results from a lack of iron. In arid regions the same color may denote a harmful concentration of soluble salts. Black and dark-brown colors in soils usually, but not always, denote a considerable content of organic matter. In many soils two or more color-forming elements are present, giving rise to intermediate colors, such as yellowish brown or grayish brown. Because soil color usually has some basis in physical or chemical conditions, it is commonly assumed with good reason that dark soils are productive and that the light-colored ones (red to white) are, by comparison, unproductive. Although this is true of many soils, it is not always so.

The color of soil changes, not only from place to place but also from the surface downward and from one time to another. Surface soils, in some regions, are prevailingly unlike their subsoils in color, and wet soils generally are darker in color than the same soils when dry. The prevalent color of the soil of a region is, therefore, some indication of the general nature of the physical and chemical properties of the soil there, and it is used as a convenient designation for soils of the different major soils groups of the world, which are to be discussed later. Soil color has some relation to soil temperature also. Dark soils are better absorbers of solar radiation than are those of light color, and therefore they tend to be warmer. However, the warmth of a soil is even more dependent upon the circulation of air and water in it. For that reason a light-colored but permeable sand may warm up quickly in spite of its color.

FACTORS IN SOIL FORMATION

605. PARENT MATERIALS AND SOIL FORMATION.   It has been noted previously that soil is developed from a parent material, which is the regolith. Although the processes of development, when carried to completion, impart new characteristics to the soil complex, they do not in all soils erase completely the effects of strong contrasts in the parent materials. Some of the latter change rapidly, whereas others are highly resistant to change. Some are highly complex mineral compounds; others are simple. Some are high in lime, others low. Sandy soils develop from very sandy parent materials regardless of environmental conditions. The effects of parent material are generally more

visible in young and imperfectly developed soils, such as river alluvium, than in old ones.

606. THE CLIMATIC FACTOR IN SOIL DEVELOPMENT. Climate influences soil formation both directly and indirectly. Directly it affects the weathering of rocks, the percolation of water through the soil, and the work of the gradational agents. The soils of humid regions are more leached than those of dry lands. They are commonly more acid also and usually have little available lime, whereas those of arid lands are little leached and usually contain lime or soluble salts. Climate also affects the development of the soil through its seasonal variations in temperature and rainfall. Prevailingly high temperatures promote rapid chemical change in the soil, and cold slows it down. Alternating seasons of rain and drought cause soils to develop color and composition different from those of soils of continuously rainy regions. Wind acts as a drying agent in soil formation, and deflation and wind deposition are important soil-forming processes in some localities. These are but a few of the many ways in which the climatic elements are concerned with the processes of soil development.

607. THE BIOLOGIC FACTOR IN SOIL DEVELOPMENT. Both plants and animals play important parts in soil formation. Microorganisms (bacteria, fungi, protozoa, etc.) cause the decay of plant and animal remains and aid in their transformation into humus. Some kinds transform atmospheric nitrogen into soil nitrogen, as previously noted. These minute organisms live and die in such vast numbers (billions per gram of soil) that their own bodies also make an important contribution to the organic content of the soil. The roots of higher plants, such as grasses and trees, penetrate the soil and help to make it porous. When they die they add organic matter within the soil. Deep-rooted plants bring mineral solutions up from the subsoil and build them into their tissues. When these die and decay the minerals are added to the upper soil layers. However, the organic acids provided by plant decay in humid regions hasten the soil-leaching process. The work of worms is most important in mixing organic remains with the mineral soil constituents and in bringing subsoil minerals to the surface. Burrowing animals perform a similar service on a smaller scale, and all animals aid, to some extent, in soil formation when plant products pass through their digestive tracts and are returned to the soil for further transformation.

608. SURFACE RELIEF AS A FACTOR IN SOIL DEVELOPMENT. In addition to the other factors mentioned, the development of the soil is influenced by its physical site. This is because differences in surface slope may greatly affect the moisture and air conditions within the

soil and the rate of its surface erosion. Ideal development is most likely to take place on rolling and well-drained uplands where there is free underdrainage and moderate surface erosion. On such sites the removal of old and leached surface material by erosion just about keeps pace with the downward progress of the soil-forming processes. Soils developing under such conditions are called *mature* or *normal* soils. The soils of steep slopes, on the contrary, generally fail to develop to maturity because much of the rain water runs off the surface instead of percolating into the ground. This produces less leaching than is normal for the climatic situation, and it accelerates surface erosion, exposing the less developed lower layers. Lack of soil water and increased erosion reduce the density of the vegetative cover and thus modify the organic contribution to the soil development also. In poorly drained or marshy areas soils do not develop normally either. But in this case it is due to the slowness of leaching and to the fact that air cannot penetrate. Hence the usual organic processes are not carried out.

SOIL ZONES, SOIL PROFILES, AND SOIL CLASSIFICATION

609. ENVIRONMENT AND SOIL ZONATION. Because of the fact that climate is an important factor in soil formation, there is a notable correlation between the world distribution of the major soil types on the one hand, and that of the great climatic regions with their characteristic vegetational associations, on the other. The relationship is most clearly seen in the distribution of the maturely developed soils. Such normal soils show great uniformity within a given set of environmental conditions regardless of the parent materials from which they are derived, and they show likewise great differences in character under different climatic environments, even though their parent materials may have been similar. Because they are characteristic of large regions or zones, which are more or less similar to the great climatic regions, these are sometimes called the *zonal* soils. There are other soil types which are found in all the climatic zones, and these are called *intrazonal*. In them some one factor, such as peculiar character in the parent material, outweighs the effects of climate and all other environmental conditions. Still other soil types seem to have no relation to the great soil zones. Generally they are found in areas of extremely youthful and undeveloped regolith, such as newly deposited alluvium, dune sand, or nearly bare rock. They are called *azonal* soils.

610. THE SOIL PROFILE. It will be apparent from the preceding discussion that some of the more important properties of zonal soils are acquired through *development*. A soil may be thought of as being

somewhat like an organism, in that it has some qualities derived from its ancestry and some that come as a result of growing up under a given set of environmental conditions. Moreover, as a soil advances in age the qualities inherited from its ancestry tend to become less important in its make-up, whereas those which are acquired through development tend to assume greater importance.

In soils that have been subjected for a long time to the soil-forming processes, the qualities acquired through development are made

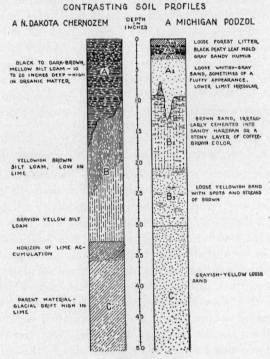

CONTRASTING SOIL PROFILES

A N. DAKOTA CHERNOZEM   DEPTH IN INCHES   A MICHIGAN PODZOL

BLACK TO DARK-BROWN, MELLOW SILT LOAM — 10 TO 20 INCHES DEEP — HIGH IN ORGANIC MATTER

YELLOWISH BROWN SILT LOAM, LOW IN LIME

GRAYISH YELLOW SILT LOAM

HORIZON OF LIME AC-CUMULATION

PARENT MATERIAL - GLACIAL DRIFT HIGH IN LIME

LOOSE FOREST LITTER. BLACK PEATY LEAF MOLD GRAY SANDY HUMUS

LOOSE WHITISH-GRAY SAND, SOMETIMES OF A FLUFFY APPEARANCE. LOWER LIMIT IRREGULAR

BROWN SAND, IRREGU-LARLY CEMENTED INTO SANDY HARDPAN OR A STONY LAYER OF COFFEE-BROWN COLOR

LOOSE YELLOWISH SAND WITH SPOTS AND STREAKS OF BROWN

GRAYISH-YELLOW LOOSE SAND

FIG. 319.

evident by an arrangement of the soil into layers, or *horizons*, of different thicknesses and different chemical and physical properties. The succession of these layers, from the surface down to the underlying parent material of the soil, is called the *soil profile*.

611. PARTS OF THE SOIL PROFILE. Three horizons are commonly recognized: an upper, or A, horizon; an intermediate, or B, horizon; and a lower, or C, horizon (Fig. 319). In most soils the A horizon is distinguished from the others in color, texture, and structure. It is that part of the soil in which organic life is most abundant, and in grassland soils it may consist almost wholly of organic material. In forest soils

it may have a thin layer of organic material while its lower portion has lost some of its mineral constituents. In humid regions, generally, its development has involved the loss of something from its original composition. Through the work of percolating water some soluble material has been leached out, and some finely divided material has been carried out in suspension, or *eluviated*. The A horizon is, therefore, in most humid-land soils a horizon of leaching and eluviation and is left poorer in soluble substances and coarser in texture as a result. The B horizon is, in contrast, one of *illuviation*. In it are deposited some of the materials carried in suspension from above and some parts of those carried in solution either from above or from below. It is a zone of enrichment, and in some soils it is made dense and impenetrable by its additions. The C horizon is the little changed parent material, or regolith, from which the soil was derived. The thickness of each of these horizons varies greatly with the type of soil. In some they are thin, and in others so thick that, for purposes of minute description, each horizon is further subdivided.

612. MATURE AND IMMATURE PROFILES. Although uniform conditions of climate and natural vegetation tend to unify soil development, not all the soils of a given locality are likely to have the same profile. It was indicated above that a mature soil is the result of the slow evolution of a soil in its given environment. Such a soil may be said to have a *mature profile* and to represent the climax of development under the given conditions. The profile cannot develop ideally if the soil-making forces are interfered with by rapid erosion or rapid aggradation or are retarded by poor drainage. Therefore, many soils have not mature profiles. Instead, their horizons show evidence of disturbance or of arrested development, so that they remain immature. Some soils, such as deep sands, have developed no horizons and therefore have no profiles.

It cannot be expected, therefore, that all the soils of a district will have the mature profile typical of that district. In fact, in some considerable areas little if any mature soil is to be found. The normal processes of agriculture such as deforestation, plowing, and heavy grazing tend to increase the rate of erosion and to intermingle and otherwise destroy soil horizons. Indeed, the typical profiles of mature soils probably are nearly, if not quite, restricted to the virgin soils of a region, whether they are the soils of forest or those of prairie. Of their virgin soils many regions of high agricultural development have left only a few scattered remnants. Yet, when mature soils are present, they show significant similarities of profile over large areas, even when they are derived from widely different parent materials. Moreover, even the soils of incompletely or imperfectly developed profiles in a region commonly have qualities that indicate a developmental progress in the direction of the regional type.

613. THE LIMITATIONS OF A GENERAL CLASSIFICATION OF SOILS. Any attempt to secure a world view of the function of soil as an element of earth environment requires that soils be grouped in a manner suited to convenient description and such that the general features of their world distribution may be understood readily. The physiographic terms that have been used heretofore to describe classes of the regolith, such as residual, transported, alluvial, aeolian, and others, are not adequate to describe all the significant soil differences. The classifications used by agricultural experts in describing the local differences of soils are too complicated to be grasped quickly. If there is any sound basis for generalization upon a subject of such infinite variety as the soil, it appears to be in a discoverable degree of regional unity in the characteristics of mature soils as expressed in their profiles. It is upon that basis that European and American soil scientists have succeeded, in recent decades, in evolving a system of classification having general application. However, the details of even that system far exceed the limits of this brief treatment, and it must here be subjected to further generalization. So general a classification must be employed with full understanding of the fact that it does not adequately account for many of the details of soil condition and soil distribution in specific localities.

614. MATURE SOILS AS A BASIS OF SOIL CLASSIFICATION. The characteristics of mature soils make a convenient basis upon which to classify the soils of the world, in spite of the fact that mature soil is almost lacking in some localities. It is a good basis because it rests primarily upon the essential properties of the soil itself and not upon the manner of soil origin. It rests upon the properties of all the soil horizons and not upon those of the surface layer alone. Classification upon that basis has the further merit of recognizing the effects of all the soil-making forces, especially climate, and makes it possible to understand the relations of the different soil types to each other.

In proceeding to a classification of the soils of the world upon the basis of mature soil type it should be reemphasized that soils of mature profile are not the only soils in most localities and that they are not everywhere the most productive soils from the agricultural viewpoint. Each region has also its intrazonal and azonal soils. In many regions they are much more abundant than the mature soils. These cannot be classified regionally upon the basis of mature soil type but must be recognized as existing in association with each of the classes so made.

Chapter XXV. The Principal Soil Groups of the World

615. Major Classes of Soils. Among the various factors that combine to transform regolith into soil, no other is more important than condition of climate. Quantity of soil moisture and prevalent conditions of soil temperature affect the soil directly, as has previously been indicated, and they also condition the growth of natural vegetation and the activity of microorganisms. It is possible, therefore, to distinguish clearly, upon the basis of their mature profiles, between the soils of humid forest regions and those of desert and steppe regions and, likewise, between the forest soils of the tropics and those of middle or high latitudes.

The mature soils of humid regions generally have developed under natural vegetations of *forest or woodland*. There the organic matter is incorporated in the soil more slowly than in the grasslands. Therefore, humid-land soils, as a whole, are much leached, prevailingly light in color, and characterized by a comparatively low content of both organic matter and mineral plant foods. However, the chemical nature of the soil-forming processes, and the results produced by them in terms of soil profiles, are notably different in warm humid regions from those which operate in cool humid regions. The dominant soil-making process of the tropical and subtropical forest regions is called *laterization*. Through this process the organic soil material is rapidly mineralized and leached out, the basic soil minerals are lost, and even the silica is largely dissolved. When this process is carried on to its extreme development there remain principally the hydroxides of aluminum and iron, and this residual material is called *laterite*. In the subarctic forest lands, on the contrary, the dominant soil-making process is called *podzolization*. Owing to differences in climate, its processes are unlike those of laterization. Half-decayed and acid organic matter accumulates on the top of the soil. The upper soil is leached of its iron and aluminum compounds, and the remaining material is high in silica. In the subsoil there is an accumulation of finely divided organic matter, iron and other mineral compounds leached from above and deposited below. The final product of this process is an acid, unproductive soil called *podzol*.

It appears, therefore, that laterites should be widespread in the humid tropics and podzols in the subarctic regions, but both these assumptions are not entirely supported by the facts. Although podzols do in fact occur widely in the higher latitudes, true laterite is not widespread in the tropics. Generally, however, tropical soils are lateritic in type and have progressed through some part of the lateritic process. Podzolization, on the other hand, is characteristic not only of the subarctic but, in modified form, extends into the forest regions of the lower middle latitudes and even to the tropics, where some soils of podzolic type exist beside, or have even developed from, those of lateritic origin. The notable thing in this connection, however, is that these two extremes do appear, that intermediate types exist, and that they form rude belts or zones corresponding roughly with the temperature modifications of the humid lands. These are the soil zones.

The mature soils of subhumid and dry regions generally have developed under natural vegetations of *grass or desert shrub*. They are, because of the lack of abundant soil moisture, characterized by a considerable, and in some places excessive, content of soluble mineral matter. Although there are some significant differences between the soils of the warm dry regions and those of the cool dry regions they are not so marked as are those between the laterites and the podzols in the humid regions. Instead, there is a greater difference between the soils of the very arid or desert regions and those of the subhumid grassland regions, whether they lie in low latitudes or farther poleward. The typical mature soil of a desert region is gray in color, high in saline or alkaline minerals, and low in organic matter, while that of the subhumid grassland region is neutral or moderately alkaline, black or dark brown in color, and high in organic matter. The desert and grassland soils are zonal also, but with respect to the moisture supply rather than to temperature.

A brief survey may now be made of each of the principal soil groups of the world with respect to its profile characteristics and its inherent capacity for human use. Attention may be directed also to the major features of the world distribution of the great soil groups, of which a generalized view is presented graphically in Plate IX. The fact that this map of the world distribution of soil groups leaves much to be desired is due to at least three conditions: (*a*) The small scale of the map requires that it be very general, but the facts of soil distribution are highly detailed. (*b*) Large areas of some of the continents are incompletely surveyed as to soil, and information about them is inadequate or almost entirely lacking. (*c*) Writers in describing the soils of other lands have not always done so in the terms employed in the present classification, or they have used the same terms but with different meanings. Attempts to harmonize such descriptions have not been attended by uniformly satisfactory results.

Soils of the Humid Forest Lands

616. It was noted above that the mature soils of the humid forest lands are of two extreme groups, with several of intermediate character. These may be considered in the following order: (*a*) the lateritic soils, found generally in regions of tropical rainforest climate or the humid subtropics; (*b*) the podzols, which are found principally in the regions of subarctic coniferous forest; and (*c*) the gray-brown podzolic forest soils, which are found in the broadleaf forest regions, intermediate between the other two (Plates VIII, IX).

617. TROPICAL AND SUBTROPICAL RED AND YELLOW SOILS. Although mature soils in the regions of warm and humid climates are developed largely by the lateritic decomposition of rocks, it does not follow that they are all alike. In fact they are of great variety, since the original rocks differ greatly, there are various degrees of laterization, and some of the lateritic materials have been more or less podzolized. Within the general regions of the humid tropics and subtropics also, there are numerous types of intrazonal or azonal soils. The resulting association of types is so complex that no attempt will be made to distinguish them in the soils map of the world (Plate IX). However, the outstanding characteristics of some of them may be noted briefly, particularly as they may be related to use of the land for agricultural crops.

618. *Lateritic Red Soils.* Soils so highly laterized as to be true laterites (L. *later*, brick) are not widespread. They seem to reach their highest development in the well-drained uplands of regions having the savanna type of rainfall regime. In general the laterites are granular, porous, and have low water-holding capacity. They are capable of being tilled immediately after heavy rains but are subject to drought. Being highly leached, they are low in plant foods, both mineral and organic, and are not capable of sustained cropping without heavy fertilization. And, since they are porous, they require irrigation in dry seasons. Most of them have red or brown A horizons and deep B horizons of dark red color. Such as are weathered from rocks high in iron are composed largely of iron oxide, and some are suitable for use

as iron ore. In certain localities the original rocks were high in feldspars and low in iron-containing minerals. The lower horizons of the laterites derived from them are buff or gray in color and consist largely of the hydrous oxides of aluminum. Some are so rich in aluminum that they are used as ores of that metal.

Far more extensive in area than the true laterites, and of much greater agricultural importance, are related types which may be called the *lateritic red and yellow soils*. Not only are they found in the rainy forest lands of the tropics, but they are also widespread in the humid subtropics, such as the cotton belt of the United States and southern China (Plate IX). They have been subjected to the process of laterization, but either the process has not been so complete as in the case of the laterites or it has taken place under slightly different conditions of rainfall and drainage. The upper horizons of these soils generally are brown, friable clays and loams. The B horizons usually are deep and more compact than in the laterites, and their colors vary from red to yellow or mottled. The lighter colors result from a less complete oxidation of the iron content, and this in turn is believed to indicate more abundant soil moisture resulting from either greater rainfall or less thorough underdrainage. Some of the red and yellow soils have been more or less affected by podzolic processes, especially such as are derived from sandy materials and are porous, as in the Atlantic Coastal Plain of the United States. In such soils, a thin upper layer of organic material is underlain by a leached gray or yellow A horizon, and this in turn is underlain by an acid B horizon of red or yellow lateritic material.

The agricultural capacity of the mature red and yellow soils is distinctly better than that of the laterites. Although, as a class, they are low in readily available lime and other alkaline substances, they still contain some reserves of unweathered rock minerals and considerable colloidal materials from which these plant foods may be made available. Their generally finer textures cause them to be more retentive of moisture, but to permit adequate drainage. However, their supplies of organic matter seldom are abundant. Under cultivation the colors of the red and yellow subsoils usually predominate. That is because cropping quickly uses the small surface reserve of organic matter, plowing tends to intermingle the A and B horizons, and the higher clay content of these soils makes them more subject to erosion than are the laterites. Although they presently become exhausted under continuous cropping, they respond well to fertilizers because of their fine textures. In some regions they are kept in continuous productivity by heavy fertilization, but in others worn-out lands are abandoned for periods of years to permit the accumulation of new reserves of plant food.

619. SOILS ASSOCIATED WITH THE LATERITIC RED SOILS. It was noted previously that mature soils of the lateritic red type, like other mature soils, attain their best development upon undulating surfaces where underdrainage is free and erosion is small but not entirely absent. From that it may be inferred that there are many localities, within the large areas shown as lateritic soils on Plate IX, that do not have mature soils of that type. The soils of some of these are intrazonal, and those of others are azonal in character. Among the former are the soils of boglands or other areas of poor drainage and such as have an unusual lime content, owing to the limy nature of their parent materials. The azonal types include the rapidly eroding surfaces of steep slopes, where the soils are thin, stony, and immature. They also include porous sands without profile development, recent deposits of volcanic ash, and especially the recent alluvial deposits of floodplains and deltas. In these latter the rate of accumulation is too rapid to permit of the slow development of the normal profile. Yet in most instances they are, where adequately drained, more productive agricultural lands than the mature soils with which they are associated. Henceforth it will be understood that the intrazonal and azonal soils exist in association with each of the great soil groups to be discussed, and particular reference to their characteristics will be brief.

620. PODZOLS. Podzols are the typical mature soils of regions having subarctic climate (Plate IX). Although it is known to occur in the humid tropics and subtropics, podzolization is much more favored by long winters and short summers. Podzolic soils are different from lateritic soils in structure, profile, and color.

The mature podzol is developed under a natural vegetation of forest, but in this case it is mainly coniferous forest. The effect of long cold winter and moderate summer temperatures and a forest litter of resinous pine needles is to retard bacterial action and to permit the formation of a brown layer of raw humus or half-decomposed organic remains, which represents the accumulation of many years. This spongy material on the forest floor retains water, becomes highly acid as the result of fermentation, and the downward-moving soil solutions are made acid by it. The strong acidity is unfavorable to the existence of earthworms, and they are few. Consequently their customary work of mingling the decaying vegetation with the upper soil layers is not accomplished, and the line of separation between raw surface humus and the mineral soil is sharp. Moreover, the effect of the strongly acid solutions upon the soil minerals is very different from that under the weakly acid or neutral solutions found in tropical soils. The acid solutions render soluble and remove from the surface soil the iron and aluminum, which, under tropical conditions, are oxidized and left at the surface. Underneath the layer of raw humus the A horizon of a mature podzol is leached of its iron and readily soluble minerals, and, by eluviation, it has lost most of its clay and colloidal constituents also. It is, therefore, poor in the mineral elements of soil fertility and nearly structureless. Through loss of iron it is bleached to a grayish-white

Fig. 320.—A forest podzol, newly cleared, east of Peace River, Alberta. The plow has turned under the surface layers and has exposed the fluffy whitish-gray sand of the lower A horizon. See Fig. 319.

color (the name podzol is derived from Russian words meaning "ashes underneath") (Figs. 319, 320). Beneath a bleached A horizon of variable thickness there is typically a brown, acid B horizon which is strongly illuviated. In it are deposited some quantities of the iron and other minerals leached from above and even part of the finely divided or colloidal clays and organic material which have passed through the A horizon. In some localities these substances bind together the mineral particles of the B horizon, cementing it into a stony layer, or *hardpan*. The C horizon is composed of the glacial drift or other parent material of the soil. Podzol is poor agricultural soil. Under cultivation the surface layer of humus soon is lost, and the grayish surface soil requires fertilization and good management to keep it productive and to prevent its poor structure from becoming a hindrance to tillage.

The main regions of podzol development, as is shown in Plate IX, are in the higher middle latitudes. However, they are not strictly confined to those latitudes. Partially podzolized soils are abundant in the humid lower middle latitudes and are to some extent found in the red-soil regions or even in the humid tropics where unusual conditions have permitted the accumulation of coverings of acid organic matter.

621. SOILS ASSOCIATED WITH THE MATURE PODZOLS. In connection with the podzols, as with the other groups, there are soils of immature or imperfectly developed profiles. Recent alluvial deposits, ice-scoured and steam-eroded slopes, glacial marshes, and other areas of high water table comprise large total areas of structureless soils or such as have abnormal or immature podzolic profiles. Podzolization proceeds most rapidly and extends deepest on light permeable materials that are low in lime, such as sand. However, there are, in the region of the podzols, considerable localities of tight glaciolacustrine clays, such as those of the Ontario Clay Belt (433). In some of these the compactness of the clay has retarded leaching, and the soils are but weakly podzolic or podzolization has reached only a short distance beneath the surface. Many of the associated soils are better for agricultural use because of their differences from the true podzols. Not even the normal well-drained soils of the region, however, are equally podzolized. They have developed under different kinds of natural vegetation which have grown in response to differences in slope, exposure to sunlight, or the nature of the underlying rock. These differences tend to modify the nature of the soil profile or to retard its full development. However, it is probable that among the many somewhat different soils of the podzolic soil regions there is a degree of unity in characteristics which is sufficient to set them well apart in appearance and utility from the soils of the other major groups.

622. THE GRAY-BROWN FOREST SOILS are the typical mature soils of the humid microthermal forest regions of the world (Plate IX). They are podzolic soils but not fully developed podzols. They may be considered as intermediate in characteristics between the podzols and the tropical red and yellow soils. They also reach their normal development under forest vegetation but mainly under deciduous forest with associated shrubs and grasses. Under these vegetational and climatic conditions there is a surface accumulation of organic material which forms a dark layer from 1 to 3 in. deep. It is less rapidly decomposed and typically more abundant than the organic accumulations associated with the tropical red soils, but it is not so abundant, so poorly decomposed, or so acid as that associated with the podzols. Moreover, the organic material derived from broadleaf forest contains more lime, potash, and other basic elements than does that from coniferous forest,

and these are returned to the soil. The A horizon of the podzolic gray-brown forest soil is leached but not impoverished or greatly bleached. It generally is stained with iron but by a brown hydroxide of iron rather than by the red oxide common in the tropics. The admixture of organic matter to the brown surface material gives the grayish-brown color from which the group name is derived. The quantity of organic material decreases downward, and the B horizon is yellowish brown and of heavier texture than the A horizon, because it has been illuviated from above. As in the podzols, the C horizon is the little-changed parent material of the soil, much of it glacial drift. The gray-brown soils have generally better structures than the other forest-land soils, keep their structures better under cultivation, and respond more readily to the application of lime and organic fertilizers. The humus of forest origin is better distributed in the upper gray-brown soil horizons than in the podzols, because of the work of earthworms and other soil organisms which thrive under the less acid conditions. This reserve of humus, together with some quantities of the critical soil minerals, causes newly cleared gray-brown soils to be productive. However, they presently lose their strength under continuous cropping unless they are carefully managed and well fertilized.

Plate IX shows the mature gray-brown podzolic soils to be typical of some of the intensively cultivated agricultural lands of the world, such as northeastern United States, northwestern Europe, and several other regions of smaller size.

623. SOILS ASSOCIATED WITH THE MATURE GRAY-BROWN FOREST SOILS.   Some of the soils associated with the gray-brown soils are without structure, such as sandy heath lands or the peat soils of the moors and glacial bogs. Moreover, many of the phases of the gray-brown soil itself have developed from parent materials of widely different kinds. These include not only different kinds of bedrock but also glacial deposits such as limy till, sandy till, and glaciofluvial and glaciolacustrine deposits. Although the soils developed upon these various parent materials tend, in time, to become much alike in regions of similar climate and natural vegetation, some of them mature more rapidly than others, and, therefore, at the present stage they differ. In any case, the time that has elapsed since the withdrawal of the continental ice sheets from northern North American and Europe has not been great enough for all the kinds of parent material to attain full soil maturity. Under cultivation the gray-brown soils lose their A horizons, especially upon hill slopes, and the yellowish color of the B horizon shows in striking contrast with the gray browns of the more level areas or the gray blacks of peaty soils in ill-drained depressions. It is not surprising, therefore, to find that soil types, especially in glaciated regions, change at short intervals and change abruptly and that only small parts of the total surface

may be covered by the mature soil which is taken to be typical of the full course of soil development in the region.

Soils of the Subhumid Grasslands and Deserts

It was previously indicated that the soils of the subhumid grasslands and the deserts are to be distinguished from those of the humid forest lands. It was noted also that a clear distinction is to be made between the dark-colored grassland soils and the gray soils of the deserts. These groups may be considered in the order just stated.

624. THE DARK-COLORED GRASSLAND SOILS. Forest ceases to be the dominant vegetation in both tropical and middle-latitude climates where dryness, as it is expressed in terms of precipitation, its distribution, absorption, and evaporation, reduces the supply of soil moisture below a critical amount. The amount of moisture required to support a forest varies with latitude, altitude, and other conditions, and it is not possible to draw a clearly defined climatic line that will everywhere coincide with the boundaries between forest lands and grasslands or with the soil boundaries associated with them.[1] However, the result of increasing dryness is that, eventually, forest ends and grass becomes the dominant vegetation. The effect of limited soil moisture, and the presence of grass cover, is to cause the development of soils very different from those of the humid forest lands.

In regions where the moisture supply is almost, but not quite, sufficient to support a forest vegetation it normally is sufficient to support a dense and luxuriant growth of grasses. The growth and annual death of a part of the thick grass sod and its fibrous roots add organic matter *in* the soil where it decomposes slowly and gives rise to a large supply of humus. However, the accumulation takes place under conditions of moderate to low moisture supply, and the humus is not prevailingly saturated, and it is not acid. Because the humus is largely of grass-root origin it is not confined to the surface but extends to depths of from several inches to 3 or 4 ft. Slow leaching leaves sufficient lime to combine with the large amount of organic colloids and colloidal clays in these dark soils, thus promoting excellent structural conditions, which are found in all the soil horizons (Fig. 321). The abundant and deep organic material also is the source of much of the agricultural strength for which these soils are famed and of their prevailing dark colors. Owing to the deep penetration of the organic material, the horizons of the grassland soils usually are not so sharply defined as are those of the forest soils, and they change only gradually to a parent material beneath.

[1] See Art. 564 and footnote.

Because the grassland soils develop under comparative dryness, they are less leached than any of the soils previously considered. There is normally a redistribution in the soil profile of the lime contained in the parent material, without a complete removal of it. In fact there is in most of these soils *a horizon of lime accumulation* which is one of the characteristics distinguishing the soils of the dry lands from those of the humid climates. Frequent periods of drought cause upward movements of capillary water. This movement brings up lime, dissolved from the parent material of the soil, and the evaporation of water from the soil surface causes its deposition. Subsequent rains tend to carry the lime down again, but ultimately a position of balance

Fig. 321.—A vertical section in a mellow grassland soil of the chernozem type, near Hythe, Alberta. The deep penetration of grass roots is shown clearly. See Fig. 319. (*Photograph by Mary McRae Colby.*)

is established. The position of that horizon depends upon the supply of soil moisture and the quantity of lime in the parent material. It is nearer the surface in regions of abundant lime and low rainfall and farther down in soils that are better supplied with moisture or are derived from parent materials poor in lime (Robinson).

Since dark soils of the general group here described are found over large areas of subhumid climate, both in middle latitudes and in the tropics, it is not to be supposed that all of them are alike. They differ as a consequence of (*a*) amount and seasonal distribution of precipitation, (*b*) conditions of temperature, and (*c*) the types of grass vegetation under which they have developed. Only three major subdivisions of the grassland group may be noted in greater detail.

625. *Prairie Soils.* Adjacent to some of the forest-soil regions, but on their drier margins, are black prairie soils that may be

thought of as intermediate in type between the true steppe soils and the forest soils. These intermediate soils, which may be called *prairie soils*, are widely developed in the United States, Russia, and South America, and there are others somewhat like them in Africa. They appear to have formed under a natural vegetation of tall grasses but in climates having sufficient moisture so that the land might have supported forests. The reason why there were not forests in these regions is not clearly understood (582).

The prairie soils are like the steppe soils in their fine granular textures and dark color. Both these qualities are derived from abundant and deep accumulations of the organic matter of grass roots. They are different from them and like the podzolic forest soils, in that they are low in lime and other alkaline substances. They have no horizon of lime accumulation; yet they are neutral rather than acid. This condition is due to the fact that they are supplied with sufficient moisture so that there is a predominant downward movement of the soil solutions that carry the readily soluble minerals below the lower limits of the soil profile and into the underground water circulation. The prairie soils are, however, excellent agricultural soils. Because of their high humus content, their good structure, and the more abundant soil moisture associated with them they are among the most productive soils of the world.

The rich corn-belt soils of central Illinois, Iowa, and Missouri are prairie soils (Plate IX). The typical mature soil is found on rolling interfluves where the natural vegetation of prairie grasses was best established. In the United States they are developed mainly in regions of older glacial drift on which are considerable admixtures of loess. On steeper slopes, especially river bluffs, fingers of woodland originally projected into the prairies. On such sites the gray-brown podzolic soils were developed.

Somewhat like the prairie soils, and included with them in the map (Plate IX), are some that appear to have passed the climax of their development and to have entered a stage of retrogression. They are called "degraded chernozems" (626). It appears that they developed originally as black steppe soils and were lime accumulating, but, owing to increased rainfall or other possible changes, they have lost much of their lime and have been more or less invaded by forest vegetation. Podzolization has set in, and the subsoil has become lighter. Still, however, the surface soil maintains the dark color and high productivity inherited from its earlier condition. Degraded chernozems are recognized especially in Russia.

In several humid regions there is another kind of dark-colored soil, high in humus, which is found in association with the red and yellow soils, the gray-brown forest soils, and perhaps others. It is similar to prairie soil in character and yet significantly different in origin. The soil type is called *rendzina*. It is developed from parent material containing lime in such abundance that the supply continues to exceed the rate of loss through leaching. Hard limestones break down too slowly to form rendzinas. In soft chalky limestones, however, or in beds of glacial or lacustrine marl, the rate of physical disintegration is more rapid than the rate at which leaching can remove the lime. Consequently, the resulting soils are high in lime in spite of heavy leaching. High lime content encouraged an original vegetation of tall prairie grasses rather than forest. This, in turn, produced a dark soil of the prairie-soil type, with which they are grouped in Plate IX. Examples of rendzinas are found in the soils of the Black Prairies of Alabama and Texas, in certain dark soils of eastern Cuba, in some of the chalk lands and glacial marls of Europe, and elsewhere. Many of the areas are too small to be shown individually in Plate IX, and they are included with adjacent soils.

626. *Chernozem Soils.* Chernozem (a Russian word meaning black earth) is the name applied to a type of soil that may be considered the finest development of the grassland-soil group. It is formed under a dense vegetation of prairie and steppe grasses and under precipitation sufficiently low so that, while the most soluble soil minerals are leached out, an abundance of lime and the less soluble alkaline minerals remain. The low precipitation also results in a lack of eluviation, and the soil has a large component of clay and colloids. In true chernozem soils the horizon of lime accumulation lies generally between 3 and 5 ft. beneath the surface and is still within reach of the grass roots, which find in it an inexhaustible source of calcium. The surface material of the chernozem is high in humus and of a black or very dark-brown color (Fig. 319). The soil structure is well flocculated, granular, and porous. Upon tillage it crumbles into a fine seedbed, and it has a large capacity for holding water. The reserves of both organic and mineral plant food in chernozems are so abundant that the soils will stand cropping for long periods without fertilization. The high colloidal content of chernozems causes them to be extremely plastic when they are wet and, on slopes, to suffer badly from surface erosion when they are cultivated. In general, however, there are no better soils than chernozems for grain, cotton, and other crops that draw heavily upon soil fertility.

Plate IX shows the probable world distribution of the chernozems. These highly fertile soils reach their most excellent development in the middle latitudes, especially on the gently undulating uplands along the prairie-steppe margin of the United States (582, 583) and in southern Russia. However, even in North America there are differences between the chernozem of the northern end of the belt, in Canada and the Dakotas, and that of Texas. The latter was developed under grass and shrub vegetation less dense than the northern sod and under higher temperatures. It has, in consequence, a lower humus content and a more brownish-black color and a redder subsoil.

In regions of subhumid tropical grassland also there are belts of dark soils which are classed as chernozem. They are shown in Plate IX. These soils have not been studied so widely as the chernozems of higher latitudes, but they appear to be like the latter in that they contain abundant organic matter and a horizon of lime accumulation. However, long-continued high temperatures hasten the decomposition of organic matter, even under subhumid conditions. It is probable that a large part of the tropical chernozems are neither so deep nor so black as those of the Dakotas. They are apparently more like those of Texas. Also, according to Shantz and Marbut, those of Africa at least are notably heavier in texture and more difficult to cultivate than similar soils in America.

627. *Brown Steppe Soils*. Adjacent to the chernozems, but on their drier margins, are soils that, although similar, show the effects of a decreased moisture supply. The line of separation seldom is sharp, and the transition from the black soils commonly passes through soils of chestnut-brown to those of reddish-brown color. These together may be called the *brown steppe soils* (Plate IX), and they are to be clearly distinguished from the podzolic gray-brown forest soils.

The brown steppe soils show the influence of decreased moisture in several ways. First, it may be noted that they have developed under a grass cover less luxuriant and deep rooted than that associated with the chernozems and the prairie soils. In general, it is a continuous sod cover of various species of "short grass," but it includes also areas of grass with intermingled desert shrub. The roots of the grasses provide an abundant but less penetrating source of humus than those of the tall grasses. The dryness of the earth has promoted the formation of brown rather than black humus, which is intermingled with a powdery surface soil and lies above a subsoil of somewhat coarser and more lumpy structure than that of the chernozems. The brown steppe soils have, like the chernozems, a zone of accumulated lime or other alkaline substances, deposited beneath the surface by the movement of soil moisture. Because the precipitation of the brown steppe-soil regions is slight, the horizon of alkaline accumulation is relatively near the surface, and, in some localities, the lime is so abundant that it forms a tough hardpan layer in the soil. In general, however, the soils are easily tilled and are found upon undulating to rolling land well adapted to cultivation. The fact that the brown steppe-soil regions, the world over, are predominantly regions of livestock grazing rather than of soil cultivation is due to the deficiency of rainfall in them rather than to deficiencies in their soils.

628. DESERT SOILS. The typical soils of the arid lands of the middle latitudes may be called the gray desert soils whereas those of the low-latitude deserts generally are tinged with red (Plate IX). They develop under sparse vegetations composed of widely spaced desert shrubs and, therefore, lack the abundant organic matter of the grassland soils. Because they are low in organic matter the lighter colors predominate in these soils, and the reds, browns, yellows, and grays of weathered rock minerals are widely exposed. This characteristic is accentuated by the accumulation of lime and other whitish substances near to, or even upon, the soil surface. The alkaline and saline materials usually are present in such abundance that commonly the surface materials, or those immediately below the surface, are cemented by them into crusts or hardpan layers. Desert soils, lacking grass, are, therefore, characteristically low in nitrogen but have large supplies of soluble minerals. In such soils as are of medium to coarse texture the concentration of alkaline materials is not generally sufficient to be harmful to plants. In some areas, however, the surface accumulation of salt and alkali is so great that cultivated plants cannot grow in it. This condition, in its extreme form, is found in playa-lake beds (438). It is, however, not only the quantity but also the quality of the salts that determines the agricultural utility of desert soils. It is commonly held that soils in which the compounds of calcium predominate maintain better structures under irrigation, whereas a predominance of sodium salts tends to destroy the soil structure and eventually to render irrigated land unfit for use.

It is probable that the larger parts of the great deserts are not covered with mature soils. Associated with the latter are patches of rock desert or stream-eroded pediments (437), expanses of desert pavement covered with the varnished pebbles left after wind deflation (440), tracts of dune sand, and areas of immature soil resulting from the recent and rapid growth of alluvial fans. Fan soils are the most widely cultivated in arid land because of their suitability for irrigation. But even desert sands contain so many undecomposed rock fragments that they are well supplied with soluble minerals, and if abundant water is available for irrigation they may be made agriculturally productive.

Soils of the Subpolar Regions

629. TUNDRA SOILS. In the treeless regions of the Arctic fringe the prevailing soil characteristics are not those of the steppe or desert. The soil profile shows evidence of excessive rather than deficient moisture. This is due to the low rate of surface evaporation and to the presence of permanently frozen subsoil at a depth of about 3 ft. The better drained sites of the Arctic-fringe regions have soils somewhat like podzols, but the usual horizons include a brown peaty surface layer which is underlain by grayish horizons, one of them characteristically plastic or even fluid. A large part of the tundra is poorly drained (380), and the prevailing soil conditions are those of bog and hummocky marshland. The soils are in several respects similar to the glacial marsh and bog soils found in middle latitudes, many of which are drained and cultivated. In the Arctic region they cannot be drained, are unsuited to tillage, and support vegetation useful only as pasture.

Soil Conservation

630. DESTRUCTIVE SOIL EROSION. There has been already abundant opportunity to observe that erosion is one of the most powerful and widespread of the processes involved in the modification of the earth's surface. The fact that, in the geologic past, soil has been removed during the slow processes of land degradation is not now a matter of great concern. On the other hand, the fact that present erosion is doing the same thing is a matter of vital concern, because human disturbance of the balance of nature has greatly accelerated the process, and it is now removing the upper horizons of developed soils much faster than natural processes can replace them. In some localities soils are fast being removed down to the parent materials of the soil or even to bare rock. This is destructive soil erosion, since there is lost in a few years or in a few generations a resource which has required thousands of years for development, a resource which cannot be replaced.

Not all kinds of soil are equally subject to destructive erosion. It may be appreciated from foregoing descriptions that some soils, such as the true laterites or eluviated sandy soils, might even benefit by the uniform removal of some depth of surface soil. This would expose less weathered minerals and less leached materials underneath. But those soils, because of their high porosity, are among those least subject to rapid erosion. On the other hand, the dark-colored soils, with the organic accumulations of the ages in their upper horizons, are highly subject to erosion, as also are certain of the forest soils of high clay content.

631. MEASURES OF THE DESTRUCTIVENESS OF SOIL EROSION. Some idea of the destructiveness of soil erosion in the United States may be had from a government report[1] which states that the annual losses of plant nutrients from the cropped lands and pastures of the country through leaching and erosion are almost six times greater than the quantity of those elements removed from the same lands in crops or forage. The same report states further as follows: "Already the utility of 35 million acres of formerly good farm land has been essentially destroyed, in so far as the production

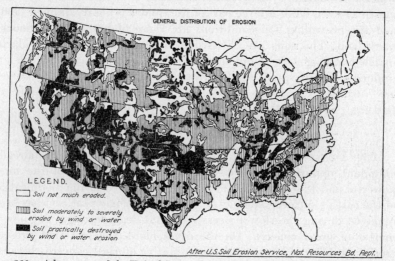

FIG. 322.—A large part of the United States already has suffered severe loss through soil erosion.

of cultivated crops is concerned, chiefly by gully erosion. This represents an area about the size of Pennsylvania, Massachusetts, and Connecticut combined, or 218,000 farms of 160 acres each. From about 125 million additional acres—land still largely in cultivation—the topsoil, representing the most productive part of the land, has been washed off or largely washed off by the erosive action of unrestrained runoff of storm waters. In addition, approximately 100 million acres of cultivated land are starting in the direction of the 125 million acres of impoverished soil-stripped land. These prodigious losses do not take into account the widespread erosional wastage that is speeding up over the vast domain of the western grazing areas" (Fig. 322).

632. THE CAUSES OF DESTRUCTIVE SOIL EROSION. The principal cause of destructive soil erosion, both by rain water and by wind, is human disturbance of the natural conditions by the removal of the natural vegetation and the loosening of the soil by cultivation. The natural vegetation is

[1] *Nat. Resources Board, Rept.*, p. 162, Washington, D. C., 1934.

destroyed by land clearing, burning, excessive grazing by livestock, and
plowing. The rate at which the soil is destroyed after these changes depends
upon the textural and structural conditions of the soil, the conditions of
climate, and especially the degree of land slope. Under natural conditions
a cover of forest vegetation tends to decrease the rate of runoff because of
the many small pits and irregularities of the forest floor and because the
litter and humus collected there is highly absorptive of moisture, tending to
hold rain water until it can escape slowly. Dense growths of prairie grasses
have much the same effect. When the natural vegetation is removed and
the tilled soil is alternately beaten by rain and dried by sun and wind the
erosive influence of both wind and water have full effect. Bennett[1] cites
experiments which show that upon very gentle slopes in Missouri and Texas
as much as 40 tons per acre of soil was eroded from bare plowed ground in a

Fig. 323.—Incipient gullies in a tilled field and serious soil erosion resulting from a
single rain. In the foregound is sand from which the finer and more fertile soil constituents have been removed. (*U. S. Soil Conservation Service.*)

single year. That is the equivalent of an inch of soil from the whole surface
every three or four years. In the Missouri experiment, land under the same
conditions of slope, soil, and climate but covered with grass lost by erosion
only about one-fourth of 1 ton of soil material per acre per year.

633. KINDS OF DESTRUCTIVE SOIL EROSION. The manner in which
soils are eroded and the kind and degree of their destruction also depend
much upon the texture and structure of the soil, conditions of climate and
land slope, nature of tillage, and other matters. One of the most widespread
and least noticed kinds of erosion on tilled land is *sheet wash* (352). This
may be accomplished by the removal of a uniform thin layer of soil, but
more commonly it results from the formation of myriads of minute gullies
(Fig. 323). These gullies are so small that they may be erased by the next
cultivation of the field, but others soon form, and the stripping process
continues. This phase of soil erosion is the more harmful because it removes
the finer and more fertile of the soil particles first.

[1] Bennett, H. H. The Geographical Relation of Soil Erosion to Land Productivity.
Geog. Rev., Vol. 18, pp. 579–605, 1928.

In some kinds of soil, especially in compact and poorly flocculated clays and silts underlain by softer materials, *gullying* rapidly becomes deep and extends itself by headward erosion of the dendritic type (Fig. 324). On rolling surfaces this process, if left unchecked, quickly destroys both soil and subsoil beyond all hope of repair (Fig. 325). Under such conditions the

Fig. 324.—A cultivated slope that has been badly damaged by gullying. See also Figs. 127 and 128. (*U. S. Soil Conservation Service.*)

whole damage does not result from the erosion of the upland soils. Adjacent lowland soils sometimes are ruined at the same time by being buried under accumulations of the coarser and less fertile alluvial products of the erosion.

In the subhumid plains of the United States great damage is in progress from wind erosion on surfaces laid bare by plowing or by overgrazing on the

Fig. 325.—Soil completely destroyed for agricultural use by unchecked gullying. (*Photograph by H. H. Bennett, courtesy of the Geographical Review, published by the American Geographical Society of New York.*)

part of livestock. In some localities the powdery soil thus exposed has been removed to a depth of several inches. As more land in this region is cultivated dust storms increase in number and severity. During the prolonged drought of 1934, millions of tons of fertile topsoil were drifted about like snow by storms or were lifted so high into the air that quantities settled far to the eastward, as has happened many times before (446).

634. THE REDUCTION OF DESTRUCTIVE SOIL EROSION. The seriousness of the soil-erosion menace is barely beginning to be realized in America, and too little is being done to reduce the loss. It certainly is not possible to stop entirely losses by solution and erosion, which have gone on since the world began. However, some things may be done to reduce the rate of destructive erosion brought about by human disturbances of the natural balance of forces. To that end a program of planned soil conservation should be supported. Such a program must include a slow return to permanent forest or permanent grass of those lands in which erosion has progressed so far as to destroy the value of the land for tillage. It must include also means of protecting, by conservative methods of tillage and management, those areas which are best suited to, and are required for, crop production, so that they may continue to be productive for hundreds or thousands of years to come. Among the methods having this latter end in view, the specialists in erosion control recommend (a) the construction of dams or obstructions to erosion in gullies already formed, (b) the plowing and tilling of land along contour levels in order to cause furrows to run across the land slope and thus reduce the rate of sheet wash, and (c) the construction of contour terraces with embankments of sod, brush, or other soil-retaining vegetation at intervals, to deflect surface drainage and prevent the formation of gullies (Fig. 147). The method last named is much employed now in the South and should have wider application. Above all, is required an awakened consciousness of the need for soil protection and of the disastrous consequences that may arise from the ruthless waste of this fundamental resource.

Chapter XXVI. The Mineral Fuels

635. WORLD INDUSTRY AND THE MINERAL FUELS. Industrial civilization of the modern type is based to a large extent upon the mineral fuels, principally coal and petroleum. Therefore, no full appreciation of the potentialities of regions or countries for human use, or of their industrial development and economic problems, is possible apart from their relation to these fundamental earth resources. For that reason it is essential that the student of geography have a clear understanding of the nature and the principal variations in quality of these substances, the comparative supplies available in the world's greatest deposits, and the major features of their patterns of distribution.

636. THE LOCATION OF MINERAL FUELS EXPLAINED THROUGH GEOLOGICAL HISTORY. Coal and petroleum are parts of the earth's crustal structure and belong to the nonrenewable class of resources (529). Their origin and present occurrence are explainable only in terms of the processes and events of earth history. When the outlines of these conditions are grasped, it becomes apparent that there are large parts of the world in which it is unreasonable to expect that valuable deposits of these substances ever will be found. It becomes equally clear why it is possible for certain other regions to have large supplies of one or even both of them.

It is desirable that the major geological time relationships of the coal- and petroleum-bearing rocks be grasped quickly when they are referred to later. To promote that understanding, without digression into the realm of historical geology, the general features of the matter are presented graphically in the simplified geological column to which previous reference has been made (Appendix E).

Coal

637. THE STRUCTURAL ASSOCIATIONS OF COAL. Coal is a form of sedimentary rock the materials of which are derived largely from the

unoxidized carbon of plant tissues. Even thin beds of coal represent
long periods of accumulation, during which the remains of luxuriant
vegetation were preserved from the ordinary processes of complete
decay by being buried underneath swamp waters and, subsequently,
beneath layers of mud, sand, or lime. The origin of coal, mainly as
deposits in ancient swamps, has several points of geographical significance. First, it may be noted that the original position of all swamp
deposits is nearly horizontal. That may be observed in modern swamps.
When such deposits are buried underneath other sediments they become members of a series of horizontal sedimentary rocks. The coal
beds of some of the greatest coal fields of the world have still an essentially horizontal position, a condition that simplifies the problems of
coal mining. In other coal fields the beds are not horizontal but,
together with their associated rocks, show evidence of disturbance
subsequent to their deposition, through warping, folding, or faulting.
In some places this has involved the metamorphism of the coal. A
second point of significance is that modern swamps seldom are of
vast extent. A few, such as those on the Atlantic Coastal Plain, contain many square miles or even some hundreds of square miles of
area, and it is probable that larger ones have existed in the past.
However, it is not surprising, considering their swamp origin, that
individual beds of coal are not of great extent. Only a few are of
such size that the same bed may be traced underground for many
miles. Although most of the individual coal beds are of relatively
small areal extent, the same is not necessarily true of the great coal
fields. In the regions now occupied by some of the larger fields, general
conditions favorable to the growth of luxuriant swamp vegetation
and the accumulation of plant remains seem to have existed widely
and for long periods of time. In such regions it is probable that individual swamps flourished and disappeared, to be buried at last underneath accumulated earthy sediments while, at the same time, other
swamps grew near by. Subsequently, conditions were altered, and
another swamp formed above the remains of the older one but separated from it by layers of sediment. All degrees of variations in the
circumstances of deposition are recorded in the present formations
of some coal fields. Large or small, thick or thin, the beds are widely
distributed in area and in vertical sequence. In some localities they
so far overlap each other that a mine shaft may pass through two or
more thin and unprofitable coal strata among the rock formations
before reaching one of desirable thickness and quality. In certain
localities a half dozen or more coal beds are known to lie one above
another, separated by various thicknesses of sedimentary rock.

Since coal is known to occur within the rocks belonging to a fairly well-defined range of geological time, it is possible, by studying the rock outcrops, to determine the general extent of a coal region and, by means of test holes, to discover the number and relative thickness of the coal beds in its various parts. Upon information gathered in that way, it is possible for geologists to approximate with fair accuracy the quantity of coal available for future use in any given field or in any country or in the world, so far as its rocks have been examined.

638. VARIETIES OF COAL DIFFER greatly from region to region, and even within the same field a considerable number of market classes and grades of coal may be produced. Several standard classes are recognized, each of which marks a stage in the evolution of swamp deposits into high-grade coal. Only four of them will be mentioned here.

It may be assumed that all coal began as *peat*, preserved but crumbled and blackened organic remains, similar to that which may be seen underlying present swamps and bogs. The higher forms of coal represent successive stages in a transformation of the peat through the weight of the overlying rocks, through diastrophism, or by any other means that involve compression and the loss of water and gases (Fig. 326). A form of deposit somewhat older and more compact than peat is the crumbly brown coal called *lignite*. Still further changes produced the soft black coals of the general class called *bituminous*.

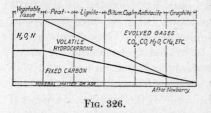

FIG. 326.

Of bituminous coal there is an almost endless list of slightly different grades and qualities. Important fields, and even different parts of the same field or different beds in the same locality, have their own recognized grades. One highly significant distinction among coals of the bituminous class is based upon suitability for the manufacture of coke of the type required in iron-smelting furnaces. Such grades as are suited to that use are called coking coals. Others are called noncoking, but they may be well suited to use as fuel for the production of power or for heating.

Further compression of coal beds, especially if it was accompanied by warping of the formations together with faulting and sometimes heating, produced the class of hard coal called *anthracite*. The transformation was accompanied by a great loss of volatile gases and water, and the resulting anthracite is low in gas and high in carbon, which makes it a nearly smokeless fuel (324).

639. COAL CLASSES AND THEIR RELATION TO GEOLOGIC AGE. Since coal is formed mainly by the accumulation of vegetation in land swamps or the swamps of coastal margins, it follows that no coal could be formed until there was abundant land vegetation. It is, therefore, not logical to expect that coal will occur in significant quantity in rocks that belong to those periods of earth history before land plants were abundant. Neither is it reasonable to expect coal deposits in igneous rocks, whether ancient or recent, because of the great heat associated with their origin. The time sequence in which the major additions of plant and animal life were made to the earth are shown in Appendix E. From that table it will be seen that the rocks of all the vast extent of time earlier than the Paleozoic bear no evidence of a land vegetation. The general world distribution of those ancient metamorphic and igneous rocks in which the occurrence of coal is impossible may be seen in Plate VI. Even the early Paleozoic periods seem not to have had vegetations of sufficiently high order of development to produce the bog deposits necessary to the abundant formation of coal. Some unimportant coal beds in association with Devonian rocks are known, but it was not until the Carboniferous period that conditions became suitable to the widespread and abundant growth and accumulation of a coal-forming vegetation.

Among the coal fields of the world are those which represent periods of accumulation dating from the early Carboniferous down to the Tertiary period and, if peat deposits be included, down to the present. In a general way, there may be recognized among the many classes of coal represented in these fields a general order of quality which is highest in the older coals and lowest or poorest in those of more recent origin. This order is not without its notable exceptions, yet the general relationship is logical in view of the fact that time is an important element in the transformation of raw peat into good coal. In certain younger coal formations (Cretaceous and Tertiary) are localities that yield coal of high grade, even some anthracite. Usually they are due to diastrophic changes or to igneous intrusion which have, by pressure, fracturing, or heat, made way for the escape of water or gas or have otherwise hastened the transformation.

It may be observed, therefore, that, in general, those world regions which include coal-bearing rocks of late Paleozoic age (Mississippian, Pennsylvanian, Permian) are most likely to possess coal of high quality and that some large areas of coal in regions of younger rocks yield only lignites. Often it is true also that those coal formations which lie in regions of disturbed rock structures have at least some localities in which the quality of the coal has been improved by the disturbance. Plate VI may be referred to again for the broader aspects of the distribution of the older and the younger sedimentary rocks. Of course, only a small part of the sedimentary rocks of either of those age groups was formed under swamp conditions such that coal beds are included among their strata.

640. THE ACCESSIBILITY OF COAL is, in part, a matter of where the coal beds are located with respect to markets, but here its meaning is

Fig. 327.—Giant furrows turned by power shovels in the process of strip mining in southern Illinois. The 4 ft.-thick bed of coal exposed in the bottom of the deep trench is mined out before the next furrow is turned.

TYPICAL CROSS SECTIONS IN AMERICAN COAL FIELDS

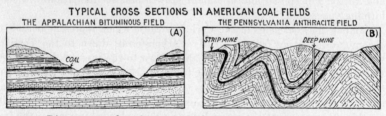

Fig. 328.—Diagrams to show in contrast the common relationships of surface and structure in the bituminous and anthracite fields of the Appalachian coal regions.

Fig. 329.—A stratum of bituminous coal outcropping, along with other sedimentary strata, in a road cut on a West Virginia hillside.

restricted to the subject of their structural and situational relations to the earth's surface. In some localities of little disturbed sedimentary rocks coal beds are found so close to the surface that they may be mined in open pits after the removal of only a few feet of overburden (surface earth or rock) (Fig. 327). In others they are so far underground as to be reached only by mine shafts of great depth. In still others, although originally they were deeply buried, the coal beds are now made readily accessible by deep stream dissection which exposes outcrops of coal among the rocks of the valley walls (Figs. 328A, 329). In regions of complicated rock structure coal beds, once horizontal but now greatly folded, present various degrees of accessibility. In some such localities erosion exposes parts of coal beds at the surface. In others the same beds are bent downward to great depths or are displaced or shattered by faulting. In such structures the difficulties of mining are greatly increased (Fig. 328B).

THE COAL REGIONS OF THE CONTINENTS

641. Because coal still is the principal source of power in manufactural industry and also is necessary to the smelting of iron, its distribution is a matter of critical importance in relation to the world centers of heavy manufacture, present and future. Although there are coal reserves in all the continents and in most of the countries of the world, the distribution of the great ones is most uneven. They are, in fact, grouped in three principal regions: (a) central and eastern North America, (b) northwestern Europe, and (c) eastern Asia. The specific fields of greatest importance in the several continents may now be considered.

642. NORTH AMERICA not only is the continent of greatest coal production but also is credited with the greatest of all coal reserves. These have been estimated at 5 trillions of tons, or nearly two-thirds of the total estimated supply of the world, although that figure may be somewhat reduced when more complete information is available concerning reputedly large deposits in Siberia. The North American coals include representatives of every class from high-grade anthracite to the lowest grades of lignite. They are contained in several fields, the location and extent of which are shown in Fig. 330.

It will be observed that certain areas of the continent are without coal. Notable among them are the ancient rocks of the Laurentian Shield of Canada and the Appalachian Piedmont and also the young sediments of the Atlantic and Gulf coastal margins. In the complicated structures and partly igneous rocks of Mexico and the regions west of the Rocky Mountains coal fields are small and scattered and, with a few notable exceptions, yield coals of low grade.

643. *The Appalachian Field.* Not the most extensive, but much the most important, among the coal fields of the continent is that of the Appalachian hill region. It is comprised of two principal subdivisions: (*a*) a small highly folded section containing anthracite coal in the Appalachian ridge-and-valley region of northeastern Pennsylvania and (*b*) a large region of little-folded rocks which contain numerous beds of bituminous coal, some of them thick and of high quality. This

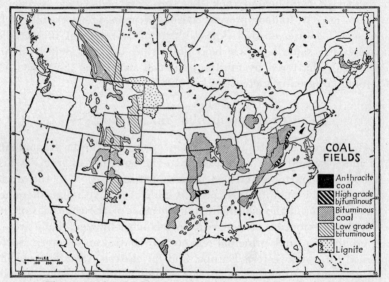

FIG. 330.—The principal coal fields of the United States and Canada distinguished as to location, extent, and principal types of coal.

latter region extends from northwestern Pennsylvania to northwestern Alabama.

The anthracite region is noted for the high carbon and low gas content of its coals and for their smokeless quality. This region is the source of most of the anthracite used in America, but the supply is limited. Moreover, the extreme folding to which the region has been subjected has inclined many of the coal formations at high angles underground, and associated faulting has dislocated them. This has greatly increased the cost and difficulty of mining, rendering anthracite an expensive fuel (Figs. 328*B*, 331).

The Appalachian bituminous region is largely, but not entirely, underlain by workable beds of coal which, in total, represent a period of accumulation which was long, even from the geological viewpoint.

Mainly, they are of Carboniferous age and of good quality. Differences in the thickness of the beds and in the conditions under which they were deposited, together with variation in degree of subsequent disturbance, have given unlike qualities to coals of different localities. Some of them are of the high quality required for the manufacture of blast-furnace coke. That is particularly true of one coal bed of great thickness and large extent in western Pennsylvania. It was the basis of Pittsburgh's early supremacy in iron and steel manufacture, and it still furnishes coke for that and several other smelting centers. Large additional supplies of coking coal are now obtained from other

FIG. 331.—Some of the pretentious structures associated with the complicated underground conditions and deep mines of the Pennsylvania anthracite region. Mountainous piles of waste result from long operation on the same site. (*Ewing Galloway.*)

sources, especially from fields in West Virginia, Alabama, and other parts of the Appalachian region.

More than three-fourths of the high-grade coal of the continent, some of which has special uses other than for coking, is obtained from the Appalachian bituminous field. The coal of that field is noted also for the ease with which it is mined. The coal-bearing rocks largely are included within the limits of the maturely dissected Appalachian hill country (481). Being traversed by innumerable deeply incised stream valleys the coal beds often are exposed along the valley walls, and mining is relatively simple. It is accomplished in large part by means of "drifts," or horizontal tunnels driven into the hillside outcrops of nearly horizontal coal seams (Figs. 328A, 332). In many mines the dip of the coal bed permits the mine workings to slope gently downward toward the mine mouth, and the removal of both coal and drainage waters is aided, or may be wholly accomplished, by gravity. The

abundance, accessibility, and high quality of these coal beds give
the Appalachian fields first importance in America and perhaps in the

FIG. 332.—A small "coal camp" situated in a narrow West Virginia valley. The
valley bottom has room for the creek bed, a road, a railway spur, and two rows of
cabins. Simple chutes or "tipples" leading from hillside mines are seen on both sides
of the road. Contrast them with the structures shown in Fig. 331.

world. It supplies the coal used in the eastern and northeastern
industrial districts and also most of the American export coal.

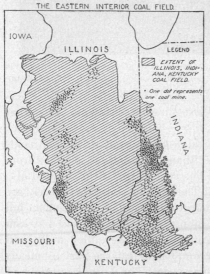

FIG. 333.—Most of the coal mines in
the synclinal Eastern Interior Field are
located upon its shallower margins.

644. *The Interior Bituminous Fields.* The interior region of the United States also is abundantly provided with coal fields. Generally the coal is Carboniferous in age and bituminous in quality. The several areas are known respectively as (*a*) the *Eastern Interior Field* (Illinois, Indiana, and Kentucky), (*b*) the *Northern Interior Field* (Michigan), (*c*) the *Western Interior Field* (Iowa, Missouri, Kansas, Oklahoma, and Arkansas), and (*d*) the *Southwestern Interior Field* (Texas). In the Eastern and Northern fields the coal-bearing rocks have broad synclinal structures, and, in the former, the coal beds of the middle

portion are so deeply buried under younger rocks that they are difficult to reach. Therefore, mining is practiced mainly about the margins of the field (Figs. 333, 327). In the Western and Southwestern fields the coal beds are inclined gently downward toward the west and pass beneath increasing thicknesses of rock. The coal is mined along the more shallow eastern edges of the fields, where it provides abundant supplies of lower grade bituminous coal for limited local markets.

645. *The Rocky Mountain fields* include many coal districts spread over a large region which extends from the ranges of central Alberta and eastern British Columbia southward to New Mexico. Most of the coal beds of the region are of younger than Carboniferous age. However, there are many localities where rock deformation or igneous intrusion has improved the quality of the coal, so that bituminous coal is abundant, and even a small quantity of anthracite is found. Rocky Mountain coal is important to the region, and some is shipped considerable distances, but the available supply is not comparable in quality or quantity with that of the East.

646. *Pacific Coast Fields.* Although much of the Pacific Coast region has no valuable coal deposits, there are a few of considerable local significance. Important among them are those of Alaska, Vancouver Island, and the Puget Sound region. The Alaskan deposits have more future than present value, but those of Vancouver Island especially are important, though limited in quantity, because they are near the American terminals of some of the major transpacific steamship routes.

647. *Coal in eastern Canada* is not abundant, because the larger part of eastern Canada is comprised of pre-Paleozoic rocks. One small field of large local importance is found in the northern end of the Province of Nova Scotia. It is a matter of great concern to Canada that its most populous and industrially developed region, which lies between Lake Huron and the city of Quebec, is practically devoid of coal (Fig. 330).

648. *North American Lignites.* In Texas and other Gulf Coast states, in the western interior plains of the United States and Canada, and in the Rocky Mountains are vast areas which are underlain by coals of lower than bituminous quality. Nearly one-half the total coal resource of the United States, and more than three-fourths that of Canada and Newfoundland, are of that class. Mainly it is lignite. The total quantity of these low-grade coals is, therefore, great, but they are not nearly so important as the better coal. Their poor quality involves greater difficulty in storing, shipping, and burning, and they have much lower heat-producing capacity than bituminous

coal. They have at present only local use, but they may be used much
more by future generations.

649. SOUTH AMERICA has the misfortune to be, of all the continents,
least well endowed with coal. There are in its entire extent only a few
areas of coal-bearing rocks. The extensive highlands of the east and
northeast are, in large part, of pre-Paleozoic rocks, and the sediments
that flank the long eastern front of the
Andes are very young. In the Andes of
Peru and on the coast of central Chile
there are small deposits of valuable
coal, and there is some of low grade in
southern Brazil. Their total reserve is
believed to be less than 1 per cent of
the quantity available in North
America.

650. EUROPEAN COAL FIELDS are
more productive than any in other
parts of the world, except those of
North America. In total coal reserves
Europe ranks third among the continents, and hardly more than one
twenty-fifth of its supply is below
bituminous grade. The average quality
is, therefore, good. However, it is estimated that the total European coal resource, of bituminous grade or better, is

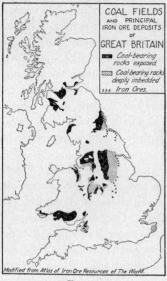

FIG. 334.

less than that of Asia and hardly one-third as great as that available
in North America. Its present value is increased by the fact that the
principal fields are so distributed that they fall within the territorial
boundaries of several European countries the industrial advancement
of which may be attributed in part to these sources of fuel.

651. *British coal fields* occupy no less than six distinct regions in
England, Scotland, and Wales. Mainly the coal beds are of Carboniferous age and contain coal of bituminous quality or better. So well
distributed are they that only two parts of the island are more than
a few miles removed from one or more of them (Fig. 334). Those two
parts are the ancient crystalline rock region of the Highlands of Scotland and the plain of southeastern England, in which London is
situated. It is probable that all the coal-bearing rocks of Scotland would
have been removed by erosion had not a section of them been preserved
in the rift, or graben, valley of the Scottish Lowlands (330). Associated
with each of the major British coal fields is an important industrial

district, and some of them, especially that of South Wales, are close
to the sea and well situated for the export of coal.

Although the quality of British coal generally is superior, it is
not always easily mined. The rocks of some of the fields have been
subjected to severe deformation or are buried beneath thick sediments.
In the South Wales field, where the highest grades of coal are found,
rock folding brought some parts of the coal beds to the surface, where
stream erosion exposed them and made mining simple. However,
most of the easily accessible coal has been mined, and some of the
workings now have followed the coal structures deep and far underground, greatly increasing the cost of production. The total quantity
remaining in Great Britain is estimated at an amount nearly one-half
as great as that in the Appalachian field of the United States, two-

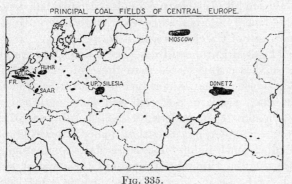

PRINCIPAL COAL FIELDS OF CENTRAL EUROPE.

Fig. 335.

thirds as great as the German reserve, and ten times greater than that
of France. It is sufficient for many years to come.

652. *The coal fields of continental Europe* are numerous, but none
covers so much area as the greater ones of North America. Moreover,
some of them contain much thin coal or coal at great depths, and a
few yield only low-grade coals. The more important fields and most
of the better grades of coal lie in an east-west belt through the center
of the continent. The ancient crystalline rocks of Scandinavia and
Finland to the north of that belt and the much disturbed rocks of the
Mediterranean Basin on the south of it contain either no coal or but
small and unimportant fields.

The central coal belt of Europe extends from northern France
through Belgium, Germany, Czechoslovakia, and Poland into Russia
(Fig. 335). Several of its fields lie wholly or in part in Germany, which
has the greatest coal reserve of any European country and nearly
three-fourths as much as the Appalachian field. The estimated reserve of Germany includes, however, considerable quantities of low-

grade bituminous coal and lignite. Low grades of coal and even peat are much more used in continental Europe than in Great Britain or the United States.

653. *Important Districts.*   Coal of good quality is mined at several points along a band of Carboniferous rocks in the western end of the central European belt. This important zone begins in northern France, crosses central Belgium, and enters Germany. Its most productive portion lies in the Ruhr Valley of Westfalen (Westphalia), east of the Rhine. That field is of particular importance because it has long been the center of the heavy iron and steel industries of Germany and because it contains a reserve of coking coal reputed to be larger than any other in continental Europe (Fig. 403). Near by is the coal field of the politically famous Saar Basin. Another highly important district is that of the middle eastern region. Its richest coal deposits lie in Poland, the Upper Silesian section of southeastern Germany, and adjacent portions of Czechoslovakia.

The coal fields of European Russia are of much larger area although they have smaller coal reserves than those of western Europe. The district of greatest present importance is that of the Donets Basin in the south, which yields coking coal and some anthracite. It is the focus of heavy industry in modern Russia. The Moskva (Moscow) field is of greater areal extent, but its coal is smaller in quantity and of lower grade, including much lignite. There are also several small coal fields on the flanks of the Ural Mountains, but the greatest potential reserves of U.S.S.R. lie in Siberia. These include some that are only partially explored. Altogether the coal reserve of U.S.S.R. is very large. It is now claimed by Russian authorities to be more than one-third as great as that of the United States of America (Figs. 335, 336, 343).

654. ASIA is believed to contain larger reserves of coal than any other continent except North America. Figures 336 and 343 indicate the location of the known fields of major importance but do not give a complete picture of coal distribution, because the quantity and quality of the coal believed to exist in some of the fields are greater than their areal extent would indicate.

Siberia.   Several coal fields are known to exist in Siberia. The one being most rapidly developed is the Kuznetsk Basin, southeast of Novosibirsk. It is estimated to be the richest and largest coal reserve in Russia. Another, but smaller, field lies west of Lake Baikal, and in the isolated forest areas of northern Siberia are extensive coal regions whose boundaries and values are imperfectly known.

655. *China.*   Although the full measure of the coal resources of Asia is not known, it is believed that China has more than three-

fourths of the total. The quantity of high-grade coal in that country is estimated to be greater than that of any other country in the world, except the United States. It includes much coking coal and what probably is the largest supply of anthracite in the world. There are several coal fields in China, but much the largest reserve lies in the northern district of Shensi-Shansi, which is reputed to have 80 per cent of the total. Because of the present inaccessibility of that field others of smaller size are now much more productive. However,

PRINCIPAL COAL FIELDS OF ASIA

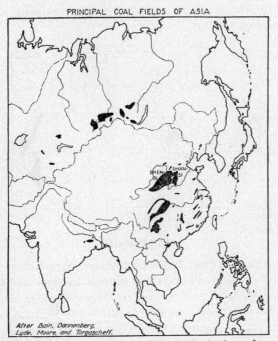

Fig. 336.—The fields of Shensi and Shansi, China, dominate the coal resources of Asia.

the future may see a notable difference from the present, both in the relative production of the coal fields of China and in the relative importance of China as a center of manufacture.

656. *Other Asiatic countries* that have important coal reserves are Japan and India. Those of India are located in the northeastern part of the Deccan and are now being much used in connection with the iron ores of the same region. However, they probably are not of a large order of magnitude. Unfortunately for industrial Japan the reserves of coal in that country are small and scattered, and many of the beds are badly faulted.

657. AFRICA AND AUSTRALASIA. Australia, although it is a much smaller continent than Africa, has a larger coal reserve (Fig. 337). Fortunately, the principal field is located near the humid east coast of New South Wales, in or near the principal centers of population. Because of its abundance, good quality, and accessibility, Australian coal is the leading source of supply in the Southern Hemisphere, but the total reserve supply is not comparable with that of the larger fields of the Northern Hemisphere. The African coal reserve is not great, but the present production is considerable. It is obtained mainly from fields in the southeastern part of the continent, especially in the Transvaal and Natal.

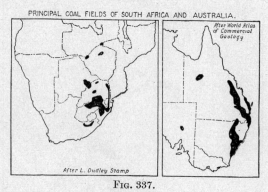

PRINCIPAL COAL FIELDS OF SOUTH AFRICA AND AUSTRALIA.

After World Atlas of Commercial Geology

After L. Dudley Stamp

FIG. 337.

Petroleum

658. THE STRUCTURAL ASSOCIATIONS OF PETROLEUM. Petroleum (rock oil) and its related substances natural gas and asphalt are earth materials, probably of organic origin. Whatever their origin may be, they have been so long included in the rocks that no trace of any organic antecedents is clearly discernible in them, and the very nature of the hydrocarbons of which they are composed is unlike that of the oils and other analogous compounds found in plants and animals. Because of its chemical nature, petroleum may be split up by fractional distillation into an array of products suited to many uses. Its cleanliness, compactness, and convenience as a fuel and the fact that new machines are continually being devised for using it in the production of heat and power have made it a critical item in the resource inventories of modern nations.

Petroleum and its related substances are found in quantity in sedimentary rocks only, probably because they are derived from microscopic marine organisms whose remains were originally intermingled with marine deposits. Generally they are held in porous rocks, especially sandstones, where they exist as filling in the pore space of the rock just as it is filled elsewhere by ground water. Petroleum is found in limestones also, and some porous or slightly cavernous limestones yield it in large quantities.

Oil- and gas-bearing rocks are found in a considerable variety of physical associations and are of different geological ages. Like coal, however, they are not found among the ancient crystalline rocks of pre-Paleozoic age. Some oil sands are found at great depths, where they are buried underneath hundreds or thousands of feet of younger rocks. In some localities there are two or more oil-bearing formations, one above the other but separated by great thicknesses of intervening

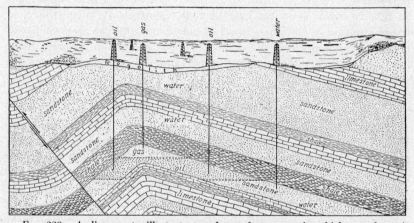

Fig. 338.—A diagram to illustrate one form of structure in which petroleum is entrapped and the relation between the locations of several wells and the nature of their products. The existence of this anticlinal structure is not evident from the surface relief.

strata, and they may be of widely different geological ages. The oil and gas accumulations usually are overlain by rocks that contain abundant ground water, and many are underlain by them also. The oil and gas seldom are distributed uniformly throughout the total extent of the rock in which they occur but are gathered together in limited areas, called *pools*. The pools are bodies of oil trapped in some form of structural pocket from which they cannot escape. Some of these "structures" are the tops of anticlines which are capped by shales, clays, or other impervious rocks that prevent the upward escape of the oil or gas. Other pools are found in pockets, domes, or lenses of many shapes and origins into which the oil or gas has migrated from surrounding areas and there collected (Fig. 338). Migration into these structural pockets has taken place, in the long geological past, because the oil and gas are lighter than water and tend to rise under the influence of ground water until they are caught and held beneath some impervious formation.

The way in which oil and gas are found has an important geographic consequence. Because the structures suitable for petroleum collection commonly are small and deeply buried (some of them more than a mile below the surface), it often is impossible accurately to predict their exact location and extent or even their presence. When one structure is found in a region it seldom is possible to predict how many others may be found near by and still less possible to estimate the volume or value of their contents. Confident appraisal of the petroleum reserves of the nation or of the world is, therefore, not so readily made as in the case of coal resources. It must suffice, in the evaluation of the importance of petroleum and gas as elements of regional equipment, for the student to become acquainted with those fields that have either present importance or proved resources for the near future.

American Oil and Gas Fields

659. Fields in the United States. Nature has endowed the United States with several regions in which petroleum and gas are found, and the production of those fuels in the United States far exceeds that of any other country. Each of the regions includes a number of subdivisions or fields and many localities in which are found individual oil structures the total number of which is great. In some of the structures both oil and gas are found together; some yield oil but not much gas, and others yield gas alone. In every productive field also are structures that already have yielded all that they are capable of producing economically, and they have been abandoned. There are some that have passed the maximum of production, and still others that are now at the peak of their productive lives. Doubtless there are, in most of the fields, additional pools which remain undiscovered and hold a reserve for the future. The active life of most pools is relatively short, and already some of the fields have declined in production until they are but minor factors in the national output. The question of how long the United States can maintain its present abundant petroleum production is not capable of assured answer, but it is believed that in a decade or little more production will be reduced much below the levels to which Americans have been accustomed.

The several principal regions of oil and gas production are indicated in Fig. 339. They are, from east to west, the Appalachian, Eastern Interior, Mid-Continent, Gulf Coast, Rocky Mountain, and California

regions. Of these the Mid-Continent is now much the most productive
region, followed by California. In the process of their discovery and
development most of the country adjoining and between these regions
has been so fully explored that there is no longer any probability of
the discovery of additional oil regions or even of new fields of great
importance. Deeper drilling and further search undoubtedly will
bring to light new horizons and many new pools to add their quotas
to the *known* reserve which, according to the National Resources
Board Report of 1934, was sufficient to last for only 15 years at the

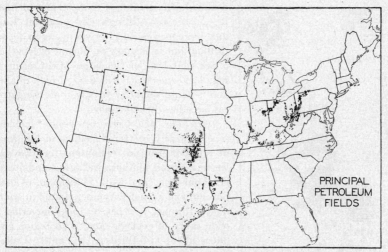

PRINCIPAL
PETROLEUM
FIELDS

Fig. 339.—Many of the pools included in the principal petroleum fields of the
United States are very small. Only the larger have been included on this map, and the
areas of many of them have been enlarged or combined to make them visible at this
map scale.

1933 rate of consumption. The need for conservative practice in the
production and use of this essential fuel is evident.

660. *The Appalachian Region.* The first oil and gas field to be developed
on a modern scale was in the Allegheny region of America. That region
was for many years the most productive in the world. The fuels are obtained
from many fields, and pools are found in the early Paleozoic rocks (mainly
sandstones) which incline gently westward from the highlands. They
extend intermittently from western New York to Tennessee, and the region,
as a whole, is of greater extent than the important coal field which includes
younger and higher rocks that are found in the same general area. Petroleum from the Appalachian field is noted for its superior quality, which
involves low sulphur content, ease of refining, and the fact that, upon distillation, it leaves a residue of paraffin rather than asphalt. Some gas is
found in association with oil in most of the pools of this field, but also there

are many pools of gas with which no oil is found. The most productive part of the field is its central portion, located in southwestern New York, western Pennsylvania, and northern West Virginia. Although its yields of oil still are considerable, it has passed, many years since, the peak of its productivity. Much natural gas remains, however—a resource of vital importance for household and industrial use in the region—and it is closely related to the growth of certain types of manufacture there.

661. *The Eastern Interior Region.* Fields of importance are located in Ohio, Indiana, Illinois, and Michigan. The Michigan fields are new but relatively small, while the others, formerly of great importance, have declined. The greater of them, that which lies in southeastern Illinois and adjacent Indiana, has experienced a revival owing to deeper drilling, but it has now an output of less than 5 per cent that of the large Mid-Continent region. Formerly it yielded oil of high quality and a large quantity of gas, but the latter resource has dwindled also.

FIG. 340.—A portion of the Mid-Continent Oil Field in southeastern Kansas, showing the many individual "pools" that lie within the area. (*After W. H. Emmons.*)

662. *The Mid-Continent region* includes several widely scattered fields and hundreds of pools in Kansas, Oklahoma, central and western Texas, southern Arkansas, and northern Louisiana (Fig. 340). Petroleum, of both paraffin and asphaltic types, is found in abundance through a series of rocks covering a wide range of geologic time. This region produces about two-thirds of the entire United States output and has been producing for many years. Some pools have been exhausted, but the practice of deeper drilling has reached oil in older rocks at lower horizons and has been responsible for the most remarkable of recent discoveries. Gas is abundant in this region also. However, owing to small urban population and slight industrial development, there is but limited local market for gas, and much of it has been wasted.

663. *The Gulf Coast region* includes numerous pools found in the young rocks of coastal Louisiana and Texas, some of them in association with the coastal salt domes or mounds underlain by deposits of rock salt (699). Although this region exceeds the Eastern in production, its output is barely one-fourth that of the adjacent Mid-Continent region.

664. *The Rocky Mountain region* is comprised of many fields distributed over a large area which is mainly in Wyoming, although it extends northward into Montana and south into Colorado. It is the least productive of the major oil regions of the United States. Although both the Gulf Coast and

Mountain regions are large in area, they are well explored, and the probability of wholly new fields' being discovered within them is not great.

665. *The California Region.* The oil and gas fields of California are distributed over a belt that extends from the environs of Los Angeles northward toward San Francisco (Fig. 341). Some of the fields are located in the

FIG. 341.—The forest of oil derricks that occupies the low arch of Signal Hill, near Long Beach, Calif.

plains and hills of the southern California piedmont district, some in the San Joaquin Valley and the Coast Ranges, and others on the very shoreline itself. As a whole, the California region is highly productive and ranks second only to the Mid-Continent in importance. Its oils mainly are heavy and of the asphaltic type.

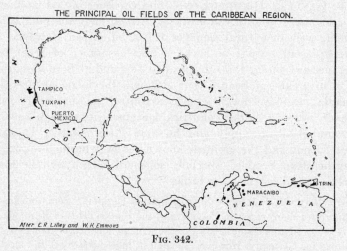

THE PRINCIPAL OIL FIELDS OF THE CARIBBEAN REGION.

FIG. 342.

666. *Canadian Regions.* Canada apparently is not so well endowed with petroleum and gas as it is with coal. A small amount is obtained in that section of Ontario north of Lake Erie, and some also in the plains of Alberta. The former area is a northward extension of the Applachian fields, and

the latter of the Rocky Mountain fields. Their present importance is relatively small.

667. CARIBBEAN REGIONS.   Bordering the Carribean Sea are two productive oil regions (Fig. 342). One of them, on the coast of Mexico, includes fields near Tampico and Túxpam. These began to yield abundantly early in the present century and for some years gave Mexico second rank among the oil-producing countries of the world. They now have passed the peak of their productivity, although the output still is considerable. A second region includes several fields distributed along the north coast of South America, mainly in Colombia, Venezuela, and the island of Trinidad. Seepage and evaporation of volatile constituents from an ancient pool in Trinidad gave rise to the famous asphalt lake of that island, where hardened asphalt, removed from the surface, is replaced by the slow upwelling of new supplies from beneath. The recent large yields of oil from several localities in Venezuela have enabled that country to rise to third place among the producing countries of the world.

668. SOUTH AMERICA, beyond the Caribbean borders, gives some evidence of widespread occurrence of petroleum. Of the several countries, only Argentina, Peru, and Ecuador now have important production.

EURASIAN OIL FIELDS

669. GENERAL DISTRIBUTION.   The presence of oil and gas is known in many localities in Eurasia, Africa, and Australia through producing wells or natural seepages of gas, oil, or tar. However, fields of large present output or such as give assurance of great future importance are confined to Europe or to Asia and its bordering islands.

It is of great significance that although the financial interests of the leading west-European countries control supplies of petroleum elsewhere, not one of the countries contains within its borders any significant petroleum supply, and the same is true of Japan. The largest present output and the greatest known reserves lie in three regions: (a) southeastern Europe, especially southern Russia; (b) the Persian Gulf region; and (c) the East Indies.

670. THE OIL FIELDS OF SOUTHEASTERN EUROPE.   Some oil has been produced for many years in Poland, and the Ploeşti fields of Rumania have lately achieved great fame because of the struggle for their control as a source of supply for Germany. However, the oldest, most persistent, and most productive fields in Europe are in southeastern Russia adjacent to the Caucasus Mountains and the Caspian Sea. Of several fields in this region those near Baku, on the peninsula of Apsheron and Grozny, north of the Caucasus, are most famous (Fig. 343). Oil from those fields enabled Russia to lead the world

in production until the opening of the present century. It fell behind the United States during the first decade of the century, was passed in turn by Mexico during the second decade, but has now recovered second place. Although its output is less than one-fifth that of the United States, Russia is much the most important oil producer in the Old World. Vast areas of land yet to be explored for oil in the country may well enable European and western Asiatic Russia to maintain at least its present rank in petroleum output, although Siberia, as a whole, appears to be poor in that resource.

THE COAL AND PETROLEUM FIELDS OF EUROPEAN RUSSIA AND CENTRAL SIBERIA

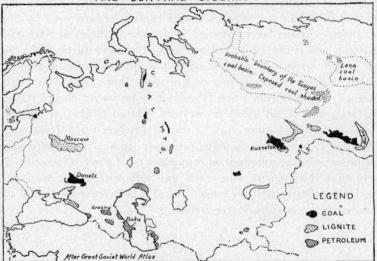

Fig. 343.—The relative importance of the Russian coal and oil fields is as much dependent upon their location as upon their size.

671. OIL FIELDS OF SOUTHERN ASIA. Although the fields of southern Asia together produce only about as much petroleum as either California or Oklahoma, it is possible that some of the world's greatest oil reserves are there. About the head of the Persian Gulf are the producing fields of Iran (Persia) and known reserves of great importance in Iraq. The control of these resources has been, in recent years, a matter of great concern in international politics and military strategy.

Some petroleum is obtained from fields in Burma, but a much larger quantity comes from the East Indies, especially Sumatra and Borneo. The output of this region exceeds that of Kansas in volume, and the reserves are believed to be considerable.

SUPPLEMENTARY OIL RESOURCES

672. OIL SHALES. The recovery of petroleum from underground ceases when the flow has decreased to the point where the cost of pumping exceeds the value of the oil recovered. That does not mean, however, that the oil supply is completely used. The movement of oil in the pore space of the rocks is sometimes impeded by the collection of tarry substances, and some oil always clings as films upon the rock particles. It is estimated that perhaps, on the average, more than half the original supply remains underground when a pool is abandoned. Improved methods of recovery may, in the future, make some of that oil available.

In addition, there are, in the United States and elsewhere, large supplies of oil-yielding organic matter contained in compact shales. The material does not flow and hence cannot be recovered by pumping. Petroleum has been obtained from rich oil shales of that kind in Scotland, and it can be done elsewhere. However, the cost of production is high, because the rock must first be quarried or mined and then treated, before the crude oil, such as now flows from wells, can be obtained. For a future, when petroleum is no longer cheap, there are large supplies of oil shale in western United States, especially in Wyoming and Colorado, and oil can be produced also from coal by subjecting it to various chemical processes. In any case, these sources will be expedients adopted to supplement a failing oil supply. It is likely that the student who reads this will, within his lifetime, live in a United States that no longer includes petroleum in the list of its abundant and cheap earth resources.

Chapter XXVII. Ores and Other Economic Minerals

673. CLASSES OF MINERAL RESOURCES. In addition to water and the mineral fuels, the earth provides many inorganic substances for human use. In the list are the raw materials of a wide array of industries. The substances are of great diversity and include some as different from each other as the crude rocks and sand used in road construction are different from the fine metals and gems that enter into the making of an expensive watch. The mineral resources drawn upon to supply these needs may be grouped, according to the purpose for which they are produced and the manner of their treatment, into (*a*) the ores of the metallic minerals and (*b*) the solid, nonmetallic, nonfuel minerals. Those of the first group are prepared for use by treating with one of several processes of mechanical concentration or chemical reduction, and from them the metals are obtained. Those of the second group sometimes are used practically as they come from the earth. The list of the metals is a long one, but that of the nonmetals is longer. In the latter are rocks, sand and gravel, clays, lime, salines, fertilizers, abrasives, gems, and many others.

The Metallic Minerals

674. THE IMPORTANCE OF METALLIFEROUS ORES. Before the beginning of written history men knew the value of certain metals and sought the materials from which they might be obtained. Copper and tin were employed to produce bronze, which was harder than either of its components. Gold and silver also were highly prized, as they are now. Later came the use of iron and other metals. Some of these are used separately in the arts and specific industries, while others are combined with each other, and especially with iron, in a number of industrially important alloys.

Of the many metals concerned, a considerable number may be classed as precious or semiprecious. These are used in relatively small quantities. While the existence of a supply of one of them, such as

577

gold, silver, chromium, or tungsten, is important to many industries, and economically important to the region in which it occurs, it can hardly be called a basic mineral resource. The very smallness of the volume of output of each of them and the limited quantity required, coupled with high specific value, enable these and similar metals to move freely in the channels of international trade. In a sense, the whole world draws upon the same sources of supply. Even a distant country enjoys almost the same advantage from such a resource, except in time of war, as does the country in which it is produced. A few metals that are used in large quantities, especially iron, may be thought of as fundamental resources. This is particularly true if they occur in close proximity to supplies of the fuel needed to smelt them. So much of iron and its ores are required, and they are of such comparatively low specific value, that they do not move in the channels of international trade with the same ease as do those of the other class. They do, indeed, move to some extent, but the possession of a domestic supply of iron ore is considered always, next to a supply of coal or petroleum, a matter of major economic importance by the great nations.

In the world of modern industry, therefore, ores of the metals, precious and nonprecious, are elements of great significance in the complex of things that go to make up the natural equipment of regions. Because of that fact, it is necessary for the student of geography to grasp at least the fundamentals of those earth conditions upon which the presence or absence of valuable ores is likely to depend and to know the broad features of the world distribution of the most important of these substances.

675. THE COMMON PHYSICAL ASSOCIATIONS OF ORE DEPOSITS.   An ore deposit is a concentration of a metallic mineral, or one of its chemical compounds, sufficiently rich in the metal so that it is profitable to use it. Some metals, *e.g.*, gold and copper, are found locally in the metallic, or "native," state. More commonly the metallic elements occur in chemical combination with other elements in the form of sulphides, sulphates, oxides, carbonates, and other compounds, from which they must be set free by processes of reduction called *smelting*. Usually, also, the valuable compounds are intermingled with some quantity of rock or earthy material, called *gangue*, from which they must be separated by mechanical means.

The local concentration of minerals by natural processes into ores of profitable quality is believed to have come about in several different ways, which may be touched upon here only because they have to do with the distribution of regions of mineral occurrence. Some, for example, appear to have originated at the same time as the igneous rocks in which they are found but to have separated from them while yet in the liquid molten state because they were heavier or for various other reasons. Others seem to have been thinly distributed in the original rocks and to have separated out later through some process of concentration, especially by the slow chemical work of ground water. Traces of metallic minerals are found in many rocks, both igneous and sedimentary. In liquid igneous intrusions it is possible, as has been stated (317), for molecules of like kind to come together and separate from the parent mass during the slow process of cooling. However, when valuable minerals are distributed through solid rocks they are more likely to be concentrated by the work of solutions. This may come about as a result of several processes which, in general, do either one of two things: (a) Some solutions that contain molecules of valuable mineral, and perhaps others as well, bring them together and deposit them in greatly enriched zones. The deposition may take place in cavities, thus forming such features as mineral veins, or it may take place by a process of replacement, similar to that of petrification (350). (b) The work of solution may largely remove the rock minerals associated with those having valuable properties, leaving the latter behind in greatly concentrated or enriched form. While these processes may be accomplished by the ordinary cold waters of the ground, it is likely that the result is brought about more readily by the steam and hot waters associated with igneous intrusions. Not only is hot water more active chemically, but those waters are likely to contain gases and solutions derived from the molten mass which, themselves, may contain some of the valuable minerals or may bring about chemical changes in the rocks with which they come in contact.

It is not surprising, in view of the foregoing facts, that rich mineral ores are more often found (a) in regions that have at some time been affected by igneous intrusions or (b) in regions of crystalline rock where the processes of metamorphism have been accompanied by great pressure and the development of heat or (c) in regions where both igneous activity and metamorphism have operated together. This association of conditions clearly has an important relation to the world patterns of distribution of the metallic mineral resources. Although there are some notable exceptions, it is broadly true that the great areas of undisturbed sedimentary rocks are poor in the ores of metals (see Plate VI). This is exactly the opposite of the relationship found to exist in connection with coal and petroleum. Conversely, it is true that the principal areas of ancient crystalline rocks, the bases of old worn-down mountains, and regions of young complex mountains are likely to have localities in which mineral ores may be found. Ore deposits are more often discovered in mountain regions not merely because of the existence there of more of the conditions favorable to their formation but also because of conditions favorable to their discovery. The vigorous erosion characteristic of mountains tends to dissect the rock structures and lay open to view those associations of physical features and rock composition by which the prospector for minerals learns to recognize the existence of ores.

Iron Ores and Their Distribution

676. The Physical Associations of Iron Ores. With the exception of aluminum, iron is the most abundant of the metallic minerals in the rocks of the earth (314). Because it is so easily oxidized or rusted, it is seldom found in metallic form but in some chemical combination. The most important of these are (a) *hematite*, Fe_2O_3, red or gray iron oxide; (b) *magnetite*, Fe_3O_4, black magnetic iron oxide; (c) *siderite*, $FeCO_3$, iron carbonate; and (d) *limonite*, $2Fe_2O_3, 3H_2O$, brown hydrous iron oxide. The red and brown oxides are particularly abundant, since they are scattered widely but thinly through a large part of the regolith and give the common red, brown, or yellow colors to it. Only a little of it is required to give a strong color, and ordinary earth has not enough iron in it to make it profitable for use as an ore (604). Pure hematite and magnetite contain as much as 70 per cent of metallic iron, but large deposits of ore seldom are pure, since they contain admixtures of gangue minerals, especially silica. Some are known, however, that yield large amounts of ore containing as much as 55 per cent of its weight in iron. Most of the ore used in the world must, in order to be profitable under present economic conditions, contain more than 30 or 35 per cent of iron. In the United States relatively little ore is mined that does not contain 50 per cent of iron or more. Some iron-ore deposits contain gangue minerals, such as phosphorus, which are not in large quantity but are difficult to get rid of in the smelting process. That makes the ores less valuable. A few ores, on the other hand, contain lime, which is an aid in the smelting process, and they are made more valuable thereby. The latter are known as self-fluxing ores.

It is clear, therefore, that, although iron is a very abundant metal, the distribution of usable ores of iron is a matter of national concern. Those deposits of largest present value are (a) high in metallic iron, (b) low in objectionable impurities, (c) capable of being inexpensively mined, and (d) situated so that they may be transported cheaply to regions where the other necessary ingredients of iron manufacture are easily assembled near to a large market for iron and steel. Few iron-ore deposits meet all those qualifications. A few, which meet enough of them, have attained international importance and should be known. Among them the outstanding deposits, measured by their present contributions to the iron industries of the world, are those of the Lake Superior region of the United States, northeastern France, Great Britain, Sweden, U.S.S.R., Germany, and Spain. Others of large potential importance require consideration also.

THE IRON ORE RANGES OF THE LAKE SUPERIOR REGION

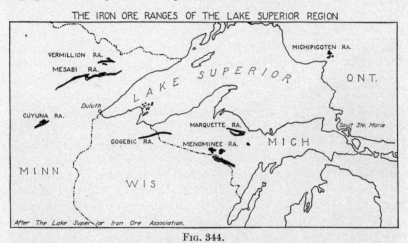

Fig. 344.

677. THE IRON ORES OF THE UNITED STATES. In the United States much more iron ore is mined and used than in any other country in the world. This is in part made possible by the high quality, ease of mining, and convenient location of some of the ores of the Lake Superior region. There are in that region, which includes parts of northern Minnesota, Wisconsin, and Michigan, several bodies of ore (Fig. 344). All of them, however, are found in the ancient crystalline rocks of the Laurentian Shield, which in that region extends southward from the principal area of those rocks in Canada. Furthermore, there are several other bodies of usable ore in the United States besides those of the Lake Superior district.

678. *The Lake Superior ores* are hematite of a desirable grade. Although the region contains large quantities of low-grade ore in which the proportions of silica and other gangue minerals are high, those mined up until the present were very rich, the average iron content being about 55 per cent. Quite as important in the development of the American steel industry is the fact that these ores are prevailingly low in phosphorus. In many iron

ores that element is as much as one-half of 1 per cent of the total. In the Lake Superior ores it generally is less than one-tenth of 1 per cent. Ores with more than that quantity of phosphorus could not be used in the manufacture of steel by the rapid and cheap Bessemer process, which played an important part in the history of the American industry, although it has largely been supplanted now by other processes.

The physical situation of the Lake Superior ores is of as great advantage as their chemical composition. They have been concentrated in the ancient rocks by the work of ground waters and lie in pockets which, in general, are

FIG. 345.—Mining iron ore in an open pit in northern Minnesota. The lighter colored material at the top is glacial drift. (*Courtesy of The Oliver Iron Mining Company.*)

near the surface. In that district of northern Minnesota called the Mesabi Range particularly, the ore deposit is a broad and shallow synclinal ridge, covered only by a relatively thin overburden of glacial drift. When the overburden is stripped away the ore may be removed by steam shovels in open pits (Fig. 345). It is the most productive body of iron ore in the world, but a large part of the highest quality ore has been mined, and the standard of required iron content already has been reduced slightly. However, there are large reserves still in the region having iron content higher than is found in many of the ores used in Europe.

The relation of the Lake Superior ores to regions of manufacture and market is fortunate also. The construction of a ship canal through the rapids of Saint Marys River, connecting Lakes Superior and Huron, provided a deep waterway for the transportation of ore almost from the mine to the very margin of the Appalachian coal field and the heart of the American industrial region. The provision of special devices and carriers for handling the ore has reduced the cost of transportation to a very low figure. For many years more than three-fourths of the iron ores mined in the United States have come from the several districts of the Lake Superior region, but the regional dominance is not likely to continue indefinitely. Following the depletion of the high-grade shallow ores the principal production will be of lower grade and deeper ores which will be forced to compete with similar ores from other regions.

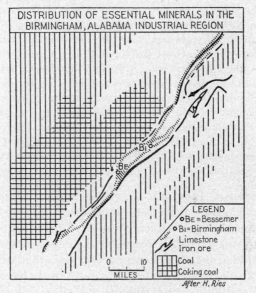

FIG. 346.

679. *Other United States ores* are available in several districts. Among the sedimentary rocks of the Folded Appalachians are discontinuous beds of hematite which are found in localities from New York to central Alabama. These ores are most used in Alabama, where they are mined in the same district with the coal and limestone required in smelting them (Fig. 346). They are of relatively low grade but have the advantage of containing sufficient lime so that they are almost self-fluxing. Other considerable deposits of ore, hematite and magnetite, are known in the Adirondack Mountains and at various places in the interior states, the Rocky Mountain region, and other western localities. What the relative importance of these several reserves may prove to be when the Lake Superior ores no longer dominate American production is not known.

680. OTHER WESTERN HEMISPHERE RESERVES OF IRON ORE. Iron ore moves so cheaply by water that even the ample United States supply has not prevented some foreign ores from moving to meet

abundant coal upon the eastern seaboard for smelting there. Most of these limited imports come from other North or South American sources, chiefly from Chile, Cuba, and Newfoundland. The two last named have large reserves of ore available for export.

681. *Canada and Newfoundland.* It is the lot of Canada to have the larger part of the ice-scoured rocks of the Laurentian Shield but, so far as is now known, the smaller part of the rich and easily mined iron-ore deposits which occur in them. Some of considerable value are known in the region north of Lake Superior, but they are not comparable in extent with those of southeastern Newfoundland, which rank among the large reserves of good ore in the world. They are now mined to a limited extent for use in Nova Scotia and for export to Great Britain and the United States.

682. *Brazilian Ore Reserves.* Although Brazil does not now compete with Cuba and Chile in the export of ore, it has a remarkable supply which, for several physical and economic reasons, is not now producing much commercially. The ore fields lie more than 200 miles north of Rio de Janeiro in the ancient crystalline rocks of the Brazilian plateau. They include a number of localities which contain ore bodies of the highest quality, some hematite, some magnetite. Altogether, the region is reputed to have what is perhaps the greatest and richest reserve of iron ore in the world.

683. EUROPEAN IRON-ORE DEPOSITS. The iron industries of Europe depend mainly upon European sources of ore. Like those of North America, the greatest centers of iron manufacture are located in, or close to, the principal coal fields. In only a few places are the ore and coal found together; hence, one or the other must usually be transported. In the United States they move freely by water over the Great Lakes, and more largely the ore moves to, or toward, the coal. In one particular respect the European situation is different. Although some of the countries contain both, the numerous political boundaries of western Europe have separated several of the more important deposits of iron from those of coal, and much of the ore, especially the high-grade ore, has had to move in international trade to reach the principal smelting centers. The large iron resources are in France, Great Britain, and Sweden. That of Sweden is less in quantity, than those of the other two but superior in quality. The U.S.S.R. also has reserves of iron ore, the most important of which are found in two localities; Krivoi Rog in the Ukraine, not far from the Donets coal field, and in the southern Ural district. Other important sources of ore are found in Germany and Spain. Those of Germany are not adequate to the large needs of the country, but those of northern Spain, a country of little coal, have provided ore for export to England and other countries until some of the deposits are nearly exhausted.

684. *The iron ores of France* include the largest single iron reserve in Europe and one of the large ones of the world. They are found in the northeastern part of the country in the province of Lorraine and extend across the boundary into Luxemburg and slightly into Belgium (Fig. 347). Prior to the treaty of Versailles, in 1919, the eastern part of this field lay on the German side of the international boundary, and as a result of military operations it is again under German control. It has been most important in the development of the German iron and steel industry. The Lorraine ores are mainly limonite and of relatively low grade, since they average only about 30 to 40 per cent of iron. However, they are sedimentary in origin and contain enough lime to make them self-fluxing, and they lie near the German, Belgian, and French coal fields and the great industrial market of Europe. They are high in phosphorus, but a special process of steel manufacture extracts that undesirable element and makes from it a valuable byproduct fertilizer.

FIG. 347.

685. *The iron ores of Great Britain* are fairly abundant but are scattered, of different kinds, and mainly of low grade. It has long been the practice of British smelters to supplement the domestic supply with other ores, especially the better grades imported from Sweden, Spain, Newfoundland, and elsewhere. However, of domestic low-grade ores Britain has a supply sufficient for many years, and war economy is enforcing a greater dependence upon them. They are distributed in several localities, the larger reserves being in the northern and central counties (Fig. 334). They are closely associated with supplies of coal and limestone.

686. *The iron ores of Sweden* are only moderately abundant, but the principal deposits are noted for their high quality. They are mainly magnetite and average from 55 to 65 per cent iron. The largest and best deposits are situated in the crystalline rocks of the far northern part of the country. Since there is almost no coal and but little iron manufacture in Sweden, the ores are exported, in normal times, to Germany, Britain, and other European countries. One phase of German military strategy has been concerned with the control of these ores and of the Norwegian port of Narvik through which they are mainly exported.

687. OTHER SIGNIFICANT IRON-ORE DEPOSITS. Through the vast expanses of Africa, Asia, and Australasia iron-ore deposits are known to exist in many places. Some of them now produce in sufficient quantity to provide abundantly for local industry, as do those of southern Australia, for example. It is probable that in localities as yet imperfectly explored other, and perhaps significant, resources may be found. However, of all the many iron-ore deposits known, only one appears

so great as to rank among the major sources of iron in the world. That one is in India. It lies adjacent to the principal, but not highly productive, coal field of the country in a district about 150 miles west of Calcutta (Fig. 336). The ores are hematite of high iron content; they are of great extent and are so near the surface that some at least are capable of being mined in open pits.

688. SIGNIFICANT FACTS ABOUT THE IRON RESOURCE.   Iron is the most important metal in the present-day world, and it is the second most abundant. Moreover, scattered over the earth are many places where there are ores of some present or future significance as sources of the metal. Of these many deposits only a few have now any great importance. Much the larger number have little present value because they are (a) small or (b) remote or (c) low in iron content or (d) combined with substances that increase the difficulty and cost of smelting them. Which of the deposits of present less importance may achieve future prominence cannot be predicted, because of the possibility that new methods of manufacture of iron may, in the future, make it feasible to use as ores substances much below the present standards of good quality.

However, since iron usually is reduced from the ore by the use of certain grades of coal in the form of coke, it is important to consider in what parts of the world these two ingredients are found close together. It was stated previously that the distribution of the world's plains was such that they contribute to the commercial supremacy of the Atlantic Ocean (374). Another reason for that supremacy may be noted here. The world regions in which abundant deposits of iron ore and of coking coal are closely associated lie on the borders of the North Atlantic Basin. These include eastern United States and countries of northwestern Europe. In them are the present world centers of heavy iron and steel manufacture and of many other industries that depend on cheap iron and steel. There seems good geographic basis for believing that those centers will long continue, because no others appear to have better natural endowment or more advantageous situation. Perhaps the world's greatest reserves of ore are in Brazil and India, but the former has not any, and the latter has only a limited supply of coking coal. China has large reserves of excellent coal but no known supply of ore of comparable importance. Also, it may be noted, Japan, now a progressive industrial nation, has but limited domestic supplies of coal and even less iron ore of usable grade. In this respect the situation of the United States is fortunate. Although the best of the readily accessible ores of the country have been used, large supplies of slightly inferior grades remain. Beyond these there are truly vast reserves of iron-bearing rocks too low in iron to be considered ore at present.

OTHER METALLIC MINERALS

689. IMPORTANT PRECIOUS AND SEMIPRECIOUS METALS. The list of metals that have importance in modern arts and industries is so long that adequate descriptions of their several regions of occurrence would require more space than is available here. In any case, a brief account of each of so many kinds of regions might well produce more confusion than enlightenment. For that reason, comment will be restricted to the locations of the major world regions that are noted for their important productions and possible reserves of the precious and semiprecious metals as a group.

690. PRODUCTIVE AND POTENTIAL MINERAL REGIONS. The earth conditions favorable to the occurrence and discovery of the ores of the several metals here included must be of great variety. The generally favorable conditions have been discussed (675), and it needs only to be stated here that the principal world regions of mineralization are those of ancient crystalline rocks or of more recent crustal disturbances or of igneous activity. Although this is true in a general way, it is a rule that has notable exceptions. One type of exception is found in the deposits of lead and zinc ores associated with sedimentary rocks. Examples of these are the lead and zinc deposits of southwestern Missouri, southwestern Wisconsin, and adjacent Illinois, or those of Belgium or of Poland.

Another exception of great importance is the ore of aluminum. This metal, even more abundant than iron, is like iron in that it is a constituent of earthy minerals which are widely distributed in the regolith. It is a component of common clay and other substances most of which are too low in grade to be utilized profitably. Only in a few places are there rich deposits of the earthy ore of aluminum called *bauxite*. Varieties of this substance are of different origins, but it seems clear that some are derived from sedimentary clays that have been changed through long-continued leaching by ground water, whereas others are known to have been derived by the complete weathering or laterization of igneous rocks of types that were low in iron (618). The notable deposits of the Ouachita Mountain region of Arkansas and of the Guianas, in South America, are of the latter type, whereas those of France are of sedimentary origin. Large reserves of bauxite available in France, Hungary, and Yugoslavia provide abundantly for European consumption, dominantly German, but the domestic reserves of the United States are not great, and much of the ore consumed is imported from British Guiana. Smaller deposits are known in many parts of the world, but, whatever their present climatic situation, there is at least the implication that, at the time of their formation, the climate of the region was hot and humid.

Potential deposits or reserves of the semiprecious and precious metals are only imperfectly known, if at all. Many of the deposits of great value that have been discovered are of small areal extent, and their existence is not marked by obvious surface features. In some cases their discovery has been a matter of chance. Whether others like them exist and, if so, their number and future productiveness cannot be said. Changes in methods of ore reduction may, in the future, change centers of production and increase the available supply of metals. Large quantities are known of substances bearing aluminum, copper, gold,

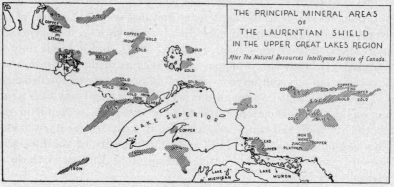

FIG. 348.

and other metals which it is not now profitable to mine because the cost of mining and smelting them is greater than the present values of their products. That may not always be true.

691. *The Laurentian Shield.*   One of the world regions highly productive of the metals, and one having large possibilities of future discoveries, is the Laurentian Shield. From the ancient crystalline rocks beneath its ice-scoured surface are obtained not only the rich iron ores of the Lake Superior region but also a wealth of other metals. These include most of the world's supply of nickel and large amounts of gold, silver, cobalt, copper, and others. Important discoveries are made in this extensive region each year, and the exploitation of mineral resources is one of the principal industries which have attracted settlements of people there (Fig. 348).

692. *The American cordilleran region,* from Alaska to Cape Horn, is one of the world regions noted for the abundance and variety of its mineral products. These include widely distributed bodies of ore, some of which have been practically exhausted while others still are in full production.

Doubtless many others remain to be discovered or are reserved for a future time when new processes shall make them profitable. Valuable deposits of copper are found in the region in localities as far separated as Chile, Peru, Arizona, Montana, and Alaska and in many intermediate places (Fig. 349). Gold, silver, lead, and zinc are sufficiently abundant so that Mexico, the United States, and Canada hold high rank in the production of each of them. The Andean countries of South America are important producers not only of copper but also of platinum, tin, and tungsten, besides having an appreci-

Fig. 349.—Looking down upon Bingham, Utah, and Bingham Canyon, where large quantities of low-grade copper ore are mined on the open mountainside. Note the linear pattern of the town. (*Photograph by Capt. A. W. Stevens, U. S. Army Air Corps.*)

able output of other metals. It was the gold of this region that gave impetus to its conquest by Spain.

693. Central and South Africa. The crystalline rocks of central and southern Africa include several productive mineral regions. Within that vast area are the world's leading gold-producing district and important centers in the production of copper and chromium, not to mention the leading localities from which diamonds are mined.

694. Other mineral regions of world renown may only be mentioned. Among them are the following: (*a*) areas of igneous and crystalline metamorphic rocks in southern and western Australia which have yielded gold, silver, lead, zinc, and minor quantities of other metals. The exploitation of those mineral ores had much to do with the progress of exploration and settlement in Australia; (b) the crystalline rocks of the highlands of eastern South America, in Brazil and the Guianas. In addition to the large deposits of iron ore, previously mentioned, these highlands yield important quantities of manganese, gold, and precious stones. They are known also to contain deposits of several other metals which are as yet little developed; (c) a large region of crystalline rocks in eastern Asia. They extend from Chosen (Korea), on the south, to the shores of the Okhotsk Sea on the north and thence westward in southern Siberia through the regions of the Yablonoi Mountains, Lake Baikal, and the Sayan and Altai Mountains. From this region is obtained a large part of the gold that makes the U.S.S.R. one of the leading producers of that metal. It contains large areas that are as yet little explored geologically; (d) the highlands of southeastern Asia. From them are now obtained the larger part of the world's tin, tungsten, and several other metals; (e) the cordilleran region of southern Europe and the Mediterranean borders. In it are included important centers in the production of several metals. They are located in Spain, North Africa, Italy, Czechoslovakia, and the Caucasus district of southern U.S.S.R.

695. SUMMARY. From the foregoing it may be concluded that the world's principal centers of actual and potential production of the precious and semiprecious metals are those of complex mountain structures or such as are associated with igneous or crystalline rocks (Plate VI). In contrast with those regions are several the surfaces of which are comprised mainly of sedimentary rocks or such as are buried deeply beneath thick mantles of alluvium. Despite the fact that the regions of sedimentary rocks contain the world's supplies of mineral fuels and certain of the ores of iron, aluminum, lead, and zinc, they are, in general, poor in the ores of the precious and semiprecious metals.

Although the larger part of the ores of the metals are found in regions of ancient rocks or of mountain structures, it may not be safely concluded that all such regions are so endowed. It is probable that lack of detailed exploration in certain of those regions may explain their present lack of known ore deposits, but that is not true of all. For example, the crystalline Highlands of Scotland and the large areas of similar rocks in Scandinavia and Finland are known by geologists in much greater detail than are those of Canada or Africa. Similarly, the geology of the Alps is known in more minute detail than that of any other mountains of the world. Yet in neither of these regions are there outstanding deposits of the precious and semiprecious metals.

The Nonmetallic, Nonfuel Minerals

696. MINERALS FOR MANY USES. In addition to the mineral fuels there are produced from the earth more than 50 other nonmetallic

minerals. Some of them are used in their natural states while others pass through processes of industrial manufacture and appear as components in goods having hundreds of essential uses. Rocks, sands, clays, salts, abrasives, fertilizers, gems, and many others make up the list. Most of them are found in a variety of grades or qualities which have equally varied uses. They are essential parts of the natural equipment of regions, but no limited portion of the earth contains all of them. Indeed, there are few regions, if any, that contain all of even the most essential.

Because of the great number of these substances, many must be omitted from this brief treatment. Others, the more essential or those required in greater quantity, may be grouped for consideration under two major headings: (a) minerals used in making utensils or in construction and (b) those used as raw materials in the chemical industries. A few minerals, such as lime, belong in both classes.

CRUDE MINERALS FOR CONSTRUCTION AND UTENSILS

697. ROCK FOR CONSTRUCTION. Many kinds of rock and large quantities of it are used in architectural and engineering structures. In the form of cut stone, crushed rock, or gravels of stream or glacial origin, some material that will serve these purposes is found in most parts of the earth. It may seem that rock, in this broad sense, is one of the universal items of regional equipment, like the air. That, however, is not true. Some regions are endowed with rocks having unusual qualities of structure, strength, beauty of color or ease of working. Others have none at all.

Because crude rock is heavy and of low value, it seldom moves far from its place of origin unless it has some particular quality to recommend it to a wider market. Regions in which rocks of special quality abound have, therefore, a valuable resource, especially if they also are near a large market for stone. Such a region is New England. There a vast quantity of crude rock, glacial boulders, and gravel is supplemented by special rocks in a region of igneous intrusion and metamorphosed sediments. Beautiful and massive granites, slates of parallel cleavage, and excellent marbles all are produced. The even-textured and easily worked gray limestones of southern Indiana have a national market, and some other stones of unique quality have practically world markets. Such are the lithographic limestones of Bavaria and the statuary marble of Italy.

A few regions of considerable size are practically devoid of rock. Among these are the great deltas of the world, where silt covers hundreds of square miles, and rock is buried to great depths. Much larger are certain of the plains of older alluvium or the regions of deep loess accumulation. Among these is the loess- and alluvium-covered Pampa of Argentina and similar areas in the American corn belt, where older drift and loess cover the rock strata deeply. In these regions are localities that have not even any crude rock or gravel with which to surface roads.

698. SANDS, LIMES, AND CLAYS FOR INDUSTRY. Sand, in crude form, enters largely into construction as an ingredient of concrete, mortar, and plaster. Also it shares with lime and clay a place of importance as a raw material of industry. Lime and clay are required in the manufacture of cement; clay is basic to the brick, tile, and pottery industries; and sand is the chief raw material in the manufacture of glass. These three substances are of common occurrence. There are, for example, river sands, beach sands, wind-blown sands, glaciofluvial sands, and pure sandstones. There are unconsolidated marls, soft chalks, and hard limestones. There are river clays, lacustrine clays, marine clays, residual clays, and shale rocks. Not many regions are without one or more of these minerals. However, qualities differ. Glacial lake clays may be good enough for the manufacture of ordinary brick and tile, but other uses have more particular requirements. Pottery clay, especially, must be pure and burn white. It usually is found in residual deposits where it has weathered from coarsely crystalline feldspars (315). Good grades of glass sand, free from iron or clay, may be sought hundreds of miles from the centers of glass manufacture. Therefore, some regions gain advantage from natural endowments of sands, limes, or clays suited to particular requirements. Some, indeed, have achieved international fame through their products, such as that which attaches to the regions of pottery clays in southern England, northern France, or Bavaria.

MINERAL RAW MATERIALS FOR THE CHEMICAL INDUSTRIES

699. SALT is one of the common rock minerals of the earth. Owing to its solubility in water, it is not abundant in the zone of free ground-water circulation. Inexhaustible supplies are available for human use, however, from the following sources: (a) the sea, which contains $2\frac{2}{3}$ lb. of salt for every 100 lb. of water; (b) natural brines, which are the waters of ancient seas trapped in sediments, now deep underground, and cut off from ground-water circulation; (c) deposits of rock salt, which probably are precipitates from the evaporation of water in the arms of ancient seas or in former arid interior drainage basins. Those deposits now are sedimentary rocks deep underground, where they are protected by the other sediments from the solvent action of ground

water; (d) another limited source of supply is found in the surface encrustations of salt in the playa and similar deposits of the interior drainage basins of deserts.

Salt is used not only as a food and a preservative of food but also in large quantities in chemical industries. It is the basic raw material from which a number of the compounds of sodium are made. For industrial uses it is obtained largely by mining rock salt or by the pumping of brines, either natural brines or those produced by pumping water down to bodies of rock salt.

Primitive peoples in many regions have found it difficult to procure sufficient salt, even for their limited requirements. Yet salt is now so readily obtained and is found in so many places that few parts of the world are without some local supply. Industrial salt, however, comes mainly from a few sources.

700. SALT-PRODUCING REGIONS. The industrial regions of North America are supplied with salt, both rock salt and brine, from abundant reserves. Thick beds of rock salt underlie large areas in central and western New York, northeastern Ohio, southeastern Michigan, and peninsular Ontario. Other large reserves are found in the buried "salt domes" of the Louisiana-Texas Gulf Coast, in deposits in central Kansas, and at various places in the southwestern states.

The industrial centers of Europe likewise are well provided with salt. There are large deposits in western England, central Germany, Austria, and southern U.S.S.R. Other populous countries, especially China and India, also are large producers of salt.

701. SULPHUR has many uses in modern industry, especially in the form of sulphuric acid and for various uses in connection with the manufacture of steel, oil, rubber, explosives, and in other chemical industries. It has long been obtained from deposits associated with recent volcanic activity. Some still is mined from these sources in Italy, Spain, Japan, and Chile. In the United States, which now produces more than four-fifths of the world's supply, the deposits have no immediate volcanic connection. Instead, they are found in association with petroleum and the rock-salt deposits of the Louisiana-Texas coast. There the sulphur is recovered by means of wells through which superheated steam is pumped underground to the sulphur beds and molten sulphur is returned to the surface.

702. THE MINERAL FERTILIZERS. Certain elements of soil fertility have been mentioned previously as especially subject to depletion by crop production and by the leaching action of ground water (595). They are calcium, potash, phosphorus, and nitrogen. For each of these

there are known sources of mineral supply which are drawn upon in the manufacture of commercial fertilizers. Some sulphur also is employed for the purpose. Soil lime, in the form of calcium carbonate, is readily available in the local limestones of many regions, and the location of supplies is not a matter of national concern. The other three are much less abundant, and notable deposits of them are items of earth resource of great importance.

703. *Nitrogen* is the most abundant element in the air, and methods are now in use for transforming it into nitrogenous compounds by means of electric energy. Until recently, however, the principal world

supply was from mineral sources. Most important of these were the surface deposits of the desert of Atacama, in northern Chile (Fig. 350). There, in areas of the salt-pan or playa type, are the accumulations of ages of seepage and surface evaporation. The valuable mineral nitrate of soda is intermingled with sand, common salt, and other substances from which it is separated by a simple manufacturing process. So much in world demand was this mineral that, for many years, taxation upon its export was the principal financial resource of the Chilean government, and the business of its extraction and shipment supported a considerable population in the midst of a desert and in several seaports.

FIG. 350.—The location of the principal nitrate-of-soda deposits in the desert of northern Chile. (*After Tower, in Miller and Singewald's "Mineral Deposits of South America."*)

704. *Potash* is a component of many plant tissues and is obtained in small quantities from the ashes of wood, seaweed, and other substances. The principal commercial sources are complex minerals containing potash which are found in beds like rock salt, with which they are in some places associated. The largest known deposits are located in western Europe, mainly in Germany and Alsace, where the greater part of the world's present supply is obtained from mines 1,000 ft. or more beneath the surface.

705. *Phosphorus* is present in certain rock minerals and from them is supplied to the soil. It is also an important constituent of the grains and other plant materials, but it is stored mainly in animal substances, especially in bones, animal manures, and fish. From these sources some is returned to the land as fertilizer. The principal mineral sources of phosphorus occur in the form of calcium phosphate, a rock. It is believed to have been formed from the alteration of limestone by

the chemical action of ground water which had passed through ancient accumulations of fish and bird remains.

Valuable beds of phosphate rock usually occur as local pockets in limestone strata and are known to exist in several parts of the world. The location of those most used is as much related to the regions of consumption as to the extent and richness of the deposits. The principal sources of supply for the European market are located near the Mediterranean coast of Africa in Tunisia, Algeria, and Morocco. The United States is largely supplied from beds in western Florida and central Tennessee (Fig. 351). Other great reserves are known to

Fig. 351.—Mining phosphatic limestone for its phosphorus content, in central western Florida.

exist in the northern Rocky Mountain region of the United States, in Russia, Siberia, and some of the islands of the Pacific Ocean.

Cultural Features Associated with Mineral Extraction

706. MINING. Potential mineral resources or ore reserves have not usually any clear surface manifestations that make them obvious elements of the landscape. The features of material culture of greatest importance associated with mining are the materials extracted from the mines, their kind, quantity, and quality, and these are not always conspicuous. This is due to the fact that in many mining localities there is no important storage of the products. As soon as they are brought from the mine they are removed from the premises for smelting, refining, and fabrication. Thereupon they become the raw materials of manufacture and are no longer a part of the mining complex.

However, that is not always the case. In the Gulf Coast sulphur-producing districts great stock piles containing hundreds of thousands of tons of gleaming yellow sulphur are a conspicuous reminder of the nature of the local resource. In some of the oil fields extensive tank farms store millions of barrels of oil awaiting shipment, and the dull red of ore piles marks the sites of some of the underground iron mines of northern Michigan. In general, however, mineral production must be visualized in terms of the number of tons of ore or coal or barrels of oil moving out by rail, truck, boat, or pipe line along various routes from the producing area.

In many mining regions the most conspicuous features of mineral production are the top works of mines with their derricks, hoisting machinery, mills, powerhouses, loading sheds, and waste dumps (Figs. 331, 327). Quarries and open-pit mines likewise leave conspicuous scars upon the surface. Various of these in association represent the typical mining landscape. But, since most mining is done by underground shafts and tunnels, the excavation features are not so readily observable. They are nevertheless, even when underground, important cultural features. Their nature and extent often are a direct reflection of the history of local mining and of the problems and prosperity of the industry there.

707. MINING POPULATION AND SETTLEMENTS. The significance of mining in a region is reflected in various ways, especially by the percentage of the total working population that is employed in mining and similar industries, such as petroleum production. In the United States there are very few spots where that ratio exceeds 50 per cent. However, a map showing the distribution of mining centers by this means suggests some interesting facts (Fig. 352). For example, in western Pennsylvania, where miners are particularly numerous, there are so many other people employed in various industries that the percentage of miners to other workers does not generally exceed 20, and in only limited districts does it exceed 30 per cent. In Nevada, on the other hand, mining is shown to be an industry of the greatest local importance by the fact that in nearly half the state the proportion of miners to other workers exceeds 20, and in one large district it exceeds 40 per cent. This is clearly due to the fact that, although miners are obviously less numerous in sparsely populated Nevada than in densely peopled western Pennsylvania, the number of those employed in manufacture is still smaller by comparison.

In mining settlements the miners' houses and their arrangement in street patterns are conspicuous elements of regional character. In general they are not noted for the beauty of their appearance or the

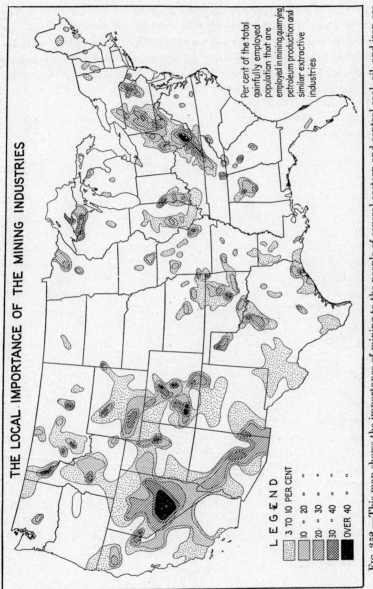

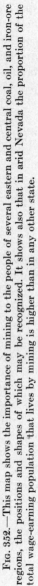

THE LOCAL IMPORTANCE OF THE MINING INDUSTRIES

Per cent of the total gainfully employed population that are employed in mining, quarrying, petroleum production and similar extractive industries

LEGEND

3 TO 10 PER CENT
10 " 20 " "
20 " 30 " "
30 " 40 " "
OVER 40 " "

Fig. 352.—This map shows the importance of mining to the people of several eastern and central coal, oil, and iron-ore regions, the positions and shapes of which may be recognized. It shows also that in arid Nevada the proportion of the total wage-earning population that lives by mining is higher than in any other state.

spaciousness or sanitation of their surroundings. It has been noted previously that a large part of the world's mining industries are conducted in regions of restricted physical environment. It is perhaps unavoidable therefore that mining settlements should fail to compare favorably with agricultural or commercial settlements in the same part of the world (Fig. 332, 349).

THE CULTURAL ELEMENTS OF GEOGRAPHY: FEATURES RESULTING FROM MAN'S USE OF THE LAND

Introduction

708. NATURAL AND CULTURAL ELEMENTS. The geographic character of most earth regions is determined by *two* sets of features: (*a*) those which are a part of the original natural or physical earth and (*b*) those which have been superimposed on the original physical area by man as a result of his living in a region and utilizing its resources. These two great groups of surface features, their forms, patterns of distribution, and characteristic associations, are the *elements* or *fundamentals* of geography. Those elements of the areal scene provided by nature, some inorganic and others organic (*physical geography*), have already been analyzed, classified, and described in Part I of this book. In the present division, Part II, those other elements, people, and the features of material culture resulting from their occupying a region and developing its resources, are analyzed and classified. This is *cultural geography*. Nowhere does man exist upon the earth without doing something to its surface; marks of his utilization are always conspicuous within inhabited areas. This human imprint, these features of *material* culture associated with agriculture, manufacturing, trade, mining, and the other economies—houses, fields, roads, factories, domesticated animals, etc.—become, then, the immediate interest and object of study in Part II of this book.

Some geographers would include among the elements of human geography, in addition to the material culture of a region, other less tangible aspects of its human development, such as the physical well-being of its people, their education, art, government, morals, and religious life. But whether these nonmaterial elements be included or not, most geographers would agree that, for the earth as a whole and for the majority of its regions, the most important elements of human geography are those associated with the efforts of human beings to make a living, *viz.*, the facts of land utilization, including agriculture, manufacturing, trade, mining, etc.

709. LACK OF A READY-MADE CLASSIFICATION OF CULTURE FEATURES. Unfortunately there does not exist any such careful and systematic ordering and classification of the earth's man-made or material-culture features, their characteristics and origins, as there is for its natural features. This, in part, may reflect the greater difficulty in classifying the less orderly array of man-induced features, as compared with those resulting from natural forces, since human beings are not governed by natural laws as are rivers and winds but by minds through which they are able to frustrate environment or adapt it to their needs. Man's acts are not entirely the result even of reason, for what he does is often influenced by moods, whims, and prejudices as well, so that the works of his hands may lack that orderliness and system characteristic of natural forms. This may help to explain why human geographies, unlike physical geographies, are rarely a classification and analysis of the elements of the subject, but rather are topical or regional treatments of associated cultural features.

A second reason for the more complete analysis and classification now available for the natural features as compared with the cultural is that a number of specialized earth sciences have been at work on the problem of analyzing and classifying physical phenomena. Geology and physiography on the nature and distribution of earth materials and landforms, pedology on soils, meteorology and climatology on atmospheric conditions, biology on plant and animal distributions— each of these sciences has aided geography by providing it with basic materials on a particular phase of the physical earth. There has been no equivalent contribution to human geography from the various social sciences.

710. Purpose of Classification and Analysis of the Elements of Human Geography. It is immediately noticeable that the size of Part II of this book dealing with the cultural elements is by no means equal to that of Part I that sets forth the natural elements. *This discrepancy between the sizes of Parts I and II in no way indicates the authors' concept of the relative importance of the natural and cultural elements in geography* (see Preface). It chiefly reflects a fundamental contrast in the nature of the two groups of elements and of the materials bearing on the genesis and distribution of them. There are clearly defined world patterns in *types* of climate, soil, and native vegetation, and it is this fact that makes possible a relatively complete analysis of the distributional aspects of those natural elements. But, as pointed out in the Preface, world patterns of *types* are not so clear for settlements, population, manufacturing, or even for agriculture. In these elements there is much greater regional individuality, and as a consequence less in the way of generalized types which are repeated

on the several continents. Any discussion of the cultural elements, therefore, is compelled to deal more with particular instances and regions than with types that are world wide in scope. Such a discussion does not warrant the same elaboration as one that is focused upon world types.

The discussion of the more important elements of human geography, included within the following chapters, attempts to introduce the beginner in geography to the general content of that field. In brief fashion it brings to his attention the more important groups of features inscribed by human beings upon the regions that they occupy. It is suggestive of the kinds of things, along with others of a physical nature, that one would observe and record on a map or in a notebook if he were making a geographic study of a region. No attempt is made to describe the human geography for the whole earth or for any part of it. The emphasis is upon *types* of land use and of material culture rather than upon a complete covering of the field of human geography. Nor has it been felt necessary to be consistent and logical in treating all the various forms of land use and their associated cultural features. For example, the extractive economies such as mining, hunting, fishing, trapping, and logging are not analyzed in separate chapters of Part II as are agriculture and manufacturing. Significant comments on these less important economies, however, are included in certain chapters of Part I, especially Chap. XXII on Water Resources, Chap. XXIII on The Biotic Resource, and Chaps. XXVI and XXVII dealing with economic minerals.

Chapter XXVIII. Population

711. To the cultural features of the earth's regions man has a dual relationship: (*a*) Collectively the people living on the earth's surface and occupying its regions are themselves one of the cultural elements; and (*b*) man is also the originator, designer, and fashioner of all that great assemblage of features that results from his living on and utilizing the earth. No doubt it is the second of these relationships that gives man his principal geographic significance. The total portion of the earth's surface actually occupied by the bodies of human beings is insignificantly small, so that man himself usually is not a very conspicuous item on the planet. In terms of mass and areal extensiveness, the work of his hands is ever so much more dominant in the geographic scene than is the creator himself. Van Loon, in his popular book on geography, emphasizes this relative insignificance of the quantity aspect of human life when he shows that the earth's 2,000,000,000+ inhabitants could all be put into a single large cubical box measuring $\frac{1}{2}$ mile on a side. Or, allowing each person 6 sq. ft. to stand on, the planet's total population would not occupy more than 450 square miles, which is about two-thirds the size of an average Wisconsin county. But in spite of the fact that human beings cover such a microscopic portion of the earth's surface, Brunhes, a famous French geographer, states that the two most important maps for all human geography are (*a*) the map of men or population and (*b*) the map of rainfall. For where human life is abundant, features of material culture are likely to be also.

It needs to be emphasized that geographers are not primarily concerned with groups of men or population from ethnographic, historical, social, political, or economic points of view but rather with their *spatial*, or *distributional*, aspects as expressed in terms of several closely related items; *viz.*, (*a*) numbers, (*b*) density, (*c*) distribution patterns, and (*d*) movements. From these facts relating to numbers, densities, distributions, and movements of population, however, stem problems of grave social, economic, and political consequences in which the geographer has primary interest.

The concepts of numbers, densities, and distribution as applied to population are much interrelated. It is difficult to think in terms of one without at the same time being conscious of the others. But, on the other hand, neither are the concepts synonymous, and so, in order to emphasize the distinctiveness of each, they are discussed separately.

1. Numbers and Distribution Patterns

712. NUMBERS OF PEOPLE. That there are on this earth somewhat more than 2,100,000,000 people is probably the most basic of all statistical facts. Compared with it, data on area of cultivated land, tons of coal mined, or number of automobiles manufactured are in the nature of embroideries. Of these 2,100,000,000 people occupying the earth, over one-half are in Asia, nearly one-quarter in Europe, and approximately 9, 7, and 4 per cent in North America, Africa, and South America. Among individual countries China leads with nearly one-quarter of the whole earth's population, while India comes next with nearly one-sixth. Far below these two Asiatic countries come Soviet Russia and the United States to be followed in turn by Japan, Germany, the United Kingdom, Italy, and France.

POPULATION STATISTICS (ESTIMATED FOR 1938. *League of Nations Statistical Year Book, 1938–1940*)

Continents

Asia	1,134,500,000
Europe	470,500,000
North America	182,810,000
Africa	155,500,000
South America	91,300,000
Oceania	10,670,000

Selected Countries

China	450,000,000
India	365,000,000
Soviet Russia	170,400,000
United States	130,000,000
Japan	72,750,000
Germany	69,486,000
The United Kingdom	46,064,000
Italy	42,919,000
France	41,907,000

The concept of numbers of people is an important one geographically, for there is usually a direct relationship between number of people in a country or region and the kind and intensity of land use prevailing there. But the simple concept of numbers becomes ever so much more important as an index of land use when it is supplemented by two other types of population facts. (*a*) The first of these involves the stage of agricultural and economic development of a people, their horsepower equipment, mental endowments, degree of health, cultural heritage, inhibitions, ambitions, and the like. A smaller number of energetic, ambitious people utilizing mechanical power may very well do more work and more completely modify the earth's surface than a larger population living on a lower plane of civilization.

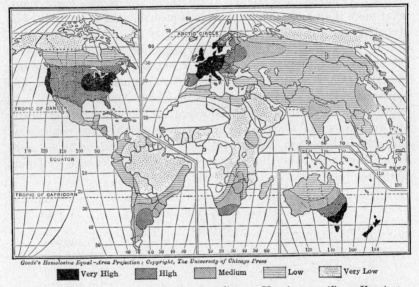

Goode's Homolosine Equal–Area Projection: Copyright, The University of Chicago Press

| ■ Very High | ▨ High | ▤ Medium | ▤ Low | ⣿ Very Low |

Fig. 353.—Distribution of civilization according to Huntington. (*From Huntington, "Principles of Human Geography," by permission of John Wiley & Sons, Inc.*)

(*b*) A second supplementary item of importance is the trend of population, *i.e.*, whether there is growth, stagnation, or decline. Any treatment of population needs to be dynamic rather than static, for the rate of growth or decline of a nation's population greatly affects its wants, institutions, and arts.

713. *Contrasts in the Cultural and Economic Well-being of Populations.* It is clearly recognized that great differences exist in the civilization of the various peoples of the earth. There are parts of the earth whose population we speak of as being advanced and progressive, and there are others that are called backward and retarded. Important regional contrasts of a geographic character grow out of these differences in cultural and economic advancement. Ellsworth Huntington

has attempted to show the world distribution of this elusive thing called civilization.[1] His map (Fig. 353) shows two major centers, one in northwestern Europe and the other in northern and eastern United States, with smaller centers in Pacific Coast United States, southeastern Australia, and New Zealand. The regions of lowest scale civilization on Huntington's map are coincident with the low latitudes of excessive heat and the high latitudes of excessive cold. Although one may question the validity of certain distributional facts shown on the map, it does nevertheless represent in a general way what an

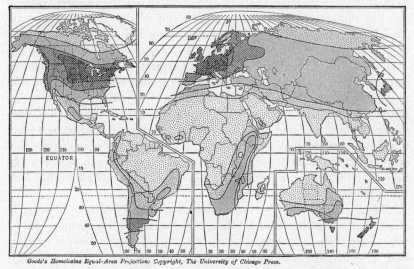

Goode's Homolosine Equal-Area Projection: Copyright, The University of Chicago Press.

FIG. 354.—Distribution of climatic energy according to Huntington. The density of shading is roughly proportional to the degree of climatic energy. (*From Huntington, "Principles of Human Geography," by permission of John Wiley & Sons, Inc.*)

Occidental would probably consider to be the broad distribution pattern of the elements of *western* civilization. A Chinese or a Hindu might not agree that it represented civilization in general.

The question may well be raised relative to what causes these great differences in stages of civilization among the world's population, which in turn result in contrasts in kind and degree of land use. Some would argue that, to a degree at least, it represents fundamental differences in racial potentialities; that the regions of highest civilization are those occupied by the most virile races possessed of physical and mental qualities that foreordained that they were to be the world's leaders. Of this type of philosophy the leaders of Nazi Germany have

[1] Huntington, Ellsworth. "Civilization and Climate." 3d ed., pp. 240–274, Yale University Press, New Haven, 1924.

been the most ardent recent advocates. Anthropologists and psychologists are of the opinion, however, that there is no scientific basis for this doctrine of superior and inferior races. Up to the present time no reliable evidence is available that shows inherent psychological and mental differences that distinguish the races fundamentally.

Huntington believes that climate, through its effects upon health and energy, is one of the most important factors having to do with regional variations in civilization.[1] It is only fair to say that many scientists discount his findings. According to Huntington three conditions of climate, (a) temperature, (b) humidity, and (c) variability are of greatest importance in affecting health and energy. The ideal climate for human progress may be summed up as follows: (a) an average annual temperature that ranges from somewhat below 40° for the coldest month to nearly 70° in the warmest month; (b) a relative humidity that is moderately high, except in hot weather, and rainfall at all seasons, and (c) a constant succession of cyclonic storms bringing frequent moderate changes in temperature. Huntington has constructed a map showing world distribution of climatic energy, and there is a close correspondence of this map with the one showing distribution of civilization (Fig. 354). He believes this coincidence between the maps of civilization and climate to be one of cause and effect, but here again there are many doubters.

Fairgrieve[2] and others have pointed out that cultural history, in other words, civilization, is the story of man's increasing control over energy. From this point of view a map of distribution of civilization is to be explained in terms of control and utilization of energy. The Industrial Revolution with its emphasis upon the use of mechanical power marks a great dividing line in history, and the parts of the world now generally recognized as most advanced are those that have made the greatest use of inanimate energy. The United States and Europe today are utilizing by far the largest amount of the world's mechanical energy and doing a disproportionate share of the world's work. Leith estimated that the United States alone (1931) had an energy output from coal, oil, natural gas, and water power amounting to nearly half the world's total and was doing nearly half the world's work.[3]

714. TRENDS IN POPULATION.   The most striking facts regarding world population during the past century are (a) the phenomenally

---

[1] *Ibid.*, pp. 291–314, 387–411.

[2] Fairgrieve, James. "Geography and World Power." 2d ed., p. 3, E. P. Dutton & Company, Inc., New York, 1921.

[3] Leith, C. K. "World Minerals and World Politics." Pp. 48–49, McGraw-Hill Book Company, Inc., New York, 1931.

rapid growth of population, particularly in the occidental countries, following the Industrial Revolution, and (b) the striking decline in rate of growth since about the first decade of the present century. Associated with the Industrial Revolution there occurred an unprecedented expansion of resources, both natural and cultural, which became available to the peoples of the countries involved. It was these greatly expanded resources that permitted the rapid growth of population For a time it began to look as though man, like plants and the lower

COMPARATIVE BIRTH RATES IN SELECTED COUNTRIES (PER 1,000 POP.)

	1881–1885	1930–1932	1933–1936
Belgium	30.9	18.3	15.8
Denmark	32.4	18.2	17.6
England and Wales	33.5	15.8	14.7
Finland	35.5	19.6	18.0
Germany	36.8	16.2	17.7
Italy	38.0	25.1	23.3
Norway	31.0	16.5	14.6
Australia	35.2	18.3	16.7

	1876–1880	1901–1905	1925	1935
Western and Northern Europe	32.7	28.4	19.8	16.8

animals, breeds up to the limits of the means of sustenance. In 1800 the white race, which was the largest single group to come under the influence of the Industrial Revolution, represented only one-sixth of the earth's population, but by 1925 it included one-third—from 225,000,000 to 625,000,000. This unusual growth of European peoples is the outstanding phenomenon of population history.

But the same industrial revolution that permitted the rapid increase in occidental peoples during the past century produced a peculiar change in people's attitudes toward size of families, so that during the twentieth century the trend has been reversed and the low birth rates prevailing in most western European countries during the past few decades cause worry that these populations may actually die out. Clearly the impact of the Industrial Revolution upon population growth may be divided into two phases; the first marked by a very rapid increase, and a second, and perhaps final phase, marked by a new stability which may turn into a decline. Since 1919 the number of future mothers born to each woman in western Europe has declined at an astonishing rate. Hardly a country in that region is actually reproducing itself at the present time. During the last few years the rapid decline in American birth rate appears to have halted, at least temporarily, but even now the country is barely holding its own. Estimates by the United States Bureau of the Census indicate a

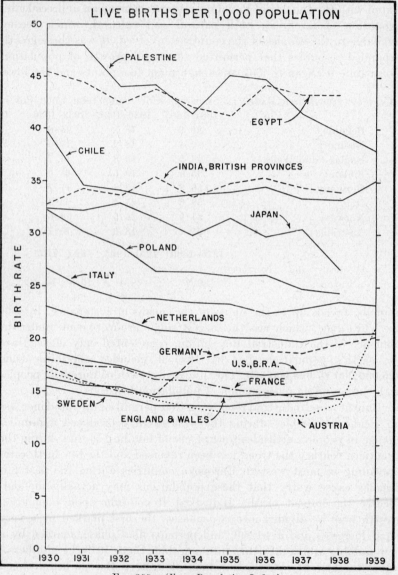

FIG. 355.—(*From Population Index.*)

steadily decreasing rate of population growth in the next several decades, with a static condition reached by about 1980–1985, after

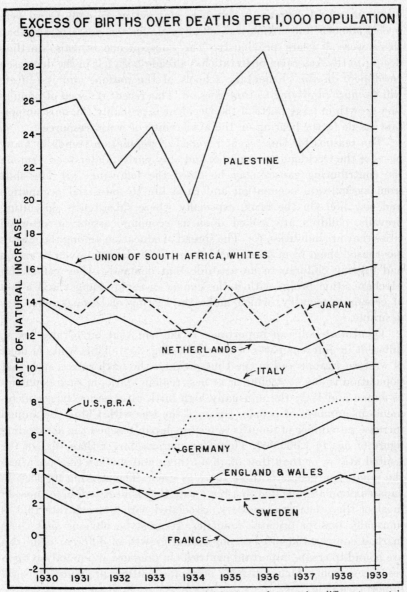

EXCESS OF BIRTHS OVER DEATHS PER 1,000 POPULATION

PALESTINE

UNION OF SOUTH AFRICA, WHITES

JAPAN

NETHERLANDS

ITALY

U.S., B.R.A.

GERMANY

ENGLAND & WALES

SWEDEN

FRANCE

RATE OF NATURAL INCREASE

FIG. 356.—Large differentials in population increase characterize different countries and different regions. (*From Population Index.*)

which an actual decrease in numbers may set in. In 1935 there were over 1,500,000 fewer American children under ten years of age than there were 5 years previously. The consequence of this startling decline in the American birth rate has already been felt in the decreased enrollment in the elementary schools of the nation, and its effects will be more ramifying as time goes on. This recent reversal of population growth in large parts of the Occident is probably the most important single factor bearing on the availability of world resources.

The reasons for this recent reversal of population trends in many parts of the Occident are complex and only partly understood. Among the contributing causes may be listed the following: (a) The shift from agricultural occupation and rural life to industrial occupation and city life. On the farm, especially where subsistence agriculture prevails, children are looked upon as economic assets; in crowded cities they are liabilities. (b) The spread of education among the masses has roused them from a satisfaction with a life largely given to eating and bearing children to an attitude that demands other values. (c) Mechanization brings with it the danger of rapid changes and a loss of economic security, which make the rearing of large families less desirable.

Of utmost political importance is the fact that birth rates are so different in different parts of the world (Fig. 355). Thus while in most of western Europe and in the United States the birth rate is such that population is due to decline or at best remain static, in such countries as Japan and Italy the unusually high birth rates assure larger increments in numbers of people. Up until the war with China the annual increase in number of mouths to feed in Japan reached the astounding figure of nearly 1,000,000. This is an increase larger than that of the United States, or than that of all northern and western Europe, where the number of people is three times as great. The striking increase in Japan's population is due to a birth rate that is nearly double those of most of the other great powers, associated with a death rate that is unusually low for oriental countries. It must be obvious that these marked contrasts in rates of population growth in different countries are bound to create important contrasts in pressure of population upon resources, from which contrasts originate political problems of world importance (Fig. 356).

Population Distribution Patterns

715. Patterns of the First Order, or World Patterns.   Even a superficial study of the world map of population is sufficient to show that over three-quarters of the earth's inhabitants are concentrated in

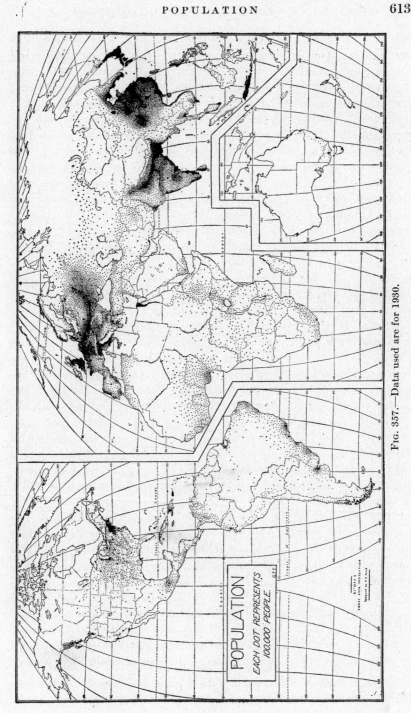

Fig. 357.—Data used are for 1930.

POPULATION
EACH DOT REPRESENTS
100,000 PEOPLE.

two or three great continental clusters (Fig. 357). One of these is in southeastern Asia or Monsoonia; a second is in western and central Europe; and a third, which is considerably smaller than the other two, is in eastern and central United States and Canada. The Oriental cluster, composed chiefly of peasant farm people, is much the largest with nearly one-half of the whole world's population. In both the European and American centers, which have been greatly affected by the Industrial Revolution, civilization is much more complex, and manufacturing and trade are more highly developed than in Asia. As a result, cities, which are the products of trade and industry, are more numerous, and a far larger percentage of the peoples of Europe and North America are urban dwellers. It is noteworthy that this monsoon region of generally high population densities is separated into two parts by the less densely populated peninsula, composed of Burma, Indo-China, and Thailand (Siam).

At the opposite extreme from the three great continental clusters of dense population are the lands of the earth that are relatively empty of people. With two principal exceptions these are areas with climatic handicaps. On the world population map the single largest empty spots are in the lands bordering the Arctic Ocean. Here shortness of growing season, cool summers with frost hazard, and miserable soils are the principal physical handicaps. At the opposite climatic extreme are the somewhat less thinly peopled wet tropics, more especially the forest lands. Notable exceptions are overcrowded Java and British India. In general the American tropics seem much less well populated than those of the Old World. This disparity may be due to the introduction of diseases by the European colonizers. Possibly modern hygiene could aid in repeopling these regions. Whether or not colonists from middle latitudes can occupy and develop the tropical forest lands is still a debated question.[1]

The third general type of thinly peopled areas is the dry lands. The possibilities for irrigation in some of these may slightly modify their present population content, but it will probably never be great. Dry farming has not been overly successful, and the possibilities of drought-resistant crops have been pretty well exploited.

716. *Will the World Pattern of Population Distribution Change?* To an unusual degree the present world pattern of population distribution reflects the productive capacities of the earth's great regions. In other words, the people of the earth are where they belong in terms of natural resources and equipment and taking into consideration their present

---

[1] Price, A. Grenfall. White Settlers in the Tropics. *Amer. Geog. Soc. Special Pub.*, 23, New York, 1939. See also Yearbook of Agriculture, 1941, pp. 237–261.

standards of living.[1] The world has been pretty well explored in terms of productive capacity, and marked shifts in population numbers and densities are not to be expected. Great mineral discoveries such as have characterized the last few centuries are extremely unlikely. In a few places, such as parts of South America, for example, extensive areas of land are held out of full settlement by the large size of the land holdings. Some parts of inner Asia fit for agriculture are prevented from being so used by their present utilization by pastoral peoples. A few relocations of population may result from (a) the discovery of new crops, (b) the vernalization of seeds, which treatment involves the shortening of their growing season, and (c) the extension of public hygiene, particularly in the wet tropics, where colonization seems to be partly, if not largely, a matter of health.

Thus, although there are large areas of the earth still potentially available for human settlement, these are mainly of a marginal nature, often because of climatic handicaps. Such regions can be occupied only with considerable effort and at high cost so that settlement is discouraged. Thus, although the frontiers of settlement have not become stagnant, their advance in the future will be much slower than has been true in the past.

717. PATTERNS OF THE SECOND ORDER. If the focus is sharpened somewhat, it is evident that within any large area of the earth there are lesser patterns of population distribution which are conspicuous and distinctive. Thus within the monsoon lands of southeastern Asia, which support such a large percentage of the world's people, the spread of population is very uneven. Here it is a much fragmented or *clustered* pattern that is conspicuous, with a relatively small part of the total land area supporting a great majority of the people (Fig. 358). Almost knife-edge boundaries frequently appear to separate areas containing several hundred, or even thousand, persons per square mile from others which are almost barren of settlement. This markedly clustered pattern of population is closely associated with surface configuration and soil characteristics, for southeastern Asia is, in general, a hilly region with restricted lowlands composed of river alluvium. The peasant farmers have tended to gravitate toward these alluvial lowlands, where soils are fertile and gentle slopes and abundant water, two items relatively necessary for the inundated rice crop, are easily available. The more difficult slope sites with thinner less fertile

[1] Sauer, Carl O. The Prospect for Redistribution of Population. Chap. I of Isaiah Bowman (Editor). "Limits of Land Settlement." Council on Foreign Relations, New York, 1937; Broek, Jan O. M. Climate and Future Settlement, in "Climate and Man," Yearbook of Agriculture, 1941, pp. 227–236.

soils are avoided. In hilly Japan only 15 per cent of the land surface is actually cultivated. One might with great fitness describe Japan and China as having "alluvial civilizations."

This concentration of agricultural effort on only the best land is explained in part by the large dependence upon hand labor and hand

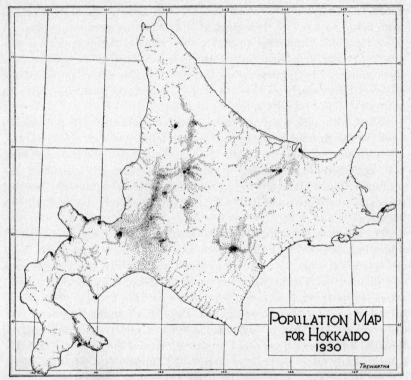

FIG. 358.—Pattern and density are both conspicuous. As in other parts of monsoonal Asia, population in this northern island of Japan proper is concentrated upon the plains of new alluvium. One dot represents 200 people.

tools. It requires approximately 15 man-days to spade an acre of land by hand so that the farmer who depends entirely on his own muscles can cultivate only an acre or two of ground. Even those who have an ox or horse can plow at most only a few acres. Since it takes just as long to dig up and cultivate poor land as good land, the oriental farmer is obliged, in order to feed his family, to put his efforts on the most productive soil. On anything else he would starve. In the United States on less productive lands the farm area is increased, and this greater area is operated through the use of more animal or motor power and the use of laborsaving machinery. But this adaptation the oriental farmer is incapable of making.

Over dry central and western Asia population is concentrated in or near the highlands where water is more abundant. In Siberia there is a marked focusing of the agricultural population on the east-west belt of fertile dark soils in western Siberia, lying between the subarctic taiga region on the north and the dry lands of the Aral-Caspian region to the south.

Europe. In western Europe as well, even on the lowlands, the clustered population pattern is conspicuous, although the boundaries of the clusters are usually not so sharp as in eastern Asia. This is particularly true in Great Britain, where only 8 per cent of the population are farmers and 80 per cent are classed as urban. In that island six of the seven most conspicuous population clusters are industrial urban concentrations coincident with important coal fields (Fig. 334). The London center, the greatest of all, is the most striking exception to this coincidence with coal, that cluster being less exclusively specialized in manufacturing and supported relatively more by trade. Most of the industrial regions have their own ports which serve them more or less locally, but London on the other hand is the port for the greater part of Britain and its political and financial capital as well.

On the continent of Europe there is a continuous belt of extremely dense population oriented east-west along the fiftieth parallel from the North Sea and English Channel to the lower Dnepr (Dnieper) in Soviet Russia. This might be called the *European population axis.* The belt broadens from east to west, and the density of population likewise increases in the same direction. It reaches its greatest density in the general vicinity of the lower Rhine, coincident with important coal and iron deposits and lying near the mouth of one of the world's great natural waterways (*cf.* Figs. 357, 335). This maximum concentration of people in the general region of northwestern Germany, Holland, Belgium, and northern France is continued eastward in somewhat less intense form through southern and eastern Germany; northern Bohemia and Moravia in Czechoslovakia, Galicia in southern Poland, and into the Ukraine of southern Soviet Russia. Throughout the length of the European population axis, which contains more than a fourth of the people of the continent, lie the most important coal basins of Europe, the power resources of which have aided the growth of numerous industrial cities (Figs. 357, 364). In Mediterranean Europe high population densities are found on a number of small isolated basins or delta plains, but these populations are based chiefly upon agriculture. Chief among these islands of population is the one occupying the large and relatively fertile Po Valley in Italy. Here both rural and urban population are represented, for this is Italy's most highly industrialized region. It thus becomes obvious that, although eastern Asia's population concentrations are of peasant agricultural peoples focused upon fertile alluvial plains, to a much larger degree western and central Europe's population is concentrated in commerical and industrial towns and cities grouped with respect to basic mineral resources, important routes of trade, or fertile plains producing raw materials and food.

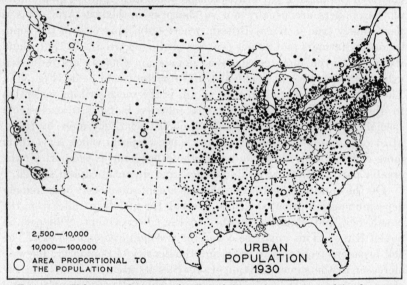

· 2,500—10,000
● 10,000—100,000
○ AREA PROPORTIONAL TO THE POPULATION

URBAN POPULATION 1930

Fig. 359.—Urban population in the United States is concentrated in the manufactural belt lying north of the Ohio River and east of the Mississippi. (*From Jones, "Economic Geography," by permission of The Macmillan Company.*)

718. *North America.* In the United States the most striking feature of population distribution is the contrast between the well-occupied humid East with its predominance of lowlands, and the meagerly occupied dry and rougher West (Fig. 357). Throughout the lowlands of much of central and eastern United States population is spread rather evenly, and marked clustering is not conspicuous. It is chiefly in the northeastern part of the country north of the Ohio River and east of the Mississippi, which includes the great manufactural belt with its large urban population, that clustering is prominent (Fig. 359). West of the Appalachians the highest densities are coincident with the industrial belts along (*a*) the southern and southwestern sides of Lake Michigan, (*b*) the southern side of Lake Erie, (*c*) the margins of

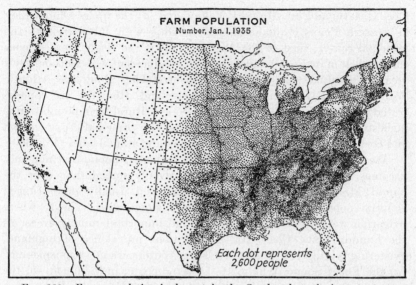

Fig. 360.—Farm population is densest in the South, where the important crops, such as cotton, corn, and tobacco, require much labor. In this region farm machinery is not abundant. (*Courtesy of U. S. Department of Agriculture.*)

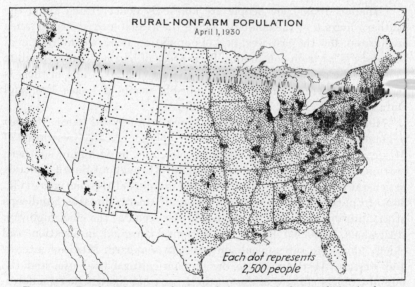

Fig. 361.—Rural nonfarm population includes nonagriculturists living in the open country or in villages and towns with fewer than 2,500 inhabitants. It is highest in suburban areas. (*Courtesy of U. S. Department of Agriculture.*)

Lake Ontario and the Mohawk Valley, and (*d*) the upper Ohio Valley in western Pennsylvania and eastern Ohio with Pittsburgh as the principal center. East of the Appalachians is the single greatest continuous belt of dense population, which is coincident with the country's greatest manufacturing concentration stretching along the Atlantic Seaboard from southern Maine to Maryland. Here too are concentrated the nation's chief foreign-trade ports. Rural farm population is highest in the South, however, where the two principal crops, cotton and corn, require large amounts of human and animal labor (Fig. 360).

West of the 100th meridian or thereabouts, population not only becomes less dense but it is much less evenly spread than over the humid Mississippi Valley. In this drier and usually more rugged country population is chiefly clustered along river valleys, where irrigation water is available, and around important mining areas. In the humid Pacific Coast states with their prevalence of highland, clustering is still very prominent. Three centers are most conspicuous: (*a*) the Puget Sound–Willamette Lowland center in the north, (*b*) the concentration in the Great Valley and the San Francisco Bay region in central California, and (*c*) the southern center occupying the smaller valleys around and back of Los Angeles and San Diego.

Canada's 10,000,000 people are markedly concentrated along the southern margin of the country, where the available agricultural lands are located. But the east-west belt of population along the international boundary is far from continuous, large areas of barren country tending to isolate the people into four or five distinct clusters. Chief of these is the one occupying the Ontario Peninsula north of Lakes Erie and Ontario, and in the St. Lawrence Valley.

719. *Latin America, Australia, Africa.* In *tropical* Latin America population is concentrated in the cooler uplands. Nearly two-thirds of Mexico's people live in the higher, cooler, and more humid southern portion of that country's central plateau. Throughout South America in general the people occupy chiefly the margins of the continent (Fig. 362). In part this reflects (*a*) the physical, chiefly climatic, handicaps of the interior lands and (*b*) the use of the ocean as the chief highway. Australia's 7,000,000 people are likewise marginal in location and chiefly along the subtropical southeastern seaboard. Much of interior and western Australia is too dry for agricultural land use, and the humid tropical climate of the northern part has likewise been a deterrent to settlement. In Africa concentrations are conspicuous (*a*) along the Mediterranean borderlands, (*b*) in the western Sudan and along the Guinea coast, (*c*) on the East African uplands including the Abyssinian Plateau, and (*d*) along the southern and southeastern

margins of the continent. Most striking of all, however, is the unusual
concentration on the floodplain and delta of the Nile in Egypt, where

FIG. 362.—Population in South America shows a clustered pattern and is concentrated along the margins of the continent. (*From James, "Latin America," by
permission of The Odyssey Press.*)

the population density reaches 1,500 per square mile while the bordering lands are nearly empty of people.

2. Density and Movement of Population

720. The Simple Man-land Ratio. How much land there is to how many people is a fundamental consideration in the life of any society. This relationship of number of men to area of land is called the *man-land ratio*, which, in its simplest form, may be expressed as the number of persons per square mile, square kilometer, or some other unit of area. This is sometimes known as the simple arithmetic density of population. In 1938, the earth's population was estimated to be somewhat more than 2,100,000,000, which, expressed in terms of the man-land ratio, was a little over 10 persons per square mile. But, quite obviously, this figure gives no genuine understanding of real density, for it fails to take into consideration the fact that over 70 per cent of the planet's surface is water, which has no permanent settlements. For the land areas of the earth only, population density is slightly over 41 persons per square mile. This, to be sure, is a more refined and accurate figure than the former but still it fails to give a very true picture of actual conditions, since human life is by no means evenly distributed over the continents. It appears, then, that the idea of density is almost inextricably tied up with that of distribution. Only where people are dispersed rather widely and evenly over an area is the figure for density alone highly significant.

ARITHMETIC DENSITY OF POPULATION FOR SELECTED COUNTRIES ABOUT 1938

	People per Square Mile
Belgium	711.3
Netherlands	638.9
United Kingdom	498.8
Japan	482.4
Germany	371.9
Italy	365.6
Switzerland	261.8
India	214:7
France	197.0
United States	42.6
Canada	3.2
Australia	2.3

721. Factors Affecting Population Density. Even in regions where human beings are widely and evenly dispersed, the simple ratio of people to land is not always a satisfactory measure of *real* density. This is because equal areas vary greatly in their capacities or resources for supporting populations. Varieties of climate, surface configuration, soil, vegetation cover, and mineral resources create wide differences in the productivity of land. If, for instance, the ice-covered continent of Antarctica, with an area estimated at 5,000,000 square miles and without permanent settlements, were to receive 100 inhabitants, it probably could be called overpopulated, since it has so few resources for supporting human life. On the other hand, the fertile Nile and Yangtze plains can support 100 persons on 1 square mile—five million times the previous density—and still not be considered greatly over-populated (Fig. 365). If, then, in the denominator of the man-land ratio, *productive capacity* is substituted for square miles, a much better estimate of *real* density is obtained. This is known as the general *economic density* of population. The figure for productive capacity of land is not so easily arrived at, however, since the natural equipment of a region is not one but a variety of items. The geographer, trained as he is in the various aspects of natural earth, is equipped to make this contribution relative to the total natural potentialities of regions.

Of somewhat greater significance than arithmetic density of population is the so-called *physiological density*, which substitutes arable land for total area in the man-land ratio. This is a more refined and accurate

PHYSIOLOGICAL DENSITY OF POPULATION FOR SELECTED COUNTRIES
ABOUT 1925
(*League of Nations Statistics*)

	Inhabitants per Square Mile of Arable Land
Japan	2,532
Netherlands	2,085
Great Britain	2,080
Switzerland	2,007
Belgium	1,664
Brazil	1,661
Norway	1,071
Italy	798
Germany	793
India	533
France	463
Sweden	413
United States	221
Canada	88

index of population density because it omits those lands that are un-productive. For example in Japan, where less than 16 per cent of the land is under cultivation, the arithmetic density figure is about 480 per square mile, whereas the physiological density in 1940 is over 3,000 per square mile, the highest for any country of the earth. In the table on p. 623 are given the physiological population densities for a number of countries. The striking feature of this list, after noting Japan's position, is the high rank of a number of European countries.

A somewhat different concept is provided by *agricultural density*, which is simply the number of agricultural people per unit of arable land. Thus Japan, which has a physiological density of 3,000+ per square mile, has an agricultural density of about 1,400, which indicates that slightly less than one-half of the country's inhabitants are agriculturists. In the following table giving agricultural densities for selected countries it is conspicuous that there has been a change in the ranks of several nations from what they were in the arithmetic and physiological density tables. It is the countries with relatively dense populations, large percentages of which are engaged in agriculture, that appear at the top of the list. On the other hand, a densely populated but highly urbanized region like Great Britain has a low rating.

AGRICULTURAL DENSITY OF POPULATION ABOUT 1930
(*After Reithinger*)

	Agricultural Population per Square Mile of Arable Land
Bulgaria	255
Poland	237
Italy	234
Belgium	187
Netherlands	185
Switzerland	172
Hungary	161
Germany	125
France	117
Denmark	99
Great Britain	49

722. THE GENERAL ECONOMIC POPULATION DENSITY IN COMPLEX CIVILIZATIONS. The problem of comparing population density and productive capacity of land becomes further complicated in those regions where men do not live directly from the soil. There is no *simple* way of expressing the potential capacity of areas for supporting population in a complex industrial and commercial civilization. In order to evaluate the general economic density of a country it is necessary to consider, in addition to the agricultural productivity, the various

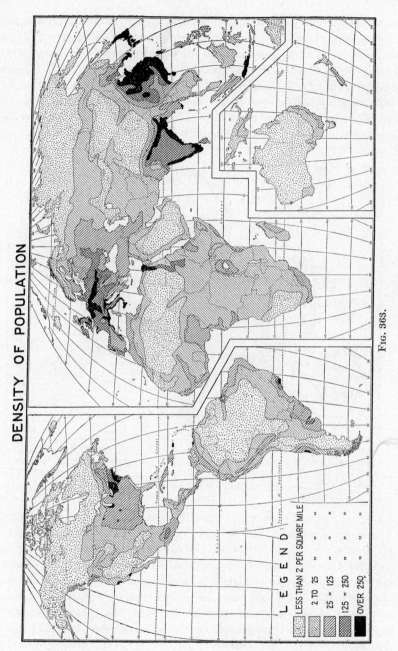

DENSITY OF POPULATION

Fig. 363.

LEGEND

LESS THAN 2 PER SQUARE MILE
2 TO 25 " " "
25 " 125 " " "
125 " 250 " " "
OVER 250 " " "

natural resources independent of the soil, such as minerals, timber, fish, and scenery. Additional items to be evaluated are the degree of actual exploitation of these resources and the proportional use of other factors such as capital, quantity and quality of labor, and degree of technical development. For example, the United Kingdom's 47,000,000 people draw only a small part of their economic livelihood directly from the soil of the 94,000 square miles on which they live. Of prime importance in evaluating that country's capacity for supporting human life is its

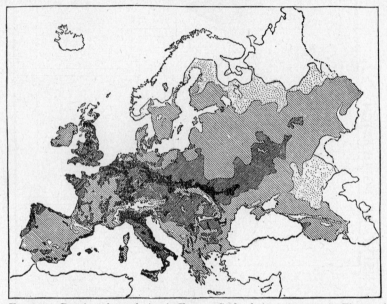

Fig. 364.—Density of population in Europe. Scale about 1:47,000,000. Five gradations of density are shown: black, 100–500 persons per square kilometer; bars 50–100; lines, 10–50; dots, 1–10; white (within political Europe), 0–1. (*Map by L. Weise in Petermann's Mitteilungen, Vol., 59, I, 1913. Reproduced by Mark Jefferson and published in the Geographical Review.*)

supply of mineral resources, especially coal. With coal as the principal source of industrial power Britain draws raw materials and food from all parts of the world, processes the raw materials in British factories utilizing her accumulated capital and her abundance of high-quality labor, and returns the finished materials again to the far corners of the earth. On the other hand, in simple rural civilizations that are composed of self-sufficient peasant families, the direct relationship between number of people and productive capacity of land is not so difficult to observe. So difficult is it to evaluate the general economic density for the various regions of the world that comparative data are as yet not available.

723. DENSITY DISTRIBUTION. In a general way Fig. 357, showing distribution of *numbers* of people, also gives an impression of relative densities, although from such a map numerical density readings are impossible. Simple arithmetic densities exceed 250 per square mile in Japan, eastern China, Chosen (Korea), Java, and the lowlands of India. Here in southeastern Asia is the world's largest region of high densities (Fig. 363). For most of the lowlands in this region the density figures greatly exceed those given above. On the Yangtze Plain of China density is nearly 900 per square mile and on the North China

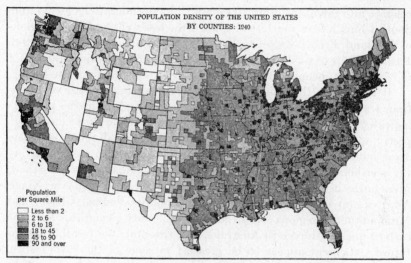

FIG. 365.—(*Courtesy of U. S. Department of Commerce.*)

Plain it is close to 650. On the plains of Bengal in northeastern India it is over 600 per square mile. After southeastern Asia the next largest region of high densities (exceeding 250 per square mile) is in Europe, with more restricted areas in northeastern United States (Figs. 363, 364, 365). Over much of the subarctic plain of Eurasia and North America and over the great deserts there are fewer than two inhabitants per square mile. Although it is true that the general lineaments of the world pattern of population densities are directly related to the productive capacities of the lands, the details of the pattern show many exceptions. Not only natural productivity of regions, but also many social, historical, and political factors are involved in understanding the details of population densities in the various parts of the earth.

724. POPULATION MOVEMENTS. At least partly because of contrasts in economic population densities in different parts of the world,

there is a tendency for peoples to move from regions of high economic density to those of low. In past centuries, before some of the earth's more productive lands were occupied by the white race, this movement of peoples was more conspicuous than it is at present. The migration of peoples from Europe to the New World continents during the past three centuries was one of the greatest flows of population in all times. At present the largest streams of population movement are in Asia. From North China there go annually over 1,000,000 people into the frontier lands of northern Manchuria. Between these two regions the population gradient is very steep, which tends to accelerate movement. Another stream of Chinese emigration chiefly from South China moves southward toward the less well populated regions of Thailand, French Indo-China, Malaya, and the islands of the Dutch East Indies, except Java. From densely populated Bengal there is a movement of people toward the less well occupied Assam Valley.

It is unlikely that there will in the future be such large and continued movements of population as have taken place in the past. As indicated previously the easily available lands of the world have been pretty well settled. For the white race the principal thinly occupied areas outside the tropics with possibilities for further settlement are (a) southern and particularly southwestern Siberia and northern Manchuria in Asia, (b) the Prairie Provinces of Canada in North America, (c) eastern Brazil, Uruguay, and the Pampa, Chaco, and Mesopotamian regions of Argentina in South America, and (d) eastern and southwestern Australia. For Orientals the possibilities for future settlement appear to be greatest in some of the East Indies, Malaya, and the southern Philippines. It is at present difficult to foresee what the future settlement possibilities are for such extensive tropical regions as the Amazon Valley and the Congo Basin.

SELECTED REFERENCES FOR CHAPTER XXVIII

Baker, O. E. Population, Food Supply, and American Agriculture. *Geog. Rev.*, Vol. 18, pp. 353–373, 1928.

Bowman, Isaiah (Editor). "Limits of Land Settlement: A Report on Present-day Possibilities." Council on Foreign Relations, New York, 1937.

Fairchild, Henry Pratt. "People." Henry Holt and Company, Inc., New York, 1939.

Hankins, Frank H. Pressure of Population as a Cause of War. *Ann. Amer. Acad. Pol. Soc. Sci.*, Vol. 198, pp. 101–108, 1938.

Pelzer, Karl J. Population and Land Utilization. Part 1 of "An Economic Survey of the Pacific Area." Institute of Pacific Relations, New York, 1941.

Population and Social Problems. *Intern. Labor Rev.*, Vol. 39, No. 3, March, 1939, pp. 291–318.

Thompson, Warren S., and P. K. Whelpton. Levels of Living and Population Pressure. *Ann. Amer. Acad. Pol. Soc. Sci.*, Vol. 198, pp. 93–100, 1938.

————. The Population of the Nation, in "Recent Social Trends in the United States." Report of the President's Research Commission on Social Trends, McGraw-Hill Book Company, Inc., New York, 1933.

Thornthwaite, C. Warren. "Internal Migration in the United States." Pp. 5–18, University of Pennsylvania Press, Philadelphia, 1934.

Zimmerman, E. W. "World Resources and Industries." Harper & Brothers, New York, 1933. Especially Chaps. IX and X.

Chapter XXIX. Settlements and Their Houses

725. By the term *settlement type*, as applied to any region, is meant the characteristic colonization or occupance unit. These units vary in size and complexity from the simple isolated one-family farmstead of the Iowa prairies on one hand, to the great urban metropolis such as New York or Chicago on the other. In either case, however, the farmstead or the metropolis, the settlement unit represents an organized colony of human beings together with the buildings in which they live or that they otherwise use and the paths and streets over which they travel.

It is unfortunately true that there does not exist at the present time sufficient reliable information to permit the writing of a satisfactory discussion of house and settlement types in terms of their world distributions and the principles involved in these distributions. Important as these geographic elements are, therefore, the following brief analysis of them is obliged to be more in the nature of comments on the characteristics of houses and settlements in a few particular regions. Any world classification into types, with accompanying maps showing distribution of these types, like those provided in this book for some other geographic elements such as climate, native vegetation, soils, and agriculture, is still impossible.

Houses

726. The House a Fundamental Geographic Element. The two most fundamental requirements of human beings are food and shelter, and much of the imprint left by peoples upon areas that they occupy results from activities associated with those two requirements. Every normal person is compelled by nature to spend a quarter to a third of the daily 24-hr. period in sleep. During this unconscious period man is an easy prey to his enemies, either animals or fellow men, who desire to attack him. Since they cannot escape sleep, all human beings are compelled to seek shelter, both from enemies and from the elements.

This sleep shelter, no matter how crude, is a critical focus in the life of any individual, since he is forced to return to it for periodic protection. The house, then, becomes a universal feature of regions permanently occupied by human beings and is one of the most fundamental elements of cultural geography.

As used here, the title "house" is meant to include not only the dwelling house, ranging from the humblest native tropical huts to the most elaborate city mansions, but all other human structures as well, where people congregate or where their goods are stored, such as schools, factories, warehouses, churches, and stores. In primitive societies the dwelling unit greatly predominates, but in more advanced

Fig. 366.—A representative rural house in subtropical Japan. Note the heavy thatched roof.

civilizations there is a much wider variety of buildings, such as storage structures for crops and food, shelters for domestic animals and machines, and numerous other types having industrial, commercial, transportational, pleasure, and religious functions.

727. DISTINGUISHING FEATURES OF HOUSES. In describing and classifying houses, one of the first problems that arises is the necessity of making a decision relative to what characteristics of houses are geographically significant, setting apart the buildings of one region from those of another. Certainly among the more important items employed in differentiating houses is the one of *building materials*— earth, stone, brick, steel, wood, etc. Likewise important are such items as *size, shape* or *form, colors, spacing,* and *function.* Sometimes it is one feature of a region's buildings that gives distinctiveness to the group; sometimes it is another. In Norway, for instance, the bright colors of the houses—blues, reds, and whites—are particularly striking,

especially so in that region where dark weather predominates. In northern Russia the carved gables, gaily painted, are a distinctive feature. The white stucco walls and red-tile roofs of the newer houses and the wooden bungalows representing an earlier period of building are both typical of southern California. Japan's houses are distinctive by reason of their close spacing, flimsy wooden construction, and heavy thatch or gray-tile roofs (Fig. 366). The Chinese house. made of adobe

Fig. 367.—A representative rural house in northern China, or Manchuria. (*Courtesy of Chinese Eastern Railway.*)

or brick, possesses individuality, in part, at least, because of its form, being characteristically built around a court (Fig. 367). In certain wealthier sections of our larger cities it is often the size and magnificence of the dwelling units that are distinctive, as is the case with those along Park Avenue and Riverside Drive in New York City and with the estates along the Hudson north of the same city. Obviously it is possible to have a great variety of house types resulting from different combinations of materials, size, color, shape, and functions.

728. HOUSE MATERIALS AS A BASIS FOR CLASSIFICATION. One of the simplest and most useful classifications of houses may be based upon the *kind of materials* used in construction, although of course such a classification would be far from complete and inclusive. In

primitive societies there is a strong tendency to use those materials readily at hand furnished by the natural earth, provided, of course,

Fig. 368.—A native house in the tropical rainforest of Ecuador. The living quarters are elevated above the ground in order to protect against floods and animals and to give better under-ventilation. (*Rau Art Studios.*)

they are suited to the prevailing climatic conditions. Noteworthy examples of this tendency are the snow huts, or *igloos,* of the American Eskimo; the *tents* and *yurts,* made of felted hair and wool from their flocks and herds, used by the nomadic peoples of dry interior and western Asia; the *thatched frame-and-wattle huts* of peoples in the tropical rainforest (Fig. 368); or the *adobe* dwellings of village peoples in dry lands.

729. *House Belts in Russia.* Brunhes, in his book "Human Geography," points out that in traveling from north to south in European Russia, where a succession of natural zones is crossed, one is struck by the regular succession of dwelling

Fig. 369.—A log house in Kentucky.

types. Thus in the tundra, where trees and cultivated crops are absent and where human life is nomadic, there are no fixed habitations, the summer dwellings of the natives being light tents made of reindeer skins, while in winter covered earthen pits serve as houses. To the south of the tundra is the wide belt of forest, coniferous and deciduous, and within that natural region the wooden house is the prevailing type. It might be added that the wooden dwelling is common to many other forested regions such as Sweden, Čechy (Bohemia), the Alps, eastern United States, and Japan. In its simplest form it is constructed of the straight trunks of trees, notched at the corners and laid one on top of the other. The log house of the American pioneer often was of this type (Fig. 369). In more advanced societies the logs are first sawed into boards, and these are used for sheathing a wooden skeleton or framework. For roofing material, shingles, bark, or thatch are common. Still farther south in Russia, where forest gives way to prairie, the wooden house becomes much less frequent, and sod and adobe dwellings roofed with thatch

Fig. 370.—A sod house on the Argentine Pampa. (*Photograph by H. G. Olds.*)

or pieces of turf are the prevailing type. Simple sod structures likewise housed the early settlers on the American prairies and were common to the Argentine Pampa as well (Fig. 370). Beyond the prairie belt in Russia, in Crimea and the Caucasus, where stony steppe prevails, houses of stone tend to replace the sod hut.

730. *Complexity of House Materials in Complex Civilizations.* In more advanced and complex societies, where transportation is better developed, there is nowhere near the same dependence upon local building materials as there is in more primitive and frontier civilizations. As a consequence, there is likely to be a greater variety of house types, even in the rural parts of regions having well-developed transportation systems. Buildings on an American farmstead, although predominantly of wood, are not infrequently constructed of brick or stone. It is in the city, however, where the danger of fire is greater, and where larger buildings are more common, requiring stronger and

more durable materials, that the greatest variety of house types prevails. In the downtown business sections there predominate closely spaced, relatively tall buildings of brick, stone, and cement supported by a steel framework. Typical of larger American cities is the many-storied skyscraper. Throughout the residential districts wooden houses still are common, although those of brick and stone are very numerous (Fig. 371). In European cities the wooden house occurs less frequently. In Japan, on the other hand, it is the prevailing type. One European writer has likened the Japanese dwelling to a wooden cage lightly placed upon the ground. It is never painted and consequently the color is that of weathered wood.

Fig. 371.—Good substantial residences in a middle-western town in the United States. One is brick and the other frame.

731. *Durability of Materials.* In those parts of the world where wood is the dominant construction material in cities, owing to the destructiveness of fires, very old buildings are rare. It is said that there are no really ancient buildings in all of Japan. In Europe, on the other hand, numerous stone and brick buildings have stood for centuries, and some for more than a millennium, preserving for this modern age some of the culture of ancient and medieval man. In Greece, Rome, and Egypt the evidences of ancient civilizations still persist in the form of magnificent stone ruins. "When the vigorous life which throbbed in such structures of stone ebbs or dies out completely, the ruins still enable one to imagine what they must have been originally." (P. Vidal de la Blache.) In Assyria and Chaldea on the other hand, where temples and palaces were built chiefly of less durable clay, their sites are now only mounds of earth.

732. *House Form and Shape.* Other than materials, the ground plan and shape of houses are basic elements differentiating the residences of one region from those of another. Previously mentioned is

the distinctive plan of the Chinese house built around a court. In the United States, as one travels the length and breadth of the country, a little pointed observation reveals basic regional contrasts in house form. By means of a 1,650-mile car traverse from Madison, Wis., to Beaumont in southeastern Texas, in which 3,464 rural houses were observed, 16 fundamentally different types of houses were distinguished.[1] Most numerous type and common to both the northern and southern sections of the country was the bungalow. In the North other than the bungalow, two-story , , and  houses were the most common types. Smaller one-story rectangular cabins and cottages were characteristic of the South (Fig. 372a,b,c). House materials were of practically no value in differentiating the structures, since 94 per cent of the total were of wood and 91 per cent of sawed lumber. Unpainted houses, chiefly in the South, comprised nearly 40 per cent of the total number, and 38 per cent were painted white.

(a)

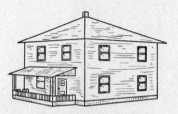

(b)

(c)

FIG. 372.—(a) A rural house type characteristic of the South. (b) and (c) Rural house types common in the North. (*Courtesy of Robert Finley and E. M. Scott.*)

To even a layman with any appreciation of architectural qualities the contrast between many of the fine old farmhouses of New England, New York, and Pennsylvania on the one hand, and the unlovely rural houses of the Middle West, built at a later period, is striking. One of the most attractive features of travel in rural New York and New England is the numerous fine old homes in the villages and on the farms. Their excellent proportions, simple lines, and straightforward sturdy appearance brand them as being architecturally good. By contrast, farm and village houses throughout the Middle West are notoriously lacking in these same qualities. Seemingly the farther back from the Atlantic Seaboard one travels the fewer farmhouses of architectural merit there are. In New

[1] Finley, Robert, and Scott, E. M. A Great Lakes-to-Gulf Profile of Dispersed Dwelling Types. *Geog. Rev.*, Vol. 30, pp. 412–419, July, 1940.

York they are numerous; in Michigan there are many fewer, and in Wisconsin they are a rarity. What is probably still more strange is that in New England, where they had good models in the Colonial farmhouses right at hand, their modern creations show a definite deterioration in quality. It is not clear why the offspring of the Colonial farmer-carpenters, whether at home or in the Middle West, seemed to lose their eye for good house form.

Settlements

733. Two Primary Types of Settlements. Although geographers are concerned with the representative house types in different parts of the world, they are even more interested in the characteristic groupings of houses, together with their inhabitants and creators, into occupance units or settlements. Based upon form

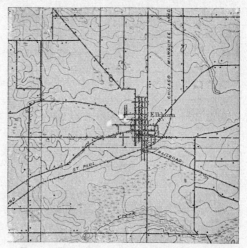

Fig. 373.—Illustrating agglomerated and dispersed settlements. A market town in Wisconsin surrounded by isolated farmsteads, the latter indicated by black dots. (*Elkhorn sheet. Scale about ½ in. = 1 mile.*)

and function, two great subdivisions of settlements are here recognized: (*a*) the *isolated*, or *dispersed*, *type* in which the single residence unit is the distinctive nucleus, as it is, for instance, on an American farmstead; and (*b*) the *agglomerated type* in which there is a collection of several or many residences, together with other types of buildings (Fig. 373). Agglomerated settlements are designated by various names according to their size and the complexity of their functions, *i.e.*, hamlets, villages, towns, and cities. In all of them, however, the two most conspicuous features are always the *house* and the *street*.

Dispersed Settlements

734. Character and Advantages of Dispersed Settlements. For the most part, dispersed settlement, where the one-family residence stands isolated and apart from others, is characteristic of agricultural areas. In some parts of the world hunters, trappers, fishers, and miners may live in open-country dwellings, and, in the United States at least, there is a sprinkling of nonfarm residences scattered throughout the rural areas. Nevertheless, for the world as a whole, the farmer is by far the most numerous open-country dweller. To such a degree is this true that the dispersed settlement unit is often taken to be synonymous with the farmstead.

The outstanding characteristic of dispersed settlement is the minute size of the settlement unit, viz., the family, and the isolation and privacy in which it exists. Such isolated living tends to separate men psychologically as well as economically. Admittedly there are both advantages and disadvantages to this system of open-country living, the advantages being chiefly economic and the disadvantages social. Economically the isolated farmstead, located on a compact and unified farm, has the advantage of keeping the farm family at its place of work and near the fields and animals that it cultivates and rears. There is not required the time-consuming movement between home and fields that is necessary when the farmer is a village dweller, with his scattered fields located at some distance from the residence. Freed from the restrictions associated with living in a village with other farmers and working the surrounding fields along lines developed for the village as a whole, the isolated farmer is much more independent as far as his methods of farm management are concerned. He is less obliged to conform to any pattern as set by others, and therefore the energetic, resourceful farmer is able to forge ahead of his less ambitious neighbors. Freer reign is given to individual initiative and enterprise so that there is less of a dead level in the farming population, and stagnation is less likely.

Many would argue that the offsetting social disadvantages of open-country dwelling more than compensate for these economic advantages. They consider that whatever economic progress has been attained by the change from the farm village to the system of individual occupation has been at a fearful cost in terms of social values. The sense of neighborly interdependence and the solidarity and strength fostered by the village communal agriculture are greatly weakened when farm families live isolated and alone. The close, warm, communal life of the farm village, the feeling of being an integral part of the life of many men, is lacking. Moreover, the only neighbors of an American farmer are other farmers and they are at some distance, and this prevalence of men of his own vocation tends to weaken his sense of economic and social interdependence. The division of labor between different classes in a farm village serves as a constant reminder to its residents of neighborhood interdependence. An additional social handicap in open-country living is that the farmer labors much of the time alone except perhaps for the company of his team of horses or a dog.

It is a lonesome labor unrelieved during long hours by association with his fellow men. Much of the farm work in rural villages, on the other hand, is done in groups or gangs, and this fellowship in labor introduces an element of the play spirit into even the most arduous work and relieves it of its boring qualities. This lightening of the load when men work together is experienced on an American farm chiefly on such occasions as silo filling and at threshing time.

735. ORIGIN AND DISTRIBUTION. The historical record is not entirely clear as to the origin of dispersed settlement, but evidence

FIG. 374.—Dispersed rural settlement in a Swiss valley. (*Courtesy of U. S. Department of Agriculture.*)

seems to indicate that the rural village was by far the most common type of agricultural settlement prior to the enclosure of English open fields. Certainly before that event the prevailing custom was for farmers to live in rural villages. The movement for enclosures and the associated disintegration of the English farm village falls into two periods, 1485–1560 and 1760–1820. It grew out of a need for a more efficient and economical system of cultivation than was possible under the village type of agricultural settlement with its characteristic pattern of scattered fields with much land held in common. These same needs have caused the dispersed type of settlement to spread to other parts of the world as well.

At the present time the open-country type of rural settlement, with the individual farmstead set down in the midst of its fields, is almost universally characteristic of rural United States and of the agricultural sections of Canada. In the United States almost the only clear-cut example of the agglomerated farm village type of rural settlement is to be found in the Mormon regions of Utah.

Outside Anglo-America dispersed rural settlement appears to be strongly characteristic of Australia and New Zealand, of the Scandinavian countries, the small Baltic States, and the British Isles in Europe, and of Argentina and Uruguay in South America. Smaller regions of dispersion or regions where that form of rural settlement is less dominant are the highland regions of Mexico, Costa Rica, western Panama, the Orinoco Lowlands in Venezuela and Colombia, the Lake Maracaibo Lowland in Venezuela, southern Portugal, western France, the highland areas of central Europe, northern Japan, northern Manchuria, Szechwan province in China, and scattered areas in South Africa and in the East African Highlands.

736. REASONS FOR DISPERSED SETTLEMENT. Numerous attempts have been made to find a logical explanation for the world distribution pattern of dispersed settlements described in the preceding paragraph, but without a great deal of success. The reasons for this type of settlement appear to be different in different regions. In more recently settled areas such as the United States, Canada, Australia, and Argentina, the abundance of cheap land, resulting in large farms, has probably been the principal factor fostering separate farmsteads. Where the unit of cultivation is several score, or even several hundred acres, all in one single holding, village type of settlement would have resulted in much loss of time and energy going back and forth between residence and fields. Nevertheless, the Russian colonists in the spring wheat belt of Siberia characteristically live in villages, this tendency to live together even in a region of new and abundant land perhaps reflecting the dominance of agglomerated settlement in European Russia.

737. *Natural Factors.* There appears in certain parts of the world to be some relationship between natural factors, particularly surface configuration, and settlement type. A number of European writers have observed that dispersion appears to increase in direct proportion to the ruggedness of the land surface. In other words, isolated farmsteads are more characteristic of hilly land, and compact rural villages reach their maximum development on plains. In Japan this is strikingly true. The relationship has been noted likewise for Switzerland, Germany, southwestern Poland, Austria, Hungary, and Slovakia. In southern Europe, the Dinaric Alps and the Carpathians stand out as marked centers of open-country dwelling. The explanation, in part, may lie in the physical character of such locations, the whole

aspect of which leads to a diffusion of resources—arable land, water, and natural sites with pleasant exposures. Vidal de la Blache writes: "The scattered manner of grouping suits localities where, as a result of the dissection of relief, soil, and hydrography, the arable land is itself divided up. The clustered village is indigenous, on the other hand, in districts where the arable area is continuous, admitting of uniform and extensive exploitation."[1] In regions of dissection and abundant slope, the scattered fragments of cultivable land are often too small to support more than a few isolated farmsteads. The inhabitants are compelled to utilize other resources, such as pastures and woodland, which in turn require larger landholdings. It should be pointed out, however, that the foregoing generalization concerning type of rural settlement and associated relief does not have universal application, for there are numerous hilly regions of the world where the farm village is characteristic. In regions where both types are common, however, there is often a tendency for the isolated farmstead to be more characteristic of the hilly portions.

Certain other natural factors are believed to act in a manner similar to relief in restricting the amount of contiguous arable land and thereby favoring dispersed settlement. Scarcity of water, marshes, forests, stony moraines, and poor soils are some of these adverse elements. In Poland, for example, areas of poor soil, marshes, and dunes are considered to be sites of ancient open-country living. In Shropshire, England, villages prevail except in the heavily wooded country without fertile alluvium. In Germany and Finland there appears to be some correlation between areas of poor soil and dispersion. Dispersion is said to be possible in Flanders because of the abundant ground water, whereas in parts of Russia and southern Belgium the restricted number of places where water is available handicaps widespread open-country living.

738. *Cultural Factors.* Type of economy and historical changes have also been instrumental in affecting the present pattern of world settlement types. In Europe dispersed dwellings are common in regions where pastoralism and transhumance are important. The moorlands of Wales and Yorkshire, used chiefly for grazing, are islands of dispersions within larger regions of village dominance. In Switzerland, Austria, and Norway the highlands are seasonally occupied by herders who live in dispersed chalets, Almhütte, or saeter huts. The pastoral Lapps appear to live in dispersed fashion except in winter, when they gather in hamlets or take lodging with some peasant.

---

[1] Vidal de la Blache, P. "Principles of Human Geography." P. 316, Henry Holt and Company, Inc., New York, 1926.

During those periods when farmers had need of defense against hostile neighbors, there was good reason for their congregating in villages, where better protection of life and property could be made. As defense needs became less significant, open-country isolated living became more prevalent. The decline in feudalism with the associated freeing of the serfs and the change from communal to private land tenure likewise favored the decline of the farm village and an associated increase in the number of separate farmsteads. The Industrial Revolution, improved transportation, and the rise of commercial agriculture had much the same effects. Recent agrarian movements in Poland, Czechoslovakia, Hungary, and other countries, where estates have been dissolved and the land divided among the peasants, has led to further dispersion. The rapid increase in population in Europe since the Industrial Revolution has been a factor leading to colonization of available agricultural land by single families. Thus on the Danube Plains, which has been one of Europe's most exclusive regions of farm villages, there is an increased number of isolated farmsteads on the Pustza lands between the older settlements. At first this took the form of summer occupance of the isolated dwellings in the midst of the fields, but with a return to the villages in winter. Recently there has been a growing tendency to continue residence away from the villages in winter as well as in summer, so that genuine dispersion is developing.

In summary, it may be repeated that no very valid generalizations having world-wide significance can be made explaining the present distribution of open-country dwelling over the earth. Most of the explanations given in the preceding paragraphs have chiefly local significance. At the present time the drift appears to be away from the farm-village type of settlement and toward open-country living. Some of the reasons for this trend have been touched upon in preceding paragraphs. With this growth of open-country living there are bound to arise serious social problems.

739. *American Farmsteads.* An American farmstead characteristically is composed of the residence, together with a collection of barns and sheds for housing livestock and for storing crops and machinery, and of their associated barnyard grounds (Figs. 375, 376). More often than not a fence encloses the farmstead, separating it from the adjacent fields. This is the heart of the farm; it is the place of concentration for animals as well as for human beings. The grounds of the farmstead may contain a number of fenced-off pens or yards including a home garden and orchard, hog yards, cattle yards, and the like. Crops for commercial use are usually not produced on the farmstead. In a study made of several hundred farmsteads in southwestern

Wisconsin, 65 per cent of them were between 1 and 3 acres in size. They were spaced from 0.4 to 0.6 of a mile apart. The number of buildings of all kinds on the farmstead was usually between 6 and 12. Conspicuous were the large barns for storing hay and housing livestock. Fourteen per cent of the farmsteads had more than one large barn. Thirty-seven per cent of the barns covered 12,000 to 20,000 sq. ft.; 63 per cent covered over 20,000 sq. ft. Sixty-five per cent had one or more corn cribs; 61 per cent had at least one silo, $8\frac{1}{2}$ per cent had two; 40 per cent had windmills.

Fig. 375.—Aerial view of an American farmstead in Illinois. (*United Photo Shop.*)

It is obvious that a farmstead on a Wisconsin dairy farm is a relatively pretentious affair. In the different agricultural regions of the country it varies markedly in appearance as its functions change. Thus a Kansas wheat farm with relatively few animal units has a much less imposing layout of farm buildings, and the truck farm of Maryland has still less. In the Piney Woods of east Texas the characteristic unpretentious farmstead is composed of an unpainted four- or five-room house and a small single-pen hay barn made of poles with attached shelter sheds for a few livestock. A poultry house and a small smoke house complete the layout of farm buildings. The grounds of the Piney Woods farmstead are chiefly a cowpen and a garden.

It needs to be emphasized that the farmstead is not, however, just an agglomeration of buildings and yards; it is, rather, the focus or nucleus of a "culture structure with functional significance," a structure composed of human beings, the buildings that they occupy and use, the fields that they cultivate, and the livestock that they raise. Unlike the medieval manor, the American farmstead is not a self-sufficient unit, for many of the farm family's needs are supplied from the shops of near-by market towns and paid for with cash received from

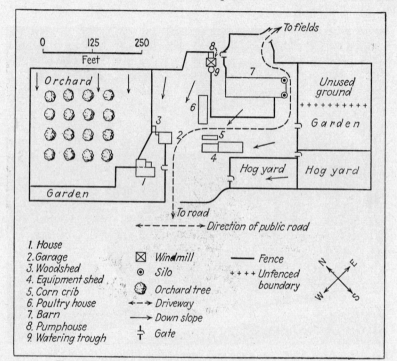

Fig. 376.—Plat of the farmstead on a Wisconsin dairy farm.

the sale of vegetable or animal products raised on the farm. The isolated farmstead is, nevertheless, the individual cell out of which America's rural-settlement structure is composed. It is such a tiny focus, however, that it is incapable of exerting an important centralizing influence as does the rural village, for instance.

AGGLOMERATED OR COMPACT SETTLEMENTS

740. As stated earlier, houses and streets in various combinations of number and pattern comprise the essential elements of all types of compact or collective settlements, from the rural village to the largest

metropolitan center. As soon as houses become grouped the necessity is immediately created for intercommunication between them, so that more or less clearly defined streets become necessary, and the spaces between the buildings become relatively regular.

Not only is the street system within the settlement a conspicuous and essential element, but beyond the boundaries of the town proper its centripetal influence is clearly marked by the road pattern. Each agglomerated settlement becomes a focus of transport lines, for one of the prime functions of towns and cities is their market services. In fact, highways (roads, canals, rivers, railroads, steamship and air lines) together with the things that flow over them—human beings as well as goods—have very likely created a majority of the towns and cities now in existence.

741. Two Classes of Compact Settlements. Two principal classes of compact settlements are here recognized: (a) those which are essentially rural in aspect and function and (b) those the functions of which are largely nonagricultural or urban. In the first group are *rural villages*, the residents of which are chiefly tillers of the soil. Such a settlement primarily is concerned with the production of agricultural goods. Within the second, or urban, group are *towns* and *cities*, the inhabitants of which "have no immediate interest in the production of the materials for their food or clothing but are engaged in transporting, manufacturing, buying, and selling these materials or in educating the people or in managing the affairs of the state or in merely 'living in town'" (Aurousseau). As a usual thing also, urban settlements are more closely built up, so that there is a denser population per unit area than in the rural villages.

THE RURAL VILLAGE

742. Nature and Development. In the rural village type of settlement, which is the commonest form over a large part of the earth's surface, farmsteads, instead of being isolated as they are in the United States, are grouped together into relatively compact communities. In such villages the predominant, sometimes almost exclusive, group is farmers. To be sure there may be some artisans, tradesmen, and professional men, but usually they are greatly in the minority. The rural village therefore is principally a place of residence and not primarily a business center. It is composed chiefly of farm dwellings and their associated outbuildings.

Community living probably is as ancient as the human race and represents an instinctive drawing together of peoples for cooperative efforts in defense, work, or some other activity. Some sort of locality groups existed even among nonagricultural tribes. Genuine village life arose, however, with the beginnings of agriculture, and there is abundant evidence that men have lived in village groups in Europe and Asia since early Neolithic times. Among primitive agricultural peoples the village was not fixed at one site, for agriculture was often of the shifting type, with moves sometimes as frequent as every two or three years. In these shifting communities the women did most of the work in the fields, with the use of only hand implements and without the aid of domestic animals. Commonly the primitive village was composed of a group of kinsmen.

At a later stage, when agriculture became more permanent, the village became fixed in its location. A definite area of land with fixed boundaries was recognized as belonging to the village. Domesticated animals were employed in conjunction with the plow and the cart, which resulted in men instead of women doing the larger part of the work. Irrigation, manuring, and the feeding of livestock became common practices. Control of the land was at first vested in the village group, or, as in the manorial villages of England, in the lord of the manor. Personal ownership of land was a matter of gradual evolution. The arable land was cultivated by individuals while the pasture, forest, and waste land was held in common by the village and was used in common.

In modern agricultural villages the land is permanently owned by families or individuals, and common land is rare. The individual farms, however, are still composed of numerous small unfenced parcels scattered in various directions and at various distances around the village. Unlike an American farm, which is usually composed of a contiguous block of land, the farm of a villager in Europe or Asia is composed of several small, unfenced, noncontiguous plots. The latter is known as the *open-field system* of agriculture. It is usually associated with the village type of rural settlement.

743. *The Latifundia Type of Rural Village* (*Hacienda, Plantation, Finca, Estate*). Throughout certain parts of the world there is a type of compact rural settlement that differs in certain fundamentals from the typical farm village. This type of clustered settlement, designated here as *latifundian*, is associated with extensive agricultural estates, often of thousands of acres, where large numbers of hired laborers are necessary to carry on the ordinary work of the estate (Fig. 377). The tea and rubber plantations of the British and Dutch in various parts of tropical southeastern Asia (Malaya, Ceylon, British India, Java, Sumatra, and others) and the haciendas of Latin America are of this type. In the United States the larger sugar-cane plantations of

Louisiana have a village type of settlement. On such extensive farms there is usually a central core area that contains the more pretentious homes of the owner and his white overseers, together with the more numerous and modest huts or cabins of the native laborers.[1] In addition there may be a commissary or store and perhaps a school, hospital, and church. Such a settlement is not composed of a group of independent

Fig. 377.—A plantation type of village on the coastal desert of Peru. (*From G. R. Johnson, Peru from the Air, The American Geographical Society of New York.*)

men, owning and cultivating their own homes and land, as is true of the modern agricultural village. The plantation is like a factory, being organized to produce commercially a particular product or crop. As a result the plantation settlement is composed of buildings owned by the estate and rented to the laborers. The latter usually are not closely attached to the land so that they may not stay long at one place. Such a settlement therefore usually lacks the permanency and close social bonds characteristic of the genuine agricultural village. The latter has its life and institutions developed by the people in the village; in the plantation settlement life is closely regulated by the

---

[1] Some plantations are operated by sharecroppers or tenants rather than by hired laborers, and under such an organization no central community is required.

estate owner. The following description is of a coffee plantation community in the state of São Paulo, Brazil:

"A characteristic group of estate buildings is associated with the cultivation of coffee. The most important building is the manager's dwelling, surrounded, at least in the older part of the state, by well-kept lawns and shrubs. Near by are the stables for the estate animals, the sheds for storage, and the extensive tile or concrete platforms on which the crop is spread to dry in the sun. And also near by are the rows of laborers' cottages which betray in their untidy and cheerless appearance the temporary nature of the relationship between owner and tenants. This group of buildings constitutes the *fazenda* and amounts to a rural hamlet in an area of agglomerated population."[1]

744. DISTRIBUTION OF THE VILLAGE TYPE OF RURAL SETTLEMENT. The farm village is the characteristic type of rural settlement throughout most of Latin America, Africa, and Asia. Certain exceptions to this generalization have already been pointed out in the discussion on dispersed farmsteads (735). Europe shows a complicated intermingling of the dispersed and agglomerated types, with Soviet Russia being the largest contiguous area where the village type strongly prevails. In somewhat less dominant form it is also characteristic of Mediterranean, central, and northwestern Europe, except in the regions mentioned in Art. 735. Aboriginal settlements in the Arctic plains of North America are chiefly agglomerated.

745. *The Agricultural Village of Colonial New England.* Although in the United States at the present time the farm village is a rare exception within the standard pattern of isolated farmsteads, this situation was not true during the early history of the country. For the first hundred years and more of its history rural New England was a land of village-dwelling farmers (Fig. 378). In part this compact type of rural settlement had its origins in the need for protection against the Indian menace. In part it reflects the nature of New England's colonization, which was by organized communities and not by individuals. Often the colonizing group had previously existed in England as a church congregation or neighborhood, so that the colonists arrived in their new home motivated by common aims and ambitions and relatively homogeneous in political and social character. Moreover, it was the policy of the New England colonizing companies to make grants of land to groups rather than to individuals. Land was not sold, but instead was awarded to responsible groups desirous of establishing a home in the wilderness. Once the community was established, Puritan ideals of religion and education tended to hold

---

[1] James, Preston E. The Coffee Lands of Southeastern Brazil. *Geog. Rev.*, Vol. 22, pp. 225–244 (236), 1932.

it together. The school and the meetinghouse were the standard focal centers of the New England farm village.

The New England town or township was a grant of land from 4 to 10 square miles in extent. Usually somewhere near the geographical center of the town the village was established, with a *common* or *green* as its nucleus. Fronting upon the common and upon the main street were the church, school, and burying ground, together with the home lots of the original settlers. The home lots contained not only the farmhouse but in addition barns and other outbuildings, a garden, and enclosures for feeding livestock and raising corn. The compactness

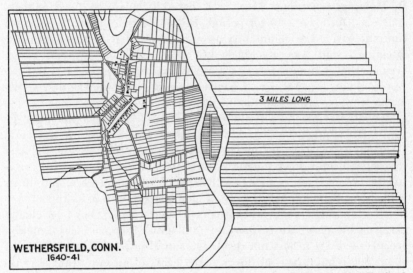

3 MILES LONG

WETHERSFIELD, CONN.
1640-41

FIG. 378.—Plat showing home lots and fields of an early rural village in New England.

of the village depended to a large degree upon the size of the home lots. Usually they varied between 1 and 5 acres in extent.

The farm of each villager was composed of several small tracts of land lying in different quarters of the town. The arable lands and mowing lands were divided into large fields of several acres, which were subsequently partitioned into strips and distributed to the settlers by lot. As a usual thing the strips were of much the same size and shape so that an orderly and regular arrangement was very conspicuous. In addition to the home lots and planting fields that were owned individually, there were also the common lands possessed and used by all the original settlers. Pasture and woodland at first were held entirely in common. And although the small planting lots were privately owned they were subject to town regulation relative to choice of crops, and they became common land for pasture after the harvest. Farms varied considerably in size and composition, but on the whole they were not large. In Hartford, Conn., the first distribution of land resulted in holdings of 27 acres, in New Haven, 44 acres. In Groton, Mass., each settler held on the average 59 acres of planting land separated into two or three parcels, and 19½ acres of meadow divided into five parcels.

Although Puritan New England was the arch stronghold of the community type of rural settlement in Colonial America, it was not unknown in other sections. For the first decade or two in Virginia stockaded communities were almost the exclusive form of settlement. In Georgia experimentation with carefully planned farm villages continued for even a longer period. In the course of a relatively short time, however, the community type of settlement in the South disintegrated and was absorbed into the plantation system, which became the dominant form of agricultural organization. Beyond the Appalachians in what is now Kentucky and Tennessee the first settlements were by groups occupying stockaded posts called *stations*.

746. THE MODERN AMERICAN VILLAGE NOT RURAL. In the United States the counterpart of the European and Asiatic agricultural village of a few score or hundred farm residences can scarcely be said to exist. Since most of America's rural population is in isolated farmsteads, even a small compact settlement of a few hundred inhabitants is likely to be composed largely of shopkeepers, artisans, and professional men, with very few farmers among them. They are chiefly places of business. Most American "villages," then, as far as function is concerned, are urban, not rural. Thus in Montfort, Wis., a village of about 600 inhabitants set down in the heart of an important agricultural area in southwestern Wisconsin, more than one-half of the population is dependent upon income from retail merchandising. Most of the others are supported by the professions, by the railway, and by other types of transportational and communicational services. Hardly a score of the 125 families may be classified as retired farmers, and certainly less than half a dozen are active farmers.[1] Such a community is fundamentally a trading center for the farmsteads of the surrounding countryside. Even an American crossroads hamlet of only a score of dwellings is largely made up of nonfarm families, although it is not unusual for such a settlement to have a few farmsteads. The hamlet, therefore, is relatively more rural than the somewhat larger village.

747. *Some Examples of Rural Villages in the United States and Canada.* The most perfect community type of rural white settlement

[1] Finch, V. C. Montfort, A Study in Landscape Types in Southwestern Wisconsin. Geog. Soc. Chicago, *Bull.* 9, pp. 15–44, 1933.

in Anglo-America is the Mormon farm villages in Utah.[1] Most of the farmers of Utah do not live on their farms, but within villages from which they commute to one or several fields outside the village. This community form of living resulted from a planned mode of agricultural settlement established by the Mormon Church during the middle decades of the last century. It was admirably suited for defense against the Indians and for the social and religious contacts that the church desired. The farm villages are laid out in rectangular pattern, most of them having a central square on which is located the church or tabernacle. In a representative village such as Escalante (1,000+ population), the usual 5-acre blocks are divided into four home lots of $1\frac{1}{4}$ acres each on which are located the farm home, together with barns, corrals, pens, and sheds. Farms are usually small, their average size in the Wasatch Oasis being only 37 acres. The average distance from the farmsteads to the scattered parcels of land composing the farms is 2.3 miles. It is significant to note that in the newly developed irrigated areas in Utah the isolated farmstead is more common than the farm village, and even in the longer settled areas dispersion is the newer mode of settlement.

At Amana in eastern Iowa is a group of seven farm villages housing nearly 1,500 persons who comprise the Amana settlements.[2] Like the Mormon villages, these of Iowa are the product of a planned mode of settlement by a religious sect. Each village has its own fields, supervised by a farm manager who allocates the labor for the village and decides on the crops to be grown in given fields. Community barns, sheds, and silos serve to store crops and farm machinery and to house livestock.

Somewhat intermediate between genuine dispersion and agglomeration is a type of rural settlement associated with long-lot farms. Under this arrangement, because of the narrowness of the farms, the closely spaced farmsteads along a single street or highway give the appearance of a loose village organization. French settlement in the Lake St. John Lowland in Canada[3] and in the Mississippi Delta is prevailingly of this type. In the Lake St. John Lowland farm lots are $\frac{1}{6}$ mile wide and 1 mile long with the narrow side facing the high-

[1] Harris, Chauncey D. Salt Lake City: A Regional Capital. Ph.D. Dissertation, University of Chicago, 1940, pp. 42, 117–121; Lowry Nelson. The Mormon Village: A Study on Social Origins. *Proc. Utah Acad. Sci.*, Vol. 7, pp. 11–37, 1930.

[2] Davis, Darrell H. Amana: A Study of Occupance. *Econ. Geog.*, Vol. 12, pp. 217–230, July, 1936.

[3] Glendenning, Robert M. The Distribution of Population in the Lake St. John Lowland, Quebec. *Geog. Rev.*, Vol. 24, pp. 232–237, 1934.

way. In certain parts of New England likewise, farmsteads are so close together along highways as to give the appearance of community settlement.[1]

748. *Rural Villages of the Far East.* The compact farm village is the basic unit of settlement in eastern and southeastern Asia, where nearly one-half of the earth's population is concentrated. Thus in China, where at least 80 per cent of the 450,000,000 people are dependent upon the land, 88 per cent live in settlements having fewer than 10,000 residents, while the most fundamental unit is the farm village of 250 to 2,500 people (Fig. 379). In Japan, where nearly 50 per cent

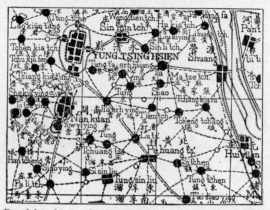

FIG. 379.—Rural hamlets and villages (black dots), together with market towns, on the North China Plain. (*From Carte de la Chine, Sheet 202, 1926 edition. Scale about* 1 *in.* = 2½ *miles.*)

of the 73,000,000 inhabitants are dependent upon agriculture, over 44 per cent of the total reside in the 9,600 rural settlements having fewer than 5,000 citizens. Nearly 20 per cent more live in villages or towns having between 5,000 and 10,000 inhabitants, and these are predominantly rural as well.

The basis of Chinese civilization is the village community (Fig. 380). Many of these villages are family villages, being composed of families all bearing the same surname and tracing their descent from a single ancestor. The units of the village are not individuals but families. Each member lives and works not for himself but for the family to which he belongs. Each family owns its own lands, possesses certain rights in the common land, and shares rights and responsibilities connected with the upkeep of the ancestral temple and the burial

[1] Scofield, Edna. The Origin of Settlement Patterns in Rural New England. *Geog. Rev.,* Vol. 28, pp. 652–663, 1928.

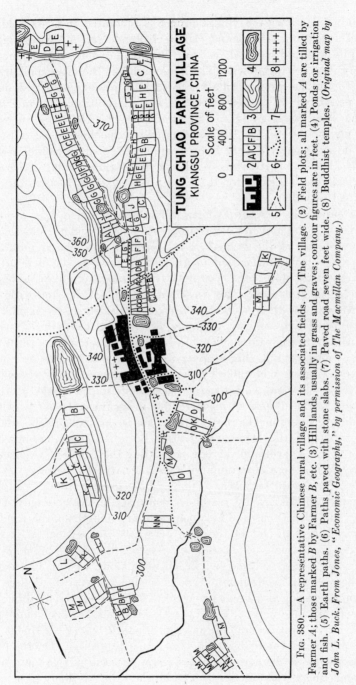

Fig. 380.—A representative Chinese rural village and its associated fields. (1) The village. (2) Field plots; all marked A are tilled by Farmer A; those marked B by Farmer B, etc. (3) Hill lands, usually in grass and graves; contour figures are in feet. (4) Ponds for irrigation and fish. (5) Earth paths. (6) Paths paved with stone slabs. (7) Paved road seven feet wide. (8) Buddhist temples. (Original map by John L. Buck. From Jones, "Economic Geography," by permission of The Macmillan Company.)

ground. Sometimes the village proper is separated from its fields by a wall as a protection against bands of plunderers. A Chinese village is a physical and cultural feature. Throughout 500 years of modern history it has changed little. The houses are like those occupied by the ancestors of the present villagers half a millennium ago. The descendants are doing what their ancestors did, cultivating the same fields in the same way, going to the same markets, following the same customs and habits. The Chinese farm village has few shops, and those that do exist carry a very limited supply of goods. Trading is done chiefly at the market towns. In the smaller farming villages there are practically no artisans, for the farmer is blacksmith, carpenter, and architect as well.

In Japan the ubiquitous farm village is striking in two respects: first, it is a social unit to a degree unknown in the Occident, and, second, the well-being of the villager is not primarily expressed in money. Tiny shops, each specialized in a single class of goods such as fish, tobacco, cakes, cloth, etc., occupy the front rooms of a few residences. These goods cost money, but they are bought not so often with cash as with rice. In other words the village still exists to a considerable degree in the rice-money economy of the fourteenth to sixteenth centuries. An almost unbelievable frugality characterizes the living of the villagers, but this keeping alive on the very cheese rind of existence is made endurable by the close communal life of the village unit. They play and work together so that life in the village is attractive and warm in spite of its incredible meagerness. It is this willing frugality of living on the part of Japan's large agricultural population that is one of the country's greatest bulwarks, keeping industrial wages at a low level and thereby permitting the Japanese exporter to compete with those of nations with greater natural resources.

749. VILLAGE PATTERNS.   Villages differ greatly from one another in shape and pattern by reason of contrasts in the arrangement of streets and their houses. These contrasts are sometimes the result of the physical character of the land on which the settlement is built (its site), but equally often they are associated with historical causes. For example, a river levee or a beach ridge along a coast may induce an elongated, or "shoestring," type of settlement with the houses laid out on either side of a single principal road or street which follows the crest of the ridge (Fig. 381). This type of village is very common in Japan on the wet inundated lowlands where floods are frequent and consequently elevated dry sites offer some protection. On the other hand, when a settlement originates at the crossing of two main highways meeting at right angles on a plain, the village is likely to be more

compact in form with its streets laid out in rectangular pattern conforming to that of the main highways. In hilly regions of uneven surface configuration, winding roads following stream divides or valley bottoms may induce very irregular and complicated street arrangements. Sometimes it happens that the original houses of a settlement were built before any road pattern developed, each house occupying what seemed to the owner a favorable site. Later, when a street system emerged, it was of necessity irregular and almost without plan. In South China, where animal-drawn vehicles are absent, village streets

Fig. 381.—A shoestring village along a coastal highway in Japan.

are narrow, crooked lanes. In North China, on the other hand, where animal-drawn carts are common, streets are fairly wide and straight and have a rectangular pattern (Figs. 332, 349, 373, 383, 384).

THE MARKET TOWN

750. DEFINITION. The market town is the smallest settlement unit in which nonagricultural or urban interests (commercial, manufactural, political, etc.) predominate. Usually the town acts in the capacity of a trading center for the surrounding rural-settlement units, composed either of isolated farmsteads or of agricultural villages. It is nearly impossible to define the market town in terms of size. In the United States, where isolated farmsteads are almost the exclusive rural-settlement type, even the so-called village of only a few hundred residents is actually a market town, with urban functions (Fig. 382). In those parts of the world, however, where farmers live in compact settlements (rural villages) and not on isolated farmsteads, the market town is usually an urban community of several thousand inhabitants.

751. FUNCTIONAL AREAS IN THE MARKET TOWN. In the agricultural village composition is relatively uniform throughout, the

settlement being composed of farm residences and associated shelter and storage sheds. Usually no "business section" exists, although there are often scattered shops. In the market town, on the other hand, where urban functions usually predominate, there are almost certain to develop distinct and specialized *functional areas*. The two that stand out prominently in almost any market town are (*a*) the commercial core, or business district; and (*b*) the residential

Fig. 382.—Aerial view of a small Illinois market town, with isolated farmsteads in the background. (*United Photo Shop*.)

portion (Fig. 383). It is in the former, where shops and stores predominate, that urban functions are concentrated. The commercial core may be distinguished from the residential area, not only by the *kind* of buildings but also by their *spacing* (Fig. 384). In the former the structures often abut against one another, while the residences are likely to be farther apart (Fig. 371). Other functions, such as manufacturing, government, education, and recreation, may be represented in the market town, but usually they are not segregated into distinct areas of conspicuous size.

Like the rural village from which most of them have grown, and for similar reasons, the town may be cast in a variety of shapes and

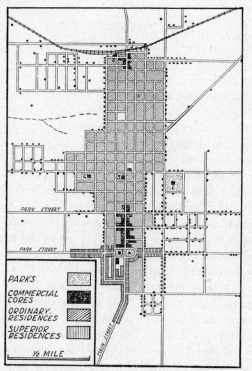

FIG. 383.—Arrangement of functional areas within a market town; Princeton, Ill. The town has grown northward toward the railroad, where a secondary business core has developed. (*Map by Stanley S. Dodge.*)

FIG. 384.—Business core of an American market town. Prairie du Chien, Wis.

patterns, both externally and internally. One of the commonest arrangements is that in which the commercial core lies somewhere near the geographical center of the town with residential areas surrounding it on all sides. Thus while the rural village has no distinct nucleus or center, this becomes a characteristic feature of cities and towns (Fig. 382).

THE CITY

752. CITIES THE PRINCIPAL FOCUSES OF MATERIAL CULTURE. The city represents the most complete modification of a portion of the earth's surface that man, through his constructive and destructive contacts with that surface, has been able to make. There human beings are crowded together in greatest numbers and density, and, partly as a result of this concentration and intensive occupying of the surface, man has here brought together his mightiest assemblage of material-culture features. So complete is the culture cover that it tends to mask, and at the same time greatly modify or possibly obliterate, the original natural features of the site. Even beyond the margins of the city proper, the settlement makes itself felt in an intricate network of communications, for these routes represent the necessary lines of contact with the countryside that it serves and that supports it. Through these channels pass tremendous quantities of food and raw material to be consumed or otherwise used by the city organization, and it is along these same routes that the city's products feed back to the surrounding countryside. "The city creates the road; the road in its turn creates the city, or recreates it. . . ."

753. FUNCTIONS OF CITIES. Numerous urban communities, the most complex of social organizations within a region, are usually indicative of an advanced stage of material civilization—a stage that many parts of the world have not yet reached. They are principally the products of commerce and industry, and where these functions have not flowered, cities are not numerous. Although it is true that large urban centers have existed from the very beginnings of great civilizations, it is more especially with the development of modern industrial-commercial nations around the margins of the North Atlantic Basin that cities have dominated the life of large regions.

The following table (after Aurousseau) attempts to classify cities and towns according to their dominant functions. The descriptive terms used in the table are self-explanatory. Illustrations of each type can easily be called to mind. Of the several classes of cities listed, Class IV, manufacturing, and Class V, commerce, contain by far the largest numbers. It needs to be emphasized that cities do not grow by themselves. They are set up by countrysides to do the tasks that must be performed in central places. They are the head offices. A city cannot exist in isolation.

CLASSIFICATION OF URBAN GROUPS ACCORDING TO DOMINANT FUNCTIONS
(*According to Aurousseau*)

Class I Administration	*Class* II Defense	*Class* III Culture	*Class* IV Production (*Manufacturing*)
Capital cities Revenue cities	Fortress cities Garrison towns Naval bases	University towns Cathedral towns Art centers Pilgrimage towns Religious towns	Manufacturing cities Craft towns

Class V Communication (*Commerce*)			*Class* VI Recreation
Group A Collection	*Group B* Transfer	*Group C* Distribution	Health resorts Tourist resorts Holiday resorts

Mining towns
Fishing towns
Forest towns
Depot towns
	Market towns
	Fall-line towns
	Break-of-bulk
	  towns
	Bridgehead towns
	Tidal-limit towns
	Navigation-head
	  towns
		Export cities
		Import cities
		Supply cities	

Entrepôt cities			

754. DISTRIBUTION OF CITIES. In 1927 there were in all the world 537 cities with over 100,000 population—224 in Asia (including all of Turkey and Russia), 182 in Europe (excluding Turkey and Russia), 90 in North America, 20 in South America, 12 in Africa, and 9 in Australasia. In 1801 there were but 21 such cities in all the world, and all were in Europe. It would appear as though urbanization was an European process and that Europeanization has been spreading rapidly throughout the world. At first glance the figures for the continents might look as though Asia were the most highly urbanized continent and Australia the least, but such is not the case. If, instead of number of great cities, the percentage of the total population living in cities of over 100,000 is used, the picture is markedly different. Australia

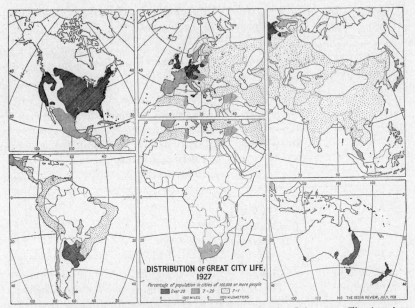

DISTRIBUTION of GREAT CITY LIFE,
1927

FIG. 385.—(*By Mark Jefferson, from the Geographical Review, July, 1931, The American Geographical Society of New York.*)

URBANIZATION BY CONTINENTS*

Continent	Great cities	Urban (millions)	Total (millions)	Percentage
Australasia	9	3.4	7.6	44.1
North America	90	38.1	156.8	24
Europe†	182	67.2	348.9	19.3
European America	90	39.4	139.2	28.3
Indian America	20	6.2	85.2	7.2
South America	20	7.4	67	10.9
Asia†	224	62.6	1,180	5.3
Africa	12	3.4	132	2.5
European Africa	12	3.4	34.8	9.8
Negro Africa	0	0	97.2	0
World	537	182	1,892.6	9.6

* Jefferson, Mark. Distribution of the World's City Folks: A Study in Comparative Civilization. *Geog. Rev.*, Vol. 21, p. 448, July, 1931.

† All of Turkey and all of Russia are included with Asia and excluded from Europe.

leads in urbanization with 44 per cent of its people in cities over 100,000 population; North America comes next with 34 per cent, Europe third with 19 per cent, South America 11, Asia 5, and Africa 2.5.

On a world map there are four widely separated regions of out-standing urbanization, where more than one-fifth of the people live in cities of over 100,000 (Fig. 385). These regions are (a) the United States and adjacent small sections of southern Canada, (b) North Sea Europe (Great Britain, Germany, Netherlands, Denmark), (c) the River Plate region in South America, and (d) eastern Australia and New Zealand. Two kinds of regions are represented: (a) regions specialized in industry and commerce as well as in agriculture, such as northeastern United States and northwestern Europe and, (b) regions that are predominantly agricultural, such as the two Southern Hemi-sphere regions, where the agriculture is of such an extensive type as to require a small amount of human labor. For this reason an undue proportion of the population resides in port cities supported by trade in agricultural products from the hinterland. In such large countries as the United States there is considerable variation in degree of urbanization in its different parts. Thus while 28.8 per cent of the total population of the United States live in cities of over 100,000, the figure is 37 for the North, 30 for the West, and 13 for the South.

755. STRATEGIC LOCATIONS FOR CITIES. It previously has been stated that cities are principally the products of commerce and industry. If this is true, it would seem to follow that there should be certain kinds of strategic locations favorable to city develop-ment, which would cause "the seed to spring to life and guarantee its growth."

756. *Commercial cities* are probably the most common type. They appear to have had their inception and growth in considerable numbers at two kinds of locations: (a) adjacent to some obstacle which hindered the further movement of men or goods and made it necessary to halt transport, break cargo, and perhaps find some further means of travel; and (b) at the convergence or crossing of important trade routes. One of the greatest obstacles to land transport is large water bodies; and likewise one of the commonest locations for great commercial cities is at the line of contact between ocean and continent, where land travel ends and water transport begins, or vice versa. The great ports of New York, London, and Hamburg are representative of this type of location. Mountains are still another type of obstacle the barrier effects of which have nurtured city growth. Thus, along the base of the Alps from Wien (Vienna) to Lyon on the north, and from Trieste to Torino (Turin) on the south, are perfect girdles of

cities, many of them located at the plain ends of mountain passes. Arid lands are likewise effective barriers to communication, so that the margins of deserts have their "ports" as do the margins of oceans. After a difficult crossing of these dry waste spaces, caravansaries, where men and animals may rest, obtain food and water, and business may be transacted, are needed. Merv and Bukhara in Russian Turkistan, and Timbuktu on the equatorward margins of the Sahara, are representative of this type of commercial city.[1] At the *end* of a barrier, where routes of travel converge as they are forced to go around the obstacle, are to be found especially favorable conditions for the growth of great trade centers. Chicago, at the southern end of Lake Michigan, is strategically situated, not only because it is at the junction of land and water routes but even more because the lake barrier converges a large number of important land routes toward its southern extremity. Atlanta, Ga., at the southern end of the Blue Ridge Mountains, profits by a similar concentration of land routes.

Istanbul (Constantinople) is a classical example of a city that has prospered as a result of its strategic location at the *crossing* of important trade routes. There the most important land route between Europe and Asia intersects at the narrow Bosporus, the equally important water route leading from southern Russia and the Black Sea to the Mediterranean. In the United States, so much of whose commercial development has taken place within the last century or since the advent of the railroad, city development has been more closely associated with the "civilizing rails" than it has in most parts of the world. St. Louis, Kansas City, Omaha, Indianapolis, and scores of other American cities owe their principal growth to the convergence and crossing of numerous rail routes.

757. Manufactural Cities. Industrial cities not infrequently are also great commercial cities, for they find in those items of location favorable to the *movement* of men and goods features that favor the *processing* of goods as well. Great commercial centers obviously are able to facilitate the assembling of raw materials and the dispersal of finished products, both of which are necessary for factory growth, and the local market and labor supply are additional factors attractive to industrial concentration. New York City; Chicago; Boston; Shanghai, China; and Osaka, Japan, are representative of a large group of cities that are specialized both in the *movement* and in the *processing* of goods.

There are many others, to be sure, which are more exclusively manufactural in their functions, whose development has not been so

[1] Vidal de la Blache, P. *Op. cit.*, pp. 473–474.

closely associated with transport advantages. Without doubt, coal, the principal source of industrial power, has been an item of first importance in the location and development of industrial cities. This relationship between mineral fuel and manufactural centers is nowhere better illustrated than in western Europe, where a high degree of coincidence is evident between coal fields and industrial cities. This is particularly true of urban clusters specialized in heavy industries, such as metals, in which large amounts of heat and power are required. In central and western Europe there is a marked concentration of cities within an irregular belt extending from the Silesian coal field in Poland and Czechoslovakia on the east to that of Wales on the west and including the other coal fields of the British Isles, the West-phalian-Belgian-north France field, and important lignite beds in central Germany. Birmingham, Manchester, Newcastle, Essen, Lille, Liége, Leipzig, and Katowice (Kattowitz) are only a few of the many manufactural cities within the great European coal belt. Where cheap and easy transport of coal is available, the manufactural city depending upon that source of power may not be located immediately upon the field. Belfast, in northern Ireland, receiving Glasgow and Carlisle coal by boat; Cincinnati with cheap river transport of coal from the Appalachian field; and Gary, Milwaukee, Cleveland, and Detroit enjoying economical lake transport from the same region all are examples of the point in question. In the last decade or two the increasing use of electric power in industry has had a significant effect upon urban development. Where electricity is generated from coal the generating plants may be located at the coal pits and the power sent wherever needed within a radius of a few hundred miles. The outstanding fact of postwar industrial development in England has been the rapid expansion of the London center so that, although it is removed from any coal field, it has been nevertheless the fastest growing of Britain's large industrial areas.

758. Distinguishing Features of a City. Mere size, expressed in terms either of number of people or of area occupied, is scarcely sufficient clearly to distinguish the city from the market town, although, to be sure, cities are characteristically larger than towns. A much more precise distinction may be made, however, in terms of (a) the number of urban functions and (b) the number of functional areas (Fig. 386). The town usually has only *one* distinct primary *urban* function (commonly market service), which serves more than just the local settlement. If what has been a market town increases its functions, so that in addition to market services it adds those of manufacturing, government, recreation, and others, then it is pluri-

functional and so may be characterized as a city. Very obviously along with the expanding urban functions or services there is a parallel growth in complexity of the city structure, with a more complete segregation of particular functions within definite areas. Thus, although the town may have, in addition to its residential areas, a definite business core, the city will have these two and also specialized areas where factories are concentrated or perhaps where warehousing services are developed. As a consequence of the several contrasting functional areas, the city *looks* different in its different parts.

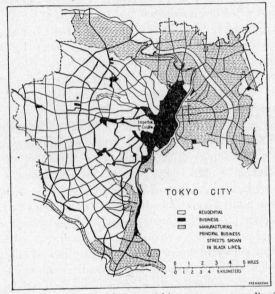

TOKYO CITY

RESIDENTIAL
BUSINESS
MANUFACTURING
PRINCIPAL BUSINESS
STREETS SHOWN
IN BLACK LINES.

FIG. 386.—Arrangement of functional areas within a great metropolis. (*After map prepared by the Tokyo Municipal Office.*)

759. Functional Areas. Within the downtown business district, tall, closely spaced substantial buildings of brick, stone, and concrete occupied by retail shops and professional offices prevail. This emphatically is the hub, or the nucleus. Upon it the street system converges so that within it traffic is usually congested. Land is so expensive that buildings tend to be tall instead of broad. It is this portion of the city which usually provides the characteristic urban skyline. Beyond the business core there may be a number of small, scattered, local business areas and likewise numerous single streets given over largely to shops and office buildings.

Wholesale, heavy-retail (lumber, feed, fuel, ice), and storage functions are concentrated outside the business core, where land is more abundant and cheaper. Very definitely this type of business is attracted by rail or water transport facilities which make easy the movement of heavy, bulky commodities. Spur railroad tracks and boxcars usually are conspicuous. Such business requires much ground space for shelter and storage, while the buildings that it occupies are relatively low and widely spaced. There is a feeling of openness about it which is absent in the business core, and congestion of traffic is less conspicuous. Exclusive manufactural areas are likewise regions of cheaper land and widely spaced buildings surrounded by storage yards and served by spur railroad tracks and canals. Water towers and tall smoking chimneys are characteristic features. Industrial areas have the reputation of being dirty and unattractive.

Residential districts within large cities vary more in quality and appearance than do those of smaller market towns, *i.e.*, greater extremes of poverty and luxury are represented. Some of the least desirable residential districts are those which have been encroached upon by expanding manufactural or business areas so that they have become decadent. The finest and most exclusive residential districts usually occupy attractive physical sites well removed from industrial and business concentrations, as, for instance, along a river or lake or on an elevated spot that provides extensive and attractive views.

SELECTED REFERENCES FOR CHAPTER XXIX

Ahlmann, H. W. The Geographical Study of Settlements. *Geog. Rev.*, Vol. 18, pp. 93–128, 1928.

Aurousseau, M. The Arrangement of Rural Populations. *Geog. Rev.*, Vol. 10, pp. 223–240, 1920.

————. The Distribution of Population: A Constructive Problem. *Geog. Rev.*, Vol. 11, pp. 563–592, 1921.

Brunhes, Jean. "Human Geography." Pp. 74–110, Rand McNally & Company, Chicago, 1920.

Demangeon, A. Agricultural Systems and Schemes of Population Distribution in Western Europe. *Geog. Teacher*, Vol. 13, pp. 199–206, 1925.

Finley, Robert, and Scott, E. M. A Great Lakes-to-Gulf Profile of Dispersed Dwelling Types. *Geog. Rev.*, Vol. 30, pp. 412–419, 1940.

Geddes, Joseph. Farm versus Village Living in Utah. *Utah Expt. Sta. Bulls.* 249 and 269, Logan, 1934–1936.

Jefferson, Mark. Distribution of the World's City Folks: A Study in Comparative Civilization. *Geog. Rev.*, Vol. 21, pp. 446–465, July, 1931.

Kniffen, Fred. Louisiana House Types. *Ann. Assoc. Amer. Geographers*, Vol. 26, pp. 179–193, 1936.

Mumford, Lewis. "The Culture of Cities." Harcourt, Brace and Company, New York, 1938.

Nelson, Lowry. The Mormon Village: A Study in Social Origins. *Proc. Utah Acad. Sci.*, Vol. 7, pp. 11–37, 1930.

Publications of the International Geographical Union on Types of Rural Settlement, 1st Report, Newton, Montgomeryshire, England, 1928 (130 pp.); 2d. Report, Florence, 1930 (91 pp.); 3d Report, Paris, 1931 (47 pp.). For the complete papers abstracted in the 3d report noted above, see *Compt. rend.* congrès intern. de géographie, Paris, 1931, pp. 8–314.

Sanderson, Dwight. "The Rural Community." Ginn and Company, Boston, 1932.

Scofield, Edna. The Origin of Settlement Patterns in Rural New England. *Geog. Rev.,* Vol. 28, pp. 652–663, 1928.

Terpenning, Walter A. "Village and Open-country Neighborhoods." Century Company, New York, 1931.

Trewartha, Glenn T. "A Reconnaissance Geography of Japan." University of Wisconsin Studies in the Social Sciences and History, 22, Madison, Wis., 1934.

Chapter XXX. Agriculture and Its Associated Features

760. In its broad sense, agriculture is the most necessary of the world's principal forms of production, and it certainly is by far the most widespread. Agricultural land is likewise the most basic and fundamental of the world's resources. It is from the land that man is fed and clothed, since the manufacturer who processes food and clothing is dependent upon the farmer for the larger part of his raw materials. The agricultural population is also one of the world's principal consumers of manufactured products. So it is that even much of the industrial and commercial prosperity of regions originates at least indirectly from the land.

761. AGRICULTURAL LAND. Agriculture requires land, but not all land is suited to agriculture. In fact, natural land seldom is capable of more than the most primitive of agricultural uses such as grazing or the collection of wild grains or hay. To prepare it for more intensive uses requires the investment of labor and money to clear, drain, fence, survey, or otherwise improve or allot it for tillage. Therefore, land as a factor in production is not, like the air, a free gift of nature. It must be won, and hence it has value.

Since agricultural land must be produced through the investment of capital and labor, it follows that much of the land of the world is incapable of becoming agricultural, since it could never be made sufficiently productive to pay adequate returns on the investment. Handicaps of one kind or another inherent in its conditions of climate, soil, or surface configuration impose limits on its utility. It was the purpose of Part I of this book to state in some detail the complex of natural elements some of which govern the quality of land, and there is no need to review them here. However, there are factors other than those of physical nature that are concerned with the value of land. Included among these are economic location, *i.e.*, an advantageous location with respect to other lands or to centers of population. Because the inherently fertile lands of the earth cannot be moved to advantageous locations, provided they do not have them, some that are inherently less productive have higher sale values because of better situation. A supply of good agricultural land is, however, one of the critical elements in the environmental complexes with which the regions of the world are endowed.

Significant Agricultural Elements and Their Classification

The distinguishable elements of culture that are associated with agricultural production are both numerous and varied. Only a few of them are noted here, and principally those that have material form and are observable. The following paragraphs comment upon those that are considered particularly significant as giving character to the various types of agriculture in the world and in making it possible to distinguish one type from another. The farm population, their houses and farmstead arrangements and structures, have been discussed previously.

762. PERCENTAGE OF THE TOTAL LAND AREA OF A REGION AGRI-CULTURALLY UTILIZED. Certainly one of the most fundamental geographic items concerning any region has to do with the percentage of its area that is agriculturally productive, i.e., is utilized for the *raising of crops* or the *pasturing of animals*. For the world as a whole there is a marked concentration of farmed land in the humid sections of the middle latitudes. Throughout the polar lands and the deserts the land is only meagerly utilized, mainly because of obvious climatic handicaps. Large parts of the wet tropics also have only sparse agricultural development, although the reasons for this are more complicated and less obvious. But even in the humid sections of the middle latitudes, where the world's agricultural lands are concentrated, there are wide variations in the percentages that are in farms. This comes about chiefly as a result of differences in climate, surface configuration, soil quality, drainage condition, location with respect to the great industrial markets of the world, and the intensity of the need for land. The last named depends in part upon the history of settlement, the cultural inheritance, and the standard of living of the inhabitants.

In the United States, where about 58 per cent of the total land area is held in farms, the percentage varies locally from less than 10, in parts of the sandy and swampy Coastal Plain, the ice-scoured crystalline rocks of the northeast, and the arid West, to more than 90 per cent in the level and fertile plains of the central Mississippi Valley region. In Japan, largely because of the rugged nature of its land surface, less than 20 per cent of the country is agriculturally productive. In Norway, where rugged surface combines with severe ice scour, the comparable figure is 5 per cent or less.

763. DISTRIBUTIONAL PATTERN OF AGRICULTURAL LAND. Not only the amount, but also the distributional aspect of farm land is geographically significant (Figs. 387, 388). In the Laurentian Upland of Canada, for example, the distributional pattern of cultivated land is an exceedingly patchy and fragmented one, concentration being upon isolated areas of glacial till and glaciofluvial plains separated

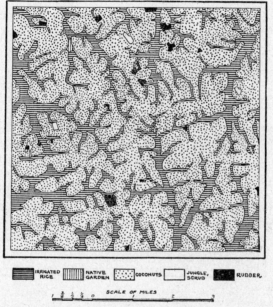

FIG. 387.—Pattern of agricultural land in humid southwestern Ceylon. Rice occupies the river floodplains and coconut groves the interfluves. (*Ceylon Survey, Avisawella sheet.*)

from each other by barren hill lands, swamps, and forests. This is quite in contrast with the distribution pattern typical of much of the Mississippi Valley, where deep soils and the general absence of rugged terrain permits farms to occupy almost the entire surface in contiguous blocks as far as the eye can reach. That is not true of all parts of the United States or even of much of the highly tilled plains of western Europe or of many other parts of the world where there are interruptions to the continuity of farm lands. Areas of unproductive sand or swamplands and hill lands in forest, owned by governmental or corporate bodies, separate certain bodies of farm land from each other, create patterns of great irregularity and provide the nonagricultural spots in the utilization fabric.

764. PLOWED OR CROPPED LAND AND PERMANENT PASTURE. Agricultural lands in general yield valuable products of several different classes such as crops, pasture, wood, and others. Undoubtedly crop land and pasture land occupy the larger areas and are much the most important. It should be emphasized that, in creating a picture of the use of farm land within a region, two elements are significant with respect to each of these uses of land: (*a*) the quantity aspect, expressed in terms of percentage of the whole area so utilized and (*b*) the dis-

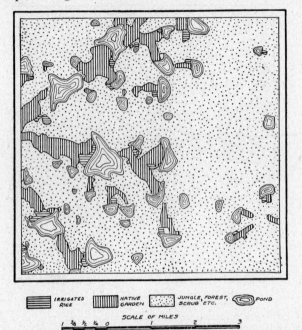

IRRIGATED RICE   NATIVE GARDEN   JUNGLE, FOREST, SCRUB ETC.   POND

SCALE OF MILES

1 ¾ ½ ¼ 0   1   2   3

FIG. 388.—Pattern of cropped land in northern Ceylon where tank irrigation is practiced. (*Ceylon Survey, Medawachchiya sheet.*)

tribution pattern of each type of land use. Unfortunately the information available from statistical sources and from field surveys is not uniformly adequate for the creation of such a picture, and if it were the details of quantity and distribution would far exceed the limits of the present space. It is possible, therefore, to present only the most general of pictures in terms of contrast, and for large areas.

In the United States, where 55 per cent of the total national area is in farms and ranches, only about 17 per cent of the total area, or 32 per cent of the farm-land area, is in tilled crops, and this is very unequally distributed. In arid parts of the western states, for example, there are many counties in which no more than a small fraction of 1 per cent of the total area is under tillage while in certain sections of the corn belt nearly all the farm land and more than three-fourths of the entire land area is tilled (Fig. 389). In the United States as a whole, more than two-thirds of the farm lands are in permanent pastures, woodlands, idle or fallow lands, and other uses. The area of land potentially available for crops is about 55 per cent larger than that actually used. In addition there are large areas of grazing lands on the public domain, in the national forests and on other lands not owned by farmers. In Japan and China proper, on the other hand, tilled land occupies a much more significant place in the land-use

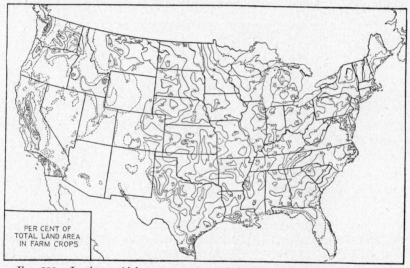

PER CENT OF
TOTAL LAND AREA
IN FARM CROPS

Fig. 389.—In three widely separate parts of the United States the proportion of the total land area, by counties, that is used for tilled crops is less than 2 per cent, but only in the corn belt does it exceed 75 per cent.

system. The human populations of these countries are dense, and most of the tillable lands are used to produce food for direct human consumption, the animal industries are only meagerly developed, and grazing lands do not occupy a significant area. In New Zealand the situation is quite the opposite. It is a newly settled country with a small population and a small requirement for the kinds of food crops that must be raised at home. Consequently a large area of potentially tillable land is devoted to pasture, and less than 3 per cent of the total area of the country is under the plow.

765. THE PROPORTIONS OF THE PLOWED LAND IN VARIOUS CROPS. A further refinement in the analysis of the uses of farm land, following the distinction of plowed land from that in other uses, would show the

subdivision of the plowed land into the kinds and amounts of the various crops raised (Fig. 390). In the United States, for example, of the farm-land area that is cropped, approximately 27 per cent is planted to corn, 20 per cent to hay, 16 per cent to wheat, 7 per cent to cotton, 10 per cent to oats, 4 per cent to sorghums, and 4 per cent to barley. These seven crops occupy about 88 per cent of the acreage of all crops. But within the country are regions of agricultural specialization, the percentages for which are greatly different from the average figure for the country as a whole. For example, one county of North Dakota, representative of the spring wheat belt, has 50 per cent of its cropped land in wheat, about 12 per cent in hay and forage crops, 18 per cent

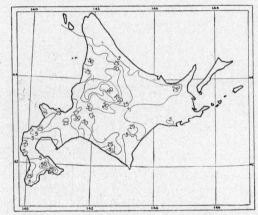

Fig. 390.—Per cent of the total cultivated area that is planted to rice in Hokkaido, the northern island of Japan proper.

in barley, 7 per cent in oats, and only 1½ per cent in corn. A county in the Iowa corn belt, on the other hand, has 48 per cent of its crop area in corn, 32 per cent in oats, 7 per cent in hay, only 1½ per cent in barley, and almost no land in wheat. These percentages show remarkable contrasts in crop emphasis and in the agricultural systems of the two regions, although the percentage of the total area in crops in the two areas is not greatly different.

766. The Amount Produced per Unit Area. Although areal spread or acreage certainly is the most fundamental geographic fact concerning agricultural land utilization, the crop yield per unit area is important supplementary information. It is an indication of the quality of the land and of the intensity of the farming practices as well. An acre of corn in terms of space occupied is identical in Iowa or Georgia, and yet the average per acre yield of corn in bushels is about 50 in the first state and only 10 in the second. This is in large part an

expression of difference in the fertility of the dark prairie soils of Iowa and the lateritic red and yellow soils of Georgia. An average acre of rice land in Japan produces approximately 2,350 lb. of clean rice; in the United States, 1,075 lb.; and in the Philippine Islands only 650 lb. The rice lands of the United States have, in the main, new dark prairie soils which certainly are not inferior to the much cropped alluvial lands of Japan. Their lower yields are indicative of much more extensive methods, where yield is sacrificed to save on cost of production, whereas in Japan vast amounts of human labor are expended to bring the yield of rice up to a high level.

767. CROPPING SYSTEMS AND PRACTICES; SEASONAL LANDSCAPES. Depending largely upon climatic conditions, the seasons of planting and harvesting vary greatly from one part of the earth to another. In the constantly wet tropics, where there is no generally dormant season for vegetation by reason of a deficiency of either heat or precipitation, definite seasons for planting or harvesting are not conspicuous. Seeds may be put into the soil at any time with assurance that conditions are satisfactory for their growth and maturing. In the savanna lands, on the other hand, where a dormant season is imposed by the drought of the low-sun period, there is a definite seasonal rhythm to agricultural practices. Except where irrigation is developed, crops are normally planted at the beginning of the rains and harvested during the dry season. Fields commonly lie fallow during the period of low sun. Throughout the middle latitudes a seasonal rhythm of agricultural operations is usually imposed by a period of cold, although in some parts a drought season may have the same effect. But over the middle latitudes as a whole, winter, or the period of low sun, is the dormant season for agriculture, whereas spring is the season of planting, summer of growth, and autumn of harvesting. This characteristic cycle is so well recognized that it has impressed itself upon the customs, habits, recreations, and literature of the inhabitants.

There are important departures from the previously noted cycle. On the tropical margins of the middle latitudes the mild winters permit some crops to flourish throughout the cool season. Thus the American Gulf Coast region, southern California, and Mediterranean Africa are important producers of winter fruits and vegetables for the markets farther north. Although oranges are picked throughout the year, the principal season is winter, when other fruits are scarce and expensive. In the dry-summer subtropical, or Mediterranean, regions where the periods of maximum heat and maximum rainfall do not coincide, the cereal crops commonly are planted in the fall at the beginning of the rains and harvested in late spring. In those regions of mild Mediterranean climate, the grains grow more or less continuously throughout the winter. Even in the long-summer-short-winter subtype of the humid continental climates, hardy cereals such as wheat and rye are fall-sown, although growth practically ceases during the winter. Most of the wheat grown in, and to the south of, the American corn belt, as well as that of western and central Europe, is designated as winter wheat, meaning that it is sown in the autumn. In the higher middle latitudes (subarctic, and humid continental climates with short summers), however, the winters are severe, and practically all crops are spring-sown, the fields being free of crops in winter.

768. *Multiple Cropping and Interculture.* It is customary in the United States to raise only one crop in a field at a time and to plant a field only once during the course of a year. After the single crop has been harvested the field is then usually allowed to lie fallow until the next year's planting season arrives. But in countries of dense population and restricted agricultural land areas, and especially in those where the growing season is relatively long, such practices as *multiple cropping* and *interculture* are common. By multiple cropping is meant the practice of replanting a field to a second crop after the first has been harvested, so that two and occasionally three harvests are obtained from the same land during the course of a year. In Japan, for example, 30 to 40 per cent of the rice fields are replanted in autumn to unirrigated crops such as wheat or barley.

Interculture is a kind of simultaneous rotation of crops in alternate rows, by which two or more different crops, planted at different times, are grown together in the same field. By this "close dovetailing rotation of crops in point of time, space, and labor" two or three harvests may be obtained in one year. In Japan summer vegetables frequently are intercultured. Four-fifths of the Italian vineyard acreage represents mixed crops, the rows of grapes being alternated with fruit trees which serve as their supports, with grain and vegetables frequently planted between the vine rows. Hay or grain crops are sometimes grown in American orchards.

769. LIVESTOCK PRODUCTION AS A PHASE OF AGRICULTURE. Two large divisions of specialized agriculture may be recognized: (*a*) the growing of crops and (*b*) the raising of animals, although frequently the two types of economy are combined, even on the same farm. Certain crops, to be sure, such as rice, wheat, flax, cotton, and tobacco, are converted directly into forms useful to human beings. Others like corn, oats, hay, and mulberry are principally used as feed for domestic animals, which in turn furnish products or services for human use. However, many of the world's economically important

domestic animals are grazers, and certain types of animal industry are found in regions where natural grass pastures, hay, and forage crops are abundant, whereas others are more sharply restricted to areas producing grain and other concentrated feeds. Since the earliest times the natural grasslands have been regions of extensive livestock production.

770. USES OF ANIMALS AND ANIMAL PRODUCTS. Under modern farming conditions the raising of livestock is done in such a variety of ways, and for such diverse purposes, that classification is not easy. Most animals, however, serve one or more of three general uses: (a) as sources of food, such as meat, milk, eggs, or honey; (b) as sources of industrial products, such as fibers (wool, hair, silk) or leather (hides); (c) as beasts of draft or burden. The kinds and quantity of animal products emanating from a region are important geographic data.

771. SYSTEMS OF LIVESTOCK PRODUCTION. The systems of economy under which livestock are raised are several. At one extreme is the *nomadic herding* practiced by the tribal peoples of dry Africa, inner Asia, and the Asiatic tundra. A somewhat more advanced stage in animal industry is represented by *livestock ranching*, a commercial form of livestock grazing such as that practiced in western United States, the steppe lands of South Africa, or the dry interior grasslands and savannas of South America. A still more intensive stage of animal raising is to be found in those humid lands of general agriculture where there is an abundance of good pasture and, in addition, a plentiful supply of grain and forage crops for feeding. In part the animals forage for their food, even though their movements are limited by fences, but heavy feeding from the crops produced on the farm is also practiced. This type of commercial *livestock farming* is well developed in western and central Europe, the American corn belt, and parts of the Argentine Pampa.

772. NUMBER OF LIVESTOCK PER UNIT OF AREA. Primary in determining the importance of any region in animal production, no matter of what kind, is information relative to the number of animals per unit of area (square mile, acre, or other unit). To obtain this in comparable terms it is necessary to reduce the various kinds of animals to a common denominator, which may be called a *livestock unit*. This may be considered to be the equivalent of one horse, one mule, one cow, seven sheep, seven goats, or five swine. On this basis one may compare the relative numbers of livestock per square mile in different regions.

773. LIVESTOCK UNITS IN RELATION TO AREA OF CROPPED LAND. Important as the above data are, however, they are not sufficient to

give a clear notion of the importance of livestock in the regional economy. As an illustration, Natrona County in east central Wyoming and Fond du Lac County in southeastern Wisconsin have respectively about 14 and 140 livestock units per square mile. On the basis of these quantity data alone, one might conclude that Fond du Lac County is highly specialized in livestock production, and that Natrona County is not. But this is not the case, since relatively the Wyoming county is more dependent upon livestock than is the Wisconsin one. The difference lies in the contrasting types of animal industry, for in semiarid Wyoming it is sheep and cattle ranching, whereas on the more productive lands of eastern Wisconsin dairy farming is the principal industry. This contrast can be brought out clearly by comparing the total number of livestock units per 100 acres in all crops for each region. The figures representing the above ratio are 340 for Natrona and only 37 for Fond du Lac County.

774. KINDS AND NUMBER OF ANIMALS.   A further important kind of data useful to a clear understanding of a region's livestock industry has to do with the particular *kind of livestock* raised. This can best be expressed as the percentage of the total livestock units in horses or cattle, or sheep and goats, etc. These data applied to Natrona and Fond du Lac counties tend further to differentiate the two regions, for although the former has 56 per cent of its livestock units in sheep and 37 per cent in cattle, the latter has 82 per cent in cattle and only 1¼ per cent in sheep. Further differentiation should be made between regions in which the cattle are being raised primarily for milk or for beef. This can be determined by data showing the quantity of milk produced annually per unit of area, per acre of land in farms, or per acre in all crops. This is clearly brought out by the last item in the table on page 677, comparing a ranching area with a dairy area and with a beef-cattle- and swine-raising area in the corn belt.

775. THE FARM—SIZE AND SHAPE; NUMBER AND SIZE OF FIELDS. A farm is defined by the United States Census as all the land that is directly farmed by one person. Thus a large plantation operated by several tenant farmers would be considered not one but several farms. The size of this operating unit varies greatly from place to place depending upon the productivity of the land, density of rural population, and several other factors. In the livestock ranching region of Wyoming and Montana, for example, the average ranch size is 1,000 to 2,000 acres, but in drier and rougher southwest Texas it reaches 10,000 acres or more. In the North Dakota spring wheat region the average operating unit is about 500 acres, in the corn belt it is about 160 acres, and in the rich cotton lands of the Mississippi flood-

plain it is 40 acres or less (Fig. 391). In Europe, where population is denser and land more scarce, farms are naturally smaller, 85 per cent of the holdings in France containing less than 25 acres. In Switzerland they average about 20 acres. Japan, representing one of the world's most densely populated rural areas, far surpasses most of Europe in the smallness of farms, the average size being only 2.6 acres, or about half an acre for each member of the farm family.

COMPARATIVE DATA FOR THREE COUNTIES, EACH REPRESENTATIVE OF A TYPE OF LIVESTOCK INDUSTRY*

	Livestock Ranching, Natrona County, East-central Wyoming	Dairy Farming, Fond du Lac County, South-eastern Wisconsin	Commercial Livestock Farming, Carrol County, West-central Iowa
1. Percentage of total land area in all crops	0.6 (very low)	57.1 (high)	63.1 (very high)
2. Total livestock units per square mile	13.8 (very low)	137.9 (very high)	116.1 (very high)
3. Total livestock units per 100 acres in all crops	340 (very high)	37.6 (medium)	28.7 (medium)
4. Percentage of total livestock units in:			
Horses and mules	6.0 (very low)	11.7 (low)	12.5 (low)
Cattle	37.5 (medium)	83.1 (very high)	70.8 (very high)
Sheep, goats	56.2 (high)	1.2 (very low)	1.6 (very low)
Swine	0.5 (very low)	4.9 (low)	14.9 (high)
5. Gallons of milk produced annually per acre of land in all crops	27.6 (low)	142.5 (very high)	27.9 (low)

776. SHAPE AND COMPOSITION. Most American farms are roughly rectangular in shape and are composed of a single contiguous block of land. The farm is further divided into several individual fields

* After Jones, Wellington D. Ratios and Isopleth Maps in Regional Investigation of Agricultural Land Occupance. *Ann. Assoc. Amer. Geographers*, Vol. 20, pp. 177–195, December, 1930. Data modified in agreement with United States Agricultural Census of 1939.

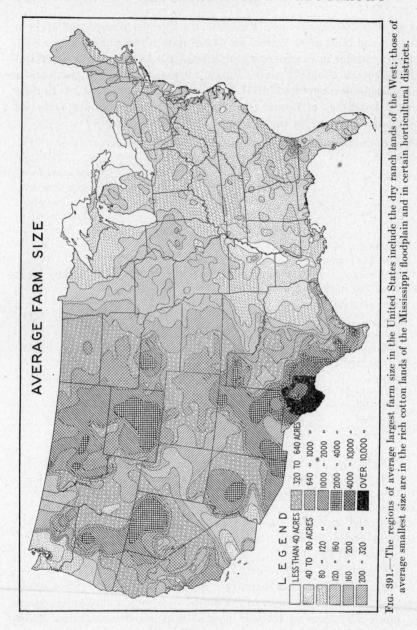

FIG. 391.—The regions of average largest farm size in the United States include the dry ranch lands of the West; those of average smallest size are in the rich cotton lands of the Mississippi floodplain and in certain horticultural districts.

of a variety of shapes and sizes but with a tendency toward rectangularity, especially where the land is not too rough (Fig. 392). The

FIG. 392.—Aerial view showing rectangular field pattern on the flattish Illinois prairie. Farmsteads can be detected by the dark clusters of trees which surround them. (*United Photo Shop*.)

prevalence of right angles in the landholding pattern of the United States is largely the result of the original land surveys by which most of the country, excepting the eastern and southern states, was subdivided by north-south and east-west lines coinciding with meridians and parallels (see Appendix C for a discussion of the American system of rectangular land survey). The section, 1 mile on a side, became the basic land-subdivision unit. Usually the American farm, as well as the individual fields, are enclosed by fences, although this is not always the case. In the flat lands of the Argentine Pampa rectangular land subdivision prevails also. It is not, however, systematically oriented with respect to compass directions (Fig. 393).

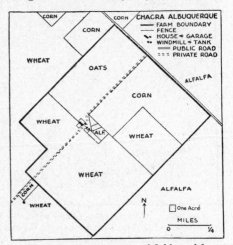

FIG. 393.—Arrangement of fields and farmstead on an Argentine farm of 554 acres. (*Map by Robert S. Platt*.)

Quite in contrast with the foregoing picture are the farms of many European countries or those of the Orient. The Japanese or Chinese farm, instead of being one contiguous plot, usually is composed of

FIG. 394.—Pattern of irrigated rice fields on a Japanese plain. The individual fields are only a fraction of an acre in area.

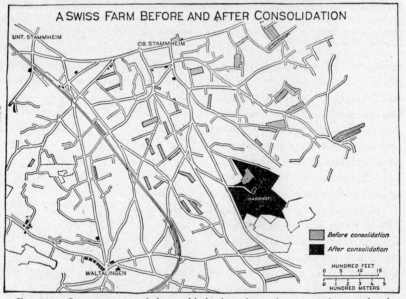

FIG. 395.—In many parts of the world the farm is not in one contiguous plot, but is composed of several isolated parcels. The average Swiss farm has a total area of 21 acres in 14 separate plots. (*Courtesy of U. S. Department of Agriculture.*)

several small, unfenced parcels of land of different sizes and shapes (Fig. 394). The parcels are scattered in various directions and distances about the rural village where the farmer dwells. For North China, where farms average 4 to 7 acres in size, there is an average of about six separate plots per farm. The plots are not far from an acre in size, and their average distance from the farmstead is slightly over half a mile. This open-field system with noncontiguous plots is also typical of France and other parts of continental Europe (Fig. 395). The representatve Swiss farm, with a total area of about 21 acres, is composed on the average of over 14 unfenced parcels.

777. REGIONAL CLASSIFICATION. The foregoing paragraphs of this chapter have attempted to outline the more significant elements in the agricultural complex of a region. The definition of an agricultural region would therefore rest upon the ability to recognize some distinctive association of these major elements. Unfortunately for the ease and clarity with which such regions may be delimited, the elements are many, some are capable of census enumeration or statistical computation, and others are not. Moreover, some parts of the world are covered by adequate and detailed agricultural census enumerations. Others have but general enumerations or none at all. From this it may be concluded that, although agricultural regions may be delimited for some parts of the world with fair precision, that is not possible for the world as a whole. Regions on this large scale must be general, and for some of them many of the desirable facts are entirely lacking. For none of them is it possible to proceed systematically though the entire list of even the known elements, since the present purpose and space does not permit so great detail. Moreover, a map to accompany such a world subdivision as is here proposed must be at a small scale and therefore general. The regional types outlined on this map may appear simple but are in fact mere generalizations of complex associations. Within each of the areas mapped as units are many variations which could be brought out only by means of a much more thorough analysis than the present purpose warrants.

The following classification and the map, of agricultural regions (Plate X) are therefore limited to a subdivision of the world into little more than a dozen agricultural types. In this it is in accord with the general classifications of climates, landforms, soils, etc., that have been employed in this book. For the basis of this agricultural classification the authors acknowledge great indebtedness to Professors Derwent Whittlesey and W. D. Jones,[1] Richard Hartshorne and Samuel N. Dicken,[2] and to Dr. O. E. Baker[3] and others whose writings

[1] Whittlesey, Derwent. Major Agricultural Regions of the Earth. *Ann. Assoc. Amer. Geographers*, Vol. 26, pp. 199–240 and plate, 1936.

[2] Hartshorne, Richard, and Dicken, Samuel N. Syllabus for the Introductory Course in Economic Geography. Pp. 26–54 and plate, Edwards Brothers, Inc., Ann Arbor, Mich., 1939.

[3] Baker, O. E. Agricultural Regions of North America. *Econ. Geog.*, Vols. II to IX.

have contributed the classifications of world agriculture most applicable to the present point of view. In the classification by Whittlesey the regional distinctions rest primarily upon a brief list of features that have recognized functions and have been noticed either in the foregoing part of this chapter or in earlier chapters of Part II. They are:

1. The crop and livestock association.
2. The methods used to grow the crops and produce the stock.
3. The intensity of application to the land of labor, capital, and organization, and the output of products that results.
4. The disposal of the products for consumption (*i.e.*, whether used for subsistence on the farm or sold off for cash or other goods).
5. The ensemble of structures used to house and facilitate the farming operations.

Major Agricultural Regions

Even the most casual survey of world agriculture shows strongly contrasting groups of regions: (*a*) those in which the major emphasis is upon the raising of animals, (*b*) those in which crop production is dominant, and (*c*) those in which these basic functions share about equally in the attention of the farmer. Each of these, however, is capable of further subdivision, and the various resulting types are of different degrees of economic intensity, some requiring a high concentration of labor, capital, and organization upon the land, and others requiring but little. In the following types it is not possible to say precisely in all cases which is a more and which a less intensive form of agriculture. However, the general arrangement is intended to present first the most primitive and least intensive forms of agricultural and pastoral enterprise and to reserve until last those of more advanced and intensive nature.

778. NOMADIC HERDING REGIONS. Nomadic herding is a primitive form of livestock industry. Those who live by means of it have no fixed habitations, but migrate with their flocks and herds in search of water and forage. They are but a step removed from the hunting stage of human economy. The animals kept by nomadic herdsmen include most of the domesticated herbivorous species such as horses, cattle, camels, sheep, goats, and reindeer. These supply their owners with most of their wants in foods and raw materials: meat, milk, wool, hair, skins, and utensils. They supply transportation also to those who live in sparsely peopled districts. This is a subsistence type of animal raising.

Nomadic herding once was widespread in Eurasia and Africa, where it evolved with primitive civilizations, but it has suffered encroachment there by higher forms of land use. This encroachment still is in progress in Asia, where Chinese farmers slowly crowd the nomads from the more humid margins of Inner Mongolia. In recent years also the agricultural revolution in U.S.S.R. has forced some of the inhabitants of the Siberian steppes to settle upon the land over which they and their ancestors have roamed for centuries. On the other hand, pastoral nomadism was not native to the American continents or Australia. In those continents the aboriginal inhabitants were either hunters of wild animals or tillers of the soil, having few domestic animals, and the later European immigrants had already developed beyond the nomadic stage. Only after the introduction of horses to the New World did the American Indians become, for a brief time, nomadic herdsmen, owning bands of ponies but little other stock. More recently the introduction of reindeer among the Eskimos of western Alaska and northwestern Canada has established a region of nomadic herding which may prove to be permanent.

The world regions that are characterized by nomadic herding (Plate X) are mainly those that are dry, either actually or physiologically: steppe lands, desert margins, and tundra. The severely dry deserts of the Old World produce little of forage and have few watering places. They are unable to support even sparse nomadic populations, although bordering tribes make temporary incursions upon them to utilize the short-lived forage that springs up following rains. The largest remaining regions of nomadic herding are those of central Asia and northern Africa.

779. LIVESTOCK RANCHING. The steppe lands and desert margins of the Americas and Australia are regions of livestock grazing also, but the economic nature of the industry there is different from nomadic herding. In the United States it is called livestock ranching, and that name may be applied to it generally. It is, from one viewpoint, a retrograde form of settled agriculture. Farmers of European origin, accustomed to tilling the soil, occupied dry lands in the new continents and took up livestock grazing because aridity did not permit of satisfactory tillage. Although they adopted the means of existence of the pastoralist they did not adopt the nomad's manner of life. Instead they retained the tradition of a settled habitation, the ranch house, and the idea of private ownership of the grazing lands, which were protected by patrol of their borders and by the ultimate building of fences to separate properties or even to divide individual holdings into great pasture fields (Figs. 396, 391).

Livestock ranching, unlike pastoral nomadism, is a commercial form of land use. The livestock products are used by the ranchman to a limited extent only. Instead they are sold on local or world markets for a cash return, with which the ranchman buys his requirements. It is also a more intensive form of agriculture than pastoral nomadism, attention being given to the selection and breeding of stock, the artificial provision of water through wells, and even some tillage of the soil where a supply of irrigation water permits. Thus supplementary feed crops may be grown and some food for the ranch family. Although the ranch animals ordinarily are confined within the ranch limits, this is not always the case. In the North American cordilleran region,

Fig. 396.—Slender fences of barbed wire divide western cattle ranches into large fields.

for example, cattle and sheep are driven from winter pastures on the lowland ranches to summer grazing on mountain pastures that are not a part of the ranch but are hired from governmental or other owners. This kind of seasonal migration of livestock is very ancient and belongs also to pastoral nomadism in the Old World and to other types of livestock management as well. It is called *transhumance*.

Within the several livestock ranching areas shown in Plate X are numerous modifications of the general type. The system of management and the kinds of livestock raised in the middle-latitude steppes of the United States and Argentina, for example, are not exactly like those of the tropical grasslands of Brazil or northern Australia. On the humid borders of the North American high plains, where good railway transportation permits of ready access to a large market, the ranches are smaller and the livestock industry more closely associated with crop tillage than in distant northern Australia. In the latter region in fact are some of the largest ranches, or "cattle stations," in the world, several of which, according to Conigrave, reach an area of 5,000 square miles each, and at least one covers more than 12,000 square miles, or nearly as much as the states of Connecticut and Massachusetts combined. On the desert margins everywhere the capacity of the land to support livestock is limited by the sparsity of the forage, and the number of livestock units per square mile is small. In the good grasslands of western Nebraska, for example, 10 acres may be sufficient to support one animal unit, but in the drier lands of central Wyoming it may require 25 to 50 acres, and in the desert lands of Arizona and Nevada more than 75 acres. Beyond a variable aridity limit, the area required to support livestock sufficient to maintain a commercial ranch unit becomes so great that it is no longer profitable to utilize it for ranching.

780. RUDIMENTARY CULTIVATION. In the tropical forest regions and upon their savanna and highland margins are vast areas of land which are used for agriculture in a rudimentary way. In the lowland areas abundant heat and moisture have given rise to a luxuriant natural vegetation, but they also promote luxuriant weeds once the original vegetation is cleared away. These mainly are the regions of the tropical red soils whose store of fertility is quickly exhausted under continuous cultivation without skillful management. This the primitive farmer cannot provide, and hence he is forced to adopt a system of cultivation that requires new lands for temporary exploitation. The inhabitants of some of these regions live under tribal organization, and in their agricultural adaptations to their surroundings they act in tribal groups.

Among the various rudimentary systems of culture two general types may be recognized. The first involves the clearing of fields in the forest, their tillage for one or more years in simple subsistence crops, such as manioc, until weeds or soil exhaustion force their abandonment. This continues until all the available field sites convenient to the settlement have been used. Then the entire group moves to a new site and establishes a new village settlement in a locality far removed. The old site quickly reverts to forest, and after some decades it may again be cleared as new land in a process of slow rotation during which the soil recovers some of its elements of fertility and the troublesome weeds have been crowded out by forest growth. This system is sometimes called *shifting cultivation*. The second type is slightly more advanced and commonly is found in tropical forest localities where the population has become somewhat more dense and especially among such groups as have some contact with the world outside and some sale for the products of their cultivation. In this system the fields are cleared of their original cover, cultivated, and abandoned as before, but the village seldom is moved. This system requires a more frequent reusing of abandoned fields and a considerable intensification of the agricultural practices, the labor for which is provided by the larger population. Tree crops, such as palm nuts and cacao, are sometimes planted in the abandoned clearings, income is derived from the land thus planted, and its reversion to forest is delayed or prevented. This is a rudimentary form of settled or *sedentary* agriculture.

The tribal farmers who till by these methods live in huts that are built of local materials. They have few livestock other than poultry and but little understanding of land fertilization or other advanced agricultural practices. They are able to clear new land by means of ax and fire, but their methods are not intensive (Fig. 285). They till the land with a sharpened stick or a hoe, tools that are inadequate for the repression of a vigorous growth of weeds. The larger part of the regions that are characterized by rudimentary tropical tillage are exceedingly remote from routes of transportation, and the products of their cultivation are for subsistence only. A smaller part only produces some crops for sale, and mainly they are the tree crops. This may be, however, a type of intensification that indicates a general encroachment upon the regions of primitive tillage. The larger of these regions as outlined in Plate X, it will be seen, are mainly within the area of the tropical rainforests. Only in parts of Africa, where infectious diseases prevent the keeping of horses or other work animals, does the rudimentary type of tropical tillage extend much beyond the forest and scrubland border.

A related form of rudimentary agriculture is practiced by the highland Indians of Central America and the Andean regions. They clear and till small fields on the mountain and valley slopes, and these, when the soils are depleted or badly eroded, are allowed to revert to pasture or bushwood. However, the settlements of the cultivators remain fixed or are moved only at long intervals when no more land is available within reasonable distance. Although these agricultural practices are rudimentary in form and similar in type to those noted above, the crops are different from those of the adjacent lowlands owing to the lower temperatures of mountain climate.

781. INTENSIVE SUBSISTENCE CULTIVATION. In parts of eastern and southern Asia are ancient centers of civilization in which agricultural skills and implements long ago made it possible to support many more people per unit of area than is possible under rudimentary

cultivation. The further growth of population required ever-increasing intensity in the use of agricultural resources and gave rise to distinctive systems of tillage. In the main they are of the subsistence type, only a small part of the farm produce being sold away from the locality of its production. Most of the readily tillable land is used, and additional areas are created at great labor through land drainage and the terracing of hillsides. Only the steepest slopes and the least productive soils remain in woodlands or pastures, but in some hilly districts woodlands occupy a significant part of the total area, nearly two-thirds in Japan, for example. The animal industries are only moderately developed, since the major part of the land, and especially the cropland, is required to produce cereals and vegetables for direct human consumption. In this respect, however, parts of the Asiatic region differ because of contrasts in religious tolerance. In China and Japan there are relatively few cattle and sheep but many swine and poultry that can be supported from agricultural and household wastes. Even ponds and streams are made to yield their maximum of food through the cultivation of fish and waterfowl. In India, on the other hand, religious custom forbids the use of flesh, and there are no swine or other animals used for food. There are, however, many cattle, water buffalo, and goats. These are used to pull the plows much more extensively than in China, where hand labor predominates, or as sources of milk and other animal products.

There is another significant agricultural contrast between parts of the general region of intensive subsistence cultivation. In the more rainy tropical and subtropical portions the cropping system is dominated by the growing of rice, and all other cultivated crops take places subordinate to this most productive of cereal grains. Rice occupies the irrigable deltas, floodplains, coastal lowlands, and terraces. Other grains occupy unirrigated lands or replace rice on the irrigated land in the cooler and drier season, after rice harvest. In the more tropical portions, where the growing season is long, multiple cropping enables two crops of rice to be harvested, which, together with beans, vegetables, and other crops, provides food for large numbers of people. These live in innumerable farm villages and till their tiny fields with endless patience and hard labor (Fig. 380), but seldom do they achieve more than a bare existence. In contrast with these rice districts are the more northerly portions and interior highlands of China and Japan and the dry interior of India, where the summers are either too short or there is not sufficient irrigation water for the cultivation of rice. There various other cereal grains, especially wheat, corn, the grain sorghums, and millets, take its place. They are associated with beans, vegetables,

and many other crops, such as cotton. The major areas of rice dominance are distinguished in the regional map (Plate X). In addition
to the major areas of intensive subsistence cultivation outlined on the
map there are others too small to be shown at that scale. Mainly they
are in the Old World, and most of them are the densely peopled oases
or irrigation regions. Of these the oasis of the Nile Valley in Egypt is a
conspicuous example large enough to be shown on the map.

782. COMMERCIAL PLANTATION CULTIVATION. Common in the
tropics, and in some areas closely associated with the rudimentary and
subsistence forms of tillage, is another type of agriculture of very
different character. Its purpose is the production of a single crop or
limited group of crops for cash sale. They are produced on an extensive
scale by efficient methods and in standard forms. The products most
susceptible to this type of management are certain world staples that
are required in large quantity, mainly in the industrial regions of the
Northern Hemisphere. Such are bananas, tea, rubber, and certain
tropical fibers. The choice of plantation site is made with reference to
its ability to produce one of these commodities in large quantity and of
superior quality, and hardly any other crops are grown. The capital
for plantation development, the skilled personnel for its management,
the machinery for its operation, fertilizers for the crop, part of the
food for the laborers, and sometimes even the laborers themselves are
brought from outside the locality, and some of them from the farthest
parts of the earth. On many plantations the laborers live in village
settlements at the plantation center and work in gangs under supervision (Fig. 377). This is notably true of rubber and tea plantations.

Like other agricultural staples, the products of plantation agriculture suffer from competition on the world market. There are few
crops so restricted by nature that they cannot be raised in more than
one region. Moreover, the great plantation establishments, once they
have created a large market and have demonstrated efficient methods
of production, begin to find competitors in the small farmers of their
respective regions. Some crops such as sugar and cotton once were
produced, and still are to some extent, under plantation systems of
management but now are grown even more largely by a modified
plantation system or by independent small farmers. The United States
cotton region is an outstanding example of this change. The abolition
of slavery, the breaking up of the great plantations, the lack of necessity for any expensive equipment in cotton growing, and the westward
expansion of cotton into the subhumid districts have almost extin-
guished the true plantation system that once prevailed. Similar if less
extensive changes have taken place in the Cuban sugar industry,

the Brazilian coffee industry, and others. In fact, small commercial farms prevail over considerable parts of these regions, and an almost complete transition is to be found between the highly centralized plantation on the one hand and the small cash-product farm on the other. Those plantations tend to resist longest the effects of private competition whose products are of such a nature that they require some kind of special handling or expensive processing or standardizing between the field and the shipping point, things the small farmer is unable to provide.

Some attempt has been made in Plate X to distinguish between the areas of highly centralized plantation cultivation and those transitional forms noted above. The simple distinction provided does not do justice to the complication of the facts. Several of the areas are so small as to require special symbols to make them stand out, and none of them is marked in such a way as to distinguish the special product for which each locality is noted. Added detail regarding these, and the reasons for their locations, is a part of the subject matter of economic geography.

783. MEDITERRANEAN AGRICULTURE. Although Mediterranean agriculture is not distinguished on quite the same basis as the other types noted here, it is an ancient association of cultural and natural features well recognized by geographers. The unique combination of dry subtropical climatic features together with hilly land surface is, in each region of its occurrence, associated with a distinctive combination of crops and livestock industries, although the relative importance of the several component cultural elements is not everywhere the same. Cereal grains, especially wheat, grow during the mild, moist winter and mature with the coming of the dry summer. Certain other crops that are sensitive to low temperatures are native to the regions of Mediterranean climate and find there the freedom from severe frost necessary to their growth. Such are the olive tree and the grapevine. Xerophytic character or deep roots that seek underground water enable them to endure the summer aridity and produce their fruits at the end of the dry season. Still other crops of humid tropical or subtropical origin have been introduced into the Mediterranean regions by man. They find there the mild winters they require, but they are not naturally adapted to the summer aridity and are able to survive only where they are supplied with water by irrigation. The citrus fruits are the outstanding example of this group of crops (Fig. 171). However, where irrigation water is available it is often supplied to other crops also, including some such as grapes and olives, which will survive without it but are much improved in yield and quality if they receive supplementary irrigation. Other irrigated crops include vegetables, sugar

beets, and alfalfa for hay and pasture. The irrigated land is used most intensively and is held in small farms that receive careful tillage and have a large investment of capital and labor per acre. It also yields large returns. However, only a comparatively small part of the total area of the Mediterranean regions is capable of irrigation, either because it is not physically suited to that use or, more commonly, because there is not sufficient irrigation water available. The larger part must produce cereals or unirrigated tree crops or is used as native pastures. Since most of the Mediterranean climatic regions include areas of hills and mountains these are used mainly as grazing lands, and they occupy much the greater part of the total area but support only a small part of the population. The dry summer pastures do not supply forage adequate for many cattle or horses but are much better adapted to the use of goats and sheep, which are the most abundant types of livestock kept there.

The world regions of Mediterranean agriculture are, of course, practically coincident with the climatic regions of that type (Plates V and X). However, the agricultural emphasis varies considerably among these regions owing to differences in historical background, density of population, accessibility to markets, and other cultural factors. In California citrus and deciduous fruits, vineyards, and vegetable crops are paramount. The industries that supply oranges, raisins, wines, peaches, figs, and other intensive crops are highly organized on a commercial basis, and they have a large national market available and the means of transportation with which to reach it. In the distant Mediterranean districts of Australia there is an even larger area of tillable land, but the supply of irrigation water is less abundant, the domestic markets are small, and the distances to outside markets great. Hence the more easily transported products of the wheat farms and sheep ranches have a higher relative importance there. In fact, both the regions of Mediterranean agriculture in the Northern Hemisphere have large near-by markets, whereas those of Australia, Chile, and South Africa find no comparable outlets for their more perishable products. Notwithstanding these differences, the basic agricultural elements of all the regions have a striking similarity and warrant their inclusion in one of the major types of agricultural regions of the world.

784. COMMERCIAL GRAIN FARMING. Commercial grain farming, like plantation culture, is a product of the modern industrial era. The two are alike in some respects but very different in others. The commercial grain farm, like the plantation, usually puts an emphasis upon some one crop that it produces for cash sale. It is, however, unlike

the plantation in its organization. It does not require a processing plant or even storage facilities, since the grain goes directly from the field to the market. It does not have gang labor, outside management, or foreign capital. Except in the communal farms of Russia, it has no workers' village, but instead has dispersed farmsteads of rather small size and unimpressive type. The commercial grain farms average large (320 to 640 or 1,000 acres in the wheat regions of the United States), and mainly they are operated by their owners or tenants upon an extensive basis, with a maximum of laborsaving machinery. The farmer supplies the management and, with his family and a hired hand or two, furnishes the labor, except for temporary help at harvest time. Wheat is usually the principal crop of commercial grain farms, but it is not the only one. In some districts corn, barley, rice, or flaxseed are raised for sale. Generally also there are secondary crops of hay, oats, and other feed crops for the farm animals. The number of animals kept is not great in proportion to the size of the farm. Most important are the horses used to pull the numerous and large tilling, seeding, and harvesting machines, but in some areas tractors have taken the place of these to a considerable extent. Other livestock includes a few cows and other animals, which are kept to furnish a domestic supply of milk and meat.

Commercial grain farming is found principally on the steppes and prairie margins of the middle latitudes, especially in the plains regions of chernozem soils. Because of the low and erratic rainfall the yields of grain average low in spite of the fertile soils, but for the same reason the land is relatively cheap. The proportion of the total area under the plow averages high, exceeding 70 per cent in parts of North Dakota, Kansas, and eastern Washington. The farms being large, the farmsteads are widely spaced. Having few livestock and little need for grain storage, they have few barns, and hence the farmsteads are unimpressive when compared with those associated with certain other types of middle-latitude farming. In fact, the whole landscape with its absence of woodlands, its large fields and widely spaced farmsteads, is one of peculiar openness.

On the semiarid margins of some of the commercial grain-farming regions part of the crop is raised by "dry-farming" methods. These are agricultural practices designed to conserve moisture by storing up in the soil part of the rainfall of more than one year, in order to produce a single crop. Thus the land is cultivated each year to make it permeable and retentive of moisture but is cropped only in alternate years. This type of farming is expensive in terms of labor, considering the possible returns, but it utilizes cheap land. It is particularly suited

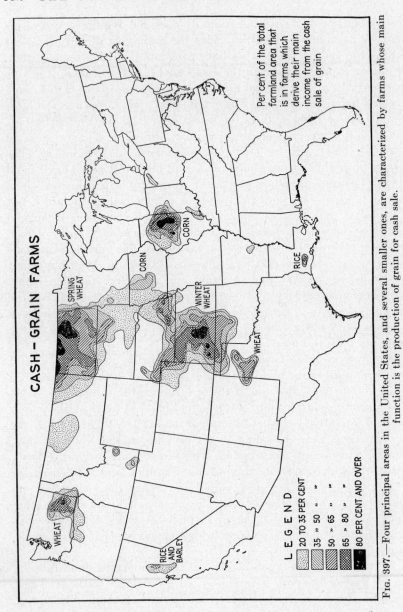

Fig. 397.—Four principal areas in the United States, and several smaller ones, are characterized by farms whose main function is the production of grain for cash sale.

to grain farming because such crops as wheat and barley have relatively small water requirements.

The world regions of commercial grain farming, shown in Plate X, are, it will be seen, distinctive of regions of European rather than Asiatic type of civilization. They occupy the new and relatively cheap lands of the world, and most of them are bordered on their drier sides by regions of livestock ranching. In part they are regions of winter wheat culture, as in Kansas, Argentina, Australia, and the Ukraine. Colder areas raise mostly spring wheat, as in southeastern Russia, western Siberia, the Prairie Provinces of Canada, and the Dakotas. Some specialize in grains other than wheat (Fig. 397). For example, corn is grown primarily for sale from the farm in a large district in eastern Illinois, also in the northern part of the Argentine grain region, and in the Transvaal and Orange Free State of South Africa. Rice, mainly a subsistence crop in the Old World, is grown entirely for sale under the American system of culture found in California and Louisiana, but these and some other cash grain districts are too small to be shown on the accompanying map.

785. Associated Crop and Livestock Farming. This name may be applied to a mixed type of agriculture in which some crops are grown as feed for livestock, some for cash sale, and some as food for local consumption. The relative importance of these three functional elements varies from one region to another. In all the regions the production of livestock is highly important, but in some it is practically the only source of cash income. The mixed farming regions may in fact be divided into two types: (a) those in which crops and livestock are raised mainly for sale, and (b) those in which they are produced mainly for local use. These may be called the commercial and subsistence types, respectively (Plate X).

The commercial type of crop and livestock farming is best exemplified by the American corn belt, where crops are raised mainly to feed hogs, cattle, and sheep, which are sold from the farm and are themselves the principal source of cash. Relatively little grain or other crops are sold from the farm and even less is used for direct human consumption. In the western European region the emphasis is more evenly divided. The significant feature of this type of farming, however, is that it is organized upon a commercial basis and that it has usually more than one source of cash income but with one of them commonly predominant. In general this type of farm is more versatile than the cash grain type, and this in turn implies regions of better climatic endowment, particularly more abundant precipitation.

The farming system of the commercial crop and livestock type varies considerably among the regions. It has, however, certain distinguishable features. Outstanding is some sort of rotation of crops that employs a succession involving (a) a tilled crop, (b) a small grain, (c) a hay crop, and (d) rotation pasture. Thus, in the American corn belt the principal tilled crop is corn, the small grain is likely to be oats or wheat, and the hay crop alfalfa, clover, soybeans, or grasses. In a succeeding year the former hay field may be used as pasture before it is plowed up and the land used again for corn. Such a rotation may run from 3 to 5 years and sometimes more. In south central Europe the sequence may involve corn, but in those sections where the summers are too cool for corn, it is replaced in the rotation by such tilled crops as stock beets, turnips, or potatoes, all of which are much used in feeding animals. In the districts of poor soil and colder winters also, wheat may be replaced by rye. In the level, dark-colored, prairie soils of the American corn belt the percentage of land under tillage is high, 75 per cent in parts of Illinois, Iowa, and Nebraska. In these areas a minimum of land is held in permanent pasture, but in regions of rougher surface and poorer soils, parts of eastern United States or Europe especially, the ratio of pasture land to crop land is much higher. However, the producing capacity of the land is high, and there normally is a surplus of feeds with which to fatten livestock in addition to those that are raised locally. Additional animals usually are purchased from neighboring areas of lower rainfall or rougher surface. The American corn belt, the Argentine alfalfa belt, and various districts in France and Germany are noted as centers of livestock feeding.

The farms of these productive regions average smaller than those of the commercial grain-farming areas, 120 to 200 acres in the American corn belt, and much less in Europe, as compared with an average of 500 in North Dakota. The manner of tillage is much more intensive, involving more investment, more labor, and a larger use of fertilizer. It is more expensive land, and the typical farm has larger and more expensive buildings to house animals and crops. According to the 1940 census, the average value of land and buildings per acre of land in farms was nearly $80 in Iowa but less than $13 in North Dakota. Also the average value of the farm buildings was nearly $4,000 per farm in Iowa but only a little more than $2,000 in North Dakota. The farm buildings in the central European mixed farming region also are large, substantial, and some of them very old as compared with the small and often barnless cabins or sod houses that characterize the farm settlements of the Russian wheat belt.

The subsistence type of crop and livestock farming is restricted largely to more primitive middle-latitude regions and especially to those that are remote from modern transportation routes. The largest region of this type is in central and eastern European Russia, where distances are great, railways and roads few, and the farming system derived from a very old form of peasant agriculture. In that region rye and oats replace the wheat and barley that predominate in the commercial grain region of southern Russia. The rye and oats are mainly consumed locally rather than sold on the cash market. Other important subsistence crops include large quantities of potatoes and cabbage and some other vegetables. The livestock density is not high, but cattle, swine, and sheep exist in moderate numbers and contribute to the local food supply. Horses are used for farm labor. Many of the Russian peasant farms have been collectivized under the Soviet regime, and doubtless the subsistence type of agriculture is being broken down, especially near the growing manufacturing towns of the Moskva (Moscow) and Ural industrial regions, which furnish new markets for farm produce. The farmers of this region live mainly in villages, their principal construction material is logs, and their barns and other farm buildings are fewer and simpler than those of the commercial mixed farming districts of western Europe. Subsistence farming produces very little cash income with which to buy improved equipment.

Other regions of subsistence crop and livestock farming are smaller and less clearly defined. The isolated Russian settlements of central and far eastern Siberia have borrowed their characteristics in part from old Russia and may be considered similar in agricultural type. There are few such districts in Anglo-America, except possibly in parts of the southern Appalachian highland and Maritime Canada, and they are small. In the highlands of Mexico and in Central and South America subsistence agriculture of the ancient Indian type has been modified by the introduction of European animals. However, in most of these districts the animals do not belong to the people who till the soil but to the great ranch owners, although they may be tended by the humbler folk. In the Central Plateau of Mexico this is not true to the same degree. The cultivators of the productive basin lands also are the owners of donkeys, cattle, sheep, and goats which graze the dry hill slopes and furnish labor in the fields, a little meat, a little milk, and some wool to their owners. These farmers, like those of Russia, live mainly in village settlements, have simple houses and few barns or other structures and little in the way of mechanical equipment. They remain peasant farmers and practically self-sufficing. The

Mexican plateau may therefore be classed as a region of subsistence crop and livestock farming. A similar condition prevails in the plateau region of southwestern Asia, especially in Turkey (Plate X).

786. COMMERCIAL DAIRY FARMING. Dairying is an intensive phase of commercial crop and livestock farming in which crops are raised to feed dairy cattle and other incidental livestock and in which milk and its products, rather than the animals themselves, furnish the principal source of cash income. Dairying is a more intensive use of land than beef production because a given quantity of feed will produce, through the medium of dairy cows, at least two or three times as much human food in the form of milk as it will in the form of beef. However, it requires more of the farmer's time and labor to produce it.

Commercial dairying prospers under varied climatic conditions, and it does not demand soils of the highest fertility. Pasture, hay, silage crops, and grain concentrates are required, but the industry is sufficiently remunerative that the concentrates may be imported if the coarser feeds are available. One condition commercial dairying must have, access to large urban markets. Milk and cream are so perishable that they must be marketed within a few hours of their production. Butter and cheese can be held longer, up to several months, provided there is means of refrigeration in storage and transit. The major dairy regions of the world are, as shown in Plate X, near the great industrial cities of northwestern Europe and northeastern United States and adjacent Canada. Dairying has not been traditional in the densely peopled subsistence farming regions of the Orient or in Mediterranean Europe with its poor summer pastures. Neither have the inhabitants of these regions the cash incomes that would enable them to support dairying on a large scale. Distant dairy regions such as those in Australia and New Zealand are of recent origin and have had the benefit of cheap land, efficient transportation, and protected access to the large British market.

The two major world regions of commercial dairy farming have advantages other than proximity to the great dairy markets. Relatively cool, moist summers are favorable to the production of pasture, hay, and other forage and fodder crops. They have also permitted the cultivation of oats and barley for grain and, in America, corn for silage. These are more suited to the feeding of dairy cows than to the fattening of beef and other meat animals. The average dairy farm in America is only slightly smaller (120 acres) than the crop and livestock farm, but its use is different. Less than half of it, on the average, is plow land, as against 50 to 75 per cent of the corn-belt farm (Fig. 389). The average value of land and buildings per acre of farm land in the two regions is about the same, but in the dairy farm the large barns and other buildings are worth more than those of the corn-belt farm and the land somewhat less. The difference in land values may be attributed to differences in soil, surface, and drainage, the dairy region being mainly one of gray-brown forest soils and recent glaciation, with areas of stony moraine and glacial marshes, which, however, are usable as pasture. The higher value of the dairy farm buildings is in consequence of the need for weatherproof structures for the protection of cows and forage crops and for the care of milk. Swine, poultry, and horses are necessary parts of the dairy farm livestock also and must be housed. Not all dairy regions require such elaborate structures. In New Zealand, especially, the winters are so mild that pasture is available all the year, no hay storage is necessary, and open milking sheds suffice for the protection of cows. There the benefits of cheaper land and lower housing costs are offset by high labor costs and especially by high freight charges to distant markets.

The form in which dairy produce is marketed varies within the parts of the great dairy regions also. Although there is no rigid separation, there is a tendency for those areas nearest the great cities to furnish the fluid milk while those farther removed furnish condensed milk and cheese, and the fringing areas supply butter. Thus, Great Britain, in normal times, is 100 per cent self-sufficient in fluid milk, about 30 per cent self-sufficient in cheese, but only 10 per cent self-sufficient in butter. The districts of New England, southern New York, and Pennsylvania supply the large eastern cities with milk, and southeastern Wisconsin and northern Illinois do the same for the Chicago metropolitan district. Northern New York State, the lower St. Lawrence Valley, and much of central and northern Wisconsin are noted for cheese manufacture, and Ontario, Minnesota, and other fringing districts are known for their butter output. In Europe, Denmark and the Baltic Sea margin are noted for butter production, but Netherlands and Switzerland, where dairy specialization is of long standing, have a large trade in cheese, for which they have become famous. Australia and New Zealand are noted for their production of butter, although the latter has a large cheese industry also.

787. COMMERCIAL GARDENING AND FRUIT CULTURE. Another form of agriculture which depends upon the existence of the great urban markets is concerned with the supply of vegetables and fruits, both in and out of their usual season. These industries are a normal part of the Mediterranean agriculture, but they are found in other regions also (Plate X). The greatest markets are those of industrial Europe and North America. In those regions are millions of people who have

not time or land for gardening but they have cash incomes with which to buy horticultural products. The great population centers of the Orient, being more largely agricultural, supply themselves during the usual season and go without during the balance of the year, as did all the rest of the world only a few decades ago. The large cities of the Southern Hemisphere are not numerous and large enough to require either the great volume of produce that flows into the European and North American centers or so vast an industry to provide it.

The vegetable and fruit crops are the produce of highly intensive cultivation. The land area utilized is relatively small, but it is made to yield an astonishing quantity of food. It is heavily fertilized and tilled with a great expenditure of labor. The farms generally are small, and the nature of the farm operations does not require large or numerous buildings. In the typical horticultural district, therefore, neat houses with small barns and few outbuildings are spaced at short intervals in a landscape of intensive cultivation. The great markets are supplied by two somewhat different types of industry. One is local and the other distant. The first takes advantage of nearness to the market. Often these small farms are located on the outskirts of the market cities or within truck-hauling distance. They supply vegetables and fruits of great variety, each in its own season, but they operate under whatever disadvantages of climate and soil the region may have. The second type operates under the disadvantage of distance from market but reaches out for localities of special advantage in climate, soil, or other environmental conditions, each according to its own requirements. The first is likely to be a general horticultural industry, growing a series of fruits and vegetables simultaneously or in sequence as the climate permits or the market requires. This type of industry is sometimes called market gardening. The second type is usually more specialized, growing one fruit or one or two vegetable specialties upon which the whole year's operations are based. Such industries commonly are called fruit farming or truck farming (Fig. 398).

In both Europe and America the great cities have their distinctive market-gardening districts. Near New York City are the extensive gardens of Long Island and the Jersey shore, areas of light permeable soils that are easily tilled. Similar industries are found northwest of Boston, in suburban Chicago, and about most other cities, roughly in proportion to their sizes. The truck-farming and fruit-growing areas, on the other hand, are farther away. Some take advantage of the temperature gradient from north to south to gain earliness of season. Beginning on the Gulf Coast or even in Cuba and Mexico, a wave of horticultural production sweeps northward through winter, spring, and summer, and finally merges with the garden products of the city environs. In Europe a similar zonal production begins in North Africa and creeps northward to areas on the channel coast of France, Belgium, Netherlands, and southern England. Many of the fruit-producing regions are highly specialized. Such are the irrigated apple districts of Washington, the peach region of Georgia, and the numerous wine districts of France. These in general are located with respect to some particular advantage of climatic condition which gives fruit of particular and uniform quality year after year while that of less

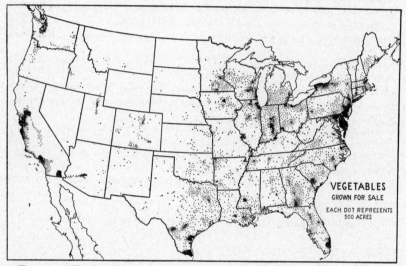

VEGETABLES
GROWN FOR SALE

EACH DOT REPRESENTS
500 ACRES

Fig. 398.—The distribution of vegetables grown for sale reflects both the advantage of mild winters in the South and West and of special soils, or closeness to city markets in the Northeast.

favored regions is variable in quality and quantity. Modern transportation has permitted even some Southern Hemisphere regions to compete in the northern markets. Apples, pears, and grapes from Argentina, South Africa, and Australia appear on United States and European markets in the season opposite to that of their normal production there, and thus they get prices that help to defray the high shipping costs. However, they are luxury items, and the trade is not large by comparison with that in wheat or some other agricultural staples.

REFERENCES FOR CHAPTER XXX

Baker, O. E. Agricultural Regions of North America. *Econ. Geog.*, Vol. 2 (1926), No. 4; Vol. 3 (1927), Nos. 1, 3, 4; Vol. 4 (1928), Nos. 1, 4; Vol. 5 (1929), No. 1; Vol. 6 (1930), Nos. 2, 3; Vol. 9 (1933), No. 2.

Cook, O. F. Milpa Agriculture. *Smithsonian Inst. Ann. Rept.*, 1919, pp. 307–326, Washington, 1921.

Hartshorne, Richard. A New Map of the Dairy Areas of the United States. *Econ. Geog.*, Vol. 11, pp. 347–355, 1935.

—— and Dicken, Samuel N. World Survey of Agricultural Land Use (and map), in "Syllabus for the Introductory Course in Economic Geography." 4th ed., pp. 26–54 and plate, Edwards Bros., Inc., Ann Arbor, Mich., 1939.

Jonasson, Olaf. The Agricultural Regions of Europe. *Econ. Geog.*, Vol. 1 (1925), No. 3; Vol. 2 (1926), No. 1.

Jones, C. F. Agricultural Regions of South America. *Econ. Geog.*, Vol. 4 (1928), Nos. 1, 2, 3; Vol. 5 (1929), Nos. 2, 3, 4; Vol. 6 (1930), No. 1.

Jones, W. D., and Whittlesey, D. S. Nomadic Herding Regions. *Econ. Geog.*, Vol. 8, pp. 378–385, 1932.

Marbut, C. F. Agriculture in the United States and Russia: A Comparative Study of Natural Conditions. *Geog. Rev.*, Vol. 21, pp. 598–612, 1931.

Pioneer Settlement. *Special Publication* 14, American Geographical Society, New York, 1932.

Shantz, Homer L. Agricultural Regions of Africa. *Econ. Geog.*, Vol. 16 (1940), Nos. 1, 2, 4; Vol. 17 (1941), Nos. 3, 4. To be continued.

Taylor, Griffith. Agricultural Regions of Australia. *Econ. Geog.*, Vol. 6 (1930), Nos. 2, 3.

——. The Distribution of Pasture in Australia. *Geog. Rev.*, Vol. 27, pp. 291–294, 1927.

Van Valkenburg, Samuel, Cressey, George B., and Hall, Robert B. Agricultural Regions of Asia. *Econ. Geog.*, Vol. 7 (1931), No. 3; Vol. 8 (1932), No. 2; Vol. 9 (1933), Nos. 1, 2; Vol. 10 (1934), Nos. 1, 2, 4; Vol. 11 (1935), Nos. 1, 2, 3, 4; Vol. 12 (1936), Nos. 1, 3.

Whittlesey, D. S. Major Agricultural Regions of the Earth. *Ann. Assoc. Amer. Geographers*, Vol. 26, pp. 199–240, 1936.

——. Shifting Cultivation. *Econ. Geog.*, Vol. 13, pp. 35–52, 1937.

——. Fixation of Shifting Cultivation. *Econ. Geog.*, Vol. 13, pp. 139–154, 1937.

Chapter XXXI. Manufacture and Its Associated Features

788. The Function of Manufacture. The essential function of manufacturing processes is to change the *form* of materials for the purpose of making them more useful or more valuable. The change in form gives to the processed material what the economist calls *form utility*. Iron ore as it comes from the mine is practically useless, but after smelting, transformation into steel, and shaping into implements or machines, it is of strategic value. Cotton in the boll has little use, but after being ginned, spun into thread, woven into cloth, and the latter made into garments, it has acquired greatly increased usefulness and value through the application of energy and skill. It is so with a majority of the products of farm, forest, and mine. Only a few, such as certain vegetables, fruits, coal, etc., are ready for human use in their primary state.

789. The Use of Land for Manufacturing. One of the characteristic features of complex modern industrial regions, such as western Europe and northeastern United States, is the great importance of manufacturing which in those regions overshadows agriculture and the extractive industries, measured either in terms of the number of people employed or in the value of the output. In fact, in the whole United States, more persons are employed in manufacture than in agriculture and all the extractive industries, such as forestry, mining, and fishing, combined. In terms of total area covered, however, the manufactural features of large regions are much less conspicuous than are those associated with agriculture. This results from the greater intensiveness of the manufactural processes and, therefore, the possibility of concentrating them on much smaller areas. One square mile of the American corn belt usually includes about four farms. This means that 640 acres are operated by 6 to 8 workers and are supporting 15 to 20 persons. This same area, however, could contain several large factories, together with their fuel yards and storage facilities, employing thousands of workers. For this reason it is difficult to construct such a map

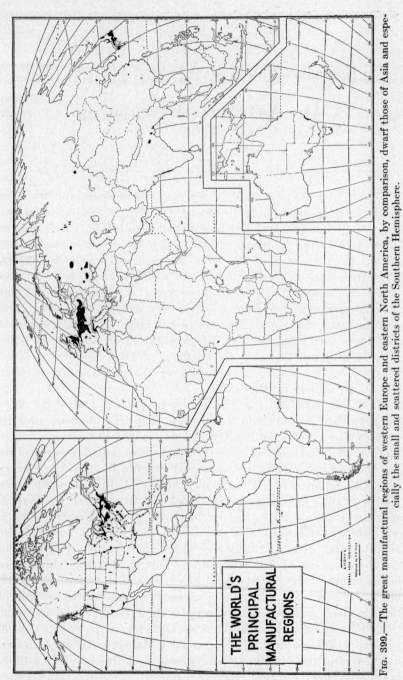

FIG. 399.—The great manufactural regions of western Europe and eastern North America, by comparison, dwarf those of Asia and especially the small and scattered districts of the Southern Hemisphere.

as Fig. 399, showing the manufactural regions of the world. The centers of industry shown there include also much land used for agricultural, commercial, and residential purposes, and only a small part of the areas indicated are occupied by factories. It may well be true that the land actually occupied by all the manufactural establishments of the world could be included within one of the smaller American states, such as Connecticut, with plenty of room to spare. It is only locally, therefore, that the buildings and equipment of the manufactural industries are conspicuous elements of the landscape, but this fact need not mislead us with regard to their great importance.

790. CLASSES OF MANUFACTURAL INDUSTRY. The United States Census of 1939 lists nearly 450 different kinds of manufactural industries, and doubtless the world list would include many more. Any attempt to compare the nature and significance of world regions of manufacture requires that industries be grouped according to some system of classification. Several such are in common use, each having its own point of view or purpose. One basic distinction commonly recognized is that which exists between the heavy and light manufactures, the former turning out such products as iron, steel, clay products, and heavy machinery, the latter such as small metal wares, textiles, or garments. Some industries also are classed as primary because they use only the crude products of the soil, forest, or mine as their raw materials. Many heavy industries are of the primary type. Other industries, especially the lighter ones, are called secondary because they employ the products of previous manufacture as their raw materials. The weaving of spun thread into cloth is a secondary industry, and so is the manufacture of a watch or an automobile from metals. These simple subdivisions fail at many points to give an adequate picture of the nature of regional industry. Other considerations are involved, and some of them are related to the nature of the industrial products. Such are the following: (a) The stage of completion to which the industrial products are carried; whether they are finished and ready for the ultimate consumer or are unfinished and require further manufacture. (b) The nature of the use for which the manufactured products are intended. There are several such distinctions to be made.[1] Some of the more important are (i) goods for immediate consumption, such as foods, newspapers, automobile tires, etc., (ii) materials for construction, such as lumber, cement, and structural steel, and (iii) capital goods, which include such machines and permanent equipment as are used by manufacturers in the

[1] Bliss, Charles A. "The Structure of Manufacturing Production." Pp. 141–166, National Bureau of Economic Research, Inc., New York, 1939.

production of other commodities. (c) The durability of the products, whether intended for long-continued or for only temporary use. Still other considerations involve the nature of the raw materials from which the manufactured products are made and the sources from which they are drawn. Thus, some industries use mainly vegetable or animal products obtained from farms. Others use wood, metals, or chemicals drawn from forests or mines. A great many manufactured products include mixed materials drawn from various of these sources.

791. MEASURES OF RELATIVE MANUFACTURAL IMPORTANCE. In judging the industrial character of a region for purposes of regional comparison it is necessary that types of manufacture be measured. The basis of such measurement can only be statistical, derived from published reports or from personal investigation. Fortunately the great industrial nations issue statistical reports in great detail. These make it possible to apply several methods of measurement, each designed to bring out its own type of comparison. Various classes of significant facts may be obtained from the statistics. Some of these are as follows: (a) Facts relating to the value of the things produced, such as (i) the value of the raw materials consumed, (ii) the value added by the process of manufacture, and (iii) the total quantity or value of the finished products. (b) Facts relating to the persons employed in the industry, such as (i) the number of wage earners and salaried employees, (ii) the total number of man-hours of labor in a month or year, and (iii) the total amount of wages and salaries paid per month or year. (c) Facts relating to the capital invested in plant, equipment, and other necessary aspects of manufacture. (d) Facts relating to the quantity and sources of the energy or power used. By using several of these measurements in combination, industries may be compared as to their relative importance in a region, or regions may be compared as to the relative importance of the several industries in them.

792. CLASSES OF MANUFACTURAL FEATURES. The factory or manufactural establishment is the point of convergence for the labor, capital goods, raw materials, and power and is the focus and heart of manufactural production, but it is by no means the whole of it. Surrounding the factory are the homes of the workers, and daily the employees move back and forth between homes and places of work. Workers in transit are a conspicuous part of the industrial scene at certain times of the day. Likewise converging upon the factory, carried by boats, railroad cars, or trucks, are large quantities of raw materials and fuel. These raw materials and fuels may not be very conspicuous at any one time, because they are a flowing rather than a stationary

mass and do not remain in one place to be seen or measured like a building or a field of corn. The best that can be done is to express their bulk in terms of tons of coal, bales of cotton, or bushels of wheat, and these symbols are hard to visualize.

Just as raw materials and power resources are converging upon the factory, so the industrial products are flowing from it toward local and distant markets. The magnitude of this outward flow is as difficult to see and appreciate as is the inflow, for this is a characteristic of all things under cover and in transit.

It should be clear, then, that the factory is only the focus, or center, of a more extensive weblike fabric which, in addition to (a) the manufacturing plant, includes (b) the workers, (c) the incoming raw materials and fuel, and (d) the outgoing factory products. These are the four principal groups, or classes, of material-culture features associated with manufactural production.

793. THE INDUSTRIAL PLANT. Of first importance in a geographical analysis of a region's manufactural appearance are facts concerning the number, kind, and size of factories. Within the Chicago industrial district, containing as it does somewhat more that 3,000 square miles, there are upward of 12,000 manufacturing establishments, representing almost every kind of industry designed to meet human wants. Among the more important are meat-packing plants, iron and steel mills and their allied industries, agricultural-implement and electrical-equipment factories, foundries and machine shops, and printing and publishing establishments. All sizes of factories are represented, from the tremendous plants associated with iron and steel and meat packing to the small printing shops employing only a few workers. Within the Pittsburgh industrial area there is less diversity of industry, with greater specialization in iron and steel. But many of these establishments are large and their number is not great. Iron-and-steel-working plants account for only 13 per cent of the number of factories in the Pittsburgh area, but they employ 58 per cent of all the workers and account for 51 per cent of all the value added by manufacture in the region.

794. SIZE OF THE INDUSTRIAL PLANT. Factories differ greatly in size and general appearance, depending upon the kind of industry they house and the part of the world in which they are located. Iron and steel plants nearly the world over are characteristically of large size, for only in large plants can the smelting of iron and the conversion of it into steel be done efficiently and economically (Fig. 400). They are distinctive also because of their typical features, such as the blast furnaces, piles of ore and coal, and the broad low buildings

that house the rolling machines. Numerous tall chimneys pour forth smoke, and everywhere there is a dirty, grimy appearance. Cotton spinning, meat packing, and flour milling are other illustrations of industries commonly housed in large plants, which, however, are essentially different in appearance from steel mills and from each other.

It is more especially in western Europe and the United States, where industrial development has been greatest, that the large factory has become the characteristic manufacturing unit. By no means all

Fig. 400.—Layout of a large iron and steel plant (National Tube Company) in Lorain, Ohio. Piles of coal, iron ore, and limestone are conspicuous along the waterway in the left foreground. (*Photograph by Somogy-Lorens.*)

the industries there are housed in large establishments, however. Most of the large cheese output of the United States is made in 1,800 Wisconsin factories which typically are one-man plants and employ altogether only a little more than 1,800 persons. The average number of persons employed in all the manufacturing industries of France normally is 10 per establishment, whereas the comparable figure for the United States is 40. One-fourth of all the workers in French industry are employed in handiwork factories that use little or no mechanical power. In Japan, and likewise in China, the inconspicuous workshop rather than the large factory is the dominant processing unit. It has been estimated that over one-half of the workers in industry in Japan are employed in establishments having fewer than five workers. In only two primary industries of Japan, cotton spinning and metal refining and processing, has the factory become the characteristic unit of production. Many Japanese cotton-weaving plants are no more conspicuous than the implement shed on an American farm.

795. THE INDUSTRIAL WORKERS. In order to measure the relative importance of manufactural production as compared with other industries in a region, it is useful to have data showing what percentage of the employed population is engaged in manufacture. In the United States as a whole, for example, about 20 per cent are so employed, but in the State of Massachusetts the comparable figure is about 32 per cent, and in Mississippi it is only 7 per cent. This is a clear indication of the much greater significance of manufacture in the regional complex of Massachusetts than in that of Mississippi. In normal times about 28 per cent of the working population of France has been engaged in manufacture; about 40 per cent in England and Wales; but less than 20 per cent in Japan. In attempting to understand the industrial character of a region it is desirable to know also the proportion of its factory workers that are employed in each of its principal types of manufacture. For example, Fall River and Lynn are both cities in eastern Massachusetts and might, without study, be assumed to be industrially similar. However, the following facts show them to be essentially different. In Lynn the three leading industries, measured by the number of persons they employ, are the manufacture of electrical machinery, of shoes, and of leather, and they employ respectively 46 per cent, 20 per cent, and 8 per cent of all the wage earners in that city. In Fall River, on the other hand, there are only two important types of industry. They are the manufacture of textiles, which occupies 63 per cent of the wage earners, and the making of wearing apparel from textile raw materials, which employs 29 per cent. The same comparison applied to other cities and industrial regions would be highly instructive.

Conditions Affecting the Location of Manufacturing

Modern manufacture rests upon certain bases, some of which have already been noted or implied. Certain of these are inherent in the features of the earth, some others depend upon the economic structure of the existing social order, and still others are the result of vague historical beginnings or grow out of individual preferences, custom, or mere human perversity. It may be assumed, however, that enterprises resting upon the latter type of base are not so likely to persist as others that have natural and economic conditions in their favor.

796. POWER AND FUEL. Modern industry differs from that of earlier times mainly as a result of the use of mechanical power. The consumption of such power in the United States, especially, is enormous. It has been estimated that, per capita of the population, it is 50 per cent higher than that of Great Britain, twice that of Germany, 10 times that of Japan, and 150 times that of China.[1] The problem of producing and transporting so large a quantity of energy is tremendous, but obviously it cannot have the same industrial significance in all localities since not all have or use power of the same kinds or in the same quantities. The principal source of mechanical energy the world over is coal, and many factories are located so as to take advantage of local coal supplies. The other principal sources, petroleum and hydroelectric energy, are sometimes more available but not always so satisfactory because some industries, such as smelting, require a great deal of heat as well as mechanical power. How an industry may locate well with respect to sources of power and fuel depends upon the nature of the industry and its energy and heat requirements and upon the relative costs of these elements from different sources. One extreme is represented by industries, such as the ferroalloy minerals, which are large users of fuel and power but whose products are compact and comparatively valuable. They find it advantageous to locate near the source of energy. The other extreme may be seen in industries such as shoe manufacture, which uses comparatively little mechanical energy and whose products are bulky. They are mainly located with respect not to sources of power but to a combination of other factors.

797. RAW MATERIALS. The location of certain manufacturing establishments is best explained by their relation to the raw materials that they use. Some of these materials are bulky, and their volume is much reduced by the processes of manufacture. It is therefore more economical to process them near their place of origin and to ship them to market in more condensed form. Such an industry is meat packing. On the average, only about 60 per cent of the live weight of market cattle dresses out as edible beef. Therefore, to ship live cattle from the great feeding grounds to the centers of consumption would be wasteful, although it formerly was done, before methods of refrigeration in transit made it possible to ship dressed beef from packing plants in central United States, Argentina, and Australia. The same conditions apply in the lumber industry. Rough sawn lumber contains only about 40 per cent of the wood in a log, 60 per cent having gone as waste or by-products. Because of that, sawmills usually locate

[1] Energy Resources and National Policy, p. 8, National Resources Committee, Washington, 1939.

near the forests and ship their rough lumber, rather than establishing themselves near their markets and receiving shipments of logs from distant sources.

Other industries require only compact and easily shipped raw materials, but their products are bulky and expensive to ship. They tend to locate with little regard to sources of raw materials. The manufacture of glass bottles, fruit jars, and similar containers is an illustration of this type. Sand is the principal raw material, but the products are bulky and fragile. Silk manufacture is another industry that locates quite without regard to the source of its raw materials.

798. LABOR. A supply of labor is a factor in the localization of industrial establishments, but not to the extent it formerly was. Some types of manufacture still require skilled labor, trained to special operations, but even these laborers can be moved in time, or new ones may be trained if other advantages offset the labor element. On the other hand, the increasing mechanization and simplification of industrial processes tend to reduce the dependence of industry upon an established group of workers to which the industry must move rather than moving the labor to the industry. In spite of this change, some types of manufacture still tend to cluster or group themselves in districts where a supply of trained or adaptable labor is known to be available. This is true of silk manufacture in the United States, for example.

799. CAPITAL. Local interest on the part of men who had money to invest in manufacturing enterprises over which they could exercise personal supervision was formerly a potent influence in the localization of industry. To some extent it still is. The growth of corporate finance has, however, much reduced the importance of this factor. The great manufacturing establishments of modern times are located with little regard to the source of the money with which they are set up. That may, in fact, come from distant and diverse origins. In some countries the money and capital goods necessary for the development of industry are supplied by government and derive from taxation. Under such conditions the location of industry follows governmental desire and may be in response to political or military discretion rather than to the operation of economic advantage. However, some parts of the world have much greater surpluses of capital savings than others, and these are likely to have greater industrial development, other conditions being favorable.

800. TRANSPORTATION. Modern industries require raw materials in great volume and from many sources, and they ship their products in large quantities to many destinations. For them good means of trans-

portation are as essential as any other element in their environment. Formerly, the small home industries supplied the local needs, and little connection with distant places was necessary or possible. This gave rise to highly decentralized manufacturing industries, and even today a lack of transport facilities, as in China, tends to decentralize industry. Great establishments, on the other hand, seek localities that are well provided with railroads, highways, and, if possible, water routes. The more efficient, cheap, and dependable these means of transportation become, the greater is the tendency for manufacturing to concentrate in areas of peculiar advantage with respect to other conditions. So potent is this factor that the great industrial centers are the great railroad centers also, and the growth of one promotes the development of the other. It is not accidental that the great manufacturing regions of America and Europe lie at the ends of the most used ocean route of the North Atlantic.

801. NEARNESS TO MARKET. Although modern transportation permits the shipping of goods cheaply to distant places, there still remain real advantages in the location of a factory near to its greatest potential market, if other conditions permit. The first of these is cost of shipment. Although arbitrary rules relating to freight charges interfere to some extent, it generally is true that shorter distances mean lower transportation costs. The advantage to be gained from that is obvious. However, proximity of factory to market has other advantages also, particularly such as grow out of an intimate knowledge on the part of the manufacturer relative to the exact needs of his customers and of sudden changes therein. Thus, in the shoe industry, there are frequent changes in style necessitating corresponding changes in the machines used in shoe manufacture. As a consequence, most of the American shoe-machine industry is located in or near the regions of shoe production regardless of whether these are centers of general machine manufacture. Similar advantages have been influential in the location of textile-machine establishments in the spinning and weaving regions, and the manufacture of automobile parts and accessories in southern Michigan. There are many illustrations of this principle, in some of which the market to be served is the general public. This is particularly true in the case of such food products as are either perishable or bulky or both. Bakery products furnish an excellent illustration of that type of manufactured goods. It is true also of such products as have particular application to the interests of only one locality. Newspapers and job printing illustrate that type of product. Because of these conditions, bakeries and printing establishments are found in nearly all cities and towns, and they belong to

that group of manufacturing industries which has been called "ubiquitous." Such industries typically are decentralized.

802. OTHER FACTORS. There are numerous factors, other than those named above, that play some part in the localization of manufacturing. Some of these are features of earth environment, such as a requirement for particular climatic conditions or for water supplies of great volume or special chemical quality. Others are of an economic or purely sentimental nature. Some industries locate adjacent to factories of an entirely different type because they use waste products from other mills as their raw materials. Some locate near others of their kind largely because the city or region bears a name famous the world over for their particular kind of product. The locations of still other industries can be attributed to nothing more substantial than the merest chance or accident. Actually, it is probable that in a large majority of cases two or more of the several classes of factors are concerned with industrial locations in a complex of relationships that cannot easily be understood.

The Great Manufactural Regions of the World

803. So many conditions are involved in the location of manufactural industries, and they are capable of combination in so many different ways, that it might appear that industrial distributions would almost be haphazard. To some extent they are so but by no means entirely. There is a recognizable grouping of the factory industries of the world into several major and some minor regional concentrations, and within these are districts of specialization that are of great importance. The oldest and most highly developed of these is in northwestern Europe. Next most important is that of eastern North America. Newer and much less complex are the centers of eastern Europe, the Orient, India, and the Southern Hemisphere (Fig. 399).

MANUFACTURAL REGIONS OF NORTH AMERICA

804. Although the American manufactural regions are exceeded in world importance by those of Europe, they are remarkable for the diversity of their products, their rapid growth, and their areal concentration. Most of the cities and towns that are dominantly manufactural in type are located in a broad belt that lies in northeastern United States and southern Canada. Its boundaries reach from southern Maine down the Atlantic Coast to Baltimore; westward to Cincinnati, Ohio; northwestward to include Chicago and the industrial towns of southeastern Wisconsin; thence eastward across central southern Michigan, peninsular Ontario, and south of the Adirondack

Mountains and the highlands of New England (Fig. 399). Within this area are concentrated about four-fifths of the industrial wage earners of the United States and Canada and like proportions of the industrial power used and of the value of manufactural output. Beyond the limits of this chief region are other centers of less significance in which the general-supply or "ubiquitous" industries hold a relatively more important place than in the major region. Of these, that of the southern Appalachian borderlands is most highly developed, whereas others in the central plains and on the Pacific Coast are newer and less devoted to the production of wares having general or world markets as opposed to local markets.

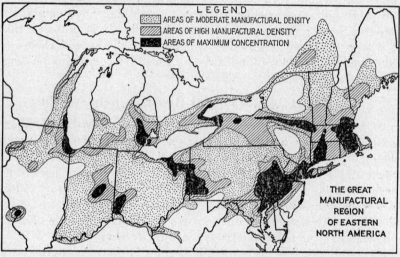

LEGEND
AREAS OF MODERATE MANUFACTURAL DENSITY
AREAS OF HIGH MANUFACTURAL DENSITY
AREAS OF MAXIMUM CONCENTRATION

THE GREAT
MANUFACTURAL
REGION
OF EASTERN
NORTH AMERICA

FIG. 401.

Many factors are concerned in the localization of these centers of manufacture, and their interaction has brought about regional specialization which, in many instances, is so striking as to give definite regional character. Even the major region is far from being a unit as to its type of development. It may in fact be subdivided into several areas of distinctive industrial character which differ in the nature of their principal industrial products and in the factors involved in their growth (Fig. 401).

805. THE NEW ENGLAND DISTRICTS. American factory industries were established in New England at an early date; textile mills in eastern Massachusetts and metalworking in the Connecticut Valley. Glaciation had produced numerous water-power sites suitable for the initial stages of industrial development; there was an abundant labor

supply available on the overpopulated farms of hilly New England and French Canada, and capital had accumulated among the merchants of the New England coastal cities. The water powers of the Merrimac, Connecticut, and other streams still are used to capacity, but they have long since ceased to be adequate. Coal is brought in from Appalachian sources by coastwise shipping and by rail, but its cost and the lack of iron ores has worked against the establishment of the heavy industries in New England. Therefore the lighter forms of manufacture prevail. The early industries have been greatly elaborated and many new products introduced, but the original forms of manufacture still leave their impress in spite of growing competition from other parts of the country. Resulting from this heritage the eastern and southwestern sections of New England still show striking contrasts.

The eastern district, extending from Rhode Island to Maine, is dominantly one of textile, leather, and shoe manufacture, and the machine trades represented there are especially those required as necessary adjuncts of textile and shoe manufacture. Southwestern New England, in contrast, is a region of light metalware manufactures. Its outstanding products are hardware, tools, electrical equipment, firearms, and machines, the outgrowth of metal trades established there more than a century ago. There are also paper, textile, and many other manufactures, but they are of less importance. Both these districts enjoy the advantage of proximity to the great eastern centers of population that are markets for part of their products, the southwestern district having particularly close relationship with the metropolitan and port area of New York City.

806. THE MIDDLE ATLANTIC METROPOLITAN DISTRICTS. The region that includes New York City, Philadelphia, Baltimore, and their immediate hinterlands, has an unusual diversity of manufactures. These reflect the interaction of many forces, among which the outstanding are the commercial or port influence, the proximity of abundant coal in the northern Appalachian bituminous and anthracite fields, and the presence there of large centers of population, which furnish both local markets and abundant supplies of labor. New York City itself is a great manufacturing center, but it is first of all a port. Its outstanding products are of the secondary type, employing as raw materials the manufactured products of other regions, domestic and foreign. The best illustration of this class of manufacture is the clothing industry, which uses cotton, woolen, and other textiles purchased from New England and other weaving centers. About 30 per cent of the workers in all the manufactures of the New York metropolitan district are employed in industries of this class.

The secondary industries are important in Baltimore, Philadelphia, and other cities of southeastern Pennsylvania also, but relatively less important than in the New York district, only about 12 per cent of the wage earners of Philadelphia and its neighboring towns being employed in the clothing industries. This district has, on the other hand, a great industrial diversity since it includes important textile, leather, and chemical manufactures and also some of the heavy industries, such as blast furnaces, steel mills and the building of ships, locomotives, and machinery. Some of the raw materials for these industries come from foreign sources through the ports of the region since they, and especially Philadelphia, are outstanding ports of import. This is true, for example, of hides, tanning materials, certain chemical raw materials, and even iron ore and other mineral ores.

807. THE CENTRAL NEW YORK INDUSTRIAL BELT, extending from Albany to Rochester, occupies the natural thoroughfare of the Mohawk Valley and the Ontario plain. Its cities have grown up along the Erie Canal and the New York Central Railroad, which link the eastern industrial districts with the Great Lakes and interior regions. The area has no local resource of coal, but the rich resources of the Pennsylvania anthracite and bituminous coal fields lie only a short distance southward, and the adjacent highlands furnish water powers that supply part of its energy requirements. It also is a region of great industrial diversity. The primary iron and steel industries are but little in evidence and neither are the primary textile trades. The secondary industries, however, are highly developed, and they include those which use many kinds of manufactures as their raw materials. Among the more important regional products are clothing, electrical and other machinery, optical instruments, chemical products, paper products, and printed matter. Some of these reflect a westward extension of the industries found in southwestern New England, but others are closely allied to those of the New York City area or of the Niagara region. This belt is clearly transitional in its position.

808. THE NIAGARA-ONTARIO REGION. Buffalo, Niagara Falls, and Toronto are the principal cities of an industrial region that reflects the advantage of location at the eastern end of the Great Lakes waterway. Cheap lake transportation permits the assembling there of grain and other agricultural produce from the interior, iron ore from the Upper Lakes region, and coal from the adjacent Appalachian fields. Industry in this region benefits also from the hydroelectric power of Niagara Falls and from its position on a main route between the interior and the eastern seaboard. The Canadian portion has also

the advantage of a tariff barrier at the international boundary, which protects certain industries that might otherwise not exist. The leading industries of the region are of the heavy type and include blast furnaces, steel works, and rolling mills and the manufacture of machinery and vehicles. Of great importance also are the chemical industries, the milling of grain, and others that use agricultural products. From this it will be seen that the industrial character of the region is more nearly like those of the regions to the westward than it is comparable with the New England or seaboard districts.

809. THE PITTSBURGH-LAKE ERIE REGION. In the Appalachian coal fields of western Pennsylvania and West Virginia the best and most abundant coking coals of America are found together with great quantities of fuel coals, some petroleum, and a large supply of natural gas. These resources gave a great advantage to the establishment there of the heavy industries, particularly the blast furnaces and steel mills of the early period of abundant steel production. The iron ore of the Lake Superior mines was unloaded at the Lake Erie ports and moved inland to the smelting centers, of which Pittsburgh was most important. Later improvements in the processes of ore reduction and a gradual decrease in the quality of the iron ores made it less necessary to move the ore to the coal region and more profitable to move coal and coke toward the sources of ore, especially to the ore-unloading points on Lake Erie. For these reasons Cleveland, Lorain, and places between them and Pittsburgh developed large iron- and steelmaking industries, and it remains still the major center of such industries in America. In most of the cities of this region from one-half to one-eighth of all the wages paid to workers in all industries go to persons employed in these primary manufactures. Associated with them are other heavy industries also, such as the heavy machine trades and the manufacture of steel pipe, structural steel, clay products, pottery, and glass. This major interest does not exclude other kinds of manufacture, such as the important clothing manufactures of Cleveland, rubber manufacture in Akron, and others, but it does give an industrial character to the region which the changes of half a century have not been able to erase.

Although the basic resource of this region is fuel and power, its development has been promoted also by position with respect to Great Lakes transportation and the trans-Appalachian rail routes to the east.

810. THE DETROIT REGION. Near the western end of Lake Erie is an industrial region whose center is Detroit, but it includes also a large section of southeastern Michigan, part of northwestern Ohio,

and western Ontario. Like the south shore of Lake Erie, it enjoys the advantages of position between the Appalachian coal fields and the northern iron mines on Great Lakes transportation. It has also some of the basic industries of iron and steel production, but they are subordinated to those that use these metals and others as raw materials, especially in the manufacture of motor vehicles. In Detroit and its industrial suburbs more than 60 per cent of all the wages paid go to workers in motor-vehicle production, and much of the remainder is paid to those employed in tool and other machine trades. In addition to the advantages of Great Lakes transportation for the assembling of power and of mineral, forest, and agricultural raw materials, this area profits by immediate access to the great markets of the agricultural Middle West by rail and highway and also to the industrial East. The development of the Ontario section of the region has been further promoted by the tariff barrier at the international boundary.

811. THE CINCINNATI-INDIANAPOLIS REGION. One of the important interior regions of manufacture includes the cities and towns of eastern Indiana and southwestern Ohio. It does not share the benefits of Great Lakes transportation or of direct access to the iron ores and forest resources of the Lake Superior region, but it has certain other advantages. It lies at the eastern end of the rich lands of the corn belt and between the Appalachian and eastern interior coal fields. To the Appalachian coal and industrial area it has access not only by rail but also through water transport on the Ohio River. Its diversified manufactures reflect an abundance of fuel and a variety of industrial raw materials, such as the products of the blast furnaces and steel mills of the Pittsburgh region and the grains and animals of midwestern and southern farms. They reflect also the large markets of the interior. In fact this region lies closest of any to the center of population of the whole United States. Highly important are its machine trades, including automotive and electrical equipment, precision tools, scales, cash registers, and many other types of mechanical products. Important also are the chemical and food-products industries, such as meat packing and the processing of grains, oil seeds, vegetables, and other agricultural raw materials.

812. THE LAKE MICHIGAN REGION. The western shore of southern Lake Michigan and its immediate hinterland comprise one of the major regions of manufacture in America. It is of great diversity, expresses the interaction of many factors, and is capable of division into several districts, which may not be considered here. Some of the principal factors include access to power resources by rail from the Illinois-Indiana coal fields and by lake transportation from those of the East,

access by lake to the northern iron-ore region, and the fact that it is the focus of rail transportation from and toward the agricultural lands of the interior plains, the Rocky Mountains, and even the Pacific Coast, which are its largest markets and its sources of raw materials. Chicago and Milwaukee are its principal centers. In them and in some of their associated towns are manufactures of nearly all classes, but a few groups of them reflect the principal industrial character of the region. These include blast furnaces and rolling mills, which, like those of the Lake Erie shore, provide raw materials for many industries. Some of these latter supply the rural markets with automotive equipment, tractors, wire fencing, and a great variety of farm machines and implements. There too are the large meat-packing plants, grain-processing mills, leather tanneries, shoe factories, and other establishments that draw their principal raw materials from the western farms and ranches and find their markets both locally and to the eastward. Also in this region are manufactories of furniture, paper, and other products whose raw materials come, at least in part, from the forests of the North and the West. Being central in position and the focus of many railroads, this region produces also large quantities of cars and other railroad equipment.

813. OTHER CENTERS OF AMERICAN MANUFACTURE. Although the great industrial region of the Northeast contains, as has previously been noted, about four-fifths of the manufacturing strength of the continent, there are others of great importance. To some extent they are scattered throughout the South and West, but among them are districts of outstanding character, whose principal products reflect the resources and other advantages of the environs. Among them are the following:

The Southern Highland Borders.   The southern Appalachian region furnishes both water powers and abundant coal; it also has access to cheap labor, forest resources, iron ores, raw cotton, and other essential raw materials. It is not surprising that it has undergone industrial development. The principal expressions of this development are seen in the cotton-textile district of the Piedmont, the blast furnaces and steel mills of northern Alabama, and in wood-products and chemical industries. In general these localities are more specialized than those of the northern regions in the manufacture of primary products and have fewer of the secondary industries using these primary products as raw materials for further manufacture. This may be an expression of its smaller degree of industrial maturity.

Industrial Cities of the Central Plains.   East of the High Plains and extending from the Prairie Provinces of Canada southward to the

Gulf of Mexico are widely spaced cities having considerable local importance in manufacture and not a small place in the whole industrial pattern of the continent. They include Winnipeg, Minneapolis-St. Paul, Omaha, Kansas City, St. Louis, Dallas-Fort Worth, and Houston. Most of them are first of all assembling points for regional produce, especially agricultural produce, and their leading manufactures are of the bulk-reducing type. Meat packing, grain milling, cotton compressing, oil refining, or similar industries take important places in them, and the more elaborate manufactures of secondary type are less developed. Of them all St. Louis is easternmost, largest, and most complex, since steel production, the machine trades, shoe manufacture, the chemical industries, and each of several others is important there, and some of them outrank meat packing.

Manufacturing Districts of the Pacific Coast. The Pacific Coast has three distinct manufacturing areas: the Puget Sound–Willamette valley group of cities, the San Francisco Bay group, and the Los Angeles–San Diego group. Each has industries of considerable variety to supply local demands, since the regions are far removed from the eastern manufacturing centers and from each other. Yet each has a distinctive character also which is determined by local resources and requirements. In the northern group, from Vancouver to Portland, sawmills and lumber-using industries normally take first rank. In the San Francisco area, petroleum refining, steel production, and shipbuilding rank high, but so great is the diversity that no one industry accounts for more than about 6 per cent of the total wages paid in the district. In the Los Angeles–San Diego region also diversity is characteristic. A large local market is served with much of its requirements in meat, clothing, furniture, machinery, and structural steel. Owing to certain advantages of climate, and its petroleum resources, and also no doubt to other cultural-historical factors, three of the many industries take high rank. These are airplane manufacture, the moving-picture industry, and petroleum refining. In normal times nearly 15 per cent of the industrial wage earners in the Los Angeles industrial district are employed in the moving-picture industry, and they receive about 20 per cent of the industrial wages paid in the area. Under wartime conditions employment in aircraft manufacture has expanded rapidly, and that industry undoubtedly has taken the leading place.

MANUFACTURAL REGIONS OF EUROPE AND ASIA

814. The continent of Europe is highly industrialized (Fig. 399). The Industrial Revolution of the eighteenth century found already

there certain of the requisite cultural and physical conditions for a progressive and rapid development of factory manufacture. These included: (a) a large population having a fairly high standard of living, which provided a large potential market; (b) a high degree of technical skills, which had resulted from the perfection and specialization of household and small workshop manufacture; (c) inventive genius, which provided new machines and adapted them to the application of mechanical power; and (d) water power at first, and eventually steam engines driven by coal. There were also widely distributed sources of water power adequate for infant industries, and when these were outgrown, there were numerous coal deposits to replace them as primary sources of energy. Europe also had the advantage of more highly developed routes of transportation than any other part of the world; good highways, canals, and canalized rivers, and a deeply indented and estuarine coastline that made large parts of Europe accessible from the sea. Under modern conditions coal is the primary source of mechanical energy, and water power takes second place. The near absence of petroleum in western Europe, significant as it may be from the standpoint of transportation and war needs, has little relation to the growth of industry since it is not, even in the United States where it is abundant, a major source of energy for manufacturing industries. It is not surprising, therefore, that the heavy and basic industries of Europe, which require great quantities of energy and fuel, are clustered about the richest coal fields (Figs. 334, 335). There are commonly associated with them many other kinds of manufacture which find various advantages in being in the great centers of industry. However, there are also several lesser manufactural districts in which the lighter forms of industry predominate, especially such as do not require great quantities of fuel and power in proportion to their demands for labor and capital or to the value of their products. Some of these are associated with the smaller and poorer coal fields or are dependent upon modern hydroelectric or steam-electric power installations. They include especially the textile manufactures, chemical industries, and many others of the lighter type.

Because of the conditions that have affected industrial development, the manufacturing centers of Europe are by no means uniformly distributed. The major districts are, in fact, arranged in a more or less continuous belt that extends east and west through the middle portion of the continent. Northern Europe, on the one hand, and the Mediterranean borderlands, on the other, are much less well endowed and less industrialized. The principal belt includes Great Britain, on the west, and extends through northern France, Belgium, western and central Germany, Czechoslovakia, and southern Poland into central and southern Russia. Various portions of industrial Europe will be given further consideration.

815. BRITISH CENTERS OF MANUFACTURE. In Great Britain coal is abundant and other sources of power scarce. It is natural therefore that the great industrial centers of the nineteenth century grew up about the coal fields (Fig. 334). To a large degree this association still exists, although new factors have come into effect and shifts are taking place.

The early iron industries of England were located especially in the Midlands region near Birmingham, and this region remains highly important in the manufacture of machinery, vehicles, arms, hardware, glass, chemical products, and many other things. Although the region has less local coal than some of the others, it has the great advantage of central location and excellent railroad connections. Power brought by transmission lines from steam-electric plants in adjacent coal-producing districts is supplemented by hydroelectric power and helps to overcome the disadvantage of a declining local coal resource.

The same flexibility with respect to power supply that has been made possible by electric transmission has aided also in making London a great and diversified manufacturing center in recent decades, although it has no local coal whatever. Its coal supply must come from the northern fields by boat and train. Formerly it was the great commercial center and port of Britain, but its manufactures were restricted and concerned mainly the processing and repackaging of a variety of products imported from abroad and designed for reexport to foreign markets. The vast labor supply of London, its connection by rail and water with the other British ports and centers of raw materials, and its ability to secure power have attracted to the city and its suburbs, in recent decades, many of the newer types of chemical and metal manufactures as well as shipbuilding and some other of the heavy mechanical trades. Efforts are now being made, however, to scatter and decentralize the industries of London in order to reduce the losses caused by aerial bombardment in the war. To some extent the scattering may be permanent, and London may not again be the great center of British manufacture that it has recently been.

In northeastern England is the principal region of heavy industry. It is located in association with the coal fields of Northumberland and Durham and one of the several principal domestic sources of iron ore in the Cleveland district of northern Yorkshire. Coastal location also favored manufactural development in this region since Swedish and Spanish iron ores came in through convenient ports, and many of the regional products were exported. However, exports have declined and so have the imports of ore and other raw materials, especially under war economy. As a consequence the coastal towns have suffered some industrial depression while the inland transportation centers have experienced comparative advantage. Important centers of manufacture in this district are the great steelmaking towns such as Middlesbrough and Hartlepool. Newcastle-on-Tyne has long been a major shipbuilding port, but the region is also a producer of railroad and structural steel, locomotives, cars, and other heavy goods. It has also a variety of lighter manufactures, including chemical industries, which are based in part upon local salt deposits.

IMPORTANT TOWNS IN THE LANCASHIRE-YORKSHIRE INDUSTRIAL REGION

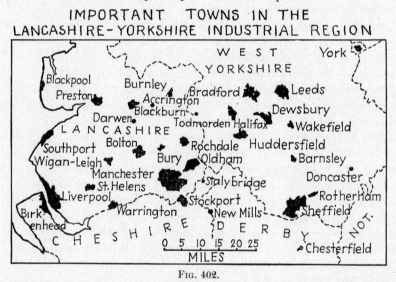

Fɪɢ. 402.

Associated with the productive coal fields of Lancashire and Yorkshire, which lie respectively to the west and east of the Pennine Hills, are industries of quite different type. These are the great centers of textile specialization. Sheep were numerous in the hilly uplands, and the manufacture of woolens was established there at an early date. When cotton spinning became important, and especially after the growth of large factories, American cotton was conveniently brought in through the west-facing port of Liverpool, and cotton textiles came to dominate the manufactures of Lancashire. For various reasons wool manufacture shifted to the eastern side of the Pennines and concentrated in western Yorkshire. A high degree of specialization grew up in both these textile regions, some towns spinning yarns of special kinds and others making only a limited class of fabrics (Fig. 402).

However, such extreme specialization has been a disadvantage during the recent depression years, and the larger and more centrally located places have had an advantage while some of the smaller and more specialized have experienced extreme distress. An industrial relocation is now in progress. The metal trades have long been represented in this region also, especially in Sheffield, where charcoal steel and an excellent variety of grinding stone gave rise to the cutlery industry for which that city has long been famous. In more recent years, abundant coal and the iron ores of the Frodingham and other deposits of eastern England have encouraged its expansion into one of the important steel-producing districts of the country.

Britain's most northern manufactural region lies in the Scottish Lowlands, between the River Clyde and the Firth of Forth. It is based upon the coal deposits of that area. It is a region of great industrial diversity but is noted particularly for its iron and steel products and its textiles. The former find particular expression in the shipbuilding of the River Clyde, near Glasgow, where the largest ocean liners are built and equipped. The latter include famous centers of manufacture in cotton, wool, flax, and jute.

The industries of the South Wales coal field are more recent and specialized than those of the other coal regions. Blast furnaces and rolling mills furnish raw materials for the manufacture of steel plates and tin plate, which are the most distinctive products of the area.

816. FRENCH AND BELGIAN CENTERS OF MANUFACTURE. On the continent of Europe, the industrial districts of France and Belgium comprise the westernmost units in the great manufactural belt that extends eastward through central Germany and into Russia (Fig. 399). All of them are related to the sources of power and minerals found in that part of the continent (Fig. 403).

The focus of French industrial development is in the northern and northeastern parts of the country. It comprises a broad belt that extends along the Belgian, German, and Swiss borders. The reason for this is found in the distribution of the critical mineral and power resources. France is not supplied with large reserves of good coal, but there are large and well-integrated water powers. These are obtained from the bordering highlands of the Ardennes, Vosges, Jura, and Alps, and also from the Central Highland and the Pyrenees. Water powers are therefore available in many parts of France but especially in the northeast and east, where they are well used in the development of textile and other light manufactures. Water power is, however, inadequate for the support of heavy industry. The principal coal deposits of France are in the north, where they are continuous with those of Belgium. They supply fuel for the heavy industries in and near the coal fields, but in recent times the fuel requirements of French industry have been fully met only by importing coal from England through the northern French ports. In the north of France also are the great iron-ore deposits of Lorraine (Fig. 403). These, in combination with the coal, are the basis of the heavy industries. In part the ore moves to the coal, and steel mills are located in the north of France and in the heavy industrial belt of Belgium, which extends along the coal fields from Mons to Liége. This belt includes not only

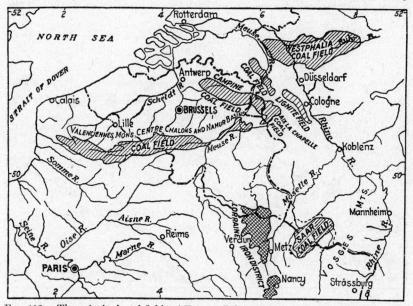

Fig. 403.—The principal coal fields of France, Belgium, and western Germany in their geographical relations to the great iron-ore deposits of Lorraine.

iron furnaces but zinc smelters and other metallurgical industries together with machine manufactures, glass, clay-working, and chemical industries. In addition to its coal this region has a dense population from which to recruit an abundant labor supply. Not all the iron is smelted in this district, however, because much of the high-grade coal moves eastward to meet the ores of Lorraine, which are rather low grade and therefore bulky. This trade is the basis for the growth of heavy industry in the ore-producing region.

Many lighter industries also have located in and adjacent to the coal fields. Such are the textile mills of the lowlands of northern Belgium and of northern France. These industries are, however, not so closely dependent on coal as are those of the heavier types, and they are found also in eastern France and in many other sections where water power is available.

Paris, like London, is a great center of manufacture even though it has no local source of power. The fact that it is a transportation center and is able to furnish a large labor supply is sufficient to attract many industries to it, but mainly those of lighter type.

817. WESTERN GERMANY has several highly important industrial districts, including those of the Saar coal basin and the upper Rhine Valley and Bavaria, but the most important are those of the lower Rhine region, which are associated with the productive coal fields of the

PRINCIPAL TOWNS OF THE RHINE-WESTPHALIAN INDUSTRIAL REGION

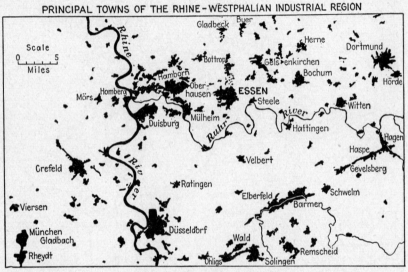

FIG. 404.

Ruhr Valley in Westphalia. This is the oldest and probably still the largest center of German heavy industry. Before 1918 it drew largely upon the iron ores of Lorraine but lost them as a result of the First World War and became dependent upon poorer domestic ores and upon imports, especially from Sweden. However, the Lorraine ores were recovered by military conquest in 1940. In the Westphalian district are more than a dozen industrial cities exceeding 100,000 population each and numerous towns of smaller size (Fig. 404). Among them, as in parts of Great Britain, is much industrial specialization. The heavy industries are grouped on the coal fields (Fig. 403) and to the east and southeast of them, the hardware and lighter metal trades lie southward, and the textile districts have developed to the westward and northward. For example, heavy iron and steel wares are the typical products of Essen, Dortmund, and Bochum in the coal area. Hardware, arms, and cutlery are the distinctive manufactures of Remscheid and Solingen, a variety of textile products is more characteristic of Duisburg-Hamborn, Krefeld, München-Gladbach, Köln (Cologne), and several others. In some part of this great Rhenish-Westphalian region are factories producing nearly every class of goods from silks to ships.

818. CENTRAL EUROPEAN DISTRICTS OF MANUFACTURE include those of south-central Germany and Bohemia. They are associated with large deposits of lignite, scattered small deposits of coal, sources of water power and various minerals, especially low-grade iron ores and the great German potash beds. Lignite is employed in the production of synthetic gasoline, and energy derived by various means from lignite, coal, and water power is integrated into a highly efficient power network. This central power resource and the exposed military position of the Westphalian region has caused a shift of industry to this more distant interior. The iron ores serve as a foundation for heavy industries, including some of the newest steel works. However, the low quality of the ores generally makes it necessary to improve them by the use of high-grade ores, especially those imported from northern Sweden. Potash and the products of coal and lignite distillation form the basis of highly developed chemical industries. The older products of the region are mainly of the lighter types, such as textiles, pottery, light machinery, optical goods, precision instruments, and the products of engraving and printing. These are the wares upon which the high industrial reputation of the region was made, and they remain important. The new political dispensation has brought others which include armament, automotive, and airplane manufactures. All are knit together into a new kind of interdependent manufactural region. Much of the shift from the west appears to have been designed as a military precaution and seems uneconomic in view of the meager supply of coal and the low-grade iron ores. How much of it may remain there when the war economy is ended only the future can tell.

In Silesia there are coal, zinc ore, and some resources in iron and other minerals. These have permitted the growth of metallurgical industries around which other manufactures, including textiles and clothing, have gathered. This area, which between 1918 and 1939 was shared by Germany, Poland, and Czechoslovakia, was developed by all three countries. It has also a most advantageous position on natural north-south corridors of central Europe, such as the Moravian Gate, at the western end of the Carpathian Mountains, and the Elbe Valley.

All these and other smaller centers of manufacture merge with those of the west in a nearly continuous belt of high manufactural development which occupies a strategic place in the industrial pattern of the world. In fact, it is a belt of such high population density (Figs. 357, 364) and manufactural concentration that it has no equal in industrial importance in any other continent.

819. SOUTH EUROPEAN CENTERS OF MANUFACTURE. Lack of coal in southern Europe has not prevented manufactural development there but has notably affected its character. Spain has abundant iron ore but little coal, and Switzerland, Italy, and the Balkan countries have no important reserves of either. However, the Alps and the Pyrenees furnish water powers that are used intensively. For that reason the heavy industries are not highly developed, and those that exist depend largely upon imported coal and raw materials. They operate in large part under government promotion and for political or military reasons. These include armament manufacture, shipbuilding, and airplane manufacture, especially in Italy. Deprived by wartime blockade of their supplies of fuel and scrap iron, they have been quickly reduced to relative unimportance. The more typical industries are of the lighter types. These include food preparation, textile manufactures, and fine metalwares, such as watches and instruments. These industries and many others can utilize the hydroelectric power and the abundant skilled labor of the Swiss valleys, the Po Basin of Italy, and Catalonia in northeastern Spain. The Balkan Peninsula is poorly developed in manufacturing. It has little coal, its water powers are much less than those of the more rainy and glaciated Pyrenees and Alps, and its people have long been troubled by political unrest that has not given manufacture the necessary condition of security.

820. REGIONS OF MANUFACTURE IN U.S.S.R. The vast expanses of Soviet Russia contain many of the requisites of a large-scale manufactural development. Prior to the Soviet regime, however, they were but meagerly employed. Large reserves of coal exist and also petroleum, iron ores, manganese, and other raw materials such as metals, timber, and agricultural products. The intense effort to achieve industrial independence initiated by the Soviet government brought about the use of these on a much larger scale than formerly, and several industrial districts have developed (Fig. 399). In part these were associated with the coal deposits of the Donets Basin and the Moskva (Moscow) region, supplemented by water powers obtained from the mountain streams of the Caucasus and from large streams of low gradient such as the Dnepr (Dnieper) (Figs. 343, 335). In the Donets Basin particularly, the proximity of the great coal fields to the iron ores of Krivoi Rog led to the development of the heavy industries, and such cities as Kharkov, Lugansk, Rostov, and others in the south made great

industrial advancement. They specialized in machinery, tractors, farm equipment, and similar products. Moskva, however, is the center of an old region of manufacture, but it suffered from a lack of coking coal and iron ores close at hand. It was formerly noted for textiles and other light manufactures, but because it is the chief city of the country, has a large labor supply, and is the principal rail center it has recently attracted a great variety of manufactures, some of them of the heavier type. Its great size and diversity make the Moskva region the greatest industrial center in Russia. Leningrad ranked second, but not because of its abundance of coal. It has, in fact, no coal and must bring its supply at great cost from the south or from foreign sources. It has more water power than Moskva but few raw materials save timber and some agricultural products. Its great development as a manufacturing center has depended largely upon its strategic position as the gateway to the Baltic Sea, the only convenient seaport of all northern Russia opening toward the industrial countries of western Europe. These great industrial centers of European Russia are now badly crippled and partly ruined by war. One may well believe however that, under any probable form of European economy, the same considerations, natural and cultural, which caused their location and growth in the first place will be strong enough to bring about their eventual recovery.

Fortunately for Russia, military precaution and the desire to bring to distant regions the benefits of manufactural industry had established other industrial centers far to the east. There are two of these, and each shows clear relations to the resources of its district. The first lies in the southern Ural region, which has a variety of resources but none in great abundance. Some small deposits of coal are found and high-grade iron ores, copper, lead, potash, salt, and other industrial minerals. Ore reduction, machinery and arms manufacture, chemical industries, and many others supplement those of the Moskva and other western districts. They also have the merit of being 800 or more miles east of Moskva and thus less exposed to military operations. The most critical shortage of materials in this region is of good coal, although some of the small deposits are of high quality. Its greatest surplus is of iron ore, mined near Magnitogorsk, and this is to some extent exchanged for coal with the central Siberian industrial district of the Kuznetsk Basin (Fig. 343), which has coal in abundance but little iron ore. This latter industrial region lies 2,000 miles east of Moskva, and, although its development has only begun, it may prove of critical importance. Not only does it manufacture metal products, but it has also at least the beginning of chemical, wood-products, paper, and general-supply industries. It has as its markets the growing population centers of central Siberia and the eastern Pacific maritime region.

821. REGIONS OF MANUFACTURE IN EASTERN AND SOUTHERN ASIA. The relation between coal deposits and the location of manufactural districts so commonly observed in Europe and America appears to be less conspicuous in the Orient. The great coal fields of northern China have no associated manufactures, whereas the high industrial development of Japan has comparatively little coal to support it. For an explanation of these facts one must turn to the industrial history of the two countries and to their comparative accessibilities from the standpoint of transportation.

822. *China*, at the beginning of war with Japan in 1937, had barely passed the threshold of modern industrial development. Such modern factory industries as it possessed, largely textile mills, were concentrated in the densely peopled lower Yangtze Valley. They drew their coal from several small fields difficult of access. The great coal fields of Shensi-Shansi (Fig. 336) were reached by only one railroad and have as yet contributed very little to the supply of industrial power. War has now devastated the factories that did exist and set Chinese manufacture back almost to the handicraft stage. Developments that may bring about regional concentrations of industry remain for the future to unfold.

823. *Japan* has only small coal fields, but they are readily accessible, and both rail and water transport permit of the movement of fuel to the centers of population. There are also widely distributed and highly developed water powers, and a great Japanese merchant marine to assemble raw materials and distribute manufactured exports. Moreover, a large and rapidly increasing population has provided cheap and abundant labor and has almost enforced modern industrialization in spite of meager resources in coal and iron. As in nearly all countries, the earlier and larger part of the manufactural development took place in the field of the lighter industries, especially silk and cotton manufactures, food preparation, and small wares of wood, paper, and metal. However, there has been a great change in the character of the Japanese industry in the last quarter of a century and particularly within the last decade. It has expanded into many new fields. Faced with the competition of rayon against the silk industry, Japanese manufacturers have themselves set up rayon industries exceeding those of any other country. The textile trades have extended also to include wool and other fibers. It is not, however, in the lighter industries alone that expansion has taken place. Abundant water powers, cheap labor, a depreciated currency which made it difficult

to buy foreign manufactures, and the desire to become independent of foreign sources of critical military needs have combined to promote the heavy industries in spite of deficiencies in the natural equipment of the islands. In order to support growing steel industries and engineering trades it has been necessary greatly to increase the coal output of Japan's limited deposits and to import coal from foreign sources. Because the home supply of iron ore is even more limited than that of coal it has been necessary also to import pig iron from Manchuria, ores from China, Malaya, and Australia, and even larger quantities of scrap iron and steel in order to avoid the use of so much coal in the smelting process. These conditions, together with the lack of domestic petroleum, make the new Japanese economy particularly vulnerable under war conditions unless it can also control all of southeastern Asia and the East Indies.

Among the heavy industries are several of large capital and great scope. They include shipbuilding and armament industries, hydroelectric and other machine equipment, and a variety of chemical industries, which are quite different from the small plants and light manufactures of the earlier period. The districts of manufacture are largely concentrated in the "industrial belt" of southern Japan. It extends westward from Tokyo to the coal fields of northern Kyushu and includes the large cities, Yokohama, Nagoya, Kyoto, Osaka, and Kobe.

824. *India*, like other lands of ancient civilization, has a long tradition in the handicrafts. For many years also factory industries have been established, especially in the textile trades, and to some extent also in metalworking. The first to develop on a large scale were the cotton mills of the Bombay district of western India. Subsequently jute mills were set up in the Calcutta region, near the source of the raw fiber. The rise of heavy industry in India is, however, of recent origin. The vast deposits of high-grade iron ore in the district northwest of Calcutta and the near-by coal fields (Fig. 336) invited the establishment of blast furnaces and steel mills of modern type, although the coal reserves are not great. The large supply of cheap labor makes it possible to produce iron there at very low cost. Until recently, however, it supplied mainly the domestic market for machines and implements. The emergency of war found in the Indian factories a nucleus capable of rapid expansion, and they quickly became an important source of supply in a variety of goods. Not only textile and leather products were provided for the armed forces, but guns of various types, explosives, vehicles, and small marine craft, and a surplus of crude iron and steel was exported for manufacture elsewhere. It is unlikely, since

industries of these varied types have been established, that they will disappear when the war emergency is past. India may, therefore, be counted as one of the important and growing manufactural regions of the world.

MANUFACTURAL REGIONS OF THE SOUTHERN HEMISPHERE

The more settled portions of the Southern Hemisphere are mainly producers and exporters of agricultural and mineral raw materials but have not engaged in their manufacture on a large scale. Hence, there are no great industrial centers there. It does not follow, however, that factory industries are entirely undeveloped or incapable of expansion. The South American countries, which have the largest domestic markets, are handicapped by lack of coal, while Australia, New Zealand, and South Africa, which have some coal (Fig. 337), have only limited markets because of small populations. In all these areas, however, manufacture has made beginnings, and in some it has advanced considerably (Fig. 399).

825. IN ARGENTINA AND BRAZIL the principal factories are those concerned with the preparation of foodstuffs and with textile manufacture. It would be expected that the forms of manufacture that could succeed there would be (a) those using raw materials produced in the region, (b) those using a comparatively small amount of coal-driven machinery, (c) those demanding a relatively small force of technically skilled employees, or (d) those producing articles that require local manufacture in order to fill immediate needs or to fit the exact nature of the local markets. In Argentina, where there is little water power and all the coal must be imported, the principal industries are meat packing, flour milling, textile mills, and manufactories of vehicles and farm implements to fit local needs. They are located mainly in the great city and port of Buenos Aires. Brazil has the advantage of large water-power resources and of a larger domestic market, and it has somewhat more diversified manufactures which include cotton and jute textiles, clothing, chemicals, and some metalwares. Through lack of coal, however, there has been little progress in the utilization of the large domestic resource of iron ore.

826. IN AUSTRALIA AND NEW ZEALAND, as in South America, the settlement and development of a large area of land by a small population has only recently permitted much attention to be given to manufacture. However, conditions there have favored manufacture somewhat more than in South America. In addition to supplies of coal there is the factor of greater distance and higher freight rates from the European and American manufacturing regions. Australians and New

Zealanders are dominantly of British stock and have somewhat greater interest in and familiarity with industrial management than those who control the capital and governmental policies of Latin America. The greater number of factories of Australia and New Zealand are concerned with the preparation of foods: flour and sugar milling, fruit preserving, meat packing, and butter and cheese manufacture. Others of long standing are the ore-reduction plants associated with the mining of gold, zinc, and other valuable minerals, also sawmills and plants turning out bulky wood products, such as furniture. During the First World War the shortage of shipping made it profitable to set up a variety of other manufactories, many of which languished in the postwar period because of their high production costs. Some have persisted, however, and Australia, particularly, enters the second great war of the century with several types of manufacture already in operation on a fairly large scale. These include blast furnaces and steel mills, near the coal fields of the east coast, textile mills in Victoria, clothing manufacture, and various types of machine and armament plants, some of them now greatly enlarged for the war emergency.

827. THE UNION OF SOUTH AFRICA, of all the Southern Hemisphere centers of population, has developed least in manufacture. However, the need of equipping military forces has recently led to industrial expansion there also. Small and local industries have enlarged their capacities and widened their manufactural scope. They are now producing military clothing, munitions, guns, and armored vehicles. South African coal and mineral ores make this possible.

WAR INDUSTRIES AND THE POSTWAR INDUSTRIAL PATTERNS OF THE WORLD

828. The distribution and the character of the world's leading centers of manufacture have resulted from a slow evolution through the operation of elements in the physical environment and economic factors which have previously been considered. In this evolution the factors of relative advantage for and experience in manufacture have expressed themselves in the comparative costs of the various classes of goods to the consumers and in the qualities of the goods. To some extent always these factors have been offset by the nationalistic objectives of governments made manifest through tariffs and other protective regulations. In the main, however, the strong forces have been good and cheap sources of fuel and power, abundant and skilled labor, available capital, and experienced management. Normally, these forces have been sufficient to overcome the disadvantages of transportation

costs on raw materials from distant sources and on finished products to distant markets.

War, however, creates an entirely different situation, and total world war brings revolution rather than evolution to bear upon the industrial patterns of the world. Goods of almost every type are required in quantity regardless of quality. Many of the products of manufacture are destined to temporary and destructive rather than long-time and constructive uses. Old industries are abandoned or moved to new sites of less natural advantage for reasons of military safety. Less adaptable raw materials are substituted for better ones which come from vulnerable sources. New industries appear in regions which previously were undeveloped. In fact, the whole industrial pattern of the world is changed within the span of a few months. However, cessation of hostilities and, we may hope world peace, must come eventually. Following that there will come a long, slow, and probably painful period of readjustment during which the world distribution of manufactural industries will reshape itself. Which ones of the abandoned industries will reappear, and where, which of the new ones will remain, and why, only the events of the future can decide. Undoubtedly the natural conditions favorable to manufacture and the usual economic forces will again exert themselves, and the old manufactural regions will resume something of their former character. Probably, however, the return will never be complete, and the patterns of the future will be in many details unlike those of either the past or the present.

REFERENCES FOR CHAPTER XXXI

Bliss, Charles A. "The Structure of Manufacturing Production." National Bureau of Economic Research, New York, 1939.

Bogardus, J. F. "Europe, a Geographical Survey." Harper & Brothers, New York, 1934.

Dickinson, Robert E. The Economic Regions of Germany. *Geog. Rev.*, Vol. 28, pp. 609–626, 1938.

Hartshorne, Richard. A new map of the manufacturing belt of North America. *Econ. Geog.*, Vol. 12, pp. 45–53, 1936.

Hubbard, George D. "The Geography of Europe." D. Appleton-Century Company, Inc., New York, 1937.

Jones, Clarence F. Areal Distribution of Manufacturing in the United States. *Econ. Geog.*, Vol. 14, pp. 217–222, 1938.

——— and Darkenwald, G. G. "Economic Geography." The Macmillan Company, New York, 1941.

Keir, Malcolm. "Manufacturing Industries in America." The Ronald Press Company, New York, 1928.

"Maps of Selected Industries Reported at the Census of Manufactures, 1937, Showing Location of Establishments, Wage Earners, Value Added by Manufacture." United States Department of Commerce, Bureau of the Census, Washington, D. C.

Mears, Eliot G. Postwar Locational Changes of British Industries. *Geog. Rev.*, Vol. 29, pp. 233–251, 1939.

Mikhaylov, N. "Soviet Geography." Bookniga Corp., New York, 1937.

Mitchell, Kate L. "Japan's Industrial Strength." Alfred A. Knopf, New York, 1942.

———. "Industrialization of the Western Pacific," Institute of Pacific Relations, New York, 1942.

Schumpeter, E. B., *et al.* "The Industrialization of Japan and Manchukuo 1930–1940." The Macmillan Company, New York, 1940.

Strong, Helen M. Regions of Manufacturing Intensity in the United States. *Ann. Assoc. Amer. Geographers*, Vol. 27, pp. 23–43, 1937.

Taylor, E. G. R. Discussion on the geographical distribution of industry. *Geog. Jour.*, Vol. 92, pp. 22–32, 1938.

Trewartha, G. T. "A Reconnaissance Geography of Japan." University of Wisconsin Press, Madison, 1934.

Van Valkenburg, Samuel, and Huntington, E. "Europe." John Wiley & Sons, Inc. New York, 1935.

Whitbeck, R. H., and Finch, V. C. "Economic Geography." 4th ed., McGraw-Hill Book Company, Inc., New York, 1941.

Wright, Alfred J. Manufacturing Districts of the United States, *Econ. Geog.*, Vol. 14, pp. 195–200, 1938.

Zierer, Clifford M. The Australian Iron and Steel Industry as a Functional Unit. *Geog. Rev.*, Vol. 30, pp. 649–659, 1940.

———. Industrial Area of Newcastle, Australia. *Econ. Geog.*, Vol. 17, pp. 31–49, 1941.

Zimmerman, E. W. "World Resources and Industries." Harper & Brothers, New York, 1933.

Chapter XXXII. Communications, Transportation, and Trade

829. FUNCTION OF COMMUNICATIONS. All forms of communication are for the purpose of facilitating the movement of man, his ideas, or his goods from one place to another. As the telephone, telegraph, cable, and radio transport man's ideas, so ships, trains, motorcars, airplanes, and animals transport him and his goods. The importance of transportation to human society is suggested by the following quotation concerning the road, which as here used is emblematic of transport lines in general.

"The Road is one of the great fundamental institutions of mankind. We forget this because we take it for granted. It seems to be so necessary and natural a part of all human life that we forget it ever had an origin or development or that it is as much the creation of man as the city and the laws. Not only is the Road one of the great human institutions because it is fundamental to human existence, but also because its varied effect appears in every department of the state. It is the Road which determines the sites of many cities and the growth and nourishment of all. It is the Road which controls the development of strategics and fixes the sites of battles. It is the Road which gives its framework to all economic development. It is the Road which is the channel of all trade and, what is more important, of all ideas. In its most humble function it is a necessary guide without which progress from place to place would be a ceaseless experiment; it is a sustenance without which organized society would be impossible; thus, and with those other characters I have mentioned, the Road moves and controls all history.

"A road system, once established, develops at its points of concentration the nerve centers of the society it serves; and we remark that the rise and decline of a state are better measured by the condition of its communications —that is, of its roads—than by any other criterion."[1]

830. PLACE UTILITY AND TRANSPORT. When a raw material has been converted by manufacturing processes into a finished product, it has been made more useful or more valuable through a change in

[1] Belloc, Hilaire. "The Road." Harper & Brothers, New York, 1925. A portion of the author's introduction.

ones. Outstanding in the mineral group are such bulky ones as coal, petroleum, iron ore, lead, and zinc. In tonnage this group takes first rank. A large group designated as miscellaneous includes a host of items, among them such outstanding ones as rubber and timber.

The striking feature of the preceding table showing per cent of world trade by continents is the unusual concentration in Europe. This reflects a similar concentration of population and of industrial development (Fig. 405). The fact that the continent is divided into a large number of relatively small but important countries naturally leads to much trade crossing international boundary lines, which thereby becomes foreign commerce. On the other hand, the immense trade between regions within a large political unit like the United States is domestic in character and consequently does not appear in the preceding table.

835. FOREIGN TRADE OF THE UNITED STATES. The diversity of American foreign trade is indicated by the table showing the 15 leading exports and imports.

Leading American Exports, 1937
(Ranked according to value)
1. Machinery
2. Petroleum
3. Cotton, raw
4. Automobile and accessories
5. Iron and steel mill products
6. Tobacco
7. Copper, including manufacture
8. Chemicals
9. Fruits and nuts
10. Coal and coke
11. Wheat and flour
12. Pulp and paper
13. Sawmill products
14. Iron and steel, advanced manufacture
15. Cotton manufactures

Leading American Imports, 1937
(Ranked according to value)
1. Rubber
2. Sugar
3. Coffee
4. Paper and paper manufactures
5. Paper base stocks, including pulp
6. Vegetable oils
7. Raw silk
8. Tin
9. Wool
10. Oil seeds
11. Cacao
12. Cotton manufactures
13. Chemicals
14. Fertilizers
15. Diamonds

The export list contains representatives of both highly manufactured wares such as machinery, automobiles, flour, paper, chemicals, and cotton cloth, and of raw materials, both agricultural and mineral. The imports include such tropical foods and raw materials as rubber, cane sugar, coffee, and cacao, which for climatic reasons cannot be produced at home. As a rule the imports include only a few manufactured products, which reflects the industrial nature of this country.

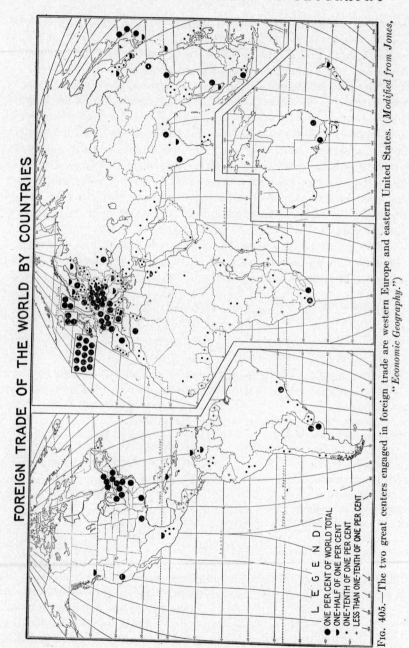

FOREIGN TRADE OF THE WORLD BY COUNTRIES

LEGEND
● ONE PER CENT OF WORLD TOTAL
◗ ONE-HALF OF ONE PER CENT
• ONE-TENTH OF ONE PER CENT
+ LESS THAN ONE-TENTH OF ONE PER CENT

Fig. 405.—The two great centers engaged in foreign trade are western Europe and eastern United States. (Modified from Jones, "Economic Geography.")

Routes of Transport and Their Carriers

836. TYPES OF TRADE ROUTES. The world's trade routes may be classified into three general types: land, water, and air. At least one fundamental difference distinguishes most land routes from those in the air and on the water, *viz.*, that in the two latter no trace is left by the vehicle after it passes. A ship slips through the water, and in a few moments all record of its passage has been obliterated. The same is true of air transport. On the other hand, the land almost invariably preserves traces of routes followed. As a consequence of this difference, it is to be expected that air and water routes are not nearly so definite in location as are those of the land. The direction and course of any route are determined, first of all, by the points that are to be connected and, second, by the obstacles that interpose themselves between these points.

But although routes may, for convenience of discussion, be divided into the three classes named above, it should not be lost sight of that they are integrally related. In modern trade a water route may be a continuation of a land route and vice versa, and the coastline is simply a point of transshipment along the route made necessary by a change in mode of transportation. Thus wheat moving to New York City reaches Duluth by rail, is there shifted to lake steamer, which may carry it to Buffalo, from which terminal it is again transshipped to rail or canal barge, which sets it down in New York.

LAND ROUTES AND THEIR CARRIERS

837. The human body is the most universal as well as the most primitive means of land transport, and human portage still prevails in many parts of the world. Animals, too, such as the horse, camel, donkey, and ox, serve in the same capacity and, because of their greater strength, are able to carry heavier loads and often with greater speed than can man. But it is usually easier to drag a burden than to carry it, and this fact very early led to such mechanical inventions as the rollers of the Assyrians, and later the wheel, upon the axle of which was built the cart. The exact place and time of origin of the wheeled vehicle is not known, but it goes back into prehistoric times. Its invention marks one of the greatest forward strides in the evolution of transport. Most of our modern means of land transport, the automobile and the train, are but modifications of the original wheeled cart, mechanically powered so as to provide greater speed and pulling strength as compared with the human- or animal-drawn vehicle.

Land routes and their carriers changed more rapidly during the nineteenth century than during the entire period of world history up to that time. Until the development of the portable steam engine land travel the world over had been by human carriers on foot, pack animals, ox- or horse-drawn wagon, or by river and canal. All these were slow, and the amount of goods that could be carried was relatively small. With the development of the railroad after about 1840, land transportation was revolutionized in some parts of the earth. However

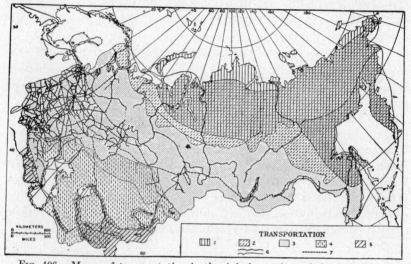

Fig. 406.—Means of transportation in the Asiatic portions of the U.S.S.R. compiled by B. Semenov-Tian-Shansky. 1, dogs; 2, reindeer; 3, horses and oxen; 4, camels; 5, mules, asses, and buffaloes; 6, principal lines of navigation on rivers and seas; 7, railroads. (*Courtesy of the Geographical Review, published by the Geographical Society of New York.*)

the earlier primitive means of travel have by no means disappeared. Over large areas of the earth, particularly those less advanced in material civilization, these forms still are the standard ones (Fig. 406). Even in the most advanced countries their least accessible and thinly populated parts are still served by the more primitive transportation facilities.

1. HIGHWAYS AND MOTOR VEHICLES

838. The Road. Of all land routes, the *road*, including everything from the humblest path to the modern concrete highway, is the most ancient as well as the most universal. Ancient Rome recognized the strategic value of roads in facilitating the quick shifting of troops to any part of the Empire, and as a result highways were constructed,

not only in Italy but over the Alps into the basins of the Danube and the Rhine, to the center of Spain, and even in England. Other ancient peoples such as the Chinese and the Incas built paved roads, but it remained for the Romans first to organize separate roads into a system or network, all parts of which fed into one another (Fig. 407). Not all peoples construct such permanent highways. Among the dunes of the Sahara are paths worn by camel trains of caravans, while porters' feet have left imprints upon the jungle soils and vegetation of the Congo. Every human establishment, no matter how insignificant, becomes a focus of roads, and the greater its attraction the greater the multiplication of trails leading to it.

FIG. 407.—Carts hauling stores to Mongolia along the old road connecting Peiping with Urga. (*Photograph by F. G. Clapp. Courtesy of the Geographical Review, published by the American Geographical Society of New York.*)

839. FUNCTIONS OF ROADS.   Most of the roads of the earth grew out of the needs for local transportation. Only to a limited extent were the public roads expected to function in long-distance movement of people or goods. In the United States the early public roads were for the purpose of providing connections between farmsteads and the market towns where the farmers traded. Only a few, such as the eastern post roads and the Cumberland Road, were planned with long-distance transportation in mind. And, although the development of the motorcar within the past three decades has had a notable effect upon trunk-line highways, it is still true that of the 3 million miles of public roads in this country, roughly $2\frac{1}{4}$ million miles are ordinary unsurfaced dirt roads serving chiefly the rural population. Surfaced roads of all kinds reach a total of 750,000 miles, of which only 150,000 miles have a hard surface of a high type. The latter are chiefly the trunk-line routes.

840. MOTORCARS AND THEIR SERVICES. The rapid expansion of surfaced highways during the past few decades has been a by-product of the phenomenal increase in the use of motor vehicles. In the pre-automobile era it was Europe that set the world standard for good roads. But when Americans began to purchase automobiles in numbers they shortly demanded good roads, for now they had a vehicle that was meant for speed and that could travel long distances. The effect upon road building and improvement in America was startling. At the present time over one billion dollars are invested each year in the construction and maintenance of roads. Other parts of the world also

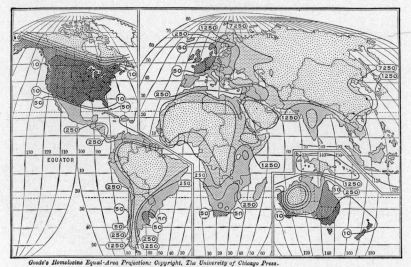

Goode's Homolosine Equal-Area Projection: Copyright, The University of Chicago Press.

FIG. 408.—Persons per motor vehicle (*From Huntington, "Principles of Human Geography," by permission of John Wiley & Sons, Inc.*)

have felt the effect of the automobile upon road building. The cost of rolling stock and right-of-way maintenance are much less for bus and truck than for railroads, and at the same time there is a far greater flexibility of usage. Countries with little capital therefore have elected to improve their transportation by providing themselves with better roads and motorbusses and trucks rather than by investing in railroads. Such a development has been striking in regions like Poland, Finland, the Baltic States, and China.

There are in the world nearly 35,000,000 passenger cars, close to 8,000,000 trucks, and 465,000 busses. Of the total number of the world's motor vehicles the United States has about 70 per cent, and nearly 60 per cent of the trucks (Fig. 408). Great Britain, France, Germany, Canada, and Australia follow in that order for total number

of cars. The increased use of passenger cars and motorbusses has cut
the passenger traffic of railroads to less than half what it was two
decades ago, and this in spite of a great general increase in travel. In
freight loadings the railroads have been reduced from 5 to 15 per cent
by the competition of trucks. It is particularly in the field of short-
distance transportation, for both freight and passengers, that motor
vehicles are able to compete with railroads. Trucks specialize principally in miscellaneous package freight that moves in small lots. For
long-distance hauls of such bulk freight as coal, iron ore, wheat, lumber,
etc., they are less satisfactory.

841. ROAD MILEAGE, DENSITY OF ROAD NET, AND PATTERN OF
ROAD DISTRIBUTION. The United States with its 3 million miles of
roads suitable for motor traffic has 40 per cent more than its nearest
rival, Soviet Russia. After Russia there follow in order Japan, Australia, Canada, France, Germany, and United Kingdom. The density
of the road net is highest in Japan, followed by Great Britain, Denmark, France, Ireland, and Belgium. The two *large* centers of high
road density are western Europe and eastern United States, regions
with large populations and relatively high standards of living. In
these regions there is usually over 1 mile of road for each square mile
of territory and in parts it is much denser. Of surfaced roads in the
United States there is about 1 mile to each 4 square miles of land
area but the ratio is only 1 to 25 for roads having a high type of hard
surfacing. The highest densities are in the northern and eastern region
of the country, extending from northern Illinois to southern New
England.

842. ROAD PATTERNS. Road arrangement or pattern is related to
both physical and historical conditions. In general roads should, as
nearly as possible, represent the shortest line between two points,
but often they deviate from this straight-line route because of surface
features, river crossings, swamps, and the like. In most sections of
Europe and North America the easiest routes of travel were discovered
by the earliest inhabitants, so that the main thoroughfares have been
the principal arteries of travel since the regions were first inhabited.
In the early settled eastern and southern parts of this country roads
tend to radiate from early settlements and follow relatively direct
routes to other settlements except as they are deflected by surface
features or drainage conditions. In those parts of the country settled
after the Ordinance of 1785, which imposed the rectangular square-
mile system of sections, townships, and ranges oriented north-south
and east-west, the road pattern is distinctive (Fig. 409, Appendix C).
Here the layout is predominantly rectangular, in the form of a checker-

SELECTED AMERICAN ROAD PATTERNS

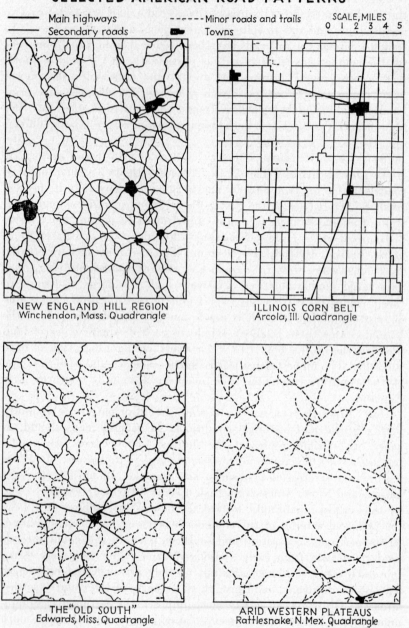

——— Main highways ----- Minor roads and trails SCALE, MILES
——— Secondary roads ▬ Towns 0 1 2 3 4 5

NEW ENGLAND HILL REGION
Winchendon, Mass. Quadrangle

ILLINOIS CORN BELT
Arcola, Ill. Quadrangle

THE "OLD SOUTH"
Edwards, Miss. Quadrangle

ARID WESTERN PLATEAUS
Rattlesnake, N. Mex. Quadrangle

FIG. 409.

board with 1-mile intervals. Some roads that antedate the survey may cut across this pattern, others deviate from it in places because of physical conditions. New paved highways pay less attention to the rectangular land survey and take their courses so as to give the shortest distances.

2. RAILROADS AND THEIR CARRIERS

843. CHARACTERISTICS OF RAILROADS. As the road is very ancient, so the railroad is a relatively modern type of land route, not

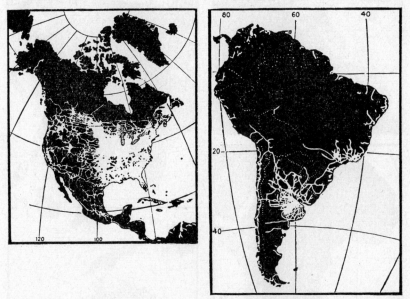

FIG. 410A.—Density and patterns of railroads. Regions and strips shown in white are not more than 10 miles from a railroad. (*From Jefferson, "Exercises in Human Geography."*)

having been in use much more than a century. The first railroad was built in England in 1825, and it has followed the expansion of occidental civilization into the four corners of the earth. It is a product of the Industrial Revolution while at the same time it has made a complex industrial-commercial civilization possible. The course taken by a rail line is often quite different from that of a road. A train cannot negotiate steep grades as can a motor vehicle so that rail lines are obliged to follow rather closely the major relief features. On the other hand, in the construction of a railroad bed use is made of cuts, fills, tunnels, and bridges in order to keep low grades so that the rail line is less influenced by minor features of the terrain. Because of the high cost of roadbed construction and the rolling stock, the railway is a paying investment only when distance and length of haul can compensate for these handicaps. Its capacity for hauling large loads long distances at a relatively high rate of speed are the principal points of advantage which urged the rapid expansion of the world's railway mileage. Unlike waterways, collections and deliveries are not restricted

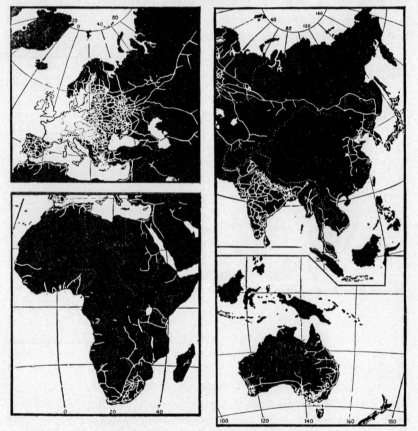

Fig. 410B.—For legend see Fig. 410A.

to main lines, for by means of secondary lines and spur tracks small towns off main lines, and even individual factories, may have connections with the markets of the country and the world.

844. Expansion of Railroads and Their Present Distribution. Rail building followed closely the spread of western civilization, and the present-day pattern of world distribution closely coincides with that machine civilization (Figs. 410A, 410B). For the entire earth there are in the neighborhood of 750,000 miles of railroad of which nearly 320,000

miles are in North America, 67,000 in South America, including Central America and the West Indies, 250,000 in Europe, 84,000 in Asia, 31,000 in Oceania, and 21,500 in Africa. Western Europe and eastern North America are the two conspicuous centers with a large railroad mileage and closely spaced rail net. In both regions there are few areas that are more than 10 miles from a line. In England, Belgium, northern France, southwestern Germany, and portions of the American Atlantic Seaboard states, most areas are even within a mile or two of rail lines. The railroad is a distinguishing feature of Euro-American culture, and its distribution is a good indicator of the spread and intensity of that culture.

845. *North American Railroads.* Only rail transportation could have made the resources of the immense spaces westward from the Appalachian barrier quickly available, and so it was that the rails marched westward with the American frontier. There was a close paralleling of railway building with the settlement and development of the land. The first lines were built to supplement waterways, but eventually they came to dominate transportation back from the seaboards. At present there are slightly under 250,000 miles of rail in the United States, which is approximately one-third of the trackage of the entire world. This immense length of rail line, like America's great length of highways, pipe lines, telephone lines, and her first rank in number of automobiles, reflect not only the country's prosperity, but also its great handicap of excessive space. Coal lies 1,000 miles from the ore, lumber is produced 2,500 miles from the principal markets, food is grown 1,000 miles and more away from the center of consumption. Our magnificent transportation facilities reflect the means by which the handicap of excess space is overcome.

846. *Density of Rail Net and Patterns of Distribution.* For different sections of the United States and Canada the *density* of the rail net varies greatly. In the poorly populated grazing regions of the western high plains and the intermontane plateaus there is only 1 mile of railroad for each 45 square miles of land. In the highly industralized northeastern part of the country from southern New England to Illinois the comparable figure is 1 mile for each 4.6 square miles, or 10 times that density. Over the Middle West and the "old" South the ratio is 1 to 10. There is a remarkable thinning out of the rail net west of the 20-in. rainfall line, where agriculture is relatively unimportant and industries little developed.

Over eastern United States the *pattern* of rail lines is that of a closely woven net. Within the general net there are a number of focal points toward which there is a general convergence of lines.

Chief among these are Chicago and Winnipeg. In both cases natural barriers or unproductive land tend to direct rail lines toward these cities. The Great Lakes and the unproductive cutover land around the Upper Lakes prevent American rail lines from taking the shortest route eastward and force them southward through Chicago at the southern end of the barrier. Winnipeg likewise has a lake barrier and unproductive land on the north, which tend to direct rail traffic through that center. Atlanta at the southern end of the Blue Ridge barrier shows a similar pattern. Great ports such as Montreal, New York, and San Francisco are important focal points for local rail nets. Such a natural gateway as the Mohawk Valley across the eastern highlands is a convergence point for several rail lines.

West of the 20-in. rainfall line the rail net disappears, and from there westward to the Pacific Coast states the single strands of the 10 great transcontinental lines with their few feeders are conspicuous. In this section passenger traffic is relatively more important than in eastern United States and freight less so, for the bulk of the inter-coastal freight goes by boat via the Panamá Canal. Canadian rail lines are crowded close to the southern margins of the country by the unproductive nature of much of northern Canada. One rail line runs northward from the main Canadian National Railway in the wheat region across 510 miles of forest and swamp to Fort Churchill on Hudson Bay. This was built by the government with the idea of facilitating the export of wheat to Britain.

847. *European Railroads.* Whereas in North America railroad building was contemporaneous with the settlement of the country, in Europe it followed the settlement. This contrast is reflected in the rail patterns of the two regions, that of Europe being much more perfectly radial with respect to major trade centers. Such great cities as London, Vienna, Paris, Berlin, Munich, and Moscow were already in existence at the beginning of the railroad era so that the rail lines were built with respect to these centers and the resulting patterns were definitely shaped by them.

This radial pattern in Europe has been fostered by another consideration, *viz.,* that of military effectiveness. Europe, made up of numerous independent countries of small size with the problem of national defense a major item, has a series of national railway systems, each system being a unit by itself. Less attention has been paid to the development of a unit system for the continent as a whole, involving international connections and transcontinental lines. Every effort was made to link the capital city and other strategic centers with the international boundaries so that troop movements to the borders could be facilitated in times of national danger. Many of Europe's railroads have been built with military rather than commercial use as the chief consideration.

The major transcontinental rail lines in Europe are the Paris-Berlin-Moscow route, the Paris-Milan-Brindisi route, and the Berlin-Vienna-Istanbul route. All these can be thought of as including London, although there is an obvious break at the English Channel. Relief characteristics of Europe are on the whole favorable to the development of rail lines, in spite of its numerous highlands. Through the highland rim of Bohemia the Elbe River has cut a famous gateway, the Saxon or Elbe Gate, that allows easy access from northwestern Europe to the Danube countries. At the western end of the Transylvanian Alps the Danube has cut the equally famous Iron Gate, which is an easy pass between central and southeastern Europe. By way of the Rhône-Saône depression western Europe finds easy access to the Mediterranean, while the lofty Alps are crossed by a series of low passes with easy approaches. Railroad ferries provide continuous rail routes between the Scandinavian countries and the German and Danish ports.

There are marked contrasts in the densities of the rail net in different parts of Europe. The highest densities per unit area for the entire world are found in western Europe. Belgium leads with 1 mile for each 3.9 square miles, but 11 other countries have densities greater than that of the United States. In southern and eastern Europe and in Scandinavia, regions of fewer people and less industrialization, the density is much lower than in western Europe.

848. *Railroads on the Other Continents.* The life of Asia is concentrated along its eastern and southeastern margins, and its chief railroad mileage is there as well. India has by far the largest amount of track, followed in turn by Japan and China. The rail net however is densest in Japan, which has a length of line per 1,000 square miles, just slightly higher than that for the United States. Each of the national railway systems in Asia is a unit within itself and is without connection with the others. Dry and high central Asia is largely without rail lines, the only significant ones being those built by the Russians into Russian Turkistan. Across Siberia reaches the long thin line of the Trans-Siberian connecting Vladivostok on the Pacific with European Russia.

African railroads are for the most part single short lines extending back at right angles from the coast for a greater or shorter distance into the interior. Between these isolated lines there are no connections, for the sea is the highway. Only in French Mediterranean Africa and in

British South Africa are there any semblances of what could be called rail nets. The most notable route of the continent is that designated as the Cape-to-Cairo route, with railroads providing the means of transport over two-thirds of the length and boats and motorcars the remainder.

In Australia, the railroads follow the concentration of population and economic life along the eastern and southern margins. Genuine rail nets occur only in the southeast and the southwest. The dry deep interior is without through railroads. A number of short lines extend back at right angles from the east and south coasts into the inland semiarid sheep, cattle, and wheat country. These end abruptly on the edge of the desert where the grazing industry is limited by drought. A long, thin, transcontinental southern line with few feeders connects the humid regions of the southeast and southwest.

Throughout most of tropical South America railroads are largely absent, the few that do exist being short isolated lines at right angles to the seacoast. In this part of South America the sea is almost the only highway connecting the principal centers of development which are along the margins of the continent. The intervening lands are barrier areas rather than connections. Around the estuary of the River Plate in Argentina and Uruguay and in the coffee region of Brazil are the greatest areas of rail development. On the flat Argentine Pampa a fanlike pattern of rail lines, with its principal focus at Buenos Aires, is very conspicuous. West of the Andes a single longitudinal rail line extends from southern Chile to Peru and is connected by numerous laterals with the seaboard. Connection is made between the Argentine rail net and the Pacific Coast in Chile and Peru by three trans-Andean lines.

WATER ROUTES AND THE MERCHANT MARINE

849. INLAND NAVIGATION. Rivers, canals, and lakes as routes of transportation have already been touched upon in Chap. XXII, Arts. 551–552. The principal handicap of rivers in general is that their courses are fixed and therefore the river trade route lacks the flexibility of a land or ocean route. The course of a river can be altered only to a minor degree. It has often been pointed out that the Mississippi would be much more useful as a trade route if its course were east-west, which is the direction of our principal trade movement, rather than north-south. In densely populated industrial regions such as western Europe, rivers and canals are used to a much greater degree than they are in the United States. This probably reflects the need for every possible trade route that can be developed.

The relative merits of rail versus river-canal transport has been vigorously debated by students of transportation. Some assert that, if the costs of river improvement and canal construction were paid for by the traffic using these routes, instead of by the government, water rates would be as high as rail. Canals are distinctly best suited to short hauls and therefore to regions of dense population. They are not profitable on long hauls. Where waterways parallel rail lines their very presence has the benefit of holding rail rates to a lower level than they would be if the competing water route did not exist. It is significant that, as the rail net in eastern and central United States was expanded

Fig. 411.—River boats moored at the sloping bank of the Ohio River at Cairo, Ill. At high water the foreground is entirely submerged.

and the efficiency of the railroads increased, practically all American waterways except the Great Lakes fell into disuse. Only in recent years have such major interior waterways as the Ohio and Mississippi Rivers and the New York Barge Canal shown evidences of a trade revival (Fig. 411).

850. *The American Great Lakes* form the greatest interior water route of the world. The great urge to build the Erie Canal was the prospect of connecting the Atlantic Coast by an all-water route with the Great Lakes and therefore the heart of the continent. The particular advantage of the Great Lakes is their depth, which permits the use of relatively deep-draft ships with great carrying capacity. The fact that the lakes are aligned in an east-west direction paralleling the flow of

trade is of major significance. Moreover, close to their shores are some of the largest wheat-, iron-ore-, and coal-producing areas of the continent, which provide ideal bulk cargo for lake shipment (Fig. 412). They connect the grain- and iron-producing regions of the Middle West with the industrial coal-producing east. Unfortunately falls and rapids in the St. Marys River connecting Lakes Superior and Huron, Niagara Falls between Lakes Erie and Ontario, and a series of rapids and falls in the upper St. Lawrence, early handicapped the use of the lakes as a through route. By canals at the St. Marys River and

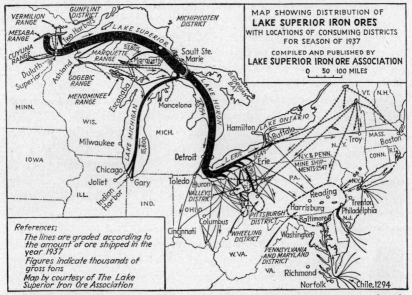

Fig. 412.—The Great Lakes are chiefly carriers of bulk freight, iron ore and grain providing a large part of the eastward-moving cargo, with coal furnishing a large part of the return freight.

dredging of the connections between Lakes Huron and Erie a 20-ft. channel is provided as far as Buffalo at the eastern end of Lake Erie. The Welland Canal connecting Lakes Erie and Ontario around Niagara Falls is 30 ft. deep, but the canals on the St. Lawrence are only 14 ft. deep so that only seagoing vessels having less than that draft can enter the Great Lakes. The new proposed plans for the St. Lawrence Waterway call for canals 27 ft. deep on the St. Lawrence, which would permit relatively large ocean freighters to enter the lake ports.

The principal cargo carried on the Great Lakes is grain, iron ore, and lumber on the eastward trip and coal from the Pennsylvania field loaded at Lake Erie ports moving westward. These are all bulk cargoes particularly suited to shipment by boat. Unfortunately, because of ice, this greatest of all interior waterways is practically useless during the colder months of the year. During this season the rail lines must carry all the freight. But in spite of that handicap the tons of traffic through the St. Clair River leading into Lake Erie is in many years greater than the combined freight passing through the Panamá and Suez Canals. Along the shores of the Great Lakes are the greatest populations, the greatest concentration of rail lines, and the principal manufacturing centers of interior North America. The route is like a great magnet drawing to it population, railroads, and industry.

OCEAN TRADE AND ITS CARRIERS

851. THE OCEAN HIGHWAY. It has been said that the nation that does not front upon an ocean is like a house that is not upon a street. This is because the oceans form a world highway that belongs exclusively to no one, reaches everywhere, and can be used by each and all that possess a bit of its shore. Here nature furnishes the roadway and there are no construction costs, no taxes, no upkeep. Costly improvements in the right of way in the form of surveying, dredging, and marking are necessary only in restricted bays, rivers, and the harbors of some of the terminal trade centers. Port cities are so eager to engage in world trade that they provide facilities for docking, loading, and unloading, and for taking on fuel at comparatively small expense to the ship. This, together with free use of the ocean highway, helps account for the cheapness of ocean transportation.

"Freedom of the Seas" has been one of the historic principles of the American nation. Of recent years the right to navigate on open ocean has not been challenged, except in time of war, but this right accomplishes little unless a ship may reach a port and there transact business. And since a nation may restrict terminal areas by enforcing restrictions over that part of the ocean within 3 miles of its coasts, and by preventing foreign nations from engaging in coastwise trade, something less than actual freedom of the seas really exists.

OCEAN TRADE ROUTES

852. THE NATURE OF OCEAN ROUTES. There was a time, and not so long ago, when oceans were looked upon as barriers separating continents. At the present time they are thought of as the highways *connecting* the continents. The ocean route in general is much less rigid than a land route, for there is no fixed track over which a ship must travel. The route belongs to no one; it is the common property of all men in times of peace. A ship with a cargo of wheat for Antwerp may be directed by radio in midocean to land instead at Marseille

without the captain's needing to ask permission of anyone to use the new right of way.

But, although the oceans are open highways to be traversed by ships in any and all directions, in reality most ocean trade is in ships that follow certain general avenues which approach definite routes. The seafaring nations have plotted on navigation charts the best routes between certain trade regions or centers. These routes are established after taking into consideration such items as sailing distances, wind and storm conditions, ocean currents, cargo possibilities, fog, ice, fueling stations, etc. An ocean trade route, therefore, is an avenue along which, because of one or more of the foregoing reasons, the tracks of numerous ships converge or coincide for a part of their ways. Such a trade route usually consists of (*a*) a central belt or trunk, and (*b*) the several branches that feed into this trunk from numerous trade centers at either end (see Fig. 413). Other things being equal the best or cheapest route is the shortest route, which on a spherical earth is a "Great Circle." Other factors, however, usually cause some deviation from the true great-circle course.

853. *The North Atlantic route* connecting eastern North America and western Europe is the most used of any. This top rank is not unusual when one considers that the regions connected are two of the most populous and highly developed regions of the earth. Passengers and freight traffic originate where people are located. In North America and western Europe are to be found the world's greatest producers of surpluses of goods of great diversity which are the basis for trade. The trunk of this route is in the form of a broad northward-curving band running in a northeast-southwest direction roughly between latitudes 40 and 50°. Owing chiefly to the hazard of icebergs at certain seasons, the route is farther north in winter than in summer. Its feeders reach from Labrador to Panamá on the west and from Norway to Spain on the east. An unusually high proportion of the world's great ports serve the route as terminals. In both volume and variety of cargo this route far exceeds any other, one-fifth of the shipping of the world being required to serve it.

854. *The Mediterranean-Asiatic route* connects the whole North Atlantic region with southeastern Asia and Australia by way of the Mediterranean Sea, Suez Canal, and the Red Sea. Its importance dates from 1869, with the opening of the Suez Canal. Unlike the North Atlantic route this one throughout much of its course follows relatively constricted waterways, which jeopardizes its safety in time of war. It is of principal importance to the European countries, particularly Great Britain, for it is the short route connecting them with their rich

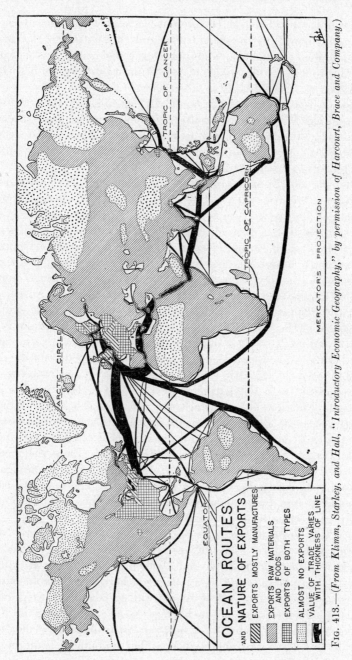

OCEAN ROUTES
AND NATURE OF EXPORTS

EXPORTS MOSTLY MANUFACTURES
EXPORTS RAW MATERIALS AND FOODS
EXPORTS OF BOTH TYPES
ALMOST NO EXPORTS
VALUE OF TRADE VARIES WITH THICKNESS OF LINE

MERCATOR'S PROJECTION

TROPIC OF CANCER
TROPIC OF CAPRICORN
EQUATOR
ARCTIC CIRCLE

Fig. 413.—(From Klimm, Starkey, and Hall, "Introductory Economic Geography," by permission of Harcourt, Brace and Company).

colonies in the Far East. In the present war one of the chief objectives
of the Axis powers is the Suez Canal and the halting of the flow of
goods and men through it to and from England. The frequency of ports
along this route provides excellent opportunities for trade of the short-
haul type.

855. OTHER ROUTES.   *The South African route* connects the same
regions as the Mediterranean route so that it in reality is an alternate
to the latter. It is 4,000 miles farther from Liverpool to Calcutta by
way of South Africa than by Suez, but many ships take the longer
route to avoid the canal tolls.

856. *The South American East Coast route* connects both sides of
the North Atlantic with eastern South America. Because Brazil
projects so far eastward into the Atlantic, American ships traveling
to eastern South America are forced to make nearly as long a trip as
those from western Europe. Under normal conditions the exchange of
eastern South America is heavier with Europe than with the United
States, with the products of farm, plantation, and range moving
north to Europe and manufactured goods south to South America.

At the *Panamá Canal* are focused routes (*a*) between the east and
west coasts of the United States, (*b*) between either side of the North
Atlantic and the west coast of South America, and (*c*) between eastern
United States and eastern Asia and Australia. The opening of the canal
has eliminated the long trip around Cape Horn together with the dan-
gers associated with navigating those waters. Greatest benefits have
accrued to American intercoastal trade and to that of North Atlantic
countries with the west coast of South America. From a military standpoint the canal is of utmost importance to the United States since it
allows a rapid transfer of the fleet to that ocean where the greatest
threat lies. It may be pointed out how fortunate for ocean navigation
it is that the land barriers were so narrow at two points on the earth,
Suez and Panamá, that canals could be cut through, thereby permitting
a continuous water route in easily navigable latitudes.

857. *The North Pacific trade routes* connect chiefly western North
America with eastern Asia. Two principal routes are recognized, (*a*)
a shorter northern great-circle route which swings northward almost
to the Aleutian Islands and (*b*) a longer southern route which connects
the two continents by way of the Hawaiian Islands. This group of
islands, the "crossroads of the Pacific," is a converging point for a
number of routes including those between Australia and Pacific North
America, and Panamá Canal and Asia. The amount of trade moving
along the Pacific routes is far less than that in the Atlantic, for the
former routes connect a region of small population with one in which,

although the population is large, the demands for foreign goods are small.

OCEAN CARRIERS

858. An additional reason, other than that the right of way is furnished by nature, why ocean transportation is cheaper than land transport is that the capital invested in the ocean freighter per ton of freight carried is less than in any form of land carrier. Other costs such as insurance, labor, terminal charges, and power per unit of freight volume and weight are also less.

859. SHIP SERVICE: LINER AND TRAMP. Ocean carriers are of two kinds, line ships and tramp ships. Liners ply back and forth across oceans on a regular time schedule and between specified ports. Generally they carry both passengers and freight, but the latter is usually of small bulk and composed of numerous packages which have a high unit value and can stand a high freight rate. Some liners, particularly the larger and finer ones, specialize in passenger traffic. These ships emphasize speed and promptness of arrival. They sail on schedule no matter what load is available. Other liners put greater emphasis on freight and the passenger service is auxiliary.

Most of the world's freight, however, is carried, not on sleek line ships, but on slower, blockier little "tramps," which go where cargo is available and are unrestricted by time schedules. Their movements are uncertain, and as they leave the home port they may not return for a year or several years. They go to the far corners of the earth, picking up and discharging cargo as they can find it. Less beautiful, slower, and many times ungraceful, the tramp steamer does the heavy and dirty work in ocean transport, yet its earnings are often more substantial than the liner's.

860. *Merchant Marines of the World.* At the time of the outbreak of the present war there were close to 31,000 ships of over 100 tons in the merchant marines of the world (Fig. 414). Britain led with 7,200; the United States was next with nearly 3,400; followed by Germany, Japan, Norway, Greece, Netherlands, and France. Compared with the United States' position in foreign trade, in which she ranks close to Great Britain, her merchant marine engaged in foreign trade is relatively small. This means that a considerable part of American foreign trade is carried in foreign ships. From the period of the Civil War down to the outbreak of the World War in 1914, in spite of an increase in American foreign trade, the country's merchant marine declined. It rose to unprecedented height during the First World War but since then has declined, until in 1938 it contained fewer ships

than in 1910. In contrast to ships in foreign trade, our ships in coast-wise trade have shown a steady increase.

THE MERCHANT FLEETS OF THE WORLD, 1938

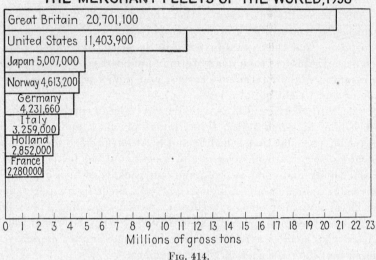

Great Britain 20,701,100
United States 11,403,900
Japan 5,007,000
Norway 4,613,200
Germany 4,231,660
Italy 3,259,000
Holland 2,852,000
France 2,280,000

0 1 2 3 4 5 6 7 8 9 10 11 12 13 14 15 16 17 18 19 20 21 22 23
Millions of gross tons

Fig. 414.

AIR TRANSPORT

861. POSSIBILITIES AND LIMITATIONS.   Air transport is a development of the past few decades and is still so recent that it has some aspects of the novel about it. People still pay for the experience of having a ride in an airplane. The particular asset of air transport is its speed; the handicap, its inability to carry heavy loads. Thus, at the present time, air transport is chiefly employed in carrying mail and passengers. Only a minor amount of miscellaneous light package freight is carried.

As in the case of ocean routes, air routes are not rigidly confined and restricted. Yet for the sake of safety and ease of navigation air routes do follow rather closely certain ground marks such as rivers or cities and, at night, lighted beacons. Unlike early rail, motor, and water transport, air transport specializes not in local, but in long-distance carrying. This means that even in those parts of the world where air transport is best developed, such as western Europe and the United States, most trade centers are not served by an air route. There is no such thing as a local air service. On the other hand, air service connects some of the most out-of-the-way places of the earth, preceding rail and motor services into such regions as interior tropical South America and Africa, and subarctic Canada. Long-distance international com-

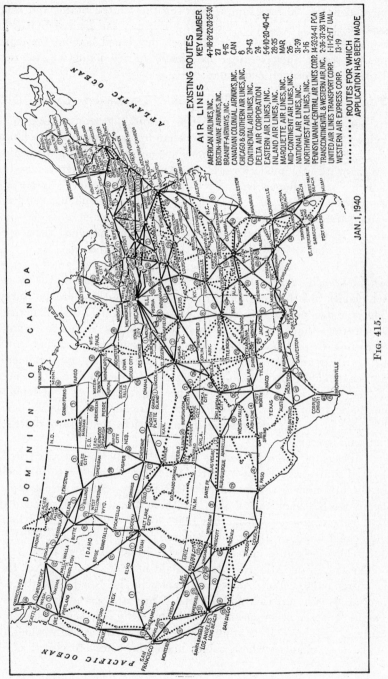

Fig. 415.

mercial flying, as for example between the United States and south-eastern Asia, the United States and Europe, the United States and South America has only recently been developed beyond the experimental stage. Such services are chiefly in the hands of American, British, and German companies.

VOICE COMMUNICATIONS—TELEPHONE, TELEGRAPH, CABLE, RADIO

862. Although they are for the purpose of transmitting man's voice and therefore his ideas rather than for transporting man himself or his goods, voice communications are nevertheless vital to trade as we know it in the modern world. One German geographer has used the number of telephones in a city as an index of the city's importance as a trade center. The outstanding merit of telephone, telegraph, cable, and radio is the ultraspeed that they make possible. Since all of them depend upon electricity for transmission, their speed is that of electricity, which is practically instantaneous.

The United States and Canada, or Anglo-America, are the regions where *telephones* are most used. About 50 per cent of the world's telephones are in the United States; over one-third are in Europe. The average per capita number of telephones in North America is seven times that of Europe. This striking contrast is due to a number of causes. In part no doubt it reflects the Americans' craving to rush things along and save time. In part it is caused by the more numerous and conveniently located public telephone booths in Europe. In many of the great European cities the per capita number of telephones compares favorably with those of the American cities. It is the dearth of them in smaller centers and rural districts that draws down the national averages.

Mileage of *telegraph* wire is likewise chiefly concentrated in the United States and Europe, nearly one-third of the world total being in the first-named region. In part this simply reflects an attempt to overcome the handicap of size, for there are a number of countries that have a greater mileage per 1,000 square miles of area, although only one, Canada, with a greater mileage per 100 population. Telegraph and telephone routes in general follow railroads and highways.

The first trans-Atlantic *cable* was laid in 1866, and even yet there is a preponderance of the world's cables in the North Atlantic connecting North America and Europe. They are scarce in the North Pacific, and the other oceans have them chiefly between coastal trade centers. Britain controls around 50 per cent of the world's cables and is the only country whose cables make the complete circuit of the earth.

Radio or wireless, the most recent of the word-transmitting facilities, has had more effect in giving more people an increased familiarity with the world about them than any other form of communication. It has become one of the greatest mediums for advertising as well as a source of news, entertainment, and education. Although radio has been in common use less than two decades, it has already become an intimate part of the lives of North Americans and Europeans. About 44 per cent of the world's receiving sets are in the United States, no other country even closely approaching our number. All of Europe has just slightly fewer than the United States. Americans should be the best informed people of the world.

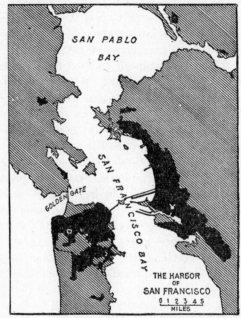

Terminals

863. NATURE OF TERMINALS. If people or commodities are to be transported by carriers over routes it becomes clear that the produce must be concentrated at certain focal points. If this concentration did not take place, a separate branch line of the route would have to connect each producer with his market. Such a system of transpor-

FIG. 416.—San Francisco has an excellent natural harbor, which is entered through the Golden Gate. Urban areas are shown in black.

tation is unthinkable. As it is, trunk lines of transportation usually connect important terminal cities where goods and people are collected and distributed. Branch lines have terminals of lesser importance. In such terminal centers facilities for loading, unloading, and storage are provided. As pointed out in an earlier chapter (XXIX) these terminal functions are the most common reason for the origin and growth of cities.

864. WATER-ROUTE TERMINALS—PORTS. Ports do not grow and prosper merely because they are on the coast, but because they are important gateways of trade. This ability to attract trade reflects certain physical and economic advantages. Among them are (a) a

good natural harbor, (*b*) a large productive and consuming hinterland, (*c*) easy access to the hinterland, (*d*) location on or close to one or more of the main world trade routes, and (*e*) mechanical facilities for handling freight and passengers. An ideal harbor is a coastal indentation safe for navigation where a ship is protected against storm waves. The term harbor has nothing to do with trade; it is simply a place of refuge. The ideal harbor is bottle shaped with an entrance wide and deep enough to accommodate traffic but narrow enough so that storm waves cannot enter. The harbors of New York, San Francisco, and Rio de Janeiro are of this type. A good harbor likewise requires ample depth of water, spaciousness, an extensive water front for pier space, freedom from ice, and small tidal range.

There are hundreds of good harbors that have no trade, and this is due either to the lack of a producing or consuming hinterland, or the absence of easy access to it. The number of high-grade harbors along such indented coasts as those of western Canada and Alaska, southern Chile, or Norway illustrate the point in question. In all these regions the hinterlands are relatively unproductive and meagerly populated so that there is little surplus to export, and import requirements are meager. As a general rule a producing hinterland is also an important consumer but not always so. For example, the western Gulf ports of the United States, such as Houston and Galveston, whose hinterlands have large surpluses of cotton, grain, and oil, are primarily export ports, Houston's exports being roughly 12 times its imports. Portland, Ore., has a similar unbalanced trade. Such a port is somewhat more handicapped than the one whose hinterland is of a kind that results in a better balance between outgoing and incoming cargo, for ships desire to carry full loads in both directions.

The effect of relative ease of access to a hinterland is well illustrated in the case of our Atlantic Seaboard ports. By way of the water-level route of the Hudson and Mohawk valleys New York has an easier natural route to the Middle West than Boston, Philadelphia, or Baltimore. By means of the Erie Canal, which followed the Mohawk Valley, New York was early provided with a water route to its hinterland which did much to establish the preeminence of that port. The gap formed by the Columbia River through the Cascades provides Portland with easier access to the interior than its rival Seattle has.

A port located on a main route of trade has a far greater chance for growth than one not so located. Ships are not attracted to isolated ports well removed from the main lines of traffic, whereas, on the other hand, trade centers with fewer advantages may become important ports of call when they are so located that numerous ships pass

Fig. 417.—Locust Point Terminal, Baltimore. An excellent illustration of the land and water relationships of a port. (*Courtesy of Baltimore and Ohio Railway Company.*)

their doors. Good illustrations of the importance of location are furnished by such ports as Churchill on Hudson Bay or Alexandrovsk at the base of the Kola Peninsula on the Arctic Ocean. In neither case have the hopes for their development been realized, and in part this is due to their far removal from any important shipping lands.

Mechanical facilities in form of wharves, warehouses, cranes, tracks, etc., are features of a port that can be provided by the trade center itself. The last few decades have seen marked competition on the part of ports for providing modern and efficient equipment for handling cargo and the quick dispatch of ships. Realizing the part that mechanical facilities play in attracting commerce, trade centers have given this feature much publicity in their advertising.

865. TYPES OF OCEAN PORTS AND THEIR SERVICES. Most ports lie at the ends of transoceanic trade routes, and they function therefore as *terminal ports*. Ships enter them to discharge cargoes that are definitely assigned to that particular port and the hinterland that it serves. New York, for example, is primarily a terminal port. There are other ports, however, whose function is more largely that of a middleman between other ports. These are called *entrepôt ports*, or, as the name suggests, "between ports"—ports for other ports. Thus London receives cargoes from the far corners of the world, and these cargoes are there redistributed in smaller amounts to other ports of northwestern Europe and beyond. At the entrepôt, warehousing and processing may occur before reshipment. Singapore is an important entrepôt port in southeastern Asia, acting as the middleman for the world's most important source of tropical raw materials. Somewhat different is the function of the *free port*, which permits ships to unload their cargoes within a fenced-off "free zone," where they are sorted, perhaps processed, or warehoused without payment of duty. Here the goods may be sold and reloaded on other ships. Payment of duty occurs only when the goods pass from the "free zone" into the city. The advantage of this free-port function is that the middleman transaction involves no customs charge and that fee is paid only once, *viz.*, when the goods enter the country of their final destination.

SELECTED REFERENCES FOR CHAPTER XXXII

Berglund, Abraham. "Ocean Transportation." Longmans, Green and Company, New York, 1931.

Clowes, Ernest S. "Shipways to the Sea." The Williams & Wilkins Company, Baltimore, 1929.

Daggett, Stuart. "Principles of Inland Transportation." Harper & Brothers, 1934.

"Foreign Commerce Yearbook." Bureau of Foreign and Domestic Commerce (annual).

Jefferson, Mark. The Civilizing Rails. *Econ. Geog.*, Vol. 4, pp. 217–231, 1928.

Johnson, Emory R., Huebner, Grover G., and Wilson, G. Lloyd. "Transportation: Economic Principles and Practices." D. Appleton-Century Company, Inc., New York, 1940.

Killough, Hugh B. "International Trade." McGraw-Hill Book Company, Inc., New York, 1938.

Long, W. R. "Railway and Highway Transportation Abroad: A Study of Existing Relationships, Recent Competitive Measures and Coordination Policies." United States Department of Commerce, Trade Promotion Series, 155, 1935.

Sargent, A. J. "Seaports and Hinterlands." A. & C. Black, Ltd., London, 1938.

Stamp, L. Dudley. Chisholm's Handbook of Commercial Geography, Longmans, Green and Company, New York, 1937.

Van Cleef, Eugene. "Trade Centers and Trade Routes." D. Appleton-Century Company, Inc., New York, 1937.

Witherow, Grace O. "Foreign Trade of the United States, 1938," Trade Promotion Series 198, Bureau of Foreign and Domestic Commerce, 1939.

Retrospect and Conclusion

866. GEOGRAPHIC ELEMENTS AND THEIR NATURAL GROUPINGS. The content of this book has been primarily concerned with the elements of geography; those groups of features, natural and cultural, that together make up the face of the earth. The treatment has been of the several groups of geographic elements singly and individually, although pains have been taken to point out the interrelations between them. This description and analysis of the geographic elements individually was considered to be necessary, for only as the separate elements are recognized and understood and their world distributions described and explained is there laid a substantial foundation for understanding the earth's surface in whole or in part. It is impossible, for example, to understand a plant as a functioning organism without first comprehending the structure and function of its individual parts—roots, stem, and leaves. No more is it possible to understand the geographic character of the earth's surface or any part of it without first being acquainted with the individual elements of its geography. But just as the botanist is ultimately concerned with the *whole* plant, so the geographer is concerned with the complex patterns of the whole earth and its separate regions, made up as they are of the interrelated and interdependent geographic elements.

867. ALL NATURAL FEATURES OF A REGION ARE INTERRELATED. It needs to be emphasized that the individual elements neither of a plant nor of a region exist separately and for and by themselves as self-sufficient units. Leaves, roots, and stems can have no separate existence apart from each other; they are only interrelated and interdependent parts of a larger whole. Climate, landforms, drainage, natural vegetation, and soils likewise never exist separately and apart from each other in nature. For any portion of the earth they exist together not only in an areal sense but likewise as interrelated elements of a region, the parts of which are geared together so that they are interdependent, each element reacting upon all the others and in

768

turn being reacted upon by them. The soil of a region, for example, can scarcely be thought of as having a separate existence apart from the bedrock, landforms, climate, vegetation, and drainage, all of which have influenced its evolution and character. The bonds of interrelationship between the several natural elements or features of a region are extremely complicated. The total assemblage of inter-related natural features, within a region is called its *natural landscape*.

868. CLIMATICALLY INDUCED NATURAL LANDSCAPES. In an earlier chapter it has been pointed out that the complex of *natural* features that characterizes any part, or the whole, of the earth's surface is the result of two sets of forces and their associated processes acting upon the solid, liquid, and gaseous earth materials. One of these two sources of energy is the forces residing within the earth; the other is provided by the sun.

It was further noted that the interior, or tectonic, forces and proc-esses (gravitational, volcanic, and diastrophic) are the cause, for instance, of variations in earth materials and likewise in many of the larger aspects of surface configuration from one part of the earth to another. The nature of these forces resident within the earth's interior are not so well known, and the distribution of types of surface features (mountains, plateaus, plains) resulting from them does not seem to follow any repeated world distribution pattern, as do climatic and soil types, for instance. Plains, plateaus, or mountains may occur at the pole as well as at the equator and along the eastern or the western sides of continents. Mineral deposits, likewise, seem to follow no apparent repeated world distribution patterns.

Solar energy, the second of the two great forces fashioning the earth's surface, expresses itself most directly through climatic processes and indirectly through a great variety of physical and chemical reac-tions, two of the most important being the weathering of rocks and the growth, death, and decay of plants. The gradational agents (streams, waves, wind, glaciers) likewise are principally of climatic and gravitational origin. Here, then, in a vast laboratory, composed of the thin outer shell of the solid earth and the adjacent lower layers of atmosphere with which it is in contact, is the focus of an unbelievably complicated set of reactions, where sun-induced processes are acting upon earth materials and major surface forms of tectonic origin to produce the present array of natural features with which the earth's surface is adorned.

869. *Mature Natural Landscape.* The very name (weathering) of the processes by which solid rock is broken down into the mantle rock or regolith cover emphasizes the role of such atmospheric conditions

or elements as temperature, moisture, oxygen, and carbon dioxide in rock destruction. Temperature and moisture conditions are likewise primary in determining the nature of the vegetation cover, while climate, and climatically induced vegetation, play significant roles in soil formation and quality. Many of the drainage, and some of the landform, features as well are the result of weathering and gradational agents, stemming indirectly from climatic energy. The regolith cover, composed of both inorganic and organic materials, and the vegetation cover develop in a region together, both responding to the conditions imposed by climate, and each in turn modifying the character of the other. It becomes evident, therefore, that within any particular region the climatic forces peculiar to it, if undisturbed over a long period of time, will produce a layer of mantle rock the depth and quality of which represent a state of balance between the rate of weathering and the rate of removal. This regolith is, in turn, covered by a mantle of vegetation, nourished by the soil layer underneath but likewise in harmony with the temperature and rainfall conditions surrounding it. Through the character and intensity of gradational forces, minor landform features and drainage conditions, in a somewhat lesser degree, likewise are brought into step with the atmospheric environment, so that the whole landscape complex bears the stamp of the regional climate. Landforms, which are so much influenced by tectonic forces, character of earth materials, and stage of development, usually bear this stamp of climatic environment much less conspicuously than do vegetation and soils, for instance. Within a large region of relatively uniform climate, there is a tendency, nevertheless, for many of its natural features, each adjusted to and in balance with all the others, to develop a considerable degree of similiarity throughout. When that state of balance has been reached, the region may be said to have a *mature* natural landscape. The reason that completely mature landscapes are rare is due in a measure to the constant operation of the tectonic forces, resulting in elevation or depression of the land. A change in climate similarly disrupts progress toward maturity. In northwestern Europe and northern North America, for instance, continental glaciation, resulting from climatic change, left a landscape which, in many respects, is lacking in perfected development. Variety in earth materials adds further disharmony. Man, too, through removing the natural vegetation cover, cultivating the soil, damming the rivers, and numerous other activities tends to disrupt the balance sought by nature.

870. CLIMATE AND THE WORLD PATTERN: GEOGRAPHIC REALMS. It has been emphasized in an earlier section of this book that (a)

climates tend to remain relatively uniform over extensive areas, and (b) similar climates are repeated on the land masses in characteristic latitudinal and continental locations. There is a definite and repeated

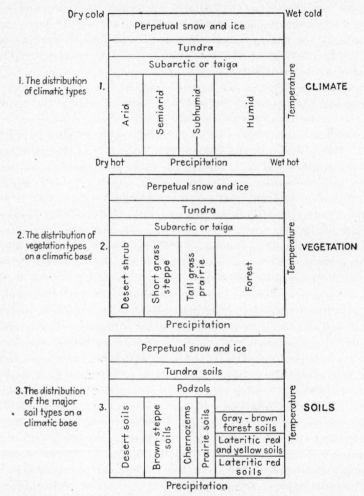

Fig. 418.—Schematic representation of the distribution of climatic, vegetation, and soil types.

world pattern in the distribution of climatic elements which permits of classifying climates into a relatively few large types. It now becomes apparent that these extensive, and often far separated, regions included within the same type of climate are likely to possess similarities in certain other natural features as well. A student cannot have progressed thus far in his study of the physical elements of geography without becoming aware of broad but clearly defined similarities in the world distribution patterns of climatic, vegetation, and soil types (Fig. 418). To these great world subdivisions, bearing as they do the stamp of a broadly similar climatic environment upon their vegetation and soil and, in a lesser degree, upon gradational landform and drainage features as well, the name *geographic realms* may be applied. For reasons noted in the previous article, too great a degree of similarity within a realm is not to be expected.

Since the character of the bedrock, size and quality of mineral deposits, and the nature of tectonic landforms are chiefly the result of interior forces, these features usually do not fit harmoniously into a scheme of world subdivisions based primarily upon climatic imprint.

871. MAN'S PLACE IN THE GEOGRAPHIC REALM. At this point the question logically arises as to whether the world patterns of population and the culture features created by human beings have any important coincidence with the pattern of the physical realms. Can it be that the inanimate earth so influences human destinies that peoples are relatively similar in their accomplishments and modes of work within similar physical environments? Within a great physical realm, possessing as it does broad similarities in natural endowments, it would not be unusual if there were a degree of similarity in some of its land-use features as well. Actually this is the case. On the other hand, man's activities within an area are influenced by so many forces, social, political, and economic, many times not directly related to the natural earth, that it is unreasonable to expect similar environments to produce similar types of land use. The influence of environment is passive, not active. It provides the natural endowments, to be sure, but it never determines how and to what degree those endowments shall be used. Physical earth sets limitations and hindrances, but it is man himself who determines the course of action. It is not to be expected that human groups with different physical and mental characteristics, with contrasting historical and social backgrounds, and in different stages of economic development, will solve their environmental problems in a similar manner. Strong coincidence between physical and cultural patterns is scarcely to be expected, therefore. Moreover man's behavior is not consistently rational and predictable, so that serious errors arise when an attempt is made to explain culture as a conscious adjustment to environment. Inherited traditions and deeply rooted habits of thought are often of greater importance in determining human behavior than is the passive environment. This is not to belittle the significance of physical earth in human affairs—to deny its importance is as erroneous as to overemphasize and oversimplify its influence.

But similar natural environments can be very significant in the life and work of two groups of peoples and those peoples still not be using the physical endowments in the same way. *In other words the environment's importance is not measured by the degree of culture uniformity prevailing within a broad realm of similar natural equipment.*

872. CULTURE PATTERNS OFTEN NOT COINCIDENT WITH PHYSICAL REALMS. As a general rule, peoples with a primitive culture or those engrossed in a simple subsistence agricultural economy appear to find fewer different ways in which to use the similar physical endowments of a realm than do complex industrial-commercial civilizations. In the low-latitude and the high-latitude realms, therefore, where civilization in general is on a lower plane of material development, there appears to be a modest amount of culture similarity. Regional differences are still conspicuous, however. In the middle-latitude realms, which include the great modern centers of western civilization on either side of the North Atlantic Ocean, as well as the center of oriental culture in eastern Asia, the fitting of culture into the pattern of the physical realms is not satisfactory. One has a feeling that such an organization is largely forced and unreal.

873. *Realms of Small Cultural Development.* It has been pointed out earlier that environment acts chiefly in a limiting sense; its effects are negative rather than positive. It may render a particular form of land use difficult or even prohibit it. This passive effect of the physical environment is clearly apparent in the distribution of man and his works over the face of the earth. Largely because of the poverty of physical potentialities, but in some instances the result of serious positive handicaps, over the greater share of the earth's surface man has made slight permanent impression, or even none at all in parts. These lands of little or no development include the *ice caps, tundra, dry lands* (semiarid *steppes* as well as *deserts*), *taiga* or subarctic forest lands, and large parts of the *tropical forests* and the *tropical savannas.* Of these only the ice caps are entirely without permanent settlements. The driest parts of some deserts are likewise without human life. Within some of these realms there are enough noteworthy exceptions to the general rule of sparse population and scant economic development to prevent one from falling into the errors of environmental determinism. Witness, for example, the cases of overcrowded and intensively cultivated Java and British India within the wet tropics.

874. *Realms of Important Cultural Development.* It is chiefly in the humid and subhumid realms of the middle latitudes that man has most completely modified the physical earth and adapted its natural resources to his needs. In these regions much of the original native

vegetation, either forest or grass, has been removed and the land put into cultivated crops. Regional specialization in production has promoted the development of communication nets of various degrees of complexity. The commerce fostered by this specialization has been instrumental in causing the development and growth of numerous towns and cities. Within these physical realms of important economic development in the middle latitudes there are fewer common cultural characteristics than is true of the less well developed realms. This appears to stem from the fact that men in more advanced stages of development are more versatile in their ways of utilizing physical environment than are primitive and backward peoples. Wider variations in kinds and intensities of land use within similar physical areas are the result. Within the well-developed parts of the middle latitudes the cultural heritage of the occupying group is usually of greater importance than the physical environment in influencing the culture patterns. For example, within the middle-latitude mixed forest lands (including marine west coast, humid subtropical, and humid continental regions), where more than half the earth's population resides, the land-utilization contrasts of the first order of importance are between the regions of occidental culture in Europe and North America on the one hand, and those of oriental culture in eastern and southeastern Asia on the other. Within the broad regions over which these two cultures are spread there exist markedly contrasting environments, but these do not result in such fundamental contrasts in land use and utilization of resources as do the dissimilar cultures.

875. A WORLD SYSTEM OF GEOGRAPHIC REGIONS IMPRACTICABLE. Considering the number of elements that enter into the geography of any region, it is highly improbable that a particular combination of *all* of them would be found repeated in widely separated parts of the earth. There are, to be sure, far separated regions that resemble each other in one, and sometimes even two or three, geographic element-complexes. For example, the Spring Wheat Region of the United States and Canada resembles the Spring Wheat Region of Soviet Russia in certain physical characteristics and likewise in its agricultural element-complex. But obviously if they were exactly alike in their agricultural elements, they would still be far from geographically alike. The notion of a world system or classification of geographic regions together with a schematic explanation of the same is clearly unsound. It seems to be based upon the erroneous concept that an area is an organic whole, an actual object. In reality an area is only the sum total of more or less related elements. It is quite possible, on the other hand, to treat the geography of the world regionally *out-*

side of any scheme of world classification, but such a description of individual geographic regions clearly lies outside the scope of the present book.

In terms of a scheme of world classification of the geographic elements the authors of "The Elements of Geography" have employed the regional concept as far as they felt it was warranted. Beginning with a world classification of the most primary physical element, climate, it was later developed that certain other natural elements, particularly native vegetation and soils, show striking similarities in their world distribution to that of climate. From this evolves the concept of a world classification of physical or natural realms (Fig. 418). But since a number of the physical elements have a world distribution quite at variance with that of the climatic pattern, the notion even of physical realms should not be pushed too far. It is a useful concept as far as it goes, but it has genuine limitations. The Amazon Valley and the Congo Basin no doubt bear resemblance in their climates, and in their plant covers and soils as well, but the two regions are far from being specimens of the same physical, let alone geographic, species. If then it appears dubiously possible to set up a scheme of world classification involving the physical geographic elements only, how much more difficult the task becomes when man and his works are included. It is the authors' belief that it is impossible to arrange the regions of the earth to form a single system that will describe the world even in outline. With this conviction in mind they have refrained from attempting to synthesize the geographic elements into any semblance of a world system.

APPENDICES

Appendix A

Supplementary Climatic Data for Selected Stations
(T., temperature in degrees Fahrenheit; Rf., rainfall in inches)

		Jan.	Feb.	Mar.	Apr.	May	June	July	Aug.	Sept.	Oct.	Nov.	Dec.	Year	Range
1.	T.	79	79	80	81	81	80	81	82	83	83	82	81	81	4.0
	Rf.	7.9	4.6	7.2	6.0	11.1	11.7	9.9	6.5	3.1	2.9	6.7	11.1	88.7	
2.	T.	80	80	82	83	83	82	81	81	81	81	80	80	81	3.2
	Rf.	3.3	1.9	4.3	9.7	10.9	7.3	4.4	3.2	4.8	13.4	11.8	5.1	80.1	
3.	T.	80	79	80	80	80	80	80	79	80	79	79	80	80	1.1
	Rf.	3.9	1.7	1.7	4.2	12.6	13.5	16.2	14.9	12.5	14.8	21.5	11.9	129.4	
4.	T.	79	81	84	86	84	82	82	82	82	81	80	79	82	7.0
	Rf.	0.9	0.1	0.3	1.7	8.3	12.6	11.1	11.0	13.3	11.1	3.7	3.1	77.2	
5.	T.	84	83	84	84	82	79	77	80	83	86	86	85	83	8.5
	Rf.	15.3	13.0	9.7	4.5	0.7	0.2	0.1	0.1	0.5	2.1	5.2	10.3	61.7	
6.	T.	70	75	83	90	89	87	87	86	85	83	76	71	82	20
	Rf.	0.1	0.1	0.2	1.1	5.8	5.5	3.3	4.6	5.7	4.7	1.6	0.4	35.1	
7.	T.	60	62	65	64	66	64	62	61	61	62	59	59	62	7
	Rf.	0.6	1.9	2.8	3.4	3.0	5.7	11.0	12.1	7.6	0.8	0.5	0.2	49.6	
8.	T.	49	54	61	71	81	90	95	94	88	80	63	53	73	46
	Rf.	1.2	1.3	1.3	0.9	0.2	0.0	0.0	0.0	0.0	0.1	0.8	1.2	7.0	
9.	T.	60	60	59	58	57	55	55	54	55	58	59	60	58	6
	Rf.	0.0	0.1	0.2	0.2	0.4	0.3	0.2	0.4	0.3	0.0	0.2	0.1	2.3	
10.	T.	58	62	68	73	79	82	82	83	78	71	64	57	71	25.2
	Rf.	0.5	0.5	0.7	1.1	1.2	2.3	2.1	2.0	4.4	2.4	1.3	1.0	19.5	
11.	T.	19	23	33	48	64	73	76	74	63	50	36	27	49	56.9
	Rf.	0.5	0.4	0.4	0.7	0.7	0.8	0.5	0.5	0.5	0.5	0.5	0.6	6.6	
12.	T.	74	74	70	64	58	54	52	54	57	62	67	71	63	22.4
	Rf.	0.7	0.6	1.0	1.7	2.8	3.1	2.6	2.5	2.0	1.7	1.2	1.0	20.9	
13.	T.	70	70	68	63	59	56	55	56	58	61	64	68	62	15.6
	Rf.	0.7	0.6	0.9	1.9	3.8	4.5	3.6	3.4	2.3	1.6	1.1	0.8	25.2	
14.	T.	49	50	53	56	61	68	73	75	70	64	57	52	61	25.4
	Rf.	4.0	2.6	3.3	2.0	1.7	0.7	0.1	0.1	1.1	3.4	4.1	3.9	27.0	
15.	T.	74	73	69	61	55	50	49	51	55	60	66	71	61	24.7
	Rf.	3.1	2.7	4.4	3.5	2.9	2.5	2.2	2.5	3.0	3.5	3.1	3.9	37.3	
16.	T.	53	55	63	69	75	81	83	83	79	70	61	54	69	30.6
	Rf.	1.4	1.6	1.8	2.7	3.2	2.7	2.5	2.6	3.5	2.0	2.2	1.8	28.0	
17.	T.	77	77	76	72	68	65	65	66	68	70	73	75	71	12
	Rf.	4.6	4.5	4.6	3.0	2.0	0.7	0.8	2.0	3.7	4.9	4.4	4.5	39.7	
18.	T.	34	34	35	42	49	55	58	58	53	45	39	35	45	24.3
	Rf.	8.5	6.4	5.9	4.1	4.5	3.8	5.8	7.5	8.7	8.9	8.3	8.5	81.0	
19.	T.	62	60	58	53	50	46	46	46	48	52	55	59	53	16.4
	Rf.	2.4	3.0	5.5	9.4	15.2	17.0	16.1	13.2	8.7	5.2	5.0	4.1	104.8	
20.	T.	39	40	43	48	53	57	60	60	56	50	45	42	49	21.1
	Rf.	4.5	3.5	2.5	1.7	1.3	0.9	0.4	0.6	2.0	2.5	6.5	5.9	32.5	

Supplementary Climatic Data for Selected Stations.—
(Continued)

(T., temperature in degrees Fahrenheit; Rf., rainfall in inches)

	Jan.	Feb.	Mar.	Apr.	May	June	July	Aug.	Sept.	Oct.	Nov.	Dec.	Year	Range
21. T.	22	25	37	51	63	72	77	75	66	55	39	27	51	55
Rf.	0.7	0.9	1.3	2.8	4.1	4.7	4.0	3.2	3.0	2.3	1.1	0.9	29.0	
22. T.	32	38	46	55	63	70	75	73	66	56	44	36	55	42
Rf.	2.4	2.3	2.7	3.4	4.1	3.3	2.8	3.2	3.5	4.7	4.3	3.0	39.8	
23. T.	8	14	30	47	60	71	77	75	61	48	29	14	44	68.4
Rf.	0.2	0.3	0.7	1.1	2.2	3.4	5.8	5.3	3.3	1.5	0.9	0.2	24.9	
24. T.	− 4	0	15	38	52	62	66	64	54	41	21	6	35	70
Rf.	0.9	0.7	1.2	1.4	2.0	3.1	3.1	2.2	2.2	1.4	1.1	0.9	20.2	
25. T.	24	23	27	38	49	57	62	59	50	41	32	25	41	39
Rf.	1.3	1.1	1.2	1.2	1.7	2.0	2.7	2.8	2.0	2.1	1.7	1.6	21.4	
26. T.	− 3	2	13	30	47	59	64	59	48	32	13	2	31	66.9
Rf.	1.1	0.8	0.8	0.7	1.5	2. 7	3.0	2.3	1.4	2.4	1.4	1.9	20.0	
27. T.	24	24	32	40	49	58	65	65	59	49	40	29	44	44.7
Rf.	6.0	4.7	5.1	4.6	3.8	3.8	3.7	4.6	4.1	5.5	5.9	5.5	57.3	
28. T.	8	9	18	30	41	53	60	56	46	34	22	12	33	52
Rf.	0.9	0.7	0.8	0.7	1.2	1.8	2.4	2.4	2.2	1.6	1.2	0.9	16.8	
29. T.	−23	−11	4	29	46	57	59	54	42	25	1	−13	23	82.4
Rf.	0.8	0.8	0.5	0.7	0.9	1.3	1.6	1.6	1.7	1.3	1.3	1.1	13.6	
30. T.	4	− 2	−2	8	23	35	42	40	32	22	11	6	13	44
Rf.	1.4	1.3	1.1	0.9	0.5	0.4	0.6	0.9	1.0	1.2	1.0	1.5	11.8	

Stations for which data are given above:
1. Georgetown, British Guiana
2. Colombo, Ceylon
3. Colón, Canal Zone
4. Saïgon, French Indochina
5. Darwin, Australia
6. Mandalay, Burma
7. Addis Ababa, Ethiopia
8. Baghdad, Iraq
9. Port Nolloth, Union of South Africa
10. Monterrey, Mex.
11. Astrakhan, U.S.S.R.
12. Adelaide, Australia
13. Capetown, Union of South Africa
14. Algers (Algiers), Algeria
15. Buenos Aires, Argentina

16. San Antonio, Tex.
17. Durban, South Africa
18. Bergen, Norway
19. Valdivia, Chile
20. Victoria, Can.
21. Omaha, Neb.
22. Milano (Milan), Italy
23. Mukden, Manchuria
24. Winnipeg, Can.
25. Uppsala, Sweden
26. Tomsk, U.S.S.R. (Siberia)
27. Halifax, Can.
28. Arkhangelsk (Archangel), U.S.S.R.
29. Dawson, Can.
30. Spitsbergen

Appendix B

Map Projections

THE NATURE OF MAP PROJECTIONS. The term map projection commonly is used in a rather broad sense, since many projections, so called, are more truly mathematical devices, and only a few are true perspective projections. The nature of the latter may be understood readily if one imagines a hemispherical basket of wire so constructed that the wires represent the parallels and meridians of the earth. The shadow of such a grid cast upon a plane touching it at a single point (tangent plane) is called a perspective projection because the observer appears to be looking through the grid. The spacing of the shadow lines obviously may be changed, and the resulting projection given different properties, by shifting the position of the light that casts the shadow to different distances from the point at which the plane is tangent to the wire grid. In certain projections the shadow is supposed to be cast not upon a plane but upon a tangent cone or a tangent cylinder, either of which is then developed into a plane. Many other "projections," and often more useful than those of the perspective class, have been devised by different scholars through mathematical computations, mainly within the last two centuries.

Some map projections are constructed so that they represent the *shapes* of earth features properly as compared to their shapes on a globe. Others represent *areas* so truly that all parts of the map are in proper areal relation to the globe. *It is impossible for any projection that includes a considerable area to accomplish both these objectives;* some accomplish neither. A projection on which the *shape* of any small area of the earth is truly rendered is called a *conformal projection.* One on which the ratio of *areas* is constant[1] between the globe and any part of the map is called an *equal-area,* or *equivalent, projection.* There are certain equal-area projections which, in achieving equality of area, produce gross distortions of the shapes of parts of the areas they show. All do so to some degree. Conversely, conformal projections in securing proper shapes do violence to the comparability of areas within the map. The name

---

[1] Areas are in constant ratio when the area of any quadrilateral included between two parallels and two meridians on a map has the same size relationship to the area on the earth that it represents that any other quadrilateral on the map has to the earth area that it represents.

of the projection employed usually will be found below each map in any scientific atlas, and often also a statement telling whether it is of the conformal or the equal-area type.

Some projections have an added quality: that of showing compass directions properly all ways from the center of the map. Such a projection is called *azimuthal* or sometimes, for no very good reason, "zenithal." One of these descriptive words may be coupled with one of those indicated above and with the name of its originator, to make the complete name of the projection, as, for example, the "Lambert azimuthal equal-area projection."

In order that the qualities of a few of the more commonly used projections may be understood they are here explained briefly and illustrated, together with some that are less used but are in striking contrast with them.

Maps of the Whole Earth

Mercator's projection, which is commonly used for maps of the world, may be understood better by first examining two other contrasting projections

Fig. A.—A cylindrical equal-area projection.

between which it effects a compromise. Figures *A* and *B* show forms of projection in which the shadow of the imaginary basket grid of the earth is cast by lights located at different points. These shadow patterns give the spacing for the parallels upon tangent cylinders. In Fig. *A* the position assumed by the light is at an infinite distance so that its rays are parallel. The result is an equal-area projection but one in which the shapes of areas in high latitudes are so stretched out east and west and so shortened north and south that they look very odd—so odd, in fact, that the projection is little used. At the opposite extreme is Fig. *B*. In this one the shadow-casting light is assumed to be at the center of the basket grid. In this projection also there is a great east-west expansion in high latitude but a still greater north-south expansion. It is neither equal-area nor conformal.

The contrast between these two makes clear the nature and purpose of Mercator's projection (Fig. *C*), first published in 1569. In it the converging meridians of the globe are represented as parallel lines spaced as they are at the equator. This obviously involves a rapid east-west expansion with increase of latitude. To balance that distortion the positions for the parallels of latitude are mathematically computed to produce north-south expansion which shall increase *at the same rate* as the east-west expansion. The result is a conformal projection; *i.e.*, any small area, like a bay or a peninsula, is shown with practically its true shape. Large areas, however, are distorted both in size and shape by the constant change of scale from place to place. Indeed, the scale of miles sometimes printed with this very common form of map is of little use outside the equatorial region, where the distortion of area is small. The expansion of the grid of this projection is a serious defect in a map for educational use, since it causes land areas in high latitudes to appear vastly larger than they really are in comparison with those near the equator.

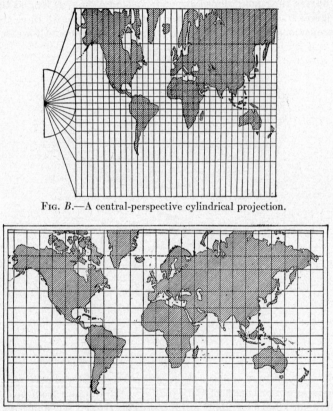

Fig. *B.*—A central-perspective cylindrical projection.

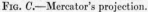

Fig. *C.*—Mercator's projection.

In addition to its conformality Mercator's projection has another quality that recommends it, especially to navigators. Straight lines drawn upon it show constant compass directions. For example, a straight line drawn at an angle of 45° to the right of a meridian on this projection trends northeast throughout its length. This is most useful for plotting ship's courses. The shortest distance between any two commercial ports follows the arc of the *great circle* of the earth passing through those ports, but that is a hard course to steer because the compass direction at any given point on the course is different from that at every other point, and the ship's course must be gradually but continuously changed. In practice, such a course is approximated by plotting on Mercator's projection a series of short straight lines (rhumb lines) which follow the general direction of the great circle but along each of which the compass direction remains constant.

THE OVAL PROJECTIONS AND THEIR COMBINATION. The projections described above portray the entire earth on one or another form of rectangular grid. There is another group of projections which mainly are oval in form, having their poles shown as points instead of lines as long as the equator. Figures D, E, and F show the plans of three of these. All three are equal-area projections, but they differ slightly in other respects. All are developed

FIG. D.—Mollweide's homolographic projection.

FIG. E.—The Sanson-Flamsteed sinusoidal projection

on polar axes that are one-half the length of the equatorial axis, which is the proper ratio of the length of the equator to the distance from pole to pole. In Mollweide's homolographic projection (Fig. D) and the sinusoidal projection (Fig. E) the meridians are equally spaced, as they are on a globe, and the parallels are truly parallel, as they also are on a globe. The difference between the two is in the shapes of their meridians and in the spacing of their parallels. Both of them distort shapes, especially near the margins of the maps and in high latitudes, but to slightly different degrees in different places. Aitoff's projection (Fig. F), while keeping equality of area, secures slightly better shapes by decreasing the spacing of the meridians from the center of the map outward and by using curved parallels. There are other projections of this general type.

In recent years also certain modified forms of projections in this group have appeared. They are characterized by interruptions of continuity for the purpose of having more than one central or principal meridian, near which there is the least distortion of shape. Goode's homolosine projection (Fig. *G*) is one of these. It is made by combining the sinusoidal projection (from the equator to latitude 40°) with Mollweide's projection (from 40° to the pole). Since it is composed of equal-area projections, it also has that quality. In addition, a proper selection of the meridians to be repeated as principal meridians causes each continent to appear as if it were in the center of the original projection where shapes are very good. The form of Aitoff's projection used in the plates accompanying this volume employs the principle of interruption also. Offsetting these two desirable properties (equality of area

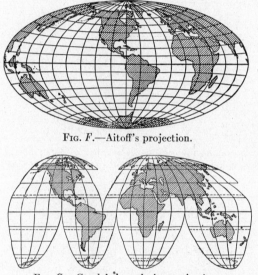

FIG. *F*.—Aitoff's projection.

FIG. *G*.—Goode's homolosine projection.

and a fairly good shape) is the necessity for the eye of the observer to bridge the gaps in the grid caused by the interruptions. Equal-area projections of the entire earth's surface are of great value for the purpose of showing the world distribution of economic data or other phenomena of any kind that require areas to be shown in their true proportion to one another.

In the first of the above groups of projections the earth poles (if they can be shown) are represented by lines as long as the equator. In the second group they are represented by points, the meeting places of all the meridians. In certain other projections neither of these conditions is fulfilled, the poles being represented by lines, not points, but by lines less long than the equator. In some of the projections of this latter group the positions of the parallels are computed so that the resulting grids are equal-area or equivalent. One of several such projections is employed for the maps of the world shown in Figs. 24, 25, and others of this book.

MAPS OF HEMISPHERES AND SIMILAR AREAS

PERSPECTIVE PROJECTIONS. The front of nearly every atlas contains maps of the hemispheres, or of the polar areas, which are circular in outline. These are constructed according to any one of several schemes of projection,

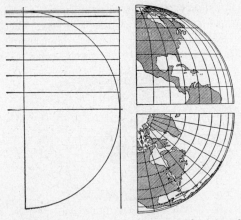

FIG. *II.*—The orthographic projection; the manner of obtaining the spacings of its parallels and meridians, and segments of its meridional and polar forms.

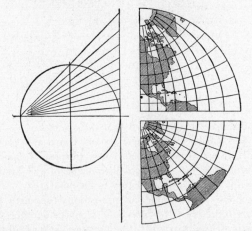

FIG. *I.*—The stereographic projection; the manner of obtaining the spacings of its parallels and meridians, and segments of its meridional and polar forms.

more or less used. Some of them have properties of peculiar value. Among them are perspective projections which are derived as if by projecting the shadows of the wire-basket grid upon tangent planes, just as in Figs. *A* and *B* they were cast upon tangent cylinders. Map grids constructed by these methods may take either the polar or the meridional form, and the illustrations show quadrants in each, together with the mode of obtaining the spacings of the meridians and parallels.

The *orthographic projection* (Fig. *H*) shows great compression about its margin but expansion of areas in its center and gives the appearance of looking into a bowl. It is much used for star charts of the heavens but not much for maps of the earth. The *stereographic projection* (Fig. *I*) shows a spacing of lines just the reverse of the preceding. It is a conformal projection and renders the shapes of limited areas accurately but greatly distorts the relative areas of different parts of the surface shown. Still more extreme in its marginal expansion is the *gnomonic projection* (Fig. *J*). In fact, the expansion of the latter is so great that no large part of a hemisphere can be shown by it, and on it both shapes and areas are so distorted that it has no value for showing either the shapes or the sizes of regions. It has, however, one unique quality that gives it a place among the valuable projections. On it every arc of a great circle of the earth is rendered as a straight line, and, conversely, every straight line drawn on the projection is an arc of a great circle. This is a most useful device for plotting great-circle (shortest possible) air or ocean routes. Because most lines that would be drawn upon this projection for the purpose of locating sail-

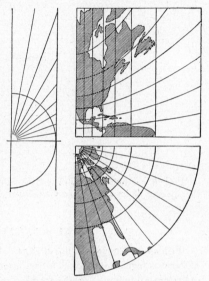

FIG. *J.*—The gnomonic projection; the manner of obtaining the basic spacings of its grid, and segments of its meridional and polar forms.

ing courses would cut parallels and meridians at various angles, compass steering by it is not easy. For that reason the significant points of latitude and longitude on the course usually are transferred from the gnomonic to a Mercator's projection and are connected by a series of short straight lines, as previously indicated. This approximates the great-circle route and makes steering much simpler. *Lambert's azimuthal equal-area projection* (Fig. *K*) illustrates the manner of constructing another of the hemispherical projections, which, however, is not of the perspective type. The spacing of the parallels or meridians from the center of the map is proportional to the chord distance of the arc of the number of degrees of earth circumference represented by the position of the line. This spacing gives the projection qualities the reverse of those of the stereographic. It is equal-area, azimuthal (*i.e.*, all points have their true compass directions from the center of the map), and the distortion of shapes, while considerable about the margins, is not great near the center of the projection. This valuable device commonly is used to show the hemispheres in school atlases. The principle employed in it, when expanded to include the whole earth, underlies the construction of Aitoff's projection (Fig. *F*)

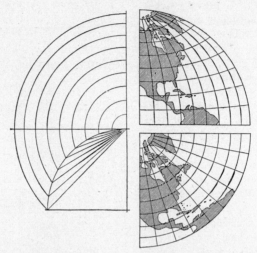

Fig. *K.*—Lambert's azimuthal equal-area projection; the manner of obtaining the spacing of its parallels and meridians, and segments of its meridional and polar forms.

The Conical Projections

Forms of Conical Projection. It has been noted previously that grids of various forms may be projected upon tangent cones as well as upon tangent cylinders and planes. Some forms of conical projection are truly perspective in type, some of even greater value are mathematically derived, whereas still others are obtained only by modification of one or more of the basic characteristics of the conical group.

To understand the simple form of the conical projection, imagine a large paper cone set down upon a globe with its apex directly above the pole of the globe. The cone is tangent to the globe along the entire circumference of some selected parallel, which is called the *standard parallel*. Because this parallel is everywhere equally distant from the apex of the cone, it becomes an arc of a circle when the cone is opened out into a plane surface, and all other parallels become arcs of concentric circles (Fig. *L*). Lines drawn on the surface of the cone from the apex through selected points on the standard parallel become the meridians of the map and always are straight lines radiating from the common center. Meridians that are radial straight lines and parallels that are arcs of concentric circles always indicate one of the several forms of the true conical projection.

In the simple form of the conical projection the scale of the map is true only along the standard parallel. North or south of that parallel the longitudinal distance expands rapidly, and the scale does not apply. Much greater area may be brought within the range of reasonable distortion if the map be constructed on *two standard parallels* instead of one. This is done by making the cone *secant* to the globe rather than tangent to it (Fig. *M*). By careful choice of position for the standard parallels an arrangement of lines may be had which, over a wide band of latitude, produces surprisingly little distortion. By mathematical adjustments of the exact positions of the parallels the distortions may be restricted either to the shapes or to the areas of the features shown. Thus both equal-area and conformal types of this projection exist.

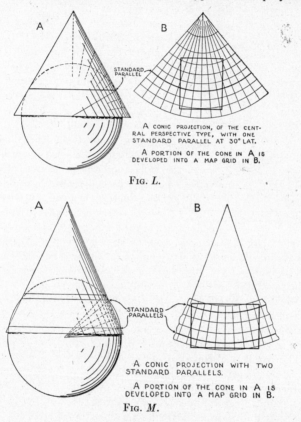

A CONIC PROJECTION, OF THE CENTRAL PERSPECTIVE TYPE, WITH ONE STANDARD PARALLEL AT 30° LAT.

A PORTION OF THE CONE IN A IS DEVELOPED INTO A MAP GRID IN B.

FIG. *L.*

A CONIC PROJECTION WITH TWO STANDARD PARALLELS.

A PORTION OF THE CONE IN A IS DEVELOPED INTO A MAP GRID IN B.

FIG. *M.*

Such are the Lambert conformal conic projection and the Albers equal-area projection, each with two standard parallels. The latter is particularly good for showing an area, like the United States, which has a greater east-west than north-south dimension. By proper selection of the standard parallels a map of the United States may be made in which the maximum scale error, which is on the northern and southern margins, is only a little more than 1 per cent. The map is, therefore, by construction equal-area and, for so large a region as the United States, very nearly conformal. The map of the geology of the United States, prepared by the United States Geological Survey in 1932, utilizes this excellent projection.

MODIFIED FORMS OF CONICAL PROJECTION. Several forms of projection adopt the basic principles of conical projection but, by modification of them in one way or another, produce grids having somewhat different qualities.

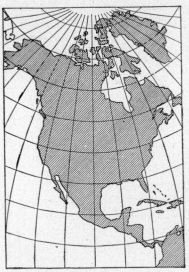

One of these is Bonne's projection, much used in atlases for maps of some of the continents (Fig. *N*). In this projection all parallels are arcs of concentric circles, as they are in the truly conical projections, and they are spaced in their proper positions relative to those on the globe. The meridians, however, are not straight lines but curves which converge at the pole and pass through points on the parallels that are spaced in true proportion to their spacing on the globe. Thus every quadrilateral of the grid has its true proportional length and breadth as compared with that quadrilateral on a globe, and the projection is equal-area. It gives good shapes near the principal meridian of a map, but distortion of shape increases rapidly with distance east or west. The projection is most properly used, therefore, for a land area, such as the continent of North America, having its greater dimension north and south rather than east and west.

FIG. *N.*—Bonne's projection.

Another modified form of conical projection often is used as a basis of detailed surveys, such as the United States topographic maps or the International Map of the World on a scale of 1:1,000,000. This projection is called polyconic (meaning many cones) (Fig. *O*). It is drawn as if many cones of different taper were fitted upon a globe, each tangent on a different parallel. The parallels of this projection are arcs of circles, as in all conical projections, but not, as in the others, arcs of concentric circles. The meridians, except a central one, also are curved.

COMPROMISE PROJECTIONS. Among the scores of map projections that have been devised some are fanciful in the extreme or have only single or very limited uses. Others make no claim to scientific value but are easily understood and generally useful, since they compromise between

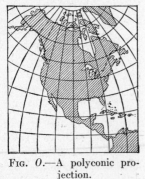

FIG. *O.*—A polyconic projection.

the distortions of shape, common in equal-area projections, and the distortions of area, usual in conformal projections. One such is the Van der Grinten projection of the earth, which has qualities intermediate between those of the Mercator and Mollweide projections. Another is the familiar globular projection of the hemispheres.

Appendix C
American Systems of Land Survey[1]

TOWNSHIP AND RANGE SYSTEM. Over a large part of the United States
the basic subdivision of the land follows a system of survey adopted by the
United States government in 1785. It was applied especially to the region of
the Great Lakes, the Mississippi Valley, and the western states. By this system public land and rural property are described and their ownership deter-

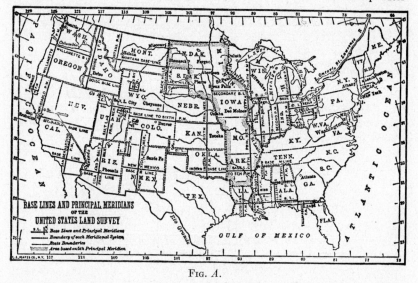

FIG. A.

mined in relation to a network of north-south and east-west lines. These
include selected meridians, which are called principal meridians, and base lines
and correction lines (Fig. A). Their use has the effect of dividing the land into
essentially rectangular blocks. The location of these blocks is indicated by
numbered *townships* and *ranges*. The ranges are north-south strips of land
6 miles wide, and they are numbered east and west from the nearest or most
convenient principal meridian. In Wisconsin, for example, the controlling

[1] Adapted from Appendix F., Bull. 36 of the Wisconsin Geological and Natural
History Survey. Illustrations by courtesy of E. F. Bean. Director.

line is the 4th principal meridian, the 1st being in eastern Indiana, and there are 30 ranges east and 20 west of it (Fig. *B*). The ranges are divided into townships by east-west lines at intervals of 6 miles, beginning at a selected southern boundary. In Wisconsin, this is the Illinois-Wisconsin state line. Thus a range consists of a north-south tier of townships each of which is supposed to be

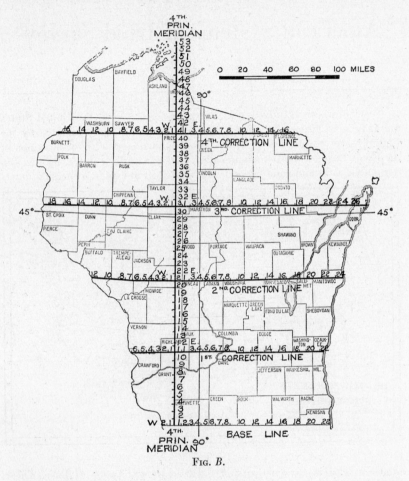

FIG. *B.*

6 miles square. There are 53 townships in the longest range in Wisconsin. By this system any township can be located by reference to its township and range numbers, *e.g.*, township 7 north, range 9 east. This is usually written T. 7 N., R. 9 E. Owing to the fact that the meridans converge toward the north certain corrections and allowances must be made. Other factors require allowance also, such as a base line which is not true east-west, errors in surveying, and the presence of lakes or streams at critical points. The four correction lines for Wisconsin are shown in Fig. *B.*

The civil, organized, or municipal towns into which counties are divided are units of political administration, and they may or may not coincide with government townships, which are for purposes of location. In thinly settled districts the civil towns often are much larger and may include two or more government townships or parts of townships. In other areas one government township may be divided into two or more small civil towns. Using Dane County, Wisconsin, as an illustration we note that most of its civil towns are also government townships, but this is not true of the two northwesternmost towns of Black Earth and Mazomanie (Fig. C). There the corner of the county

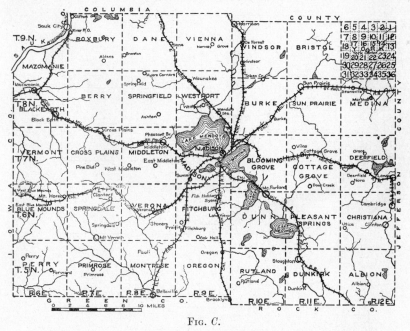

Fig. C.

is not rectangular, owing to the presence of the Wisconsin River. The boundaries of civil towns also are subject to change by appropriate legislation, but the government townships remain.

Every government township is divided into 36 *sections*, each 1 mile square. The sections are numbered, beginning at the northeastern corner and ending at the southeastern, as is shown in the northeastern township in Fig. C. The locations of the township and section corners are supposedly marked by a stake, stone, mound, tree, or other device, but too often these are impermanent features and are now difficult to locate. Since each section is 1 mile square, its area is 640 acres. For purposes of more detailed location and description the section is divided into quarters, each containing 160 acres, and the quarter sections are further divided into quarters of 40 acres each (Fig. D). These are commonly called "forties." The quarter sections are indicated by the points of the compass, and so also are the forties. To describe and locate a given forty, therefore, one might say that it is the NE$\frac{1}{4}$ of SW$\frac{1}{4}$ of Sec. 31, T. 18 N., R. 9 E. Such a location is almost as precise as if it were given in latitude and longitude, and it tells also the area of the parcel of land in question.

METES AND BOUNDS. In the Atlantic Coast states and certain others the original land grants and surveys were made prior to the adoption of the township and range system of survey. In those states parcels of land are described by a system known as "metes and bounds." In that system an arbitrary point is taken, such for example as a projecting rock, a tree, or some significant point on the bank of a river or lake. The property is then bounded by lines

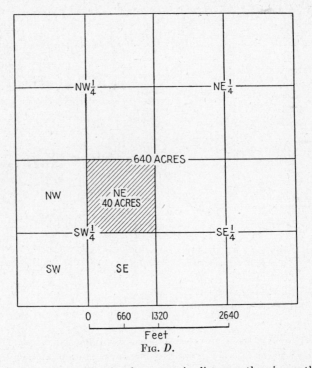

FIG. D.

run in a given compass direction for a certain distance, then in another direction for a specified distance, and so on around to the point of beginning. This system has often led to conflict over property lines because after a time the tree, stone or other arbitrary beginning point has been lost or its location has changed. Moreover, the stated distances were sometimes measured inexactly, as in parts of Texas, for example, where some of the early Spanish land grants are said to have been measured in terms of the length of a lariat rope or of how far a horse could walk in a given time. Such lines often did not surround rectangular parcels of land, and seldom did the plots of land have any consistent pattern of shape with respect to the cardinal compass directions.

This lack of coordination is plainly apparent in the road patterns to be seen in detailed maps of New England, Texas, and other states. In some North

American localities the present small parcels of land are subdivisions of grants made by the kings of England, France, or Spain to noblemen or to the sponsors of settlement projects. In French Canada, for example, the present farms often are rectangular but are very long and narrow, their narrow frontage being upon a river and their length extending at right angles from the river, regardless of compass direction. Some of the counties of the Province of Quebec may be seen to have the same shape. They were established at a time when river frontage was a most prized possession but the land of the interior had little value. Various systems more or less like that of metes and bounds are prevalent in most of Europe and, in fact, in the larger part of the world.

Appendix D

The topographic quadrangles indicated below have been selected from those published by the United States Geological Survey because they illustrate in map form certain of the landforms discussed in the text. Some of the subjects discussed, ice-scoured plains, for example, do not find clear illustration in any of the United States Topographic Quadrangles now published and are therefore omitted from the list.

Certain of the maps named below may be used to illustrate more than one class of features, and their names are repeated. Such maps are indicated by the asterisk. In some instances two or three adjacent quadrangles are required to show adequately the extent of the feature in question. Such are indicated as a series by being listed in series.

These topographic quadrangles may be obtained from the United States Geological Survey, Washington, D. C. In the following list, sheets of sizes other than standard are marked " (special)."

PLAINS OF STREAM DEGRADATION

Newly emerged plains:
  Bladen and Everett City, Ga.
  Cambon, Fla.
  Chicora, S. C.
  Moniac, Ga.-Fla.
Higher and better drained coastal plain:
  Bamberg, S. C.
  Forest, Miss.
  Springhope and Rocky Mount, N. C.
Plains with cuestaform ridges and escarpments:
  Blanchardville and Blue Mounds, Wis.
  Epes, Ala.
  Fond Du Lac and Neenah, Wis.
  Kendall and Mauston, Wis.*
  Llano, Tex.*
  Nashville, Tenn.*
  New Boston and Linden, Tex.

Niagara, N. Y.
  Pelahatchie and Morton, Miss.
Knobs and outliers on cuestaform plains:
  Big Clifty, Ky.*
  Franklin, Tenn.
  Kendall and Mauston, Wis.*
  Llano, Tex.*
  Nashville, Tenn.*
Young plains (mainly in glacial drift):
  Gillespie, Ill.*
  La Salle, Ill.*
  Macon, Mo.
  Paulding, Ohio*
  Ray, N. D.*
Rough, maturely dissected plains:
  La Farge, Wis.
  Newcomerstown, Ohio
  Nortonville, Ky.

796

Dissected river bluffs (river breaks):
  Ray, N. D.*
  Porcupine Valley and Spring Creek,
    Mont.
Old-age plain:
  Mount Carmel, Ill.-Ind.
  Owensboro, Ind.-Ky.
Peneplains with monadnocks:
  Atlanta and Marietta, Ga.

Gastonia, N. C.
Kings Mountain, N. C.
Karst plains:
  Big Clifty, Ky.*
  Interlachen, Fla.
  Mammoth Cave, Ky.
  Princeton, Ky.
  Williston, Fla.

PLAINS OF STREAM AGGRADATION

Delta margin:
  East Delta, La.
  Timbalier, La.
Narrow levees:
  Bayou de Large, La.
  Pt. a la Hache, La.
  Quarantine, La.
  Shell Beach, La.
Wide levees:
  Baton Rouge, La.
  Donaldsonville, La.
  New Orleans, La.
Wide alluvial floodplains:
  Bayou Sara, La.
  Clarksdale, Miss.
  Marks, Miss.
  Memphis, Tenn.-Ark.
  Vicksburg, Miss.
Narrow floodplains:
  Chester, Ill.

Gays Mills, Wis.
Ogallala, Neb.*
Prairie du Chien, Wis.*
Alluvial terraces:
  East Cincinnati, Ohio
  Malaga, Wash.
  Prairie du Chien, Wis.*
  Tarboro, N. C.
Alluvial fans and piedmont alluvial plains:
  Cucamonga and San Bernardino, Calif.
  Levis, Calif.
  Pacoima and Sunland, Calif.
  Whittier, Calif.
Plains of older alluvium:
  Assinniboine, Mont.
  Colorado Springs, Colo.
  Eaton, Colo.
  Sanborn, Colo.
  Vilas, Colo.

GLACIAL DRIFT PLAINS

Till plains (younger drift):
  Poorly drained
    Chokio, Minn.
    Lansing, Mich.
    Neshkoro, Wis.
  Well-drained
    La Salle, Ill.*
    Slater, Iowa
    Upper Sandusky, Ohio
  With drumlins
    Boston, Mass.*
    Clyde and Weedsport, N. Y.
    Palmyra, N. Y.
    Sun Prairie and Stoughton, Wis.
  With eskers
    Fowlerville, Mich.
    Rives Junction, Mich.*

St. Francis, Minn.
Till plains (older drift):
  Albia and Pella, Iowa
  Gillespie, Ill.*
Till plains (relief controlled by bedrock
    features):
  Baraboo, Wis.
  Stonington and Moosup, Conn.
  Youngstown, Ohio
Marginal moraines:
  Kettle-moraine regions (large area)
  Pelican Rapids and Vergas, Minn.
  Kettle-moraine belts (with associated
    pitted outwash plains)
    Rives Junction* and Stockbridge,
      Mich.
    Schoolcraft, Mich.

St. Croix Dalles, Wis.
Whitewater, Wis.
Lake plains (glacial):
Detroit, Mich.

Fargo, N. D.-Minn.
Paulding, Ohio*
Ridgeway, N. Y.

PLAINS IN DRY CLIMATES

Eolian sand plains:
Brown, Neb.
Lakin, Kans.
North Platte, Neb.
Ogallala, Neb.*

Loess plains (stream eroded):
Omaha and Vicinity, Neb. and Iowa
(*special*)
Red Cloud, Neb.
York, Neb.

SHORE FEATURES OF PLAINS

Ria shorelines:
Bath and Boothbay, Maine
Boston, Mass.*
Choptank, Md.
Kilmarnock, Va.
Deposited shore features:
Offshore bars:
Atlantic City, Sea Island, and Barnegat,* N. J.
Lopena Island and Saltillo Ranch, Tex.

Spits and hooks:
Cape Henlopen, Del.*
Erie, Pa.
Provincetown, Mass.
Sandy Hook, N. Y.
Shore dunes:
Barnegat, N. J.*
Cape Henlopen* and Reheboth, Del.
Fenville, Mich.
Three Oaks, Mich.

DRY-PLATEAU FEATURES

Plateau valleys and escarpments:
Abajo, Utah*
Bisuka, Idaho
Bright Angel, Ariz.
Diamond Creek, Ariz.
Escalante, Utah
Hanford and Scooteney Lake, Wash
Henry Mountains, Utah*
Kanab, Utah

Mesas and buttes:
Mesa de Maya, Colo.
Mount Trumbull, Ariz.
Raton, N. M.
Tascotal Mesa, Tex.
Plateau bolsons:
Carson Sink, Nev.*
Cienega Springs, N. M.
Disaster, Nev.*
Silver Peak, Nev.*

HILL LANDS

Stream-eroded hills in horizontal strata:
Arnoldsburg, W. Va.
Bald Knob, W. Va.
Confluence, Pa.
Fayetteville, W. Va. (plateau features)
Parkersburg, W. Va.-Ohio
Badlands:
Rock Springs, Wyo.
Hills in folded sedimentary strata:
Hyndman, Pa.
Millersburg, Lykens, and Pine Grove, Pa.

Mount Union, Pa.
Winding Stair, Okla.
Hills in complex rocks:
Asheville, N. C.-Tenn.
Knoxville, Tenn.-N. C.
Hills in areas of linear faulting:
McKittrick, Calif.
Priest Valley, Calif.
San Mateo, Calif.
Glaciated hill lands:
In crystalline rock
Allagash, Maine

Bolton, N. Y.
Greenlaw, Maine

In horizontal strata
Bath and Hammondsport, N. Y.

MOUNTAINS

Volcanic peaks:
  Crater Lake National Park, Ore.
  Lassen Volcanic National Park, Calif.
  Maiden Peak, Ore.
  Mount Hood, Ore.
  Mount Rainier National Park, Wash.*
Laccolithic mountains:
  Abajo, Utah*
  Fort Benton, Mont.
  Henry Mountains, Utah*
Fault-block mountains:
  Ballarat and Furnace Creek, Calif.
  Carson Sink, Nev.*
  Disaster, Nev.*
  Sequoia and General Grant National
    Parks, Calif. (*special*)*
  Silver Peak, Nev.*
*Mountain foothills of the hogback-ridge
  type:*
  Boulder, Colo.

Loveland, Colo.
Rapid, S. D.
Glaciated mountains:
  Glacier National Park (*special*)
  Hamilton, Mont.
  Hayden Peak, Utah.
  Mount Rainier National Park, Wash.*
  Sequoia and General Grant National
    Parks, Calif. (*special*)*
Emerged highland shore features:
  La Jolla, Calif.
  San Diego, Calif.
  San Luis, Calif.
  Santa Ana, Calif.
  Solstice Canyon and Las Flores, Calif.
Fiords:
  Reconnaissance Map—Alaska Railroad,
    Seward to Matanuska Coal Field
    (*special*)
  Takoma and Snohomish, Wash.

Appendix E

PRINCIPAL SUBDIVISIONS OF EARTH HISTORY AND SOME OF ITS EVENTS AS THEY ARE RECORDED IN THE ROCKS OF NORTH AMERICA

Left vertical margin (bottom to top): MORE RECENT TIME ↑ — THE ENTIRE SPAN OF EARTH HISTORY IS ESTIMATED TO BE MORE THAN 1,500,000,000 YEARS. PROBABLY TWO THIRDS OF IT HAD ELAPSED BEFORE CAMBRIAN TIME. — EARLIER TIME

Right vertical margin: PREVAILING CLASSES OF ROCKS IN THE GEOLOGIC REGIONS OF NORTH AMERICA

ERA	PERIOD	TOPOGRAPHIC DEVELOPMENTS	BIOLOGIC DEVELOPMENTS	(Prevailing rocks)
THE SPACES ALLOTTED BELOW TO THE ERAS AND PERIODS ARE NOT IN PROPORTION TO THEIR ESTIMATED DURATION				
CENOZOIC ERA OF MODERN LIFE — DUR. EST. AT ± 4% OF ALL GEOL. TIME	QUATERNARY — RECENT (ESTIMATED AT ± 25,000 YRS.)	PRESENT TECTONIC AND GRADATIONAL LAND FORMS	THE DEVELOPMENT AND DOMINANCE OF INTELLIGENT MAN	ALLUVIUMS-OLD & NEW- GLACIAL DRIFT, LOESS
	PLEISTOCENE	CALIF. COAST MTS. APPEAR THE GREAT ICE AGE	NEW SPECIES OF PLANTS AND ANIMALS APPEARANCE OF PRIMITIVE MAN	
	TERTIARY — PLIOCENE / MIOCENE / OLIGOCENE / EOCENE	ELEVATION OF ROCKY, SIERRA NEVADA & CASCADE MTS., THE COLORADO & COLUMBIA PLATEAUS, AND THE GREAT BASIN	DEVELOPMENT OF MAMMALS (PRIMITIVE TYPES OF ELEPHANTS, HORSES, DEER, CATS, DOGS, WHALES & MANY OTHERS, INCLUDING FIRST APES) BIRDS & TREES SIMILAR TO MODERN TYPES	
GENERAL EROSION INTERVAL				
MESOZOIC ERA OF MEDIEVAL LIFE — DURATION EST. AT ABOUT 8% OF ALL GEOL. TIME	CRETACEOUS (ROCKY MT. COAL DEPOSITS)	LAST GREAT SUBMERGENCE, GULF OF MEXICO TO ALASKA, FOLLOWED BY UPHEAVAL & BEGINNING OF ROCKY MTS.	RISE OF MAMMALS & BIRDS—DECLINE & EXTINCTION OF DINOSAURS. DEVELOPMENT OF MODERN FLOWERING PLANTS & DECIDUOUS TREES	YOUNGER, SEDIMENTARY ROCKS LOCAL IGNEOUS ROCKS
	JURASSIC	APPALACHIAN MTS. BASELEVELED — PACIFIC COAST VULCANISM~SUBMERGENCE FROM COLO. TO ALASKA.	GIANT REPTILES (DINOSAURS)—FIRST BIRDS — PRIMITIVE MAMMALS—MANY INSECTS SIMILAR TO PRESENT FORMS	
	TRIASSIC	LARGE LAND AREA—ARIDITY CONTINUED — SOME ROCKS OF LAND-DEPOSITED ORIGIN~VULCANISM	REPTILES (CRAWLING, WALKING & FLYING, SWIMMING) DIVERSE & ABUNDANT. MANY COMPLEX MARINE ANIMALS—FORESTS MAINLY CONIFEROUS	
GENERAL EROSION INTERVAL				
PALEOZOIC ERA ERA OF ANCIENT LIFE — DURATION VARIOUSLY ESTIMATED AT ABOUT 20 PER CENT OF ALL GEOLOGIC TIME	PERMIAN	GENERAL EMERGENCE—FOLDING OF APPALACHIAN MTS. — WIDESPREAD ARIDITY	DECLINE OF FERN TREES & RISE OF CONIFERS — GREAT VARIETY IN REPTILES & INSECTS—MANY MARINE INVERTEBRATES DISAPPEAR	OLDER AND MORE RESISTANT, SEDIMENTARY ROCKS LOCAL INTRUSIVE AND EXTRUSIVE IGNEOUS ROCKS
	CARBONIFEROUS "THE COAL AGE" — PENNSYLVANIAN	FLUCTUATING SEAS IN THE INTERIOR — FORMATION OF EXTENSIVE SWAMPS	VAST FORESTS OF FAST-GROWING TREES AND OTHER PLANTS. COMPLEX MARINE LIFE – RISE OF REPTILES AND INSECTS	
	MISSISSIPPIAN	WIDESPREAD SUBMERGENCE AND DEPOSITION OF SEDIMENTS	DEVELOPMENT OF SHARKS AND OTHER FISH—NUMEROUS AMPHIBIANS—ABUNDANT FORESTS OF FERNS & PRIMITIVE CONIFERS.	
	DEVONIAN	WIDESPREAD SUBMERGENCE – MOUNTAIN UPLIFT AND VULCANISM IN NEW ENG.	ABUNDANT FISHES WITH VERTEBRA AND PAIRED FINS, FIRST AMPHIBIANS, FIRST FORESTS (TREE FERNS)	
	SILURIAN	WIDESPREAD DEVELOPMENT OF PLAINS BY EROSION AND BY EMERGENCE	DEVELOPMENT OF FISHES—FIRST LAND ANIMALS (SPIDERLIKE) — FIRST LAND PLANTS—ABUNDANT CORALS	
	ORDOVICIAN	SEDIMENTS DEPOSITED — MOUNTAIN BUILDING IN NEW ENGLAND AND CANADA	ABUNDANT MOLLUSKS AND TRILOBITES — EARLY FORMS OF FISH — NO EVIDENCE OF LAND ANIMALS OR PLANTS	
	CAMBRIAN	WIDESPREAD SUBMERGENCE AND DEPOSITION OF SEDIMENTARY ROCKS	FIRST ABUNDANT FOSSILS MAINLY OF SHELLED MARINE INVERTEBRATES (MOLLUSKS AND TRILOBITES)	
LONG INTERVAL OF UPLIFT AND EROSION				
PROTEROZOIC		MUCH MOUNTAIN BUILDING, METAMORPHISM OF ROCKS, AND VULCANISM	PRIMITIVE MARINE LIFE, MAINLY WITHOUT SHELLS, LEAVING ONLY MEAGRE FOSSIL REMAINS	ANCIENT CRYSTALLINE ROCKS
LONG INTERVAL OF UPLIFT AND EROSION				
ARCHEOZOIC		MOUNTAIN BUILDING AND VULCANISM — MANY EVENTS OBSCURED BY VAST LAPSE OF TIME	PRIMITIVE FORMS OF MARINE LIFE, PERHAPS ALGAE-LIKE — NO DIRECT FOSSIL EVIDENCE	
EARTH HISTORY EXTENDS BACK AND MERGES WITH EARTH ORIGIN				

INDEX

Pages on which illustrations appear are in **boldface** type.